FEATURES AND BENEFITS
Core-Plus Mathematics, Course 3 TEACHER'S GUIDE PART A ©2009

Content and Organization

See page(s):

- Alignment to the NCTM Grades 9–12 Content Standards. — x
- Introduction and Organization of Course 3. — xi–xvii
- Access, Equity, and Differentiation. — xvi–xvii
- Implementing the Curriculum. — xvii–xxviii

Student and Teacher Friendly

- Engaging student-centered applications invite students to read and do more mathematics on their own. Read *Reasoned Arguments* and *Out of Control Signals*. — 3, 285
- Lesson development organizes problems for students into easy-to-understand instructions. See *Reasoning About Parallel Lines,* Investigation 2. — 35–39
- Full color **Student Edition** page alongside **Teacher Guide** page for easy reference. — 1–T1
- Effective **Teacher Guide** design provides point-of-use support to make it easier for you to focus on managing students' progress in completing investigations. — T2–T9

Extensive and Varied Practice

- **Applications** tasks help students use and apply ideas from each lesson. — 62–66
- **Connections** tasks connect each lesson's topics with other mathematics students know. — 66–68
- **Reflections** tasks help students avoid developing misconceptions and help them rethink key ideas that were developed in the lesson. — 69
- **Extensions** tasks provide opportunities to explore further or more deeply important ideas developed in the lesson. — 70–72
- **Review** tasks help students maintain important skills and provide just-in-time review. — 72–73

Test Preparation and Assessment

- **Think About This Situation** assesses students' prior knowledge before the start of the lesson. — 3
- **Summarizing the Mathematics** assesses students' ability to correctly articulate the mathematics developed after each investigation in the lesson. — 34
- **Check Your Understanding** assesses students' ability to solve problems based upon the mathematics developed in each investigation in the lesson. — 34
- **Looking Back** lessons help students review and practice key ideas that were developed in the unit. — 102–106

Technology

- *CPMP-Tools*™ expands student use of technology by including software tools for algebra, geometry, statistics, and discrete mathematics and time-saving access to selected lesson data sets. **www.wmich.edu/cpmp/CPMP-Tools/** — xi
- *StudentWorks*™ CD-ROM includes the Student Edition and more on CD.
- *ExamView® Assessment Suite* CD-ROM is a powerful state-of-the art test generator that combines ease of use with enormous flexibility in creating customized assessments.
- *TeacherWorks*™ *Plus* CD-ROM is the latest in all-in-one planners and teaching resource center including the ability to edit many of your print resources.
- *Core-Plus Mathematics* Web site resources at **www.glencoe.com**.

Course
3 Core-Plus Mathematics
Contemporary Mathematics in Context

2nd Edition

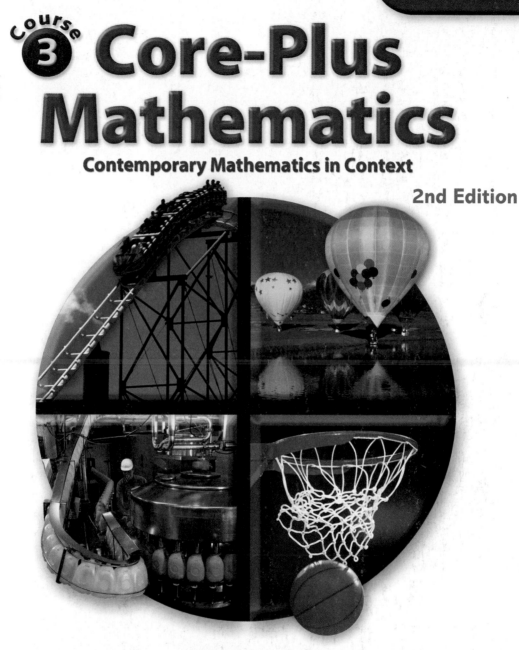

**James T. Fey • Christian R. Hirsch • Eric W. Hart
Harold L. Schoen • Ann E. Watkins**

with

**Beth E. Ritsema • Rebecca K. Walker • Sabrina Keller
Robin Marcus • Arthur F. Coxford • Gail Burrill**

 **Glencoe**

New York, New York   Columbus, Ohio   Chicago, Illinois   Woodland Hills, California

Glencoe

The *McGraw·Hill* Companies

 This material is based upon work supported, in part, by the National Science Foundation under grant no. ESI 0137718. Opinions expressed are those of the authors and not necessarily those of the Foundation.

Send all inquiries to:
Glencoe/McGraw-Hill
8787 Orion Place
Columbus, OH 43240-4027

ISBN: 978-0-07-877262-7   **Core-Plus Mathematics**
MHID: 0-07-877262-1   *Contemporary Mathematics in Context*
                               Course 3 Teacher Edition, Part A

ISBN: 978-0-07-877263-4   **Core-Plus Mathematics**
MHID: 0-07-877263-X   *Contemporary Mathematics in Context*
                               Course 3 Teacher Edition, Part B

Printed in the United States of America.

1 2 3 4 5 6 7 8 9 10 071/055 17 16 15 14 13 12 11 10 09 08

Core-Plus Mathematics 2 Development Team

Senior Curriculum Developers

James T. Fey
University of Maryland

Christian R. Hirsch (Director)
Western Michigan University

Eric W. Hart
Maharishi University of Management

Harold L. Schoen
University of Iowa

Ann E. Watkins
California State University, Northridge

Contributing Curriculum Developers

Beth E. Ritsema
Western Michigan University

Rebecca K. Walker
Grand Valley State University

Sabrina Keller
Michigan State University

Robin Marcus
University of Maryland

Arthur F. Coxford (deceased)
University of Michigan

Gail Burrill
Michigan State University
(First edition only)

Principal Evaluator

Steven W. Ziebarth
Western Michigan University

Advisory Board

Diane Briars
Pittsburgh Public Schools

Jeremy Kilpatrick
University of Georgia

Robert E. Megginson
University of Michigan

Kenneth Ruthven
University of Cambridge

David A. Smith
Duke University

Mathematical Consultants

Deborah Hughes-Hallett
University of Arizona / Harvard University

Stephen B. Maurer
Swarthmore College

William McCallum
University of Arizona

Doris Schattschneider
Moravian College

Richard Scheaffer
University of Florida

Evaluation Consultant

Norman L. Webb
University of Wisconsin-Madison

Technical Coordinator

James Laser
Western Michigan University

Collaborating Teachers

Mary Jo Messenger
Howard County Public Schools, Maryland

Jacqueline Stewart
Okemos, Michigan

Graduate Assistants

Allison BrckaLorenz
Christopher Hlas
University of Iowa

Madeline Ahearn
Geoffrey Birky
Kyle Cochran
Michael Conklin
Brandon Cunningham
Tim Fukawa-Connelly
University of Maryland

Dana Cox
Dana Grosser
Anna Kruizenga
Nicole Lanie
Diane Moore
Western Michigan University

Undergraduate Assistants

Cassie Durgin
University of Maryland

Rachael Kaluzny
Jessica Tucker
Western Michigan University

Core-Plus Mathematics 2
Field-Test Sites

Core-Plus Mathematics 2 builds on the strengths of the 1st edition, which was shaped by multi-year field tests in 36 high schools in Alaska, California, Colorado, Georgia, Idaho, Iowa, Kentucky, Michigan, Ohio, South Carolina, and Texas. Each revised text is the product of a three-year cycle of research and development, pilot testing and refinement, and field testing and further refinement. Special thanks are extended to the following teachers and their students who participated in the testing and evaluation of 2nd Edition Course 3.

Hickman High School
Columbia, Missouri
  Sandra Baker
  Lindsay Carlson
  Melissa Hundley
  Stephanie Krawczyk
  Tiffany McCracken
  Dana Meyer
  Ryan Pingrey

Holland Christian High School
Holland, Michigan
  Brian Lemmen
  Mike Verkaik

Malcolm Price Lab School
Cedar Falls, Iowa
  Megan Balong
  James Maltas

Riverside University High School
Milwaukee, Wisconsin
  Cheryl Brenner
  Scott Hanson
  Alice Lanphier

Rock Bridge High School
Columbia, Missouri
  Cynthia Francisco
  Donna Lillard
  Linda Shumate

Sauk Prairie High School
Prairie du Sac, Wisconsin
  Joan Quenan
  Mary Walz

Washington High School
Milwaukee, Wisconsin
  Anthony Amoroso

Overview of Course 3

UNIT 1 — REASONING AND PROOF

Reasoning and Proof develops student understanding of formal reasoning in geometric, algebraic, and statistical contexts and of basic principles that underlie those reasoning strategies.

Topics include inductive and deductive reasoning strategies; principles of logical reasoning—Affirming the Hypothesis and Chaining Implications; relation among angles formed by two intersecting lines or by two parallel lines and a transversal; rules for transforming algebraic expressions and equations; design of experiments including the role of randomization, control groups, and blinding; sampling distribution, randomization test, and statistical significance.

UNIT 2 — INEQUALITIES AND LINEAR PROGRAMMING

Inequalities and Linear Programming develops student ability to reason both algebraically and graphically to solve inequalities in one and two variables, introduces systems of inequalities in two variables, and develops a strategy for optimizing a linear function in two variables within a system of linear constraints on those variables.

Topics include inequalities in one and two variables, number line graphs, interval notation, systems of linear inequalities, and linear programming.

UNIT 3 — SIMILARITY AND CONGRUENCE

Similarity and Congruence extends student understanding of similarity and congruence and their ability to use those relations to solve problems and to prove geometric assertions with and without the use of coordinates.

Topics include connections between Law of Cosines, Law of Sines, and sufficient conditions for similarity and congruence of triangles, centers of triangles, applications of similarity and congruence in real-world contexts, necessary and sufficient conditions for parallelograms, sufficient conditions for congruence of parallelograms, and midpoint connector theorems.

Overview of Course 3

UNIT 4 SAMPLES AND VARIATION

Samples and Variation extends student understanding of the measurement of variability, develops student ability to use the normal distribution as a model of variation, introduces students to the binomial distribution and its use in decision making, and introduces students to the probability and statistical inference involved in control charts used in industry for statistical process control.

Topics include normal distribution, standardized scores, binomial distributions (shape, expected value, standard deviation), normal approximation to a binomial distribution, odds, statistical process control, control charts, and the Central Limit Theorem.

UNIT 5 POLYNOMIAL AND RATIONAL FUNCTIONS

Polynomial and Rational Functions extends student ability to represent and draw inferences about polynomial and rational functions using symbolic expressions and manipulations.

Topics include definition and properties of polynomials, operations on polynomials; completing the square, proof of the quadratic formula, solving quadratic equations (including complex number solutions), vertex form of quadratic functions; definition and properties of rational functions, operations on rational expressions.

UNIT 6 CIRCLES AND CIRCULAR FUNCTIONS

Circles and Circular Functions develops student understanding of relationships among special lines, segments, and angles in circles and the ability to use properties of circles to solve problems; develops student understanding of circular functions and the ability to use these functions to model periodic change; and extends student ability to reason deductively in geometric settings.

Topics include properties of chords, tangent lines, and central and inscribed angles of circles; linear and angular velocity; radian measure of angles; and circular functions as models of periodic change.

Overview of Course 3

UNIT 7 RECURSION AND ITERATION

Recursion and Iteration extends student ability to represent, analyze, and solve problems in situations involving sequential and recursive change.

Topics include iteration and recursion as tools to model and analyze sequential change in real-world contexts, including compound interest and population growth; arithmetic, geometric, and other sequences; arithmetic and geometric series; finite differences; linear and nonlinear recurrence relations; and function iteration, including graphical iteration and fixed points.

UNIT 8 INVERSE FUNCTIONS

Inverse Functions develops student understanding of inverses of functions with a focus on logarithmic functions and their use in modeling and analyzing problem situations and data patterns.

Topics include inverses of functions; logarithmic functions and their relation to exponential functions, properties of logarithms, equation solving with logarithms; and inverse trigonometric functions and their applications to solving trigonometric equations.

Contents

Contents

NCTM Standards

Core-Plus Mathematics and the instructional and assessment practices it promotes address the focal points of the National Council of Teachers of Mathematics' *Principles and Standards for School Mathematics*. By design, the **process standards** on Problem Solving, Reasoning and Proof, Communication, Connections, and Representation are an integral part of each lesson of every unit in the curriculum. The chart below correlates Course 3 units with the **content standards** for grades 9–12 in terms of focus (Ⓕ) and connections (©).

Correlation of Course 3 to NCTM Standards

NCTM Grades 9–12 Content Standards	Unit 1 Reasoning and Proof	Unit 2 Inequalities and Linear Programming	Unit 3 Similarity and Congruence	Unit 4 Samples and Variation	Unit 5 Polynomial and Rational Functions	Unit 6 Circles and Circular Functions	Unit 7 Recursion and Iteration	Unit 8 Inverse Functions
Number and Operations								
Understand numbers, ways of representing numbers, relationships among numbers, and number systems	©	©						
Understand meanings of operations and how they relate to one another	©	©						©
Compute fluently and make reasonable estimates	©	©						
Algebra								
Understand patterns, relations, and functions	©	Ⓕ			Ⓕ	Ⓕ	Ⓕ	Ⓕ
Represent and analyze mathematical situations and structures using algebraic symbols	©	Ⓕ			Ⓕ	Ⓕ	Ⓕ	Ⓕ
Use mathematical models to represent and understand quantitative relationships	©	Ⓕ			Ⓕ	Ⓕ	Ⓕ	Ⓕ
Analyze change in various contexts	©	Ⓕ			Ⓕ	Ⓕ	Ⓕ	Ⓕ
Geometry								
Analyze characteristics and properties of two- and three-dimensional geometric shapes and develop mathematical arguments about geometric relationships	Ⓕ		Ⓕ			Ⓕ		
Specify locations and describe spatial relationships using coordinate geometry and other representational systems			©			©		
Apply transformations and use symmetry to analyze mathematical situations			Ⓕ			©		©
Use visualization, spatial reasoning, and geometric modeling to solve problems	©		Ⓕ			Ⓕ	©	
Measurement								
Understand measurable attributes of objects and the units, systems, and processes of measurement	©					©		
Apply appropriate techniques, tools, and formulas to determine measurements	©					©		
Data Analysis and Probability								
Formulate questions that can be addressed with data and collect, organize, and display relevant data to answer them	Ⓕ			Ⓕ				
Select and use appropriate statistical methods to analyze data	Ⓕ			Ⓕ				
Develop and evaluate inferences and predictions that are based on data	Ⓕ			Ⓕ				
Understand and apply basic concepts of probability	©			©				

Overview

Introduction

The first three courses in *Core-Plus Mathematics* provide a significant common core of broadly useful mathematics for all students. They were developed to prepare students for success in college, in careers, and in daily life in contemporary society. Course 4 continues the preparation of students for success in college mathematics and statistics courses. The program builds upon the theme of mathematics as sense-making. Through investigations of real-life contexts, students develop a rich understanding of important mathematics that makes sense to them and which, in turn, enables them to make sense out of new situations and problems.

Each course in *Core-Plus Mathematics* shares the following mathematical and instructional features.

• Integrated Content

Each year, the curriculum advances students' understanding of mathematics along interwoven strands of algebra and functions, statistics and probability, geometry and trigonometry, and discrete mathematics. These strands are unified by fundamental themes, by common topics, and by mathematical habits of mind or ways of thinking. Developing mathematics each year along multiple strands helps students develop diverse mathematical insights and nurtures their differing strengths and talents.

• Mathematical Modeling

The curriculum emphasizes mathematical modeling including the processes of data collection, representation, interpretation, prediction, and simulation. The modeling perspective permits students to experience mathematics as a means of making sense of data and problems that arise in diverse contexts within and across cultures.

• Access and Challenge

The curriculum is designed to make mathematics accessible to more students, while at the same time challenging the most able students. Differences in student performance and interest can be accommodated by the depth and level of abstraction to which core topics are pursued, by the nature and degree of difficulty of applications, and by providing opportunities for student choice of homework tasks and projects.

• Technology

Numeric, graphic, and symbolic manipulation capabilities such as those found on many graphing calculators are assumed and appropriately used throughout the curriculum. The curriculum materials also include a suite of computer software called *CPMP-Tools* that provide powerful aids to learning mathematics and solving mathematical problems. (See pages xviii–xix for further details.) This use of technology permits the curriculum and instruction to emphasize multiple representations (verbal, numerical, graphical, and symbolic) and to focus on goals in which mathematical thinking and problem solving are central.

- ## Active Learning

  Instructional materials promote active learning and teaching centered around collaborative investigations of problem situations followed by teacher-led whole-class summarizing activities that lead to analysis, abstraction, and further application of underlying mathematical ideas and principles. Students are actively engaged in exploring, conjecturing, verifying, generalizing, applying, proving, evaluating, and communicating mathematical ideas.

- ## Multi-dimensional Assessment

  Comprehensive assessment of student understanding and progress through both curriculum-embedded assessment opportunities and supplementary assessment tasks supports instruction and enables monitoring and evaluation of each student's performance in terms of mathematical processes, content, and dispositions.

Core-Plus Mathematics is designed to make mathematics accessible and more meaningful to more students. Developing mathematics along multiple strands nurtures the differing strengths and talents of students and simultaneously helps them to develop diverse mathematical insights. Developing mathematics from a modeling perspective permits students to experience mathematics as a means of making sense of data and problems that arise in diverse contexts within and across cultures. Engaging students in collaborating on tasks in small groups develops their ability to both deal with, and find commonality in, diversity of ideas. Using technology as a means for learning and doing mathematics enables students to develop versatile ways of dealing with realistic situations and reduces the manipulative skill filter which has prevented large numbers of students from continuing their study of significant mathematics. In addition, technology-produced graphics offer powerful new ways of visualizing mathematics across each of the strands.

Integrated Mathematics

Core-Plus Mathematics replaces the traditional Algebra-Geometry-Advanced Algebra/Trigonometry-Precalculus sequence of high school mathematics courses with a sequence of courses that features concurrent and connected development of important mathematics drawn from four strands.

Algebra and Functions

The Algebra and Functions strand develops student ability to recognize, represent, and solve problems involving relations among quantitative variables. Central to the development is the use of functions as mathematical models. The key algebraic models in the curriculum are linear, exponential, power, polynomial, logarithmic, rational, and trigonometric functions. Modeling with systems of equations, both linear and nonlinear, is developed. Attention is also given to symbolic reasoning and manipulation.

Geometry and Trigonometry

The primary goal of the Geometry and Trigonometry strand is to develop visual thinking and ability to construct, reason with, interpret, and apply mathematical models of patterns in visual and physical contexts. The focus is on describing patterns in shape, size, and location; representing patterns with drawings, coordinates, or vectors; predicting changes and invariants in shapes under transformations; and organizing geometric facts and relationships through deductive reasoning.

Statistics and Probability

The primary role of the Statistics and Probability strand is to develop student ability to analyze data intelligently, to recognize and measure variation, and to understand the patterns that underlie probabilistic situations. The ultimate goal is for students to understand how inferences can be made about a population by looking at a sample from that population. Graphical methods of data analysis, simulations, sampling, and experience with the collection and interpretation of real data are featured.

Discrete Mathematics

The Discrete Mathematics strand develops student ability to solve problems using vertex-edge graphs, recursion, matrices, systematic counting methods (combinatorics), and voting methods. Key themes are discrete mathematical modeling, optimization, and algorithmic problem-solving.

Connected Strands

Each of these strands of mathematics is developed within focused units connected by fundamental ideas such as symmetry, matrices, functions, data analysis, and curve-fitting. The strands also are connected across units by mathematical habits of mind such as visual thinking, recursive thinking, searching for and explaining patterns, making and checking conjectures, reasoning with multiple representations, inventing mathematics, and providing convincing arguments and proofs.

   The strands are unified further by the fundamental themes of data, representation, shape, and change. Important mathematical ideas are frequently revisited through this attention to connections within and across strands, enabling students to develop a robust and connected understanding of mathematics.

Organization of Course 3

Course 3 consists of eight units. Each of the units is comprised of two to four multi-day lessons in which major ideas are developed through investigation of rich applied problems. Units vary in length from approximately two to six weeks.

Unit 1 *Reasoning and Proof*   **Unit 5** *Polynomial and Rational Functions*
Unit 2 *Inequalities and Linear Programming*   **Unit 6** *Circles and Circular Functions*
Unit 3 *Similarity and Congruence*   **Unit 7** *Recursion and Iteration*
Unit 4 *Samples and Variation*   **Unit 8** *Inverse Functions*

   The 2nd Edition of Course 3 builds on the strengths of the 1st Edition. It includes mathematical content which the developers believed is the most important mathematics all students should have the opportunity to learn. In particular, the content of the last units in the text are not viewed as optional as is often the case with traditional textbooks. Depending on the mathematics standards and content expectations for your state, you may wish to have students complete all Course 2 units before they embark on Course 3 of the *Core-Plus Mathematics* series.

Instructional Model

The manner in which students encounter mathematical ideas can contribute significantly to the quality of their learning and the depth of their understanding. *Core-Plus Mathematics* units are designed around multi-day lessons centered on big ideas. Each lesson includes 2–4 focused mathematical investigations that engage students in a four-phase cycle of classroom activities, described in the following paragraphs—*Launch, Explore, Share and Summarize,* and *Apply.* This cycle is designed to engage students in investigating and making sense of problem situations, in constructing important mathematical concepts and methods, in generalizing and proving mathematical relationships, and in communicating, both orally and in writing, their thinking and the results of their efforts. Most classroom activities are designed to be completed by students working collaboratively in groups of two to four students.

LAUNCH class discussion

Think About This Situation

The lesson launch promotes a teacher-led discussion of a problem situation and of related questions to think about. This discussion sets the context for the student work to follow and helps to generate student interest. It also provides an opportunity for the teacher to assess student knowledge and to clarify directions for the investigation to follow.

EXPLORE group investigation

Investigation

Classroom activity then shifts to investigating focused problems and questions related to the launching situation by gathering data, looking for and explaining patterns, constructing models and meanings, and making and verifying conjectures. As students collaborate in pairs or small groups, the teacher circulates among students providing guidance and support, clarifying or asking questions, giving hints, providing encouragement, and drawing group members into the discussion to help groups collaborate more effectively. The investigations and related questions posed by students and teachers drive the learning.

SHARE AND SUMMARIZE class discussion

Summarize the Mathematics

This investigative work is followed by a teacher-led class discussion (referred to as Summarize the Mathematics) in which students summarize mathematical ideas developed in their groups, providing an opportunity to construct a shared understanding of important concepts, methods, and approaches. This discussion leads to a class summary of important ideas or to further exploration of a topic if competing perspectives remain. Varying points of view and differing conclusions that can be justified should be encouraged.

APPLY individual tasks

Check Your Understanding

Students are given a task to complete on their own to check and reinforce their initial understanding of concepts and methods.

Overview

Homework

In addition to the classroom investigations, *Core-Plus Mathematics* provides sets of On Your Own tasks, which are designed to engage students in applying, connecting, reflecting on, extending, and reviewing their evolving mathematical knowledge. On Your Own tasks are provided for each lesson in the materials and are central to the learning goals of each lesson. These tasks are intended primarily for individual work outside of class. Selection of homework tasks should be based on student performance and the availability of time and technology. Also, students should exercise some choice of tasks to pursue, and, at times should be given the opportunity to pose their own problems and questions to investigate. The chart below describes the types of tasks in a typical On Your Own set.

On Your Own: Homework Tasks	
Applications	These tasks provide opportunities for students to use and strengthen their understanding of the ideas they have learned in the lesson.
Connections	These tasks help students to build links between mathematical topics they have studied in the lesson and to connect those topics with other mathematics that they know.
Reflections	These tasks provide opportunities for students to re-examine their thinking about ideas in the lesson.
Extensions	These tasks provide opportunities for students to explore further or more deeply the mathematics they are learning.
Review	These tasks provide opportunities for just-in-time review and distributed practice of mathematical skills to maintain procedural fluency.

Additional Summarizing Activities

In *Core-Plus Mathematics*, students learn mathematics by doing mathematics. However, it is important that students prepare and maintain summaries of important concepts and methods that are developed. Students should create a Math Toolkit that organizes important class-generated ideas and selected Summarize the Mathematics responses as they complete investigations. Math Toolkit Prompts are provided in this *Teacher's Guide* to assist in identifying and summarizing key concepts and methods as they are developed by students.

In addition, the final lesson in each unit is a Looking Back lesson that helps students review and synthesize the key mathematical concepts and techniques developed in the unit. The Summarize the Mathematics questions in this lesson are focused on key ideas of the unit. The Check Your Understanding asks students to prepare a summary of the important concepts and skills developed in the unit. Templates to guide preparation of these unit summaries can be found in the *Unit Resource Masters*. Completed Unit Summaries should become part of students' Math Toolkits.

Students should retain their Math Toolkits as they continue on to Course 4. In some districts, teachers collect these resources at the end of the school year and return them to students in the fall.

Multiple Approaches to Assessment

Assessing what students know and are able to do is an integral part of *Core-Plus Mathematics*. There are opportunities for assessment in each phase of the instructional cycle. Initially, as students pursue the investigations that comprise the curriculum, the teacher is able to informally assess student understanding of mathematical processes and content and their disposition toward mathematics. At the end of each investigation, a class discussion to Summarize the Mathematics provides an opportunity for the teacher to assess levels of understanding that various groups of students have reached as they share and explain their findings. Finally, the Check Your Understanding tasks and the tasks in the On Your Own sets provide further opportunities to assess the level of understanding of each individual student. Quizzes, in-class tests, take-home assessment tasks, and extended projects are included in the teacher resource materials.

A more detailed description of the complete assessment program is given on pages xxi–xv of this text and in *Implementing Core-Plus Mathematics*.

Practicing for Standardized Tests

Opportunities for additional review and practice are provided in eight Preparing for Standardized Tests practice sets included in the *Unit Resource Masters*. Each Practicing for Standardized Tests master presents 10 questions and a test-taking tip. The questions are presented in the form of test items similar to how they often appear in standardized tests such as state assessments tests, the Scholastic Aptitude Test (SAT), or the ACT test. By using these practice sets, students can become familiar with the formats of standardized tests and develop effective test-taking strategies for performing well on such tests.

Access, Equity, and Differentiation

Several research studies have provided evidence that introducing activities through class discussion, teaching students to explain and justify, and making real-world contexts accessible to students promote greater access and equity in mathematics classrooms. (Boaler, J. "Learning from Teaching: Exploring the Relationship Between Reform Curriculum and Equity," *Journal for Research in Mathematics Education*, 2002, Vol. 33, No. 4, 239–258, and Brown, C.A., Stein, M.K., and Forman, E. A. "Assisting teachers and students to reform their mathematics classroom," *Education Studies in Mathematics*, 1996, 31–93). These practices that help promote equity are briefly discussed below.

Introducing Activities Through Class Discussions Group and class discussions of the aim of activities, the meaning of contexts, the challenging points within problems, and possible problem access points to which students might turn make tasks more evenly accessible to all students.

Teaching Students to Explain and Justify their Thinking Giving explicit attention to explaining thinking and evaluating what makes a good piece of work helps students improve their work.

Making Real-world Contexts Accessible Considering the constraints that real situations involve and connecting these situations with issues and topics in their own lives helps students view mathematics as something that will help them interpret their world.

Other Practices that Promote Equity Mixed-ability classes, a focus on problems solving, high expectations for all students, attention to a broad array of mathematical topics, and allowing students to restate problems in their own words also appear to help students from different racial, ethnic, and linguistic groups be more successful in mathematics.

Overview

Core-Plus Mathematics offers many opportunities for teachers to incorporate these practices into daily routines. One such built-in opportunity is the Think About This Situations (TATS) used to introduce lessons through discussions. Although no TATS questions are in the student text for individual investigations there are often suggestions in the *Teacher's Guide* for class launches of investigations. Since much of the mathematical content is based on real contexts, it is important that all students understand the contexts and draw on their own or a classmates background knowledge. Opportunities for students to explain and justify their thinking are built into all curriculum features. Look for opportunities to encourage the habit of mind of justifying one's thinking as students work individually and participate in small-group or class discussions.

The *Teacher's Guide* periodically includes notes that provide specific ideas for differentiation at point of use. Look for the margin notes.

Implementing the Curriculum

Considering mathematics topics and knowledge presented at each grade level and how that knowledge is built upon in succeeding grades is key to improving student learning. To support building the teacher expertise to effectively implement *Core-Plus Mathematics* the developers recommend that districts begin adoption with Course 1 and add a course level each year. Encourage teachers to progress from Course 1 to Course 4 in stages, so they can develop an understanding of the growth of mathematical ideas in the curriculum. Realize that teachers will need time and support to improve instruction for their students.

Additional advice related to successful implementation is on the Core-Plus Mathematics Project (CPMP) Web site at www.wmich.edu/cpmp under Implementation.

Planning for Instruction

The *Core-Plus Mathematics* curriculum is not only changing what mathematics all students have the opportunity to learn, but also changing how that learning occurs and is assessed. Active learning is most effective when accompanied with active teaching. Just as the student text is designed to actively engage students in doing mathematics, the teacher's resource materials are designed to support teachers in planning for instruction; in observing, listening, questioning, and facilitating student work, and orchestrating classroom discussion; and in managing the classroom.

The *Teacher's Guide* provides suggestions, based on the experiences of field-test teachers, for implementing this exciting new curriculum in your classroom. You probably will find new ideas that can at first be overwhelming. The developers highly recommend that teachers who are teaching *Core-Plus Mathematics* for the first time do so at least in pairs who share a common planning period.

Each of the items listed below is included in the *Teacher's Guide* for each unit.
- Unit overview and lesson overviews
- Objectives, suggested timeline and assignments, and materials needed
- Instructional notes and suggestions
- Solutions for investigations and homework tasks
- Promoting Mathematical Discourse scenarios

Overview

Each *Unit Resource Masters* includes reproducible masters for teaching, student activities, technology tips, a unit summary, and practicing for standardized tests. Also included in each *Unit Resource Masters* is the assessment package for the unit as outlined on pages xxi–xxiv.

A first step toward planning the teaching of a unit is to review the scope and sequence of the unit. This review provides an overall feel for the goals and coherence of the unit. The *Scope and Sequence* guide (www.glencoe.com) shows where specific mathematical topics fit in the complete four-year curriculum. Working through the student investigations, if possible with a colleague, provides help in thinking about possible student responses and understanding mathematical ideas that may be unfamiliar.

In the *Teacher's Guide*, at the beginning of each unit, you will find a Planning Guide to assist in overall planning. This resource gives a quick overview of lessons, suggested assignments, materials needed, and pacing suggestions.

You will also find teaching notes for each lesson, including instructional suggestions and sample student responses to investigations and homework sets. Thinking about the range of possible responses and solutions to problems proves to be very helpful in facilitating student work.

Some teachers choose to post the homework assignment at the beginning of a lesson along with the due date—usually a day or two following planned completion of the lesson. Other teachers prefer to assign particular tasks at appropriate points during the course of the multiday investigation, and then assign the remaining tasks toward the end of the lesson. Review tasks can be assigned before the completion of the investigation. Note that all recommended assignments include provision for student choice of some tasks. This is but one of many ways in which this curriculum is designed to accommodate and support differences in students' interests and performance levels.

It is strongly recommended that student solutions to Connections tasks be discussed in class. These tasks help students organize and formalize the mathematics developed in context and connect it to other mathematics they have studied. Structuring the underlying mathematics and building connections are best accomplished by comparing and discussing student work and synthesizing key ideas within the classroom.

Some recommended assignments include Just-in-Time Review tasks. It is important that these tasks be assigned as indicated in the Planning Guide to help ensure understanding of ideas or procedures needed in the next investigation.

Technology in Course 3

In the 21st century, anyone who faces the challenge of learning mathematics or using mathematics to solve problems can draw on the resources of powerful information technology tools. Calculators and computers can help with calculations, drawing, and data analysis in mathematical explorations and solving mathematical problems. (See the NCTM position paper on technology at: www.nctm.org/about/content.aspx?id=14233)

Graphing Calculators: Graphing calculators with iteration capabilities are assumed for class work and homework. Computer algebra system (CAS) capabilities are desirable.

Overview

Computers: Periodically, it would be valuable to have one classroom computer for whole class discussions, 4–6 classroom computers for groups to use as stations during investigations, portable classroom sets of computers, or computer lab access. For some homework tasks, school or home computer availability is also desirable.

Computer software: The use of spreadsheet, interactive geometry, data analysis, simulation, and function iteration software and computer algebra systems (CAS) is incorporated into Course 3 units. The curriculum materials include computer software called *CPMP-Tools* specifically designed to support student learning and problem solving.

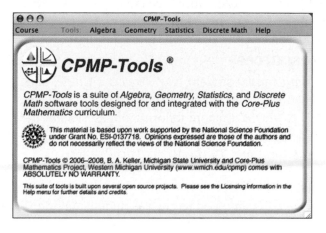

The software toolkit includes four families of programs:

Algebra The software for work on algebra problems includes an electronic spreadsheet and a computer algebra system (CAS) that produces tables and graphs of functions, manipulates algebraic expressions, and solves equations and inequalities.

Geometry The software for work on geometry problems includes an interactive drawing program for constructing, measuring, and manipulating geometric figures and a set of custom tools for exploring properties of figures and geometric models of physical mechanisms.

Statistics The software for work on data analysis and probability problems provides tools for graphic display and analysis of data, simulation of probabilistic situations, and mathematical modeling of quantitative relationships.

Discrete Mathematics The software for work on graph theory problems provides tools for constructing, manipulating, and analyzing vertex-edge graphs.

In addition to the general purpose tools provided for work on tasks in each strand of the curriculum, *CPMP-Tools* includes files of most data sets essential for work on problems in *Core-Plus Mathematics* Course 3. When students see an opportunity to use computer tools for work on a particular investigation, they can select the *CPMP-Tools* menu corresponding to the content involved in the problem. For problems involving built-in or student-provided data sets, they can select the submenu items corresponding to the required mathematical operations and data sets. Each unit overview in the *Teacher's Guide* provides general information related to *CPMP-Tools* use in the unit. Technology notes at point of use alert teachers to applicable software and specific data sets included in the software.

Materials Needed for Course 3

The following is a complete list of items used in the eight units of Course 3. Each unit Planning Guide indicates the items used in that unit.

Necessary

Compass, straightedge, protractor
Pennies (100 per group)
Quarters (1 per pair)
Rulers with metric and English markings
Linkage strips (Glencoe order number 39494)
Pipe cleaners, dental floss, or string

Electronic Resources

The *Core-Plus Mathematics* student text, *Teacher's Guide,* and *Unit Resource Masters* are included for viewing and printing from the *Core-Plus Mathematics TeacherWorks Plus* CD-ROM. Custom tailoring of assessment items can be accomplished by using the *ExamView* Assessment Suites. *CPMP-Tools* is available on both the *StudentWorks* and *TeacherWorks Plus* CD-ROMs.

Orchestrating Lessons

Core-Plus Mathematics is designed to engage students in a four-phase cycle of classroom activities. The activities in Course 3 often require both students and teachers to assume roles quite different than those in more traditional mathematics classrooms. Students successfully completing Courses 1 and 2 should have become accustomed to these new roles. Although realistic problem solving and investigative work by students are the heart of the curriculum, how teachers orchestrate the launching of an investigation and the sharing and summarizing of results is critical to successful implementation.

Students enter the classroom with differing strengths, experience, and knowledge. These differences can be viewed as assets. Engaging the class in a free-flowing give-and-take discussion of how students think about the launch situations serves to connect lessons with the informal understandings of data, shape, change, and chance that students bring to the classroom. Try to maximize the participation of students in these discussions by emphasizing that their ideas and possible approaches are valued and important and that definitive answers are not necessarily expected at this time.

Overview

Once launched, an investigation may involve students working together collaboratively in small groups for a period of days punctuated occasionally by brief class discussion of questions students have raised. In this setting, the investigation becomes driven primarily by the instructional materials themselves. Rather than orchestrating class discussion, the teacher shifts to circulating among the groups and observing, listening, and interacting with students by asking guiding or probing questions. These small-group investigations lead to (re)invention of important mathematics that make sense to students. Sharing, and agreeing as a class, on the mathematical ideas that groups are developing is the purpose of the Summarizing the Mathematics (STM) in the instructional materials.

Class discussions at STMs are orchestrated somewhat differently than during the launch of a lesson. At this stage, mathematical ideas and methods still may be under development and may vary for individual groups. So class discussion should involve groups comparing their methods and results, analyzing their work, and arriving at conclusions agreed upon by the class.

Periodically, you will find samples of class discussions centered around Think About This Situation or Summarize the Mathematics questions at point of use. These sample discussions, called Promoting Mathematical Discourse, may provide some ideas for your class discussions. These sample discussions are indicated by PROMOTING MATHEMATICAL DISCOURSE .

Assessment

Throughout the *Core-Plus Mathematics* curriculum, the term "assessment" is meant to include all instances of gathering information about students' levels of understanding and their disposition toward mathematics for purposes of making decisions about instruction. You may want to consult the extended section on assessment in *Implementing Core-Plus Mathematics*.

The dimensions of student performance that are assessed in this curriculum (see chart below) are consistent with the assessment recommendations of the National Council of Teachers of Mathematics in the *Assessment Standards for School Mathematics* (NCTM, 1995). They are more comprehensive than those of a typical testing program.

Assessment Dimensions		
Process	**Content**	**Disposition**
Problem Solving	Concepts	Beliefs
Reasoning	Applications	Perseverance
Communication	Mathematical Representation	Confidence
Connections	Procedures	Enthusiasm

Overview

Sources of Assessment Information

Several kinds of assessment are available to teachers using *Core-Plus Mathematics*. Some of these sources reside within the student text itself, some of them are student-generated, and some are materials designed specifically for assessment. Understanding the nature of these sources is a prerequisite for selecting assessment tools, establishing guidelines on how to score assessments, making judgments about what students know and are able to do, and assigning grades.

Curriculum Sources

Two features of the curriculum, questioning and observation by the teacher, provide fundamental and particularly useful ways of gathering formative assessment information. The student text uses questions to facilitate student understanding of new concepts, of how these concepts fit with earlier ideas and with one another, and of how they can be applied in problem situations. Whether students are working individually or in groups, the teacher is given a window to watch how the students think about and apply mathematics as they attempt to answer the questions posed in the curriculum materials. In fact, by observing how students respond to the curriculum-embedded questions, the teacher can assess student performance across all process, content, and attitude dimensions described in the chart on page xxi.

Specific features in the student material that focus on different ways students respond to questions are the Summarize the Mathematics, Check Your Understanding, and the On Your Own homework sets. Summarize the Mathematics features are intended to bring students together, usually after they have been working in small groups, so they may share and discuss the progress each group has made during a sequence of related activities. The questions in the Summarize the Mathematics are focused on the mathematical concepts and procedures developed in the investigation. They should help the teacher and the students identify and formalize the key ideas of the investigation. Each Summarize the Mathematics is intended to be treated as a whole-class discussion, so it should provide an opportunity for teachers to assess, informally, the levels of understanding that the various groups of students have reached.

Following each Summarize the Mathematics, the Check Your Understanding tasks are meant to be completed by students working individually. Student responses to these tasks provide an opportunity for teachers to assess the level of understanding of each student.

The tasks in the On Your Own homework sets serve many purposes, including post-investigation assessment. Each type of task in the On Your Own homework sets has a different instructional purpose. Applications tasks provide opportunities for students to demonstrate how well they understand and can use the ideas they learned in the investigations of the lesson. Work on Connections tasks demonstrates how well the students understand links between mathematical topics they studied in the lesson and their ability to connect those topics with other mathematics that they know. Reflections tasks provide insight into students' mathematical thinking and strategic competence. Extensions tasks reveal how well students are able to extend the present

Overview

content beyond the level addressed in the investigations. The Review tasks allow for pre-assessment of students' understanding of ideas or procedures needed in the upcoming lessons and also provide information on how well students are retaining previously learned mathematics. The performance of students or groups of students on each of these types of tasks provides the teacher with further information to help assess each student's evolving ability to use, connect, and extend the mathematics of the lesson.

Finally, an opportunity for group self-assessment is provided in the last element of each unit, the Looking Back lesson. These tasks help students pull together and demonstrate what they have learned in the unit and at the same time provide helpful review and confidence-building for students.

Student-Generated Sources

Mathematics Toolkits Students should create a Math Toolkit that organizes important class-generated ideas and selected Summarize the Mathematics responses as they complete investigations. Constructing a Math Toolkit prompts are provided in the *Teacher's Guide* to assist in identifying key concepts and methods as they are developed by students.

Unit Summaries A summary template intended to help students organize and record the main ideas learned in the unit is provided in each *Unit Resource Masters*. The synthesis of ideas that occurs during completion of the "Looking Back" lesson and the final unit Summarize the Mathematics discussion should provide the background for student completion of the unit summary.

Assessment Resources

Each *Unit Resource Masters* includes lesson quizzes and unit assessments in the form of tests, take-home tasks, and projects. There are also banks of questions and projects from which you can form end of semester exams following the Unit 4 and Unit 8 assessment masters. Calculators are assumed in most cases and are intended to be available to students. Teacher discretion should be used regarding student access to their textbook and Math Toolkit for assessments. In general, if the goals to be assessed are problem solving and reasoning, while memory of facts and procedural skill are of less interest, resources may be allowed. However, if automaticity of procedures or unaided recall are being assessed, it is appropriate to prohibit resource materials.

The *ExamView* software can be used to modify the curriculum provided assessment items or to create formal assessments using a combination of curriculum supplied items and ones by the teacher.

Lesson Quizzes Two forms of a quiz covering the main ideas of each lesson are provided. These quizzes are comprised of problems meant to determine if students have developed understanding of the important concepts and procedures of each lesson. The two forms of each quiz are not necessarily equivalent, although they assess essentially the same mathematical ideas. Since many rich opportunities for assessing students are embedded in the curriculum itself, you may choose not to use a quiz at the end of every lesson.

Overview

Unit Tests Two forms of tests are provided for each unit and are intended to be completed in a 50-minute class period. The two forms of each test are not necessarily equivalent, although they assess essentially the same mathematical ideas. Teachers should preview the two versions carefully to be sure that the unit assessment aligns with the learning goals emphasized.

Take-Home Assessments Take-home assessment tasks are included for each unit. The students or the teacher should choose one or, at most, two of these tasks. These assessments, some of which are best done by students working in pairs or small groups, provide students with the opportunity to organize the information from the completed unit, to work with another student or group of students, to engage in in-depth problem solving, to grapple with new and more complex situations related to the mathematics of the unit, and to avoid the time pressure often generated by in-class exams. These problems may also require more extensive use of technology than is often available in the regular classroom during testing situations. You may wish to use these more in-depth problems as a replacement for a portion of an in-class end-of-unit exam.

Projects Assessment traditionally has been based on evaluating work that students have completed in a very short time period and under restricted conditions. Some assessment, however, should involve work done over a longer time period and with the aid of resources. Thus, assessment projects are included in unit assessments. These projects, which are intended to be completed by small groups of students, provide an opportunity for students to conduct an investigation that extends and applies the main ideas from the unit and to write a summary of their findings. Many of these might also allow for students to present their work in a variety of ways. You may have students who would rather prepare and present their work orally or visually using computers and/or video equipment. In this way, the projects can provide an opportunity for students to use their creativity while demonstrating their understanding of mathematics.

Midterm and Final Assessments A bank of assessment tasks, from which to construct midterm and final exams that fit your particular class needs and emphases, are provided in the Unit 4 and Unit 8 *Unit Resource Masters*. In addition to problems similar in form to those on the quizzes and tests, these assessment banks include several multiple-choice problems for each unit.

Extended assessment projects are also included with the end-of-year assessments. These projects are investigations that make use of many of the main ideas encountered in the curriculum. They require use of material from more than one unit. The projects are intended to be completed by small groups of students working over a period of time. You may wish to have different groups work on different projects and then give presentations or create posters of their work.

Portfolios The *Core-Plus Mathematics* assessment program provides many tasks that can be placed in students' portfolios, including reports of individual and group projects, Math Toolkits, teacher-completed observation checklists, unit assessments (especially the take-home tasks), and projects. See *Implementing Core-Plus Mathematics* for additional portfolio information.

Overview

Scoring Assessments

High expectations of the quality of students' written work will encourage students to reach their potential. Assigning scores to open-ended assessments and to observations of students' performance requires more subjective judgment by the teacher than does grading short-answer or multiple-choice tests. It is therefore not possible to provide a complete set of explicit guidelines for scoring open-ended assessment items and written or oral reports. However, some general guidelines may be helpful. When scoring student work on open-ended assessment tasks, the goal is to reward, in a fair and consistent way, the kinds of thinking and understanding that the task is meant to measure. To score open-ended assessment tasks, teachers should have a general rubric, or scoring scheme, with several response levels in mind; a specific rubric and anchor items. (See *Implementing Core-Plus Mathematics* for more details.) The general rubric is the foundation for scoring across a wide range of types of open-ended tasks. The following general rubric can be used for most assessment tasks provided with *Core-Plus Mathematics*.

General Scoring Rubric	
4 points	Contains complete response with clear, coherent, and unambiguous explanation; includes clear and simple diagram, if appropriate; communicates effectively to identified audience; shows understanding of question's mathematical ideas and processes; identifies all important elements of question; includes examples and counterexamples; gives strong supporting arguments
3 points	Contains good solid response with some, but not all, of the characteristics above; explains less completely; may include minor error of execution but not of understanding
2 points	Contains complete response, but explanation is muddled; presents incomplete arguments; includes diagrams that are inappropriate or unclear, or fails to provide a diagram when it would be appropriate; indicates some understanding of mathematical ideas, but in an unclear way; shows clear evidence of understanding some important ideas while also making one or more fundamental, specific errors
1 point	Omits parts of question and response; has major errors; uses inappropriate strategies
0 points	No response; frivolous or irrelevant response

Assigning Grades

Since the *Core-Plus Mathematics* approach and materials provide a wide variety of assessment information, the teacher will be in a good position to assign appropriate grades. With such a wide choice for assessment, a word of caution is appropriate. *It is easy to overassess students.* The developers believe it is best to vary assessment methods from lesson to lesson, and from unit to unit. If information on what students understand and are able to do is available from their homework and in-class work, it may not be necessary to take the time for a formal quiz after each lesson. Similarly, information from take-home assessments or project work may replace all or portions of an in-class test.

Deciding exactly how to weigh the various kinds of assessment information is a decision that the teacher will need to make and communicate clearly to students.

Managing Classroom Activities

Active Learning and Collaborative Work

The *Core-Plus Mathematics* curriculum materials are designed to promote active, collaborative learning and group work for two important reasons. First, a collaborative environment fosters students' ability to make sense of mathematics and develop deep mathematical understandings. Collaborative learning is an effective method for engaging all the students in the learning process, particularly students who have been under represented in mathematics classes. Second, practice in collaborative learning in the classroom is practice for real life: students develop and exercise the same skills in the classroom that they need in their lives at home, in the community, and in the workplace.

Value of Individuals

Perhaps the most fundamental belief underlying the use of collaborative learning is that every student is viewed as a valuable resource and contributor. In other words, every student participates in group work and is given the opportunity and time to voice ideas and opinions. Implementing this concept is not easy nor does it happen automatically. In order to set a tone that will promote respect for individuals and their contributions, classroom norms should be established. Teachers should initiate a discussion and together write all the student formulated classroom rules for both individual and group behavior. The positively stated rules of behavior should be posted in the classroom and every member of the learning community should be held responsible for adhering to them.

Importance of Social Connections

Even in classrooms in which the rules for showing respect have been clearly established, experience has shown that students still cannot talk with one another about mathematics (or social studies, or literature, or any other subject) if they do not first have positive social connections.

One way to develop this kind of common base is through team-building activities. These short activities may be used at the beginning of the year to help students get acquainted with the whole class, and may be used during the year whenever new groups are formed to help groupmates know one another better. Team-building activities help students learn new and positive things about classmates with whom they may have attended classes for years, but have not known in depth. The time taken for these quick team builders pays off later in helping students feel comfortable enough to work with the members of their group.

Need for Teaching Social Skills

Experience also has shown that social skills are critical to the successful functioning of any small group. Because there is no guarantee that students of any particular age will have the social skills necessary for effective group work, it often is necessary to teach these skills to build a collaborative learning environment.

These social skills are specific skills, not general goals. Examples of specific social skills that the teacher can teach in the classroom include responding to ideas respectfully, keeping track of time, disagreeing in an agreeable way, involving everyone, and following directions. Though goals such as cooperating and listening are important, they are too general to teach.

One of the premises of collaborative learning is that by developing the appropriate skills through practice, anyone in the class can learn to work in a group with anyone else. Learning to work in groups is a continuous process, however, and the process can be helped by decisions that the teacher makes.

One method of teaching social skills is to begin by selecting a specific skill and then having the class brainstorm to develop a script for practicing that skill. Next, the students practice that skill during their group work. Finally, in what is called the processing, the students discuss within their groups how well they performed the assigned social skill. Effective teaching of social skills requires practicing and processing; merely describing a specific social skill is not enough. The *Teacher's Guide* includes specific collaborative skills to practice and processing prompts for student self-assessment.

The culture and teaching-learning norms created within the classroom are crucial to the success of this curriculum. It is important to inculcate in students a sense of inquiry and responsibility for their own learning. Without this commitment, active, collaborative learning by students cannot be effective. Some students seem satisfied with the rationale that collaboration is important in workplace. Others may need to understand that the struggle of verbalizing their thinking, listening to others' thinking, questioning themselves and other group members, and coming to an agreement increases their understanding and retention of the mathematics while contributing to the formation of important thinking skills or habits of mind.

Issues of helping students to work collaboratively will become less pressing as both you and your students experience this type of learning. *Implementing Core-Plus Mathematics* provides additional information related to the challenge of facilitating collaborative work including support to help teachers make decisions about group size, composition, method of selection, the duration of groups and dealing with student absences. This resource also offers a number of practical suggestions from *Core-Plus Mathematics* teachers on effectively pacing instruction in a student-centered classroom.

Additional Resources

Implementing Core-Plus Mathematics contains expanded information on:
- the scope and sequence of Courses 1–4,
- managing classroom activities,
- differentiation built into the program,
- the assessment program,
- communication with parents, and
- mathematics program evaluation.

You will find it useful to have the implementation guide available for reference throughout the school year. This booklet can found on the *TeacherWorks* CD.

Scope and Sequence contains information on:
- the scope and sequence of Courses 1–4
- units in which key mathematical ideas are developed

You can download this booklet at: glencoe.com and www.wmich.edu/cpmp/pdfs/scopeandsequence.pdf

Math Link articles related to *Core-Plus Mathematics* written by developers and teachers are available on the *Core-Plus Mathematics* Project Web site at www.wmich.edu/cpmp under Publications. These articles were written based on first edition experiences, but in many cases are still applicable to the second edition materials.

Topics include:
- selecting and implementing *Core-Plus Mathematics*,
- effectively using collaborative groups,
- the four-year mathematics program,
- options for acceleration paths to AP Calculus or AP Statistics,
- meeting the needs of ELL and LEP students,
- college placement,
- the International Baccalaureate Program, and
- achievement in Science.

Annotated Bibliography Available on the CPMP Web site under Publications are references to articles, book chapters, dissertations, papers presented at conferences, and field-test reports based on the program. Some of these resources can be downloaded.

Professional Development Opportunities A variety of professional development opportunities are provided by Glencoe and the Core-Plus Mathematics Project. Workshops are listed on the CPMP Web site www.wmich.edu/cpmp under Implementation. Experienced *Core-Plus Mathematics* teacher-consultants can be contracted to provide onsite inservice. Contact your Glencoe sales representative or the CPMP office (cpmp@wmich.edu) for provider names.

Parent Resource Information and resources for parents including helping with homework, research supporting *Core-Plus Mathematics*, evidence of success, and frequently asked questions is available at www.wmich.edu/cpmp/parentresource/index.html.

REASONING AND PROOF

Life presents many opportunities to use logical reasoning in solving problems and drawing conclusions from information. Whether it is developing a winning strategy in a favorite game, figuring out how to build or repair something, or learning how to drive defensively, the ability to ask yourself "What will happen if … ?" is fundamental. Quite often, it is the ability of an athlete, a detective, or a lawyer to use reasoning that makes that person stand out from the crowd.

In this unit, you will examine more carefully the reasoning strategies you have used in your prior mathematics study. You will learn some basic principles of logical reasoning that underline those strategies and develop skill in applying that understanding to mathematical questions in geometry, algebra, and statistics. The key ideas will be developed through work on problems in four lessons.

Lessons

1 Reasoning Strategies

Analyze and use deductive and inductive reasoning strategies in everyday situations and in mathematical contexts.

2 Geometric Reasoning and Proof

Use inductive reasoning to discover and deductive reasoning to prove relations among angles formed by two intersecting lines or by two parallel lines and a transversal.

3 Algebraic Reasoning and Proof

Use symbolic notation to represent numerical patterns and relationships and use rules for transforming algebraic expressions and equations to prove those facts.

4 Statistical Reasoning

Know the characteristics of a well-designed experiment and use statistical reasoning to decide whether one treatment causes a better result than a second treatment.

REASONING AND PROOF

Unit Overview

In the first two courses of *Core-Plus Mathematics*, students have come to understand mathematics as an active science of exploring, discovering, explaining, and applying patterns in quantity and change, shape and motion, and data and change. Beginning with Course 3, informal mathematical explanations and reasoning are extended to more formal arguments and proofs. This first unit signals the new expectations and provides a logical foundation for proof. Key geometric ideas from Course 1 and Course 2 that will be useful in Course 3 are listed on pages T1C–T1E. A Student Master containing these ideas is available.

Lesson 1 *Reasoning Strategies* In this unit, students begin to develop an understanding of mathematical reasoning in geometric, algebraic, and statistical contexts. They begin by examining arguments presented in differing forms and using differing reasoning strategies. They are asked to judge these arguments on the basis of how well the arguments convince them that the asserted proposition is true. From these experiences, they are asked to identify characteristics of arguments that make them convincing and logically correct.

Lesson 2 *Geometric Reasoning and Proof* Once an initial understanding of desirable characteristics of a mathematical argument is developed, students are asked in Lesson 2 to construct arguments for familiar geometric relationships involving lines and angles. It is here that the need for certain assumptions (postulates) is introduced. The assumption about linear pairs states that adjacent angles formed by two intersecting lines have angle sum 180°. The assumption about parallel lines asserts the equality of measures of corresponding angles formed by two lines and a transversal. These two assumptions are used to prove familiar relations involving perpendicular lines and measures of angles when parallel lines are cut by a transversal.

Lesson 3 *Algebraic Reasoning and Proof* In Lesson 3, students continue to develop their reasoning skills in the context of algebra. The first investigations focus on the use of algebraic reasoning to show that a numerical pattern observed to be true for several specific cases (inductive reasoning) is true for all cases. The second investigation focuses on situations in which one wants to establish a general relationship between two or more variables by proving that an equation or inequality is true for all or most values of the variables.

Lesson 4 *Statistical Reasoning* In Lesson 4, students extend their ability to reason statistically. They learn how to design a good experiment to compare two different treatments and how to use randomization to produce a sampling distribution in order to decide if one treatment is more effective than another treatment. Finally, they learn the difference between sample surveys, experiments, and observational studies.

Unit Objectives

- Recognize the differences between, as well as the complementary nature of, inductive and deductive reasoning
- Develop some facility in analyzing and producing deductive arguments in everyday contexts and in geometric, algebraic, and statistical contexts
- Know and be able to use the relations among the angles formed when two lines intersect, including the special case of perpendicular lines
- Know and be able to use the necessary and sufficient conditions for two lines to be parallel
- Use symbolic notation to represent numerical patterns and relationships and use rules for transforming algebraic expressions and equations to prove those facts
- Distinguish between sample surveys, experiments, and observational studies; know the characteristics of a well-designed experiment
- Use statistical reasoning to decide whether one treatment causes a better result than a second treatment

Developing Proof-Writing Skills

Students who find writing proofs difficult, can often benefit from examining and critiquing the proofs of others. You might also consider providing them with plans for proofs to ctitique. In some cases, you might also have students write a proof based on a provided plan. Providing variations in proof outlines may provide a transition to more formal language.

Student masters have been developed to provide scaffolding as students develop their proof-writing skills. The first proof-support master provides a partial paragraph proof for students to complete. Other masters provide statements and reasons in two-column format. The statements and reasons are formatted as strips that teachers can cut, mix, and place in envelopes for distribution and later storage. Students find that initial work with these strips helps them in making important decisions about where they might begin a proof and the sequencing of statements in a proof. This sequence of masters is designed to gradually withdraw the proof-writing support as students progress through this and other units in Course 3. Notes and Teacher's Resources minis indicate the problems for which this support is provided.

When students write their own proofs, encourage them to use phrases like "it follows that ..." or "we know ... , so we can conclude that ... ." Students will continue to develop proof-writing skills throughout Courses 3 and in Course 4.

Writing Thorough Responses

Helping students develop skills in writing complete and concise solutions is one of the goals of this curriculum. However, always writing thorough responses can unnecessarily slow student progress through the investigations. As a guideline, we suggest that during investigations, students should make notes of their thinking and discussion of ideas rather than use complete sentences. Investigation time can be thought of as draft work or getting ideas out for examination and discussion. For investigation problems that ask students to explain reasoning, compare, etc., you may want to require complete sentence responses. Student responses to the Summarize the Mathematics and Mathematics Toolkit entries should be more complete. If these responses are

Teaching Resources

Student Master 2.

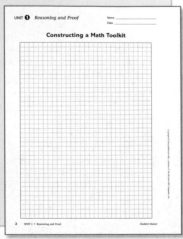

written following the class summary of important mathematical ideas, students will be able to write more thorough responses. Solutions to homework tasks from the On Your Own set should also be thoroughly written.

CPMP-Tools

CPMP-Tools software is a suite of Java-based mathematical software specifically designed to support student learning and problem solving in each strand of *Core-Plus Mathematics*. The software includes four families of programs: *Algebra* (spreadsheet and CAS), *Geometry* (coordinate and synthetic), *Statistics*, and *Discrete Math*. Additional information about the course-specific software for Course 3 is included in the front matter of this *Teacher's Guide*.

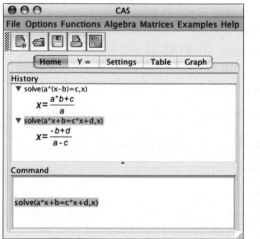

In this unit, students will be encouraged to use a CAS to check their solutions for equations that they have solved as shown below. The "Randomization Distribution" feature in *CPMP-Tools* has been developed to quickly perform random assignments of responses from experiments. The distribution can be used to estimate the probability that you would get a difference in means that is at least as extreme as the observed difference in means even if there is no difference in the effect of the treatments. A Technology Tip is provided in the *Unit 1 Resource Masters* to help students use this feature.

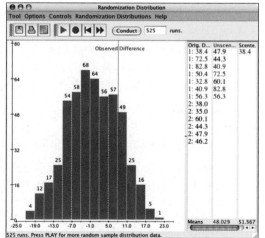

Assessment for Unit 1

In this unit, students continue to develop their skills and dispositions toward careful reasoning and proof. It is important to provide feedback on student work during investigations and on their homework tasks. This can be accomplished by having groups of students share their arguments and supporting reasoning for whole-class discussion. For selected homework tasks, students could compare their work with others prior to whole-class discussion.

Be careful not to over-assess in this unit. By carefully observing students at work and monitoring progress toward unit objectives, it is sufficient to simply administer a quiz after each of the four lessons.

Students will continue to develop reasoning and proof facility throughout Course 3 and Course 4.

Review Tasks in the On Your Own Homework Sets

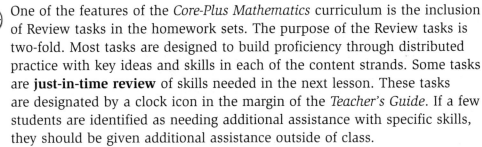
One of the features of the *Core-Plus Mathematics* curriculum is the inclusion of Review tasks in the homework sets. The purpose of the Review tasks is two-fold. Most tasks are designed to build proficiency through distributed practice with key ideas and skills in each of the content strands. Some tasks are **just-in-time review** of skills needed in the next lesson. These tasks are designated by a clock icon in the margin of the *Teacher's Guide*. If a few students are identified as needing additional assistance with specific skills, they should be given additional assistance outside of class.

Practicing for Standardized Tests

In order to provide practice with multiple-choice questions and additional review, eight Practice Sets are available in the *Unit Resource Masters*. You will notice that a couple of the questions are related to ideas from the unit just completed, but the majority are designed to provide additional review and practice in multiple-choice format as is common on standardized tests. You will also find a test-taking tip with each practice set. One of these sets should be assigned following each unit test. For more detail on this feature see the front matter of this Teacher's Guide and the Unit 1 URMs page 86.

Key Geometric Ideas from Courses 1 and 2

This unit builds on important geometric concepts and relationships developed in the previous *Core-Plus Mathematics* geometry units. Specifically:

Definitions

Isosceles triangle A triangle with at least two sides of equal length

Median of a triangle The line segment joining a vertex to the midpoint of the opposite side.

Parallelogram A quadrilateral with two pairs of opposite sides of equal length; or, equivalently, a quadrilateral with two pairs of opposite sides parallel (See student text p. 205.)

Rectangle A quadrilateral with four right angles

Kite A convex quadrilateral with two distinct pairs of consecutive sides the same length

Rhombus A quadrilateral with all four sides the same length

Congruent figures Figures that have the same shape and size, regardless of position or orientation

Complementary angles Two angles whose measures sum to 90°

Midpoint of a segment The point on the segment that is the same distance from each endpoint

Perpendicular bisector of a segment A line that is perpendicular to a segment and contains its midpoint

Slope of a segment The slope of a segment that contains two points with coordinates (x_1, y_1) and (x_2, y_2) is $\dfrac{y_2 - y_1}{x_2 - x_1}$ $(x_1 \neq x_2)$.

Line reflection A motion determined by a "mirror line" (or line of reflection) that is the perpendicular bisector of the segment connecting a point and its reflected image; a point on the line reflection is its own image.

Translation A sliding motion that is determined by a distance and direction; the coordinate rule for a translation h units horizontally and k units vertically is $(x, y) \rightarrow (x + h, y + k)$.

Rotation A turning motion determined by a point called the center of rotation and a directed angle of rotation

Size transformation of magnitude k A size transformation of magnitude k centered at the origin is defined by the rule $(x, y) \rightarrow (kx, ky)$.

Trigonometric functions; $0° \leq \theta \leq 360°$.

tangent of $\theta = \tan \theta = \dfrac{y}{x}$ $(x \neq 0)$

sine of $\theta = \sin \theta = \dfrac{y}{r}$

cosine of $\theta = \cos \theta = \dfrac{x}{r}$

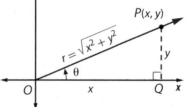

Trigonometric ratios for right triangles

tangent of $\angle A = \tan A = \dfrac{a}{b} = \dfrac{\text{length of side } opposite \angle A}{\text{length of side } adjacent \text{ to } \angle A}$

sine of $\angle A = \sin A = \dfrac{a}{c} = \dfrac{\text{length of side } opposite \angle A}{\text{length of } hypotenuse}$

cosine of $\angle A = \cos A = \dfrac{b}{c} = \dfrac{\text{length of side } adjacent \text{ to } \angle A}{\text{length of } hypotenuse}$

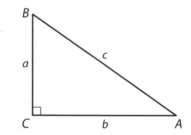

Relationships

Pythagorean Theorem If the lengths of the sides of a right triangle are a, b, c, with the side of length c opposite the right angle, then $a^2 + b^2 = c^2$.

Converse of the Pythagorean Theorem If the sum of the squares of the lengths of two sides of a triangle equals the square of the length of the third side, then the triangle is a right triangle.

Triangle Inequality The sum of the lengths of any two sides of a triangle is always greater than the length of the third side.

Triangle Angle Sum Property The sum of the measures of the angles in a triangle is 180°.

Quadrilateral Angle Sum Property The sum of the measures of the angles in a quadrilateral is 360°.

Polygon Angle Sum Property The sum of the measures of the interior angles of a polygon with n sides is $(n-2)180°$.

Base Angles of Isosceles Triangle A triangle is an isosceles triangle if and only if it has two congruent angles.

Side-Side-Side (SSS) congruence condition If three sides of a triangle are congruent to the corresponding sides of another triangle, then the two triangles are congruent.

Side-Angle-Side (SAS) congruence condition If two sides and the angle between the sides of one triangle are congruent to the corresponding parts of another triangle, then the two triangles are congruent.

Angle-Side-Angle (ASA) congruence condition If two angles and the side between the angles of one triangle are congruent to the corresponding parts of another triangle, then the two triangles are congruent.

Opposite Angles Property of Parallelograms Opposite angles in a parallelogram are congruent.

Condition ensuring a parallelogram If the diagonals of a quadrilateral bisect each other, then the quadrilateral is a parallelogram.

Conditions ensuring a rectangle (1) If a parallelogram has one right angle, then it is a rectangle. (2) If the diagonals of a parallelogram are the same length, then the parallelogram is a rectangle.

30°-60° right triangle relationship For a right triangle with acute angles of measures 30° and 60°, the length of the side opposite the 30° angle is half the length of the hypotenuse. The length of the side opposite the 60° angle is $\sqrt{3}$ times the length of the side opposite the 30° angle.

45°-45° right triangle relationship For a right triangle with acute angles of measures 45°, the length of the hypotenuse is $\sqrt{2}$ times the length of either of the equal legs of the right triangle.

Distance formula The distance d between two points with coordinates (x_1, y_1) and (x_2, y_2) is $d = \sqrt{(x_2 - x_1)^2 + (y_2 - y_1)^2}$.

Equation of a circle The equation of a circle with center at the origin and radius r is $x^2 + y^2 = r^2$.

Law of Sines In any triangle ABC with sides of lengths a, b, and c opposite $\angle A$, $\angle B$, and $\angle C$, respectively: $\frac{\sin A}{a} = \frac{\sin B}{b} = \frac{\sin C}{c}$.

Law of Cosines In any triangle ABC with sides of lengths a, b, and c opposite $\angle A$, $\angle B$, and $\angle C$, respectively: $c^2 = a^2 + b^2 - 2ab \cos C$.

Unit 1 Planning Guide

Lesson Objectives	On Your Own Assignments*	Suggested Pacing	Materials
Lesson 1 _Reasoning Strategies_ • Recognize the role of inductive reasoning in making conjectures and recognize the limitations of inductive reasoning • Recognize the need for proof and be able to create a simple deductive argument to prove a mathematical assertion • Create a counterexample to prove a claim is false • Write if-then statements and their converses and use if-then reasoning patterns in arguments	**After Investigation 1:** A1 or A2, A3, C10, R14, R15, E20, Rv25–Rv30 **After Investigation 2:** A4–A6, A7 or A8, A9, C11–C13, R16, R17, choose one of E21–E24, Rv31–Rv33	8 days (including assessment)	• Compass and straightedge for Rv32 • Pennies/counters for polygon game • Unit Resources
Lesson 2 _Geometric Reasoning and Proof_ • Know and be able to use the angle relationship theorems involving of two intersecting lines • Know and be able to use the theorems justifying the construction of a line perpendicular to a given line through a given point and the construction of a line parallel to a given line through a given point • Know and be able to use the angle relationship theorems involving two parallel lines cut by a transversal and their converses • Know and be able to use the angle sum theorem and the exterior angle theorem for triangles	**After Investigation 1:** A1, A2ab, C10, E22, Rv27–Rv33 **After Investigation 2:** A2c, A3, A4, A5 or A7, A6, A8, C10–C13, C15, R16, R18, R19, E22, choose one of E23–E25, Rv33, Rv34	8 days (including assessment)	• Protractor, compass, and straightedge • Unit Resources
Lesson 3 _Algebraic Reasoning and Proof_ • Use algebraic notation—letters, expressions, equations, and inequalities—to represent general patterns and relationships among variables • Use algebraic transformations of expressions, equations, and inequalities to establish general propositions about quantitative relationships	**After Investigation 1:** Choose two of A1–A5, A6, C17, C18, R23, choose one of E26–E29, Rv31–Rv36 **After Investigation 2:** A9, A10, A13, A14, C15 or C16, C19 or C20, R25, E30, Rv37	7 days (including assessment)	• Computer-algebra system (TI-89, TI-92, or comparable calculators or _CPMP-Tools_) • Unit Resources
Lesson 4 _Statistical Reasoning_ • Know the characteristics of a well-designed experiment • Understand the importance of subject and evaluator blinding and the placebo effect • Under the hypothesis of no treatment effect, construct an approximate sampling distribution for the difference of two means by rerandomizing; identify extreme events • Use a randomization test to decide if an experiment provides statistically significant evidence that one treatment is more effective than another • Distinguish between three types of statistical studies—sample surveys, experiments, and observational studies—and understand what inference can be made from each	**After Investigation 1:** A1, A2, C7, R11, Rv18, Rv19 **After Investigation 2:** A3, A4, choose two of C8–C10, E15 or E16, Rv20, Rv21 **After Investigation 3:** A5, A6, choose one of R12–R14, E17, Rv22, Rv23	7 days (including assessment)	• Pennies (at least 100 per group) • Copy of Factoring Test for each student • _CPMP-Tools_, "Randomization Distribution" • Unit Resources
Lesson 5 _Looking Back_ • Review and synthesize the major objectives of the unit		3 days (including assessment)	• Unit Resources

* _When choice is indicated, it is important to leave the choice to the student._

Note: _It is best if Connections tasks are discussed as a whole class after they have been assigned as homework._

Reasoning Strategies

In Courses 1 and 2 of *Core-Plus Mathematics*, you frequently used *inductive reasoning* to discover general patterns or principles based on evidence from experiments or several cases. You also used *deductive reasoning* to justify statements or conclusions based on accepted facts and definitions. In this unit, you will expand your ability to reason carefully in geometric, algebraic, and statistical contexts.

Careful reasoning is important not only in mathematics. It is a key to success as a consumer, in careers, and even in recreational activities. Setting up a play in basketball or volleyball, winning a friendly game of CLUE® or MONOPOLY®, or solving a crossword puzzle involves careful strategic reasoning.

Consider the game of Sudoku (pronounced sue-doe-koo), a number game similar to a crossword puzzle, that has recently become popular around the world. Sudoku is a Japanese word meaning "single number." The goal of the game is to fill in the empty squares with the digits 1 to 9 so that each digit appears exactly once in every row, column, and outlined 3 × 3 block.

8				6				1
4	5	7	8					9
			2	5	9			4
2	3	9		8				
6	8						9	3
	7			9		1	6	8
7			9	2	8			
9			4		5	7	3	
1				7	3			2

Adapted from: www.knightfeatures.com

Reasoning Strategies

The two investigations in this lesson help students appreciate the need for proof in mathematical settings and provide opportunities for students to analyze and construct deductive arguments. The first investigation introduces students to the important fact that there are often many different ways to present a convincing argument. The goals are for students to understand the role of assumptions in proof and to begin to identify features of a good deductive argument, such as:

- uses correct assumptions and accepted mathematical information,
- uses general statements rather than illustrative examples,
- uses valid reasoning patterns based on principles of logic, and
- is complete.

The second investigation contrasts deductive and inductive reasoning patterns. It introduces students to basic ideas about implications, converses, and if-and-only-if statements in the context of number properties, algebra, geometry, and discrete mathematics. It discusses why one counterexample can disprove a conjecture while no number of examples can prove a conjecture (unless the examples exhaust all cases). Two valid reasoning patterns are introduced—*Affirming the Hypothesis* and *Chaining Implications*—and students are provided opportunities to utilize them in several contexts. Students should understand the complementary nature of inductive and deductive reasoning. Inductive reasoning often leads to a conjecture, which may or may not always be true. Deductive reasoning provides a way to establish that conjecture is always true.

Assure students from the start that it takes time and practice to become comfortable writing valid arguments and that they will have lots of opportunities to work on developing their proof-writing abilities throughout Course 3 and in future mathematics courses. Consider spending a bit more time than usual on the On Your Own tasks. They offer a good opportunity for students to practice creating proofs and thereby gain some confidence in this area.

Lesson Objectives

- Recognize the role of inductive reasoning in making conjectures and recognize the limitations of inductive reasoning
- Recognize the need for proof and be able to create a simple deductive argument to prove a mathematical assertion
- Create a counterexample to prove a claim is false
- Write if-then statements and their converses and use if-then reasoning patterns in arguments

PROMOTING MATHEMATICAL DISCOURSE Periodically, when this icon appears, you will find a sample discussion offering possible teacher-student discourse around Think About This Situation and Summarize the Mathematics questions at point of use.

Think About This Situation

Think about strategies you would use to solve the Sudoku puzzle shown at the bottom of the previous page.

a How would you decide where to begin?

b Which square would you fill in first? Which one would you fill in next? Explain your reasoning.

c Describe a strategy (or a combination of strategies) you would use to fill in the remaining squares.

d When the game is completed, what will be true about the sums of the row entries, the sums of the column entries, and the sums of the 3 × 3 block entries? Explain.

In this lesson, you will learn how to examine arguments in terms of reasoning strategies, assumptions, and logical soundness. You will also learn how to use *if-then* reasoning patterns in deductive arguments or proofs.

Investigation 1 — Reasoned Arguments

Careful reasoning, whether it is concerned with mathematics, science, history, or daily affairs, is important if you want to have confidence in the conclusions reached. A *valid argument* shows that a conclusion follows logically from accepted definitions and assumptions or previously established facts. If the assumptions are true, you can be confident that the conclusion is true. As you analyze the situations and arguments in this investigation, look for answers to this question:

How can you determine whether a conclusion follows logically from information and facts you know are correct or on which everyone would agree?

1 **Reasoning about Crime Scenes**
In popular television shows like CSI and NUMB3RS that involve crime investigations, the detectives use careful reasoning to identify suspects, motives, and evidence that can be used to solve cases.

LESSON 1 • Reasoning Strategies   **3**

Informal if-then (and indirect) reasoning will most likely come out of student explanations and reasoning. Students should be encouraged to think about the soundness and clarity of responses, a skill they will need in the writing and analysis of proof.

In order to ensure that a variety of puzzle-solving strategies emerge, allow students to individually think about Parts a and b before having a class discussion. You may wish to use a think-pair-share technique.

Despite its name, Sudoku originated in the U.S. in 1979 under the name *Number Place*. It was popularized in Japan during the mid and late 1980s. However, it was not until early 2005 that Sudoku became a craze around the world. It now appears in dozens of U.S. newspapers. For information on the history of Sudoku and solution strategies, you may wish to read the short article, "The Sudoku Epidemic," by Robin Wilson that appeared in the January 2006 issue of *Focus* (www.maa.org/pubs/pastissues.html). A Web site that gives useful information about all aspects of Sudoku and is updated regularly is en.wikipedia.org/wiki/Sudoku.

Think About This Situation

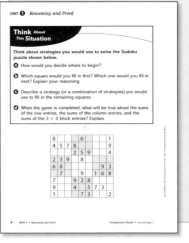

a Students will likely suggest looking for a row, column, or 3 × 3 block that is missing very few numbers.

b Student responses will vary. Some examples follow.

(1) The 1st column has the most entries filled in. The only digits that are missing are the 3 and the 5. A 5 cannot go in the missing square in the 3rd row because there is already a 5 in that row. Thus, a 3 fills in the square in the 1st column, 3rd row, and a 5 fills in the 6th row of that column.

(2) The gray 3 × 3 block on the left side of the puzzle is missing only three entries. The digits missing are 1, 4, and 5. Neither a 1 nor a 4 can be used to fill in the square in the first column, sixth row, since both already appear in the first column of the puzzle. So, 5 must fill that square leaving a 1 and 4 to be used for the two remaining squares. By examining the rows in which the last two empty squares lie, it is evident that a 1 must fill the square in the fifth row (since a 4 already exists in that row) and a 4 must fill in the square in the sixth row, thus completing the 3 × 3 block.

(3) There are many 9s in the puzzle. Only two 3 × 3 blocks are missing a 9—the top-left and bottom-right ones. Looking at the top-left 3 × 3 block, only the first row of the puzzle can have a

9 because the second and third rows already contain 9s. Using column information, a 9 cannot be placed in the third column. This process of elimination places a 9 in the first row and second column. Similar reasoning identifies the last row and seventh column of the bottom-right block to be filled with a 9.

c Students may use a variety of strategies. The focus of responses should be on whether or not students understand the strategies used by others. Possible strategies include:

- Find the row, column, or 3 × 3 block that has the least amount of empty squares and then use reasoning about surrounding rows, columns, and 3 × 3 blocks to fill in the empty squares.
- Start in a 3 × 3 block and fill in as many squares within it as possible by determining which numbers *could* go in each square and reason to find the correct one.
- Start with a particular number in mind, identify a 3 × 3 block that is missing that number, then use rows and columns to determine which squares that particular number could go in, and then reason to identify the correct square for that number.

d The focus of responses to this question should be on the reasoning that the row sum, the column sum, and the block sums will all be the same, the sum of the digits from 1 through 9, which is 45.

ASSIGNMENT NOTE
Review Task 25 on page 26 should be assigned before students do Problem 4 in Investigation 1.

Students should make careful note of the strategy or strategies they are using.

8	9	2	7	6	4	3	5	1
4	5	7	8	3	1	6	2	9
3	1	6	2	5	9	8	7	4
2	3	9	1	8	6	5	4	7
6	8	1	5	4	7	2	9	3
5	7	4	3	9	2	1	6	8
7	6	3	9	2	8	4	1	5
9	2	8	4	1	5	7	3	6
1	4	5	6	7	3	9	8	2

Investigation 1 Reasoned Arguments

This investigation opens with a crime-scene problem to help students learn about the role of evidence and assumptions in making and proving claims. This problem is followed by three problems that illustrate convincing and not-so-convincing arguments presented in different forms. Problem 4 introduces the definition and area formula of a trapezoid. A variety of arguments are proposed, and students are asked to analyze them, identify the assumptions made, evaluate them, and begin to pick out features of arguments that are both convincing and correct. In this investigation, students should recognize that reasoning based on a few examples is not a correct argument. In Investigation 2, students more carefully consider deductive and inductive reasoning.

COLLABORATION SKILL
To build effective group collaboration, collaboration skills are suggested at the beginning of some investigations. The prompt to evaluate the use of this skill is on page T9. Skill: Encourage contributions by all group members.

Promoting Mathematical Discourse

Think About This Situation, *page 3*

Teacher: In Courses 1 and 2, you frequently used inductive reasoning to look for general patterns and principles. You also used deductive reasoning to justify statements you made that were based on accepted facts and definitions. In this unit, we will continue to work on your ability to reason carefully. In the Think About This Situation, we are going to analyze how we might reason to solve a puzzle called Sudoku, pronounced sue-doe-koo. *(The teacher writes Sudoku phonetically on the board.)* Have any of you worked on a Sudoku puzzle? *(Several students indicate that they have.)* Would someone explain the goal of the puzzle for those of us who have not worked on one before today?

Karen: You have to use all the digits, 1 through 9, in each row and in each column.

Juleen: You also have to use the digits 1 through 9 in each of the 3 × 3 blocks inside the puzzle.

Teacher: Let's take a minute for each of you to look at the puzzle individually. After a couple of minutes, I am going to ask you which square you decided to fill in first and why you chose that square. Then, which one you decided to fill in second and why. *(The teacher gives students a few minutes to think individually while he observes their puzzle entries.)* Okay, it's time to put your pencils down so we can all listen to each other's ideas about ways you solved the puzzle. *(The teacher waits until all pencils are down—he knows that some students will be tempted to continue filling in the puzzle.)* Who would like to share their choices with us for the first and second squares to fill in and reasons for those choices?

Asha: I will. I noticed that the first column had the most numbers filled in, so I started there. I knew that the two numbers I could use were 3 and 5 since they weren't already used in that column. I also noticed that I could not use a 5 in the third row of the first column since 5 appears in that row already. So, I put a 3 in the square in the third row of that first column and put a 5 in the square in the sixth row. Then, I checked the sixth row to see if that worked. It did.

Teacher: What do you mean when you say that it "worked"?

Asha: I mean that there wasn't already a 5 in that row.

Teacher: Did anyone else use the same column and method as Asha? *(The teacher notes who indicates they used the same method to call on someone later to describe this strategy.)* Did anyone use the same column but a slightly different tactic?

Tony: I did. I thought, like Asha, that I needed to place a 3 and a 5 in the column but I looked at the grey 3 × 3 block at the middle-left to decide. I guess that was because I immediate saw the 3 in that block, so I knew that the 5 had to go in the grey box in the first column. This left the 3 for the white box.

Sam: I used the gray 3 × 3 block on the bottom of the puzzle. I chose that block because it had a lot of squares already filled in.

Teacher: How did you work with that block? Can you tell us which squares you filled in first and second? *(The teacher continues to monitor students for listening, not filling in the blocks. Students will finish the puzzle for homework.)*

Sam: Well, I saw that the block was missing only a 1 and a 6. Since the last row of the puzzle already has a 1 in it, the lower left-hand corner square of my 3 × 3 block had to be a 6. That left a 1 to put in the other empty square.

Teacher: Hmm, did anyone else use the same block as Tony? *(Some students indicate that they did.)* Let's describe these strategies to see if they are similar or somewhat different. Jan, you indicated that you used the same method as Asha. How would you describe your method?

Jan: Let's see. I looked for a column or row that was almost filled. Then I figured out which numbers were missing. I was looking at the first column. Then I looked at the row that went with the empty box to eliminate one of my two options. I could eliminate one option, so that left the other one for the box.

Sam: That is basically what I did with the block. But I found the missing numbers in the block and used the row all the way across the puzzle to eliminate one of my options.

Teacher: Do the rest of you agree with these descriptions of the approaches to solving the puzzle that we have talked about? *(Students indicate agreement.)* Would anyone like to offer a different way they started the puzzle? Karen.

Karen: When I looked at the puzzle, all the 9s seemed to grab my attention. Did anyone else notice that only the top and bottom rows were missing a 9? *(No one else noticed that.)* Then I just looked at the rows and columns to figure out where to put the 9s.

Teacher: Tell us more about the method you used once you noticed the 9s.

Karen: Okay. I think it would be best if I could point to the puzzle as I explain this. *(She comes to the class display of the puzzle.)* So, I knew that the first row needed a 9. I used the columns and put a mark by the cells that could not have a 9. That left me with only two possibilities for the 9. This one and this one. But the rows could not tell me the final answer. So, then I looked at the 3 × 3 blocks on the top. The one on the left gave me no information to decide where to place the 9 but the one on the right already had a 9. So, then I knew that the 9 must go in row 1 column 3.

Teacher: What square did you fill in second?

Karen: Then I went to the last row to see where to put a 9. That was easy now because every column except the third to the last column already had a 9.

Teacher: How is Karen's strategy similar to or different from the other strategies we have seen today?

Deshaun: Well, Karen seemed to be looking at the whole puzzle at the beginning. She also picked one specific number, 9, to put in each row. So, it is really quite different than looking at a row, column, or 3 × 3 block to find out which numbers are missing.

Todd: But she was checking against other rows, columns, or blocks to make a decision. So, she did the process of elimination that we were using.

Teacher: That is an interesting strategy. Do you think Karen's strategy could be used again in this puzzle? I will be handing back your puzzles so that you can complete them tonight for your homework. As you finish the puzzle, keep track of the strategies that you are using. Tomorrow when we begin class, we will see if any other strategies were used and which strategies seem the most powerful. *(The teacher knows that a strategy of selecting a specific number to complete in a puzzle is not always possible. This particular puzzle can be started this way.)* When you do have the puzzle completed, what will be true about the sums of the row entries, the sums of the column entries, and the sums of the 3 × 3 block entries?

Stacy: The sums will all be whatever the answer is to adding up the numbers from 1 to 9. Do you want us to add these numbers?

Teacher: No. That is not necessary. Let's begin the investigation work.

(The teacher collects the puzzles to hand back to students as they leave the classroom. They will finish the puzzle for homework.)

Teacher Notes

Consider the following plot from a crime case.

At 7:00 P.M., Mrs. Wilson's maid served her tea in the library. The maid noticed that Mrs. Wilson seemed upset and a little depressed. At 8:45 P.M., the maid knocked on the library door and got no answer. The door was locked from the inside. The maid called Inspector Sharpe and a professor friend. When the door was forced open, Mrs. Wilson was found dead. The maid burst into tears, crying, "I feel so bad that we haven't been getting along lately!" Nearby was a half-empty teacup, a tiny unstopped vial, and a typewritten note that said, "Blessed are the poor for they shall be happy." The window was open. When the two men went out-side to inspect the grounds, Charles, the wealthy widow's sole heir, arrived. He was told his aunt was poisoned and said, "How terrible! Poisoned? Who did it? Why was the door locked? Had my aunt been threatened?" He explained he had been working late at the office and was stopping by on his way home.

Source: Ripley, Austin. (1976). *Minute Mysteries*. New York: Harper & Row Publishers. pages 22–23.

a. Who are the possible suspects in this case?

b. For each suspect, identify the evidence that exists that could be used to charge them with the crime.

c. Write a convincing argument to charge the prime suspect with the crime.

d. Compare your prime suspect and argument with those of others. Resolve any differences.

2 **Reasoning about Games** Games based on strategy—such as Tic-Tac-Toe, Checkers, and Chess—have been played for thousands of years. The following two-person game can be played on any regular polygon. For this problem, assume the game is played on a regular nonagon. To play, place a penny on each vertex of the polygon. Take turns removing one penny or two pennies from adjacent vertices. The player who picks up the last coin(s) is the winner.

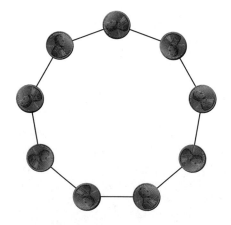

1

a. The possible suspects in this case are Mrs. Wilson's maid, Mrs. Wilson, and the nephew Charles because they all had access to Mrs. Wilson.

b. The maid brought Mrs. Wilson her tea and admitted that they had not been getting along. The locked library door, unstoppered vial, typewritten note, and the maid's comment that Mrs. Wilson seemed upset and a little depressed could be evidence that points to Mrs. Wilson herself. The open window and the nephew's knowledge that the library door was locked make him a suspect.

c. Students' arguments may vary. A convincing argument might include motive, opportunity, alibi, and evidence.

d. Students should compare their arguments and resolve any differences. The Minute Mysteries solution states that the nephew "knew that the library door was locked; a fact he could not possibly have known without guilty knowledge." Students should consider whether or not their arguments are based on assumptions or facts.

> **TRAPEZOID DEFINITION**
> There is more than one accepted definition of a trapezoid. The one used in this text on page 7, a quadrilateral with two opposite sides parallel, means that a parallelogram is a special trapezoid. Students should add this definition to the student master provided.

Unit 1

a. Working with a partner, play the nonagon game a few times. Make mental notes of strategies you used.

b. Tianna, Jairo, Nicole, and Connor each thought they found a strategy that would guarantee that they could always win the game if they played *second*. Analyze their reasoning. In each case, decide if the proposed strategy will always result in a win for the second player. Explain your reasoning in each case.

Tianna: Each time the first player removes one or two pennies, I'll remove only one penny. That way, there will be more pennies left to choose from and at least one for me at the end.

Jairo: Each time the first player removes one penny, I'll remove one penny. If the first player removes two pennies, then I'll remove two pennies. Then the remaining number of pennies will be an odd number, so there will be at least one penny for me at the end.

Nicole: Each time the first player removes one penny, I'll remove two pennies; if the first player removes two pennies, I'll remove one penny as shown by the triangles in the diagram below. Since there are 9 pennies, I can always win on the third round.

Connor: If the first player removes one penny, I'll visualize the line of symmetry containing the "empty" vertex and remove the two adjacent pennies on opposite sides of the symmetry line. If the first player removes two pennies on the first move, then I'll visualize the line of symmetry between the two empty vertices and remove the penny on the symmetry line.

This strategy will always leave three pennies on each side of the symmetry line after we each make our first move. After that, I'll match each play the first player makes by choosing the mirror image. So, I'll be able to remove the final coin(s).

②

a. Students only need to play enough games so that they begin to develop strategies to try to win the game. This will prepare them for analyzing the validity of the strategies suggested in Part b.

b. **INSTRUCTIONAL NOTE** For each strategy, students may need to (quickly) play the polygon game once or twice to understand the strategies described. You might want to put a time limit on this problem so that students remain focused on the questions to be answered.

Tianna's strategy will not always result in a win for the second player. Students may reason as follows. (1) If the first player always takes one penny and Tianna also takes one penny, then the first player will pick up the last penny. (2) There may be two nonadjacent pennies left on Tianna's last play. She would not be able to remove both which would cause her to lose the game.

Jairo's strategy will not always result in a win for the second player because dividing an odd number of pennies between two people will always result in a remainder of one. Based on turns, the remainder will always go to the first player.

Nicole's strategy will not always result in a win for the second player. The last two plays will require splitting up three pennies. But the first player will decide how they are split up, leaving the second player one penny, two adjacent pennies, or two nonadjacent pennies. If the two pennies are nonadjacent, the first player will win.

Connor's strategy will always result in a win because the symmetry line will split the board in half and will always allow him to mirror his opponent's move. The line of symmetry guarantees that Connor will always get the last mirrored play.

③ Reasoning about Numbers You may have noticed that when you add two odd numbers, for example $3 + 7$, the sum always seems to be an even number. Alex, Maria, Nesrin, and Teresa were asked to write an argument to justify the following claim.

If a and b are odd numbers, then a + b
(the sum) is an even number.

Carefully study each student's argument.

Alex: I entered odd numbers in list L1 of my calculator and different odd numbers in list L2. I then calculated L1 + L2. Scanning the calculator screen, you can see that in every case the sum is an even number.

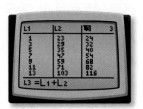

Maria: Odd numbers end in 1, 3, 5, 7, or 9. When you add any two of these, the answer will end in O, 2, 4, 6, or 8. So, the sum of two odd numbers must always be an even number.

Nesrin: I can use counters to prove the sum of any two odd numbers is an even number. For example, if I take the numbers 5 and 11 and organize the counters as shown, you can see the pattern.

You can see that when you put the sets together (add the numbers), the two extra counters will form a pair and the answer is always an even number.

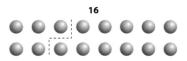

Teresa: I know that a and b are odd numbers.
By definition, $a = 2m + 1$ and $b = 2n + 1$, where m and n are integers.
So, $a + b = 2m + 1 + 2n + 1$.
Then $a + b = 2m + 1 + 2n + 1 = 2m + 2n + 2 = 2(m + n + 1)$.
Therefore, $a + b$ is an even number since the sum is a multiple of 2.

a. Of the four arguments, which *one* is closest to the argument you would give to prove that the sum of two odd numbers is an even number?

KEY IDEA One key point here is that examples alone prove nothing (unless they exhibit all possible cases). Examples make a conjecture more plausible, but they can never constitute a proof of the truth of a statement for an infinite number of cases. However, in this case, the visual argument here does suggest the main idea of a more general proof. Student groups should be able to work through this problem on their own, but be sure that this key idea surfaces in a full-class discussion, either at the end of the class period or at the Summarize the Mathematics.

a. Answers will depend on each student's choice of a specific argument.

b. For each of the arguments, answer the following questions.

  i. Does the argument have any errors in it?

  ii. Does the argument show the statement is *always true* or does the argument *only* show the statement is true for *some* numbers?

  iii. Does the argument show *why* the statement is true?

  iv. Does the argument provide an easy way to convince someone in your class who is uncertain of the claim?

c. Select one of the arguments you think is correct. How, if at all, would you modify the argument to justify that the sum of *any* two odd numbers that are square numbers (like 9 and 25) is an even number? Explain your reasoning.

④ **Reasoning about Areas** In the Course 1 *Patterns in Shape* unit, you saw that by assuming the formula $A = bh$ for the area of a rectangle with a base of length b and height h, you could derive a formula for the area of a parallelogram. You also saw that if you knew the formula for the area of a parallelogram, you could derive a formula for the area of a triangle. A standard formula for calculating the area of a **trapezoid**—a quadrilateral with two opposite sides parallel—is given by:

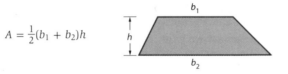

$$A = \tfrac{1}{2}(b_1 + b_2)h$$

where b_1, b_2, and h represent the lengths of the two bases and the height of the trapezoid.

Study each of the following five arguments offered by students as justification of this formula for the area of a trapezoid.

Angela: I can split the trapezoid into two triangles by drawing a diagonal. One triangle has area $\tfrac{1}{2}b_1h$. The other has area $\tfrac{1}{2}b_2h$. So, the area of the trapezoid is $\tfrac{1}{2}b_1h + \tfrac{1}{2}b_2h$ or $\tfrac{1}{2}(b_1 + b_2)h$.

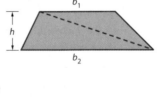

Dylan: In a parallelogram, opposite sides are the same length. Any side can be used as the base. In the trapezoid shown,

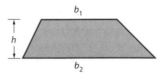

  b_1h will underestimate the area.
  b_2h will overestimate the area.

To find the correct area, you average the two estimates.

$$\frac{b_1h + b_2h}{2} = \tfrac{1}{2}(b_1h + b_2h)$$

$$= \tfrac{1}{2}(b_1 + b_2)h$$

b. *Alex's argument*:

   i. has no errors.

   ii. does not show the argument is always true, rather that it is true for the numbers in L1 and L2.

   iii. does not show why the statement is true.

   iv. gives no justification as to why the statement is true for odd numbers not in L1 and L2.

Maria's argument:

   i. has no errors.

   ii. indicates that the statement is always true since it considers all odd numbers by examining the units digit.

   iii. shows why adding any two numbers ending in an odd digit gives an answer that ends in an even digit.

   iv. justifies the claim by saying that the sum will always end in a digit 0, 2, 4, 6, or 8 and thus be an even number. To completely justify the claim to someone uncertain, she might need to show that all possible sums of any two of 1, 3, 5, 7, and 9 end in 0, 2, 4, 6, or 8.

Nesrin's argument:

   i. has no errors.

   ii. shows the statement is true for only one pair of odd numbers.

   iii. shows why by using a visual model to form pairs of numbers but does not explain that any even number would form pairs of counters and that odd numbers will be made up of pairs of counters plus one more counter.

   iv. The visual model may help convince students why the statement is true, but would have to be generalized to all odd integers. The generalization can be argued with the visualization of one case used as an illustrative example. (See Katrina's proposed proof in the Check Your Understanding on page 9.)

> **COMMON ERROR** Some students may think Nesrin's argument is a correct proof. In the class discussion, be sure they understand that justification for specific examples does not constitute a proof.

Teresa's argument:

   i. has no errors.

   ii. shows the statement is true for all odd numbers by using letters to represent arbitrary odd numbers $2m + 1$ and $2n + 1$.

   iii. explains why by using the definition of odd and even integers and adding any two odd numbers to get an even number.

   iv. is easy to follow because it is a logical sequence of statements with connecting words such as "so," "then," "therefore," and "since." (Some students might suggest that the argument provide some specific examples first to help them understand the general argument.)

c. Maria's and Teresa's arguments prove that the sum of any two odd numbers is an even number. Since square odd numbers are already odd numbers, this is just an application of their arguments. (If students select Nesrin's argument, they should improve the argument to include *any* two odd numbers.)

> **MATH TOOLKIT** Students may wish to add the definitions of an odd and even number, as in Teresa's argument, and the relationship that the sum of two odd numbers is an even number to their notes.

Hsui: If I rotate the trapezoid 180° about the midpoint M of one side, the trapezoid and its image form a parallelogram.

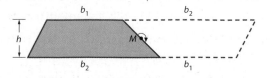

The length of the base of the parallelogram is $b_2 + b_1$ and the height is h. The area of the parallelogram is $(b_2 + b_1)h$. The area of the trapezoid is $\frac{1}{2}$ of this area, or $\frac{1}{2}(b_1 + b_2)h$.

Barbara:

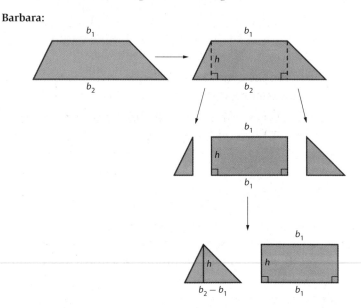

So, the area of the trapezoid is $\frac{1}{2}(b_2 - b_1)h + b_1h$, which equals $\frac{1}{2}(b_1 + b_2)h$.

Jorge: The area of the trapezoid is $\frac{1}{2}(b_1 + b_2)h$ because you can cut up the shape and find the areas of the individual pieces.

a. Which of the five arguments is closest to the argument you would have provided to justify the formula for the area of a trapezoid?

b. Which of these arguments show correct reasoning and which do not? Compare your responses with those of others and resolve any differences.

c. Select one of the arguments you think provides a correct proof of the area formula. Describe the features of the argument that you thought were good. What, if anything, would you add to that argument to make it easier to understand?

(4) **INSTRUCTIONAL NOTE** You may wish to use coordinated combinations of small-group and full-class thought and discussion in completing Parts b and c. Ask the groups to look at each argument and to identify and describe the features of the argument that are positive. Then, discuss these ideas as a full class. Ask students what they can add to make each argument even clearer.

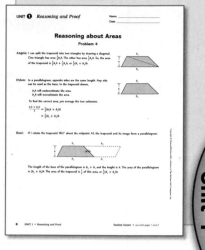

a. Answers will depend on each student's choice of argument.

b. The arguments presented by Angela, Hsui, and Barbara show correct reasoning and do a good job justifying the formula. (Students may identify some parts of the proof that could use more explanation. See Part c below.) Dylan's argument provides no mathematical justification for "averaging" the two estimates as a legitimate way to compute the area. Jorge's argument is too vague and incomplete. He does not identify the pieces into which the trapezoid is to be cut, nor does he indicate how the areas combine to produce the formula for the area of a trapezoid. Thus, he does not do a good job of reasoning to the conclusion.

c. Students should choose to look at either Angela's, Hsui's, or Barbara's argument. The good features might include that the argument uses correct assumptions (such as the area of a shape is the sum of the areas of its pieces, or the area of a shape is not changed when it is moved in the plane), uses general reasoning rather than specific cases, and explains the reasoning.

 Students may or may not have suggestions for improvements. The suggestions below are slight improvements but not necessary for a correct proof.

 To improve Hsui's argument, you could provide further explanation and justification for why the rotation about the midpoint forms a parallelogram.

 To improve Barbara's argument, adding some notes explaining where $b_2 - b_1$ came from and clarifying how the two algebraic expressions for the area are equivalent would make the argument clearer for some students.

Summarize
the Mathematics

In this investigation, you examined reasoning strategies and arguments in mathematical and nonmathematical contexts.

a Look back at the mathematical statements that the students were attempting to prove in Problems 3 and 4. In each case, answer the following questions.

  i. What information was given?

  ii. What conclusion was to be established?

  iii. How was the given information used by Teresa to reason logically to the conclusion in Problem 3? By Angela to reason to the conclusion in Problem 4?

b How can you tell whether an argument provides a correct proof of a claim?

Be prepared to share your ideas with the rest of the class.

✔Check Your Understanding

Analyze each student attempt to prove the following statement.

The sum of two even numbers is an even number.

Art: I tried many different pairs of even numbers. It was impossible to find a counterexample to the claim that the sum of two even numbers is an even number. So, the claim must be true.

Sherita: Even numbers are numbers that can be divided by 2. When you add numbers with a common factor of 2, the answer will have a common factor of 2.

Bill: If a and b are any two numbers, then $2a$ and $2b$ are any two even numbers.

$$2a + 2b = 2(a + b)$$

Katrina: Even numbers can be represented by rectangular arrays of counters with two rows.

The sum of any two even numbers will be a rectangular array of counters with 2 rows. So, the sum is even.

Full-class discussions that have punctuated this investigation can be summarized along with this Summarize the Mathematics. You may wish to reread the notes and solutions included with Problems 1–4 preceding this Summarize the Mathematics to better guide the discussion.

Summarize
the Mathematics

a Problem 3:

  i. Given: a and b are odd integers.

  ii. Conclusion: $a + b$ is an even integer.

  iii. The definitions of odd and even integers were used as a basis of the argument.

  Problem 4:

  i. Given: The figure is a trapezoid with bases of length b_1 and b_2 and height h.

  ii. Conclusion: The area is given by $A = \frac{1}{2}(b_1 + b_2)h$.

  iii. Connecting opposite vertices of the trapezoid forms two triangles, each with the given height.

b An argument or proof is correct if it contains no errors, uses general reasoning rather than reasoning about a few cases, and explains the reasoning. It also shows how the conclusion follows logically from the given information, accepted definitions, assumptions, and previously established facts.

Teaching Resources

Transparency Master 8.

UNIT **1** *Reasoning and Proof*

Summarize
the Mathematics

In this investigation, you examined reasoning strategies and arguments in mathematical and nonmathematical contexts.

a Look back at the mathematical statements that the students were attempting to prove in Problems 3 and 4. In each case, answer the following questions.

  i. What information was given?

  ii. What conclusion was to be established?

  iii. How was the given information used by Teresa to reason logically to the conclusion in Problem 3? By Angela to reason to the conclusion in Problem 4?

b How can you tell whether an argument provides a correct proof of a claim?

Be prepared to share your ideas with the rest of the class.

8   UNIT 1 • *Reasoning and Proof*   *Transparency Master* • *see work page 7*

Unit 1

COLLABORATION PROMPT
Ways we encouraged one another to contribute ideas are:
1. _____
2. _____
3. _____

MATH TOOLKIT Students should begin a list of the characteristics found in a correct proof. The list can be expanded and improved as students see more examples of good proofs. The list may also be referred to as students begin to create their own proofs. They should ask, "Does my proof meet all of the conditions we listed as part of a correct proof?" You may also wish to begin a class poster of the characteristics of a correct proof.

NOTE Solutions to the CYU are on page T10.

a. Which argument is closest to the argument you would give to prove that the sum of two even numbers is always an even number?

b. Which arguments are *not* correct proofs of the claim? Explain your reasoning.

c. Modify one of the correct proofs to justify the following statement.

The sum of an even number and an odd number is always an odd number.

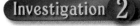 **Reasoning with If-Then Statements**

Statements of the form *"If ... , then ..."* occur frequently in everyday life and in mathematics. For example, consider the two statements: *"If it is raining on game day, then the game will be rescheduled for next Tuesday,"* and *"If x > 5, then 2x > 10."* Other mathematical statements, such as definitions, can be interpreted in *if-then* form. For example, consider the definition of a trapezoid from Investigation 1.

> A trapezoid is a quadrilateral with two opposite sides parallel.

This definition means that   *If* a quadrilateral is a trapezoid, *then* two opposite sides are parallel,

and the *converse*   *If* two opposite sides of a quadrilateral are parallel, *then* the quadrilateral is a trapezoid.

If-then statements are frequently used in deductive arguments because they imply that if some condition (called the **hypothesis**) is satisfied, some other condition (called the **conclusion**) follows. As you work on the following problems, look for answers to these questions:

> *How can you use if-then statements in deductive reasoning?*

> *How is deductive reasoning with if-then statements different from inductive reasoning from patterns?*

1 You may recall that the numbers 2, 3, 7, and 11 are called prime numbers. By definition, a **prime number** is an integer greater than 1 that has exactly two factors, 1 and itself.

    a. Write two if-then statements that together mean the same thing as the above definition of a prime number.

    b. Is 23 a prime number? Explain your reasoning.

    c. Which of the two if-then statements in Part a was used in your reasoning in Part b?

The reasoning you used in Problem 1 Part b is based on a fundamental principle of logic called **modus ponens** (Latin: mode that affirms) or **Affirming the Hypothesis**.

If you have a known fact   an (if-then) statement that is always true,
    and you also know   the "if" part is true in a particular case,
      you can conclude   the "then" part is true in that case.

✓ Check Your Understanding

a. The answer will depend on each student's choice of argument.

b. Art's argument is not a correct proof. No number of examples can prove a conjecture about even numbers, and just because Art has not found a counterexample does not mean that one does not exist.

   Sherita's argument is correct but incomplete, since it gives no explanation of why the answer will have a common factor of 2.

   Bill's argument should have started with any two even numbers, not any two numbers.

c. Bill's modification might work as follows:

   An even integer can be written as $2a$, and an odd integer can be written as $2b + 1$. Then $2a + 2b + 1 = 2(a + b) + 1$, which is an odd integer.

   Katrina's might be modified as follows:

   An even integer can be represented by a rectangular array of counters with two rows (e.g., : : :), and an odd integer can be represented by a rectangular array and one additional counter (e.g., : : : .). The sum will be an array of counters that can be visualized as a rectangular array, representing an even number, plus one additional counter. So, the sum is odd.

Investigation 2 — Reasoning With If-Then Statements

This investigation has two main goals. The first is to help students understand the need for careful analysis of the meaning of mathematical statements. The second is to make clear the nature of true if-then statements. These ideas will help students as they begin constructing their own proofs.

The investigation is comprised of seven problems that naturally fall into three groups: conditional statements, inductive reasoning leading to conditional statements, and deductive reasoning to prove conditional statements. In Problem 1, students reason by using a fundamental principle of logic called *Affirming the Hypothesis*, or *modus ponens*.

In Problem 2, students are asked to make deductions by applying general known facts in specific instances. Students should consider each statement, check their mathematical knowledge, and decide what can be logically concluded. Note that these statements deal with mathematics across all four strands of the curriculum. Arguments and proof are *not* unique to geometry.

Problem 3 introduces notation and vocabulary that summarizes the reasoning pattern in Problems 1 and 2. You may wish to treat this problem as a progress checkpoint and complete it as a class.

Problems 4–6 help students develop an understanding of using inductive reasoning to make conjectures as well as the role of counterexamples and careful if-then reasoning for proving or disproving a statement.

Problem 7 introduces students to reasoning with a chain of conditional statements.

> **COLLABORATION SKILL**
> Keep on task.

> **NOTE** Solutions to Problem 1 are on page T11.

2 Decide what can be concluded, if anything, from each of the following sets of statements. Be prepared to explain how reaching your conclusion involved Affirming the Hypothesis.

a. *Known fact:* If a person has a Michigan driver's license, *then* the person is 16 years of age or older.

Given: Andy has a Michigan driver's license.

Conclusion: ?

b. *Known fact:* If a person in Michigan has a driver's license, *then* the person is 16 years of age or older.

Given: Janet is 18 years old.

Conclusion: ?

c. *Known fact:* If two sides of a triangle are the same length, *then* the triangle is isosceles.

Given: $\triangle ABC$ has sides of length 2 cm, 5 cm, 5 cm.

Conclusion: ?

d. *Known fact:* If $f(x) = ax^2 + bx + c$ is a quadratic function with $a < 0$, *then* $f(x)$ has a maximum value.

Given: $g(x) = -8x^2 + 5x - 2$

Conclusion: ?

e. *Known fact:* If a connected vertex-edge graph has vertices all of even degree, *then* the graph has an Euler circuit.

Given: G is a connected vertex-edge graph with 6 vertices.

Conclusion: ?

f. *Known fact:* If a data set with mean $\bar{x}$ and standard deviation s is transformed by adding a constant c to each value, *then* the mean of the transformed data set is $\bar{x} + c$ and the standard deviation is s.

Given: The Oak Park hockey team has a mean height of 5 feet 9 inches and a standard deviation of $2\frac{1}{2}$ inches. Wearing ice skates adds approximately $1\frac{3}{4}$ inches to the height of a skater.

Conclusion: ?

g. *Known fact:* If S is a size transformation with center at the origin and magnitude k and A is the area of a figure, then $k^2 \cdot A$ is the area of the image of the figure under S.

Given: $\triangle P'Q'R'$ is the image of $\triangle PQR$ under a size transformation with center at the origin and magnitude 3. $\triangle PQR$ has area 32 cm^2.

Conclusion: ?

Developing the Ability to Prove Statements Encourage students
to use the correct proofs they write and read to build a repertoire of strategies
to be used in proofs. Students should note that proofs, like so many other
problems in mathematics, can be completed correctly in many different ways. It
is reasonable to expect that initial proofs may be incomplete, but all students
should be urged to use complete, reasonably sequenced statements. Rigor and
skill will follow.

Also, notice that no particular form for a proof is required. You and your class
should develop acceptable formats for presenting proofs. It may be paragraph,
a string of connected conditionals, or other formats. Lesson 2 introduces a
two-column statement-reason form for reporting proofs. The logical argument
is the important emphasis, not an arbitrarily predetermined, inflexible format.
Students should be encouraged to think in if-then format:

> *If* I know such-and-such, *then* I also know this-and-that.

This kind of thinking is the key to deduction!

1 **a.** If an integer greater than 1 has exactly two factors, 1 and itself, then
the integer is a prime number.

   If an integer is a prime number, then the integer is greater than 1 and
   has exactly two factors, 1 and itself.

   b. Yes, 23 is a prime number. 23 has exactly two factors, 1 and 23.

   c. The if-then statement, "*If an integer greater than 1 has exactly two
   factors, 1 and itself, then the integer is a prime number,*" was used to
   determine that 23 is a prime number.

2 **a.** *Conclusion*: Andy is 16 years of age or older.

   b. *Conclusion*: No conclusion can be made.

   c. *Conclusion*: $\triangle ABC$ is isosceles.

   d. *Conclusion*: $g(x)$ has a maximum value.

   e. *Conclusion*: No conclusion can be made.

   f. *Conclusion*: With ice skates on, the Oak Park hockey team has a mean
   height of 5 feet $10\frac{3}{4}$ inches and a standard deviation of $2\frac{1}{2}$ inches.

   g. *Conclusion*: $\triangle P'Q'R'$ has area $3^2 \cdot 32 = 288$ cm^2.

3 If-then statements can be represented symbolically as $p \Rightarrow q$ (read "if p, then q" or "p implies q") where p represents the hypothesis and q represents the conclusion. The arrow signals that you move from the hypothesis p to the conclusion q. The reasoning pattern you used in Problem 2 (Affirming the Hypothesis) can be represented as follows.

	Words	Symbolic Form
Known fact:	"If p, then q" is always true,	$p \Rightarrow q$
Given:	**and** p is true in a particular case,	p
Conclusion:	**then** q is true in that case.	q

In the symbolic form, everything above the horizontal line is assumed to be correct or true. What is written below the line follows logically from the accepted information.

a. In Problem 2 Part c, identify p and q in the general statement $p \Rightarrow q$. Identify the specific case of p. Of q.

b. In Problem 2 Part d, identify p and q in the general statement $p \Rightarrow q$. Identify the specific case of p. Of q.

The "known facts" used in Problem 2 Parts c–g are definitions or principles and relationships you discovered and, as a class, agreed upon in previous mathematics courses. Your discoveries were probably based on studying several particular cases or conducting experiments and then searching for patterns.

4 Select one of the statements given as a known fact in Problem 2 Parts d–g. Discuss with classmates how you could explore specific cases that might lead to a discovery of a pattern suggesting the given statement. Be prepared to explain your proposed exploration to the class.

Reasoning from patterns based on analysis of specific cases as you described in Problem 4 is called **inductive reasoning**. This type of reasoning is a valuable tool in making discoveries in mathematics, science, and everyday life. However, inductive reasoning must be used with caution.

5 The famous mathematician Leonard Euler (1707–1783) worked on a wide range of problems including questions of traversability of networks as you may have studied in Course 1. Like others of his time, he was interested in finding a formula to create prime numbers. An early attempt was:

If n is a positive integer, then
$n^2 - n + 41$ *is a prime number.*

a. Test this conjecture by examining some specific cases. Choose several positive values for n and see if the expression gives a prime number. Share the work with others.

③　**a. General statement:**

p: Two sides of a triangle are the same length.
q: The triangle is isosceles.

Specific instance:

p: Two sides of $\triangle ABC$ are length 5 cm.
q: $\triangle ABC$ is an isosceles triangle.

b. General statement:

p: $f(x) = ax^2 + bx + c$ is a quadratic function with $a < 0$.
q: $f(x)$ has a maximum value.

Specific instance:

p: $f(x) = -8x^2 + 5x - 2$ is a quadratic function with $a = -8$.
q: $f(x) = -8x^2 + 5x - 2$ has a maximum value.

INSTRUCTIONAL NOTE
You may choose to do Problem 3 as a full class as a means of summarizing work in Problems 1 and 2.

④　Responses will vary. One possible experiment or case study for each statement is provided here.

d. You could use the calculator to graph many functions of the form $f(x) = ax^2 + bx + c$ with $a < 0$ and notice that they all have a maximum value.

e. You could draw many vertex-edge graphs in which all the vertices have even degree. You could then verify that each of them has an Euler circuit.

f. You could make up a data set and find the mean and standard deviation of that data set. Then you could add different constants c to each element in the data set and recalculate the mean and standard deviation. You should see that the mean increases by c and the standard deviation does not change.

g. Using various figures, you could find the area of many preimage and image figures using different scale factors. You should notice that with magnitude k, the area of the image is k^2 times the area of the preimage.

INSTRUCTIONAL NOTE
Students need not write solutions to Problem 4. Ask groups to share their proposed explanations after they work on this problem for a few minutes.

⑤　**a.** The expression will work for most values of n. An efficient method for testing several values of the function is to put the expression into the functions list on a calculator and then look at a table of values. You can also put specific values for n into a data list and enter the function into another, using the first list for the variable. (Students may need some guidance on how to determine if a number is prime.)

KEY IDEA This problem underscores the need for deductive reasoning and reviews the idea that only one counterexample is needed to disprove a statement.

b. Based on your calculations, does the conjecture seem correct? Can you conclude for sure that it is always true? Explain your reasoning.

c. Test $n^2 - n + 41$ when $n = 41$. Is the result a prime number? Why or why not?

d. To prove an if-then statement is *not* true, you only have to find one counterexample. What is a counterexample to the statement, "if n is a positive integer, then $n^2 - n + 41$ is a prime number"?

6 Now it is your turn to do some mathematical research. Recall that the *degree* of a vertex in a vertex-edge graph without loops is the number of edges touching the vertex. Use Parts a–c and inductive reasoning to develop a conjecture about the *sum* of the degrees of the vertices of a vertex-edge graph with no loops. Share the work with a partner.

a. For each of the graphs shown, determine the number of edges, the degree of each vertex, and the sum of the degrees of the vertices. Organize your results in a table. Leave room to extend your table vertically.

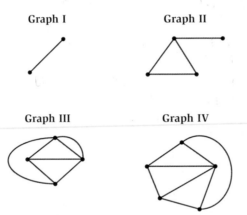

Graph I

Graph II

Graph III

Graph IV

b. Draw four additional vertex-edge graphs without loops. Find the number of edges and the sum of the degrees of the vertices for each graph. Record your findings in your table.

c. If you have a vertex-edge graph with 10 edges and no loops, what do you think is the sum of the degrees of the vertices? Check your prediction with a drawing.

d. Write a conjecture relating the number of edges E and the sum S of the degrees of the vertices.

e. Write your conjecture in if-then form.

f. Can you be absolutely positive that your conjecture is true for all possible vertex-edge graphs with no loops? Explain.

b. From the work done in Part a, it seems as though the conjecture is probably correct. However, you cannot conclude it will be true for all values of n just because a few, or many, values work.

c. The result is not a prime number. $41^2 - 41 + 41 = 41^2 = 1,681$, which has 41 as a factor.

d. The counterexample is $n = 41$. It shows that the statement is not correct because it is not true for *all* positive integer values of n.

INSTRUCTIONAL NOTE
If students are trying to find factors for 1,681 using their calculators, encourage them to set them aside to analyze Part c.

6 **a.**

Graph	Edges	Degrees	Sum of Degrees
I	1	1, 1	2
II	4	3, 1, 2, 2	8
III	7	4, 3, 4, 3	14
IV	8	3, 3, 4, 3, 3	16

b. Students should record their findings in their table in Part a.

c. The sum of the degrees will be 2×10, or 20.

d. The sum S of the degrees of the vertices of a vertex-edge graph (no loops) with E edges will be $2 \times E$. (This relationship can be represented by the formula $S = 2E$.)

e. If a vertex-edge graph with no loops has E edges, then the sum S of the degrees of the vertices is $2E$, or $S = 2E$.

f. No; inductive reasoning was used here. As in Problem 5, it may lead to a conjecture that is not true for all cases.

Inductive reasoning may lead to an if-then statement that is plausible, or seems true. However, as you saw in Problem 5, the statement may not be true for all cases. **Deductive reasoning** involves reasoning *from* facts, definitions, and accepted properties *to* conclusions using principles of logic. Under correct deductive reasoning, the conclusions reached are certain, not just plausible.

 In this problem, you will examine how deductive reasoning is used to *prove* the relationship you discovered in Problem 6. Compare your if-then statement in Part e of that problem with the following statement.

> *If G is a vertex-edge graph with E edges, none of which are loops, then the sum S of the degrees of the vertices is equal to 2E.*

Here is an argument that is claimed to be a proof of this conjecture. Study it carefully.

> If G is a vertex-edge graph with E edges, none of which are loops, then each of the E edges joins two vertices.
>
> If each of the E edges joins two vertices, then each of the E edges contributes 2 to the sum S of the degrees of the vertices.
>
> If each of the E edges contributes 2 to the sum of the degrees of the vertices S, then $S = 2E$.
>
> Therefore, if G is a vertex-edge graph with E edges, none of which are loops, then the sum S of the degrees of the vertices is $2E$.

a. Does this argument convince you that the conjecture is correct? Why or why not?

b. Why do you think the argument started with, "If G is a vertex-edge graph with E edges, none of which are loops"?

c. Is the argument based on information that is known to be correct? Look critically at each of the first three if-then statements. Are they correct? Explain why or why not.

d. The argument is based on valid reasoning with a *chain of if-then statements*, given symbolically at the right. In the first implication $p \Rightarrow q$,

Chaining Implications

$$p \Rightarrow q$$
$$q \Rightarrow r$$
$$\dfrac{r \Rightarrow s}{? \Rightarrow ?}$$

p is the statement, "G is a vertex-edge graph with E edges, none of which are loops,"

q is the statement, "each of the E edges joins two vertices."

Analyze the form of the argument and then complete this symbolic representation. Identify the statement represented by each letter in the symbolic chain.

7 **a.** Most students will find this argument convincing and will correctly believe that this argument proves the conjecture.

b. Because that condition is given information

c. Each statement is known to be correct. Reasons supporting each statement follow.

First statement: Each edge connects 2 distinct vertices when there are no loops.

Second statement: Each edge will contribute 1 degree to 1 vertex and 1 degree to another vertex, so each edge contributes 2 degrees to the sum.

Third statement: $2 + 2 + 2 + \cdots$ for E edges is 2 summed E times, or $2E$.

d.

$$p \Rightarrow q$$

$$q \Rightarrow r$$

$$\underline{r \Rightarrow s}$$

$$\boldsymbol{p \Rightarrow s}$$

p: G is a vertex-edge graph with E edges, none of which are loops.

q: Each of the E edges joins two vertices.

r: Each of the E edges contributes 2 to the sum of the degrees of the vertices S.

s: The sum of the degrees of the vertices is $2E$.

Summarize the Mathematics

Inductive reasoning and deductive reasoning are each important; they are complementary aspects of mathematical reasoning. Inductive reasoning often leads to conjectures of new relationships or properties that can be proven using deductive reasoning. Consider this conjecture.

The sum of any two consecutive odd numbers is divisible by 4.

a How could you arrive at this conjecture by using inductive reasoning?

b Write this conjecture in if-then form.

   i. What is the hypothesis of your statement?

   ii. What is the conclusion?

c How could you use deductive reasoning to prove this conjecture?

Be prepared to share your ideas and reasoning strategies with the entire class.

✓Check Your Understanding

Make a conjecture about what happens when you choose any four consecutive whole numbers, add the middle two, and then subtract the smallest of the four from that sum.

a. Describe the procedure you used to create your conjecture.

b. Write your conjecture in if-then form.

32, 33, 34, 35

c. If n represents the smallest of four consecutive whole numbers, how would you represent each of the next three numbers?

d. Use your representations in Part c to write an argument that proves your conjecture is always true.

Summarize
the Mathematics

a Inductive reasoning could be used to arrive at this conjecture by repeatedly picking two consecutive odd numbers and adding them. Then notice that the result is divisible by 4.

b If a and b are two consecutive odd numbers, then $a + b$ is divisible by 4.

   i. The hypothesis: a and b are two consecutive odd numbers.

   ii. The conclusion: $a + b$ is divisible by 4.

c If a is any odd number, then $a = 2m + 1$, where m is an integer. It follows that the next consecutive odd number $b = 2m + 1 + 2 = 2m + 3$. So, $a + b = (2m + 1) + (2m + 3) = 4m + 4 = 4(m + 1)$. Since 4 is a factor of $a + b$, the sum is divisible by 4.

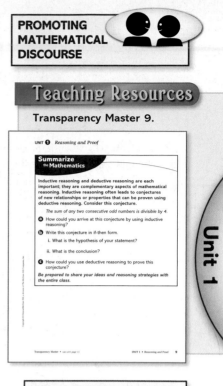

✓ Check Your Understanding

Conjectures may vary slightly; however, adding the middle two numbers and subtracting the smallest number gives the largest number.

a. To create a conjecture, students will most likely test a number of specific cases.

b. If you add the middle two whole numbers from a list of any four consecutive whole numbers and subtract the smallest from that sum, then the result will be equal to the largest of the four whole numbers.

c. $n + 1, n + 2$, and $n + 3$

d. If n represents the first of any four consecutive whole numbers, then the following three numbers can be written as $n + 1, n + 2$, and $n + 3$. The sum of the middle two numbers is $(n + 1) + (n + 2) = 2n + 3$. Subtracting the smallest of the four numbers from that sum is $(2n + 3) - n = n + 3$. This result is the largest of the four consecutive whole numbers.

Teacher: In this lesson, we have been examining how to construct arguments using both inductive and deductive reasoning. I would like each of you to think individually for a moment and then talk with a partner about the conjecture proposed in the Summarize the Mathematics for this investigation:

The sum of any two consecutive odd numbers is divisible by 4.

How could you arrive at this conjecture using inductive reasoning? Think first by yourself and then with a partner. *(The teacher gives students individual time and then makes certain that each student has found a partner. She then walks around the room listening to the conversations.)*

Teacher: It sounds like most of you used similar inductive reasoning. Shari, would you mind sharing the reasoning you and Jon used?

Shari: We just took three sets of odd numbers and added them up and divided by 4. We used 15 and 17, which gave us 32, which is divisible by 4. Then we tried larger numbers. 103 plus 105 is 208. 4 goes into 208 exactly 52 times. Finally, we used 1,111 and 1,113, which gave us 2,224. 4 goes into 2,224 exactly 556 times.

Teacher: Did anyone use different reasoning than that used by Shari and Jon? *(No students offer different reasoning.)* Talk about how you would write this conjecture in if-then form with your partner and identify both the hypothesis and the conclusion of your statement. *(The teacher allows a brief time for the conversation as students should be well practiced by their work in the investigation.)*

Teacher: Who would like to share their if-then statement? *(Several students raise their hands and the teacher chooses one pair of students.)*

Jian: We wrote: If two numbers are odd and consecutive, then their sum is divisible by 4.

Teacher: Thank you, Jian. Would anyone like to offer another if-then statement different from Jian's and Carolyn's?

Tia: We had: If you add two consecutive odd numbers, then you get a number that is divisible by 4.

Teacher: Any others?

Assad: We used variables to write: If a and b are consecutive odd numbers, then $a + b$ is divisible by 4.

Teacher: Would all three of these statements be acceptable? *(Students indicate acceptance of all three.)* Let's take a look at all three statements and identify both the hypothesis and the conclusion. I have all three written on the overhead projector. I

would like to have a "volunteer" come up and underline the hypothesis of each statement. *(The teacher draws a popsicle stick from her collection of sticks with each student's name on them.)* Isla. It looks like you are my "volunteer." *(Isla comes to the overhead and underlines the three hypotheses.)*

Teacher: Is there any disagreement with what Isla has underlined as the hypothesis in each statement? *(No students indicate disagreement.)* Okay then, Lorna, you are my second "volunteer." Would you please underline the conclusion for each statement. *(Lorna correctly underlines the conclusion for each statement.)* Any disagreement? *(None is offered.)* Thank you, Isla and Lorna. Let's consider Part c in the STM. How could you use deductive reasoning to prove this conjecture? Work for just a minute or two with your partner to develop an argument for this conjecture using deductive reasoning. If you get really stuck, you can look back at your work in this investigation or the first investigation. *(As the teacher walks around the room, she looks for different approaches that can be used in the whole-group conversation.)*

Teacher: I noticed a couple different kinds of arguments. Thomas and Mark, you used variables to represent your odd numbers. Would you write your argument on the board for us to consider? *(Thomas talks through the argument while Mark writes on the board.)*

Thomas: Since both numbers are odd, we wrote the first one as $2m + 1$. Then, since we skip a number to get to the next odd number, we called the second number $(2m + 1) + 2$. Then we added them to get $4m + 4$. Then we said that $4m + 4$ is divisible by 4 since 4 obviously goes into both $4m$ and 4.

Teacher: What do the rest of you think? Are you convinced? *(No students ask questions of Thomas or Mark.)* Well, then I have one question. When you say that 4 obviously goes into $4m$ and 4, what are you thinking?

Mark: We were thinking that since $4m$ means 4 times m then 4 is a factor of $4m$ and obviously 4 is a factor of 4.

Teacher: Any other questions for Mark and Thomas?

Gabe: We did the same thing. But to show that the final number was divisible by 4, we factored and got $4(m + 1)$. It seems more obvious that 4 is a factor when you write it that way.

Rebecca: We did that, too. But I see what Mark and Thomas are saying. It makes sense that if two parts of a sum are divisible by 4 then the sum must be divisible by 4. I guess it is just two different ways to write the sum.

Teacher: Any other comments? Okay. Lily and Kyle, would you please share your argument by writing and talking about it like Mark and Thomas did?

Lily (talking while Kyle writes): We used counters like we saw in the investigation. Since the first number is odd, we wrote a rectangular array with one extra dot. Then, for the second number, we wrote the first number again and added 2 more dots. When we add them together, this part is kind of hard to see, we moved the one dot from our first number down to the second number. Then you can see that the sum has four rows with the same number of dots and 4 extra dots. *(Kyle circles the four rows of dots in blue and the four extra dots in red.)* So, the sum is divisible by 4.

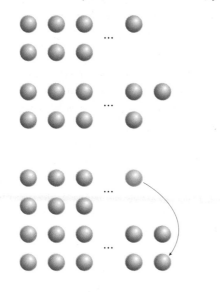

Mackenzie: I just noticed that this is the same as we were just talking about with the variables.

Teacher: Can you say more about what you are thinking? *(The teacher is not certain what point Mackenzie is trying to make.)*

Mackenzie: Well, Lily and Kyle are thinking the same way as Mark and Thomas. They said that the sum is divisible by 4 because the two parts of their array are divisible by 4. But you can think of it another way, too.

Teacher: What other way do you see?

Mackenzie: *(Goes up to the board and rearranges the dots as shown below)* Instead of moving the one dot down, move one of the bottom dots up, so then you have four rows that are exactly the same. It's like Gabe was saying.

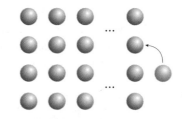

Isaac: That's a cool way to look at that!

Teacher: It is, isn't it? Are there other deductive arguments anyone wished to offer? *(No offers given.)* Let's take a look then at what you are asked to do for the Check Your Understanding.

On Your Own

Applications

These tasks provide opportunities for you to use and strengthen your understanding of the ideas you have learned in the lesson.

1 Carefully study the following plot from a detective story.

> Detectives Walker and Stanwick were called to the Engineering division of the Centipore medical building where it was discovered that someone had tampered with a sensitive computer disk. The security chief, Freedman, said he kept Engineering a restricted area. DiCampli, the vice-president of engineering, said that the disk was fine when used last Wednesday, the 11th, but was found to be altered last Friday, the 13th. Miller, a senior engineer, discovered the problem and immediately reported it to DiCampli who confirmed it and reported it to Parke, the executive vice-president of operations who, in turn, contacted the detectives.
>
> Upon further investigation, the detectives learned that the door to the room housing the computer disk was unforced and thus must have been accessed by either DiCampli, Miller, Parke, or one of two other senior engineers, Donlan and Delaney. However, Donlan was new to the company and for now could only access the room with verification by Freedman, who was out with the flu for the past week. The company was able to verify use on the 11th and use on the 13th, when Miller discovered the problem. The disk was not used on the terminal between those times. Using the disk on another computer required a decryption code which was changed on the 9th and automatically issued to senior engineers. The code was issued to other higher-ups through Freedman.
>
> Before arriving at Centipore, the detectives were given a tip that one of Centipore's competitors bribed one of the Centipore employees. With this information and the evidence they discovered at the crime scene, the detectives were sure they could figure out who the culprit was.

Adapted from: Smith, Stan. (2000). *Five-Minute Crimebusters: Clever Mini-Mysteries.* New York: Sterling Publishing Company, Inc. pp. 51–53.

    a. Identify the prime suspect in this case. Explain the evidence you could use to charge that person and write a convincing argument to do so.

    b. Write a series of arguments that could be used to exonerate or clear the other possible suspects of blame.

    c. In what ways is the reasoning used to identify the prime suspect similar to the reasoning used to solve the Sudoku puzzle on page 2?

Applications

1. **a.** The prime suspect is Delaney. Since only the senior engineers automatically received access to the new code, the culprit must be Miller, Donlan, or Delany. However, Donlan was new to the company and had not yet received the new code. Miller discovered the problem and reported it, so he seems an unlikely suspect. That leaves Delaney.

    b. Anyone other than a senior engineer could not have had the new code since Freedman was out sick. If Miller was the culprit, he would have at least delayed his pretend discovery. Donlan did not have the code, so he could only be involved if he had cooperation from another senior engineer.

    c. The reasoning used identifies which persons are possible suspects and then eliminates those who, for various reasons, cannot have committed the crime. In Sudoku, you identify which numbers could be possible to fill a blank space and then eliminate all but one based on the rule that each column, row, and 3 × 3 block must have exactly one of each of the digits from 1 to 9.

2 The following two-person game is played on a rectangular board, like a large index card. To play, players take turns placing pennies on the board. The coins may touch but cannot overlap or extend beyond the game board. A player cannot move the position of an already placed coin. The player who plays the last coin is the winner. The diagrams below show the first play of each of two players.

1st Player

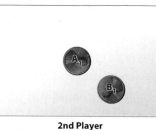

2nd Player

a. Play the game a few times with a partner, noting how the shape of the game board influences your play.

b. Use the symmetry of the game board to devise a strategy that will always result in a win for the *1st player* when he or she places the first coin in position A_1 as above.

c. On a copy of the second diagram at the right above, show the next play of a 1st player who is using your winning strategy. Then show the next two possible plays of each player.

d. Write a description of your winning strategy for the 1st player. Provide an argument for why that strategy will guarantee a win for the 1st player.

e. What other game board shapes can you make so that the strategy will work?

3 *Consecutive numbers* are adjacent integers on a number line, such as 5 and 6. Nathan, Trina, Kasib, and Ivana were trying to prove the following statement.

The sum of any two consecutive numbers is always an odd number.

Study each of the arguments below.

Nathan: If the first number is even, then the second number must be odd. This combination will always add up to an odd number.

Kasib: Two consecutive numbers are of the form n and $n + 1$. $n + (n + 1) = 2n + 1$ which is, by definition, the form of an odd number.

Trina: No matter what two consecutive numbers you take, their sum is always odd as shown below.

$$5 + 6 = 11$$
$$22 + 23 = 45$$
$$140 + 141 = 281$$

2 **a.** Students should play the game three or four times with a partner.

b. After the 1st player places a penny in the center of the board, he or she should visualize the position of the half-turn image of the 2nd player's penny and place his or her next penny at that position. Continuing with this strategy, the 1st player will have the last play. (*Note*: This symmetry strategy is guaranteed to win only if the first penny is placed at the center of the rectangle.)

c. Students' diagrams will vary depending on their strategy. In the strategy outlined in Part b, the sketch could look like:

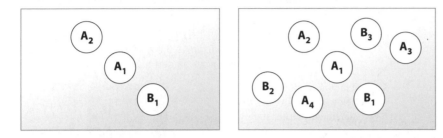

d. After playing the first penny at the center of the board, the 1st player always places a penny at the position A_{n+1} so that it is a half-turn image of B_n about A_1. Another way to describe the position of A_{n+1} is that A_1 is the midpoint of the segment $B_n A_{n+1}$.

e. The strategy outlined here will work for game boards that have half-turn or 180° rotational symmetry.

Ivana: For any two consecutive numbers, one will be even and the other will be odd. In Part c of the Check Your Understanding task on page 9, I gave an argument justifying that the sum of an even number and an odd number is always an odd number. So, the sum of any two consecutive numbers is always an odd number.

  a. Which proof is the closest to the argument you would give to prove that the sum of any two consecutive numbers is always an odd number?

  b. Which arguments are *not* correct proofs of the statement? Explain your reasoning.

  c. Give a "visual proof" of the statement using arrays of counters.

  d. How would you prove or disprove the assertion, "The sum of three consecutive numbers is always an odd number"?

4 Examine each of the arguments below. Assuming the if-then statement is true, state whether the argument is correct or incorrect. Give a reason for your answers.

  a. If the price of gas rises, then demand for gas falls. Demand for gas has risen. Therefore, the price of gas has risen.

  b. If the price of gas rises, then demand for gas falls. The price of gas has risen. Therefore, the demand for gas has fallen.

  c. If the price of gas rises, then demand for gas falls. The price of gas has fallen. Therefore, the demand for gas has fallen.

5 Suppose it is true that "all members of the senior class are at least 5 feet 2 inches tall." What, if anything, can you conclude with certainty about each of the following students?

  a. Darlene, who is a member of the senior class

  b. Trevor, who is 5 feet 10 inches tall

  c. Anessa, who is 5 feet tall

  d. Ashley, who is not a member of the senior class

6 Suppose it is true that "all sophomores at Calvin High School enroll in physical education."

  a. Write this statement in if-then form. What is the hypothesis? The conclusion?

  b. If Tadi is a sophomore at Calvin, what can you conclude?

  c. If Rosa is enrolled in a physical education class at Calvin, what can you conclude? Explain your reasoning.

3 **a.** The answer will depend on each student's choice of an argument.

b. Nathan's proof is not correct because it is incomplete. He does not provide justification for his concluding statement.

Trina's proof is not correct since she only shows the argument is true for three consecutive pairs of numbers.

Both Kasib and Ivana provide correct proofs.

c. The sum of two consecutive numbers will have this kind of representation:

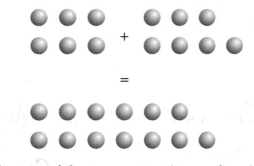

Therefore, the sum of the two consecutive numbers is an odd number.

d. A counterexample could disprove the assertion. For example, 3, 4, and 5 are three consecutive numbers; but 3 + 4 + 5 = 12, which is even.

4 **a.** Not correct. We only know that *if* the price rises, demand falls. Nothing is known about what conditions (assumptions) led to a rising demand in gas.

b. Correct. The agreement correctly uses affirming the hypothesis reasoning. It uses the known if-then statement and a particular case of the hypothesis to make the conclusion.

c. Not correct. The if-then statement tells nothing about what happens *if* the first hypothesis is false.

5 **a.** Darlene is at least 5 feet 2 inches tall.

b. Nothing can be concluded about Trevor.

c. Anessa is not a member of the senior class.

d. Nothing can be concluded about Ashley.

6 **a.** If a student is a sophomore at Calvin High School, then the student enrolls in physical education.

Hypothesis: A student is a sophomore at Calvin High School.

Conclusion: The student enrolls in physical education.

b. Tadi enrolls in physical education.

c. Nothing can be concluded about Rosa. The fact we have is that *if* a student is a sophomore, then he or she enrolls in physical education; however, students in other classes may be able to enroll in physical education also.

(7) In 1742, number theorist Christian Goldbach (1690–1764) wrote a letter to mathematician Leonard Euler in which he proposed a conjecture that people are still trying to prove or disprove. Goldbach's Conjecture states:

Every even number greater than or equal to 4 can be expressed as the sum of two prime numbers.

a. Verify Goldbach's Conjecture is true for 12. For 28.

b. Write Goldbach's Conjecture in if-then form.

c. Write the converse of Goldbach's Conjecture. Prove that the converse is not true.

(8) Examine the following if-then statements about properties of numbers.

I. If a, b, and c are consecutive positive numbers, then $a + b + c$ is divisible by 3.

II. If a, b, and c are consecutive positive numbers, then $a + b + c$ is divisible by 6.

III. If x is a real number, then $-x < x$.

IV. If x is a nonzero real number, then $x > \frac{1}{x}$.

V. If x is the degree measure of the smallest angle of a triangle, then $\cos x > 0$.

a. Use inductive reasoning to help you decide which statements might be correct and which are incorrect. For each statement that is incorrect, give a counterexample.

b. For each correct statement, use deductive reasoning to write a proof that could convince a skeptic that it is true.

(9) Tonja made the following conjecture about consecutive whole numbers.

For any four consecutive whole numbers, the product of the middle two numbers is always two more than the product of the first and last numbers.

a. Test Tonja's conjecture for a set of four consecutive whole numbers.

b. Find a counterexample or give a deductive proof of Tonja's conjecture.

7 **a.** $12 = 7 + 5$; $28 = 11 + 17$ or $28 = 5 + 23$

b. If a number is an even number greater than or equal to 4, then it can be expressed as the sum of two prime numbers.

c. If a number can be expressed as the sum of two prime numbers, then it is an even number greater than or equal to 4.

A counterexample suffices as a proof that the converse is not true. A counterexample: $2 + 3 = 5$, but 5 is not an even number.

8 **a.** Students should use examples to conjecture that **I** is correct.

A counterexample to **II**: $6 + 7 + 8 = 21$, 21 is not divisible by 6.

A counterexample to **III**: If $x = -5$, then $-(-5) = 5$ is not less than -5.

A counterexample to **IV**: If $x = \frac{1}{2}$, then $\frac{1}{2}$ is not greater than $\frac{1}{\frac{1}{2}} = 2$.

Students should use examples to conjecture that **V** is correct.

b. A possible proof for **I**:

Let x, $x + 1$, $x + 2$ represent three consecutive positive integers. Since $x + (x + 1) + (x + 2) = 3x + 3 = 3(x + 1)$, 3 is a factor of the sum. So, the sum is divisible by 3.

A possible proof for **V**:

If x is the degree measure of the smallest angle in a triangle, then the angle is an acute angle with $0 < x < 90°$. For all x in this range, $\cos x > 0$.

9 **a.** Students should test the conjecture.

b. Represent four consecutive whole numbers as x, $x + 1$, $x + 2$, and $x + 3$. The product of the middle two is $(x + 1)(x + 2) = x^2 + 3x + 2$. The product of the largest and smallest is $x(x + 3) = x^2 + 3x$. So, for any four consecutive whole numbers, the product of the middle two numbers is always two more than the product of the smallest and largest numbers.

Connections

These tasks will help you connect the ideas of mathematical reasoning in this lesson with other mathematical topics and contexts that you know.

10 *Factorial* notation is a compact way of writing the product of consecutive positive whole numbers. For example, $5! = 5 \times 4 \times 3 \times 2 \times 1$. $5!$ is read "5 factorial." In general, $n! = n \times (n-1) \times (n-2) \times \cdots \times 2 \times 1$.

   a. Calculate $3!$.

   b. The names of three candidates for the same office are to be listed on a ballot. How many different orderings of the names are possible? Compare your answer to that found in Part a.

   c. Provide an argument that $(n+1)! = (n+1) \times n!$.

   d. Kenneth Ruthven of Cambridge University proposed the following conjectures about $100!$ to a class in Great Britain. For each conjecture, write an argument that proves the conjecture or explain why it is not true.

      I. $100!$ is an even number.   **II.** $100!$ is divisible by 101.

      III. $100!$ is larger than $101! - 100!$.   **IV.** $100!$ is larger than $50! \times 10^{50}$.

11 Problem 3 of Investigation 2 (page 12) illustrated a symbolic model for reasoning with an if-then statement. You can also represent if-then statements geometrically using *Venn diagrams*.

   a. Examine these if-then statements and the corresponding Venn diagrams.

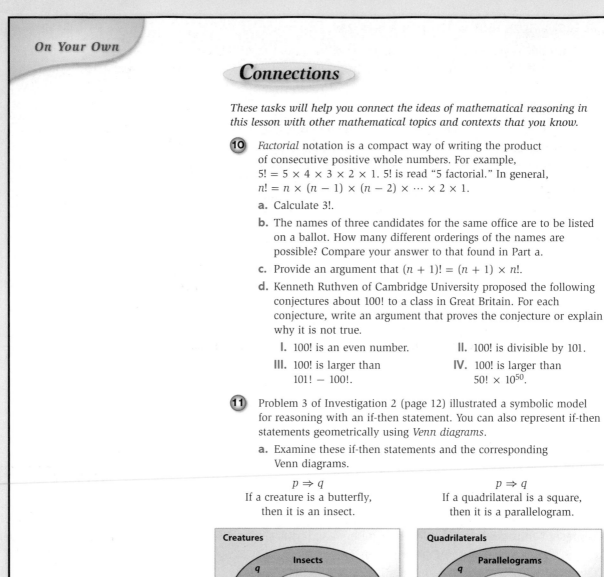

$$p \Rightarrow q$$
If a creature is a butterfly, then it is an insect.

$$p \Rightarrow q$$
If a quadrilateral is a square, then it is a parallelogram.

      i. If you know that a monarch is a butterfly, what can you conclude?

      ii. If you know that quadrilateral *WXYZ* is a square, what can you conclude?

   b. Refer to Applications Task 6 (page 18). Represent the if-then statement you wrote in Part a with a Venn diagram. How can you use the Venn diagram to reason about Tadi's situation in Part b?

Connections

10 **a.** $3! = 6$

b. Candidates A, B, and C could be ordered:

A, B, C	C, A, B	B, A, C
A, C, B	C, B, A	B, C, A

to give 6 different orderings. This is 3! different orderings.

c. $(n + 1)! = (n + 1) \times (n) \times (n - 1) \times (n - 2) \times \cdots \times 2 \times 1$
$= (n + 1) \times n!$

d. **I.** True. 100! is an even number since by definition an even number has a factor of 2. $100! = 100 \times 99 \times \cdots \times 2 \times 1$ has a factor of 2.

II. False. 100! is not divisible by 101. 101 is a prime number larger than 100. Since $100! = 100 \times 99 \times \cdots \times 2 \times 1$, it does not have a factor of 101.

III. False. $101! - 100! = 101 \times 100! - 100! = 100! \times (101 - 1) = 100! \times (100)$. $100! \times (100)$ is larger than 100! by 100 times, so $101! - 100!$ is larger than 100!.

IV. True. $100! = 100 \times 99 \times \cdots \times 51 \times 50!$; so, we need only compare $100 \times 99 \times \cdots \times 51$ to 10^{50}. 10^{50} is 50 factors of 10. $100 \times 99 \times \cdots \times 51$ is 50 factors of numbers much larger than 10. So, 100! is much larger than $50! \times 10^{50}$.

11 **a.** **i.** You can conclude that a monarch is an insect.

ii. You can conclude that quadrilateral *WXYZ* is a parallelogram.

b. If a student is a sophomore at Calvin High School, then the student enrolls in physical education.

Since Tadi is a sophomore at Calvin High School, he would be placed inside the inner region. Since this region is entirely inside the physical education students region, Tadi must be a physical education student.

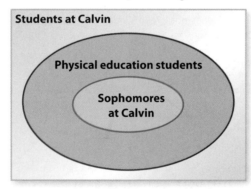

Students at Calvin
Physical education students
Sophomores at Calvin

> **COMMON ERROR** Since assuming that the converse of a statement is true is such a common error, it is crucial that Task 11 receives a full-class discussion.

c. A common error in deductive reasoning is to assume that whenever an if-then statement $p \Rightarrow q$ is true, the *converse* statement $q \Rightarrow p$ is also true.

   i. For each statement in Part a, write the converse and decide whether or not the converse statement is true. If not, give a counterexample.

   ii. How do the Venn diagrams in Part a show that the converse of a statement is not always true? How is this analysis related to your reasoning about the case of Rosa in Applications Task 6 Part c (page 18)?

12 Suppose a statement $p \Rightarrow q$ and its converse $q \Rightarrow p$ are both true. Then the statement $p \Leftrightarrow q$ (read "p if and only if q") is true. In Course 1, you proved that both the Pythagorean Theorem and its converse were true. This fact can be stated in if-and-only-if form. *In $\triangle ABC$, $\angle C$ is a right angle if and only if $a^2 + b^2 = c^2$.*

a. Write the definition of a trapezoid from page 7 in if-and-only-if form.

b. Write the definition of a prime number from page 10 in if-and-only-if form.

c. Consider this statement about real numbers. If $a = b$, then $a + c = b + c$.

   i. Write the converse of this statement.

   ii. Is the converse always true? Explain your reasoning.

   iii. Write an if-and-only-if statement summarizing this property of equality.

13 Consider the true statement, "If a person lives in Chicago, then the person lives in Illinois," and the corresponding Venn diagram below.

a. Which of the following statements are always true?

   i. If a person does not live in Chicago, then the person does not live in Illinois.

   ii. If a person does not live in Illinois, then the person does not live in Chicago.

b. How are your answers to Part a illustrated by the Venn diagram?

c. The if-then statement in Part ai is called the *inverse* of the original statement. In symbols, the inverse of $p \Rightarrow q$ is *not* $p \Rightarrow$ *not* q. Use a Venn diagram to explain why the inverse of a true if-then statement may not always be true.

c. **i.** If a creature is an insect, then it is a butterfly. If a quadrilateral is a parallelogram, then it is a square. Neither converse is true. Students should provide a counterexample for both by naming an insect that is not a butterfly and drawing or naming a parallelogram that is not a square.

ii. The Venn diagrams in Part a show that one can be in the insect region without being in the butterfly region and that one can be in the parallelogram region without being in the square region. The case of Rosa in Part c of Task 7 states she is enrolled in physical education. So, we only know that she is in the physical education part of the Venn diagram; we have no information to conclude whether she is or is not in the sophomore region inside the PE region.

12 **a.** A quadrilateral is a trapezoid if and only if it has two opposite sides parallel.

b. A number is prime if and only if it is an integer greater than 1 and has exactly two factors, 1 and itself.

c. **i.** If $a + c = b + c$, then $a = b$.

ii. Yes, the converse is true. Subtracting c from both sides of the equation results in $a = b$.

iii. $a = b$ if and only if $a + c = b + c$.

13 **a.** **i.** Not always true

ii. Always true

b. **i.** There is a ring representing people who live in Illinois but do not live in Chicago.

ii. The region representing Chicago residents is totally inside the region representing Illinois residents.

c. *Not p* means outside the region labeled *p*. It is possible to have some points outside the region *p* but inside the region *q*. Only those outside the region *q* are *not q*.

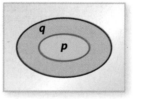

> **NOTE** *not p* $\Rightarrow$ *not q* is also written as $\sim p \Rightarrow \sim q$.

d. The if-then statement in Part aii is called the *contrapositive* of the original statement. In symbols, the contrapositive of $p \Rightarrow q$ is *not* $q \Rightarrow$ *not* p. (An implication and its contrapositive are *logically equivalent statements*.) Use a Venn diagram to explain why the contrapositive of a true if-then statement is always true.

Reflections

These tasks provide opportunities for you to re-examine your thinking about ideas in the lesson.

14 Look back at Connor's strategy to guarantee that the second player can always win the nonagon game. (Investigation 1, page 5)

  a. Will his strategy work if the game is played on the vertices of a regular pentagon? Explain your reasoning.

  b. Will his strategy work if the game is played on the vertices of a regular octagon? Explain.

  c. Describe as precisely as you can all regular polygons for which Connor's strategy will work.

15 Look back to page 6 at the arguments that Nesrin and Teresa provided to justify that the sum of two odd numbers is always an even number.

  a. How can Nesrin's counter model help you to better understand Teresa's argument?

  b. How could Nesrin's argument be revised to make it more general?

16 If-then statements are sometimes called *conditional statements*. Why does that term make sense?

17 In this age of the Internet and World Wide Web, advertising has become big business. Advertisers often use if-then statements to sell their products and services. The straightforward ad:

> *Use your money wisely—shop at FlorMart superstore.*

is worded to suggest the implication:

> *If you shop at FlorMart, then you use your money wisely.*

Often, with some added help from the advertiser, the statement is interpreted by consumers:

> *If you do not shop at FlorMart, then you do not use your money wisely.*

  a. Why might the wording of the second implication have a stronger psychological effect upon most shoppers than the first implication?

  b. Are the two statements logically the same? Explain.

d. Points that are *not q* would have to be outside the region labeled *q*. These points are also outside the region labeled *p*. Thus, points that are *not q* are also *not p*; in other words, *not q* implies *not p*.

Reflections

14 **a.** Connor's strategy will work for a regular pentagon since the line of symmetry will separate the board into two identical halves, so any move the first player makes can be mirrored by the second player.

b. The basic strategy with slight changes will work for an octagon. If the first player selects one penny, then Connor should visualize the symmetry line and select the one other penny on that symmetry line. Then mirror the opponent's play. If the opponent selects 2 adjacent pennies on the first move, then Connor should select the 2 vertices of the opposite side and mirror the opponent's play.

c. The original strategy works for all regular polygons with an odd number of vertices. The revised strategy (described in Part b of this task) works for all regular polygons with an even number of vertices.

15 **a.** Nesrin's argument could be generalized to provide a visual representation of the expressions $(2m + 1)$ and $(2n + 1)$ in Teresa's argument.

b. Nesrin could eliminate the 5, 11, and 16 in her argument and say instead that any odd number can be represented by one counter added to a rectangular array of counters with two rows. Then the sum of any two odd numbers would form a new two-row rectangular array with no extra counters, and is therefore an even number.

16 Conditional statements may make sense to students if they think of the conclusion, or "then statement," being true only on the condition that the hypothesis, or "if statement," is true.

17 **a.** The second statement implies poor judgment and thus has a more accusatory tone to it.

b. No. $p \Rightarrow q$ is not logically the same as *not p* $\Rightarrow$ *not q*.

> **ASSIGNMENT NOTE**
> Be sure to assign and discuss Task 17. It raises *incorrect reasoning* that is commonly used.

Unit 1

18 If you think about it, inductive reasoning is a common form of reasoning in the world around you. Give an example of how inductive reasoning might be used by the following people.

   a. An automobile driver

   b. A consumer

   c. A medical researcher

19 Explain how inductive and deductive reasoning differ. In doing mathematics, how does one form of reasoning support the other?

Extensions

These tasks provide opportunities for you to explore further or more deeply the ideas you studied in this lesson.

20 Look back at the nonagon game in Investigation 1 (page 4). Another student, Sofia, claimed she found a strategy using symmetry that guaranteed that the *first player* could always win the game. What is wrong with her argument below?

> As the first player, I'll remove the one penny at the top. Then in my mind, I divide the remaining 8 pennies by the line of symmetry determined by the removed penny. Now, whatever the other player does, I'll do the symmetric move. So, there is always a move for me to make. Therefore, I can never lose by having no coins to remove.

21 In his book, *Proofs without Words*, mathematician Roger Nelsen offers the following two visual "proofs." Although not proofs in the strictest sense, the diagrams he provides help you see why each particular mathematical statement is true.

   a. How does the diagram below help you see that for any positive integer n, the sum of the integers from 1 to n is $\frac{1}{2}n(n + 1)$?

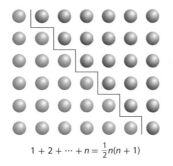

$$1 + 2 + \cdots + n = \frac{1}{2}n(n + 1)$$

Unit 1

18 Student examples will vary.

  a. An automobile driver might use inductive reasoning by observing that since most of the cars are not speeding on a certain section of the highway, it is a well-patrolled section and exceeding the speed limit there may be more likely than usual to lead to a ticket.

  b. A consumer might notice that gas prices rise on summer holiday weekends.

  c. A medical researcher might use inductive reasoning to help form conjectures that will be further explored. For example, if many people with common symptoms had all recently visited the same foreign country, the researcher might reason that it was something in that country that made all of the people sick.

19 Inductive reasoning begins with examples, looks for a pattern or relationship, and then conjectures that the relationship holds for all similar situations. Deductive reasoning begins with known information and logically reasons to the truth of some statement. Inductive reasoning leads to plausibility (or refutation), while deductive reasoning leads to certainty. Inductive reasoning is often used to develop or check conjectures that will be proved deductively.

Extensions

20 Sofia has not recognized that the second player can take two adjacent pennies, one on each side of the symmetry line at the opposite edge. That is a move that cannot "mirror," and we know that move can lead to a win for the 2nd player.

21 **a.** The numbers of light (or dark) colored counters in each row represent the numbers 1, 2, 3, 4, 5, and 6. Continuing the pattern in this diagram, one could represent any positive integer n by a row of colored counters. The rectangular array of light and dark counters is n by $(n + 1)$, so it contains $n \times (n + 1)$ counters. The sum of the n positive integers is half the total number of counters, or $\frac{1}{2}n(n + 1)$.

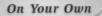

On Your Own

b. How does the diagram at the right help you see that the "infinite sum" of fractions of the form $\left(\frac{1}{2}\right)^n$, $n \geq 1$ is 1?

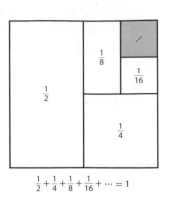

$$\frac{1}{2} + \frac{1}{4} + \frac{1}{8} + \frac{1}{16} + \cdots = 1$$

22 Many people, such as auto technicians, make a living out of repairing things. Often, repairs can be done at home if you have the right tools and can reason deductively. The first step in making a repair is to identify the problem. Examine the troubleshooting chart below for diagnosing problems that often occur with small engines, such as the one on a lawn mower.

a. What are the first things you should check if the engine runs but the mower does not?

Four-cycle engine with horizontal crankshaft

Fuel tank · Piston · Spark plug · Valve · Air filter · Cylinder · Connecting rod · Crankshaft · Carburetor · Muffler · Camshaft drive gear

PROBLEM	Starter doesn't turn engine	Engine turns, will not start	Engine starts, then stalls	Runs unevenly, lacks power	Engine stalls at idle speed	Engine dies during use	Engine runs too fast	Engine runs, device doesn't	Engine vibrates excessively	Engine smokes profusely	Engine overheats	Engine backfires	Engine is extra-noisy	POSSIBLE CAUSE
	●													Starter rope jammed or broken
	●													Recoil starter spring weak or broken
	●													Electric starter battery low, connections loose or corroded, or power cord damaged
		●	●	●	●		●							Clogged air filter
		●	●		●									Fuel tank empty; add fuel
		●	●	●	●	●								Contaminated fuel
		●	●											Fuel cap breather holes blocked
		●	●		●									Clogged fuel filter
		●	●		●									Obstructed or damaged fuel line
		●	●	●			●							Sticky choke; clean with solvent (you may have to disassemble the carburetor)
				●	●									Idle speed incorrect; see owner's manual to adjust
						●	●	●						Governor linkage out of adjustment
		●	●	●	●		●		●	●	●			Carburetor fouled or poorly adjusted
		●	●		●				●	●				On two-cycle engine, incorrect fuel mixture
		●	●		●						●			On two-cycle engine, faulty reed valve
		●	●	●	●									Fouled spark plug or damaged cable
						●				●			●	Insufficient oil in crankcase; add oil to oil tank
						●								Overheated; allow engine to cool, then restart
						●					●	●		Valves sticking, burned, or need adjusting
		●	●	●	●						●	●		Breaker points dirty or improperly set
		●	●	●	●				●					Low compression
				●	●	●					●		●	Clogged muffler or exhaust port
								●						Slipping belt
								●	●					Faulty clutch
											●			Cooling fins dirty; clean fins
		●	●	●	●			●				●		Flywheel key bent, broken, or worn
											●		●	Flywheel loose or fins damaged; tighten or replace
		●	●					●						Crankshaft bent; have engine replaced

b. The square represents a square unit. It is subdivided into sections representing areas of $\frac{1}{2}$, $\frac{1}{4}$, $\frac{1}{8}$, $\frac{1}{16}$, and the remaining area. If you keep taking $\frac{1}{2}$ of what remains of the 1-unit square forever, it would represent the infinite sum of areas, $\frac{1}{2} + \frac{1}{4} + \frac{1}{8} + \frac{1}{16} + \cdots$ that completely fill the square, and be equal to 1.

22 **a.** If the engine runs but the mower does not, you should check for a slipping belt or a faulty clutch.

b. What should you check if the engine runs too fast? If it backfires?

c. Some of the "possible causes" listed in the troubleshooting chart often suggest a next course of action. Explain how if-then reasoning is used in these cases.

23 Recall that the basic if-then reasoning pattern, Affirming the Hypothesis, can be represented as shown on the left below. In symbolic form, everything above the horizontal line is assumed to be correct or true. What is written below the line follows logically from the accepted information.

Affirming the Hypothesis   **Denying the Conclusion**

$p \Rightarrow q$ $\text{not } q \Rightarrow \text{not } p$ $p \Rightarrow q$

$\underline{p \hphantom{xxxxx}}$ $\underline{\text{not } q \hphantom{xxxx}}$ $\underline{\text{not } q \hphantom{xxxx}}$

q $\text{not } p$ $\text{not } p$

a. Explain why the second reasoning pattern above is valid.

b. Use the result of Connections Task 13 Part d to explain why Denying the Conclusion, shown above on the right, is a valid reasoning pattern.

c. Use Denying the Conclusion to decide what can be concluded from the following two statements.

Known fact: If a triangle is an isosceles triangle, then it has two sides the same length.

Given: △PQR has no pair of sides the same length.

Conclusion: ?

24 *Number theory* is a branch of mathematics that has flourished since ancient times and continues to be an important field of mathematical activity, particularly in the applied area of *coding* (encrypting messages so only the intended recipients can read them). One of the first definitions appearing in the theory of numbers is a definition for *factor* or *divisor*. An integer b is a factor or divisor of an integer a provided there is an integer c such that $a = bc$.

a. One of the first theorems in number theory follows.

> If a, b, and c are integers where a is a factor of b and a is a factor of c, then a is a factor of $b + c$.

Test this theorem for some specific cases to develop an understanding for what it says. Then write a deductive argument to prove that the theorem is always true.

b. If the engine runs too fast, you should check to see if the governor linkage is out of adjustment or the carburetor is fouled or poorly adjusted.

If it backfires, you should check to see if the carburetor is fouled or needs adjusting; if the valves are sticking, burned, or need adjusting; if the breaker points are dirty or improperly set; or if the flywheel key is bent, broken, or worn. On a two-cycle engine, check to see if the reed valve is faulty.

c. The possible cause corresponds to the "if" part of the statement, and the next course of action corresponds to the "then" part. For example: If the fuel tank is empty, then add fuel.

23 **a.** The second reasoning pattern is an application of *Affirming the Hypothesis* where *not q* implies *not p* is the known fact (Connections Task 13 Part d) and *not q* is the hypothesis.

NOTE *Denying the Conclusion reasoning is also called modus tollens.*

b. In Connections Task 13 Part d, students used Venn diagrams to show that $p \Rightarrow q$ and *not q* $\Rightarrow$ *not p* are logically equivalent. You can combine the reasoning in the first two reasoning patterns in the student text to support the validity of Denying the Conclusion as follows.

$$\left. \begin{array}{l} not\ q \Rightarrow not\ p \\ \underline{not\ q} \\ \quad\quad not\ p \end{array} \right\} \text{is an application of Affirming the Hypothesis.}$$

Replacing *not q* $\Rightarrow$ *not p* in the above statement with its logical equivalent $p \Rightarrow q$ gives:

$$\left. \begin{array}{l} p \Rightarrow q \\ \underline{not\ q} \\ \quad\quad not\ p \end{array} \right\} \text{Denying the Conclusion}$$

c. $\triangle PQR$ is not isosceles.

24 **a.** Students should test this theorem for specific cases. For example, 3 is a factor of 6 because $6 = 3 \cdot 2$. Three is a factor of 15 because $15 = 3 \cdot 5$. So, 3 is a factor of $(6 + 15)$, or 21, since $21 = 3 \cdot (2 + 5)$.

A possible deductive proof:

Since a is a factor of b, we know that $b = a \cdot m$, for some integer m. Since a is a factor of c, we know that $c = a \cdot n$, for some integer n. Then $b + c = am + an = a(m + n)$. So, a is a factor of $b + c$ since a times the number $(m + n)$ is the same as $b + c$.

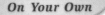

b. Form a new if-then statement as follows. Use the hypothesis of the theorem in Part a, and replace the conclusion with "*a* is a factor of $bm + cn$ for all integers *m* and *n*."

   i. Do you think this new if-then statement is always true? Explain your reasoning.

   ii. If you think the statement is true, write a proof of it. If not, give a counterexample.

c. Prove or disprove this claim.

   If a is a factor of b and b is a factor of c, then a is a factor of c.

Review

These tasks provide opportunities for you to review previously learned mathematics and to refine your skills in using that mathematics.

25 Find the area of each trapezoid.

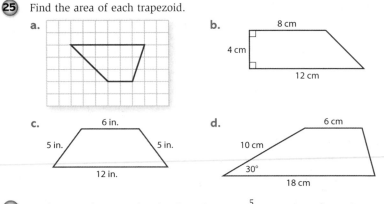

a.

b. 8 cm / 4 cm / 12 cm

c. 6 in. / 5 in. / 5 in. / 12 in.

d. 6 cm / 10 cm / 30° / 18 cm

26 Evaluate each expression for the values $x = \frac{5}{6}$, $y = -3$, and $z = 6$.

a. xz^2

b. x^{-1}

c. $|y - z| + y^2$

d. $x + \frac{4}{y}$

27 Determine if the pairs of lines are parallel, perpendicular, or neither.

a. The line containing $(8, 2)$ and $(-4, 6)$ and the line containing $(-2, 3)$ and $(1, 4)$

b. The lines with equations $y = 6x + 5$ and $y = -6x - 5$

c. The lines with equations $4x + 3y = 10$ and $3x - 4y = 10$

b. If a, b, and c are integers where a is a factor of both b and c, then a is a factor of $bm + cn$ for all integers m and n.

i. This new if-then statement is also true. Students may reason that if a is a factor of b, then a is a factor of any multiple of b, bm. Similarly, if a is a factor of c, then a is a factor of any multiple of c, cn. Using what they found in Part a, a will be a factor of the sum of the multiples of b and c.

ii. If $a \mid b$, then $b = a \cdot k$ for some integer k. Multiplying both sides of that equation by m, we see that $bm = a \cdot km$, which implies that $a \mid bm$. If $a \mid c$, then $c = a \cdot \ell$ for some integer ℓ. Multiplying both sides of that equation by n, we see that $cn = a \cdot \ell n$, which implies that $a \mid cn$. Now we see that $bm + cn = a \cdot km + a \cdot \ell n = a(km + \ell n)$. Therefore, $a \mid (bm + cn)$, or a is a factor of $bm + cn$.

c. Theorem: If a, b, and c are integers where a is a factor of b and b is a factor of c, then a is a factor of $b + c$.

Proof: If a is a factor of b, then $b = ak$ for some integer k. If b is a factor of c, then $c = b\ell$ for some integer ℓ. Substituting, we can write $c = ak\ell$. Then,

$$b + c = ak + ak\ell = a(k + k\ell),$$

which shows that a is a factor of $b + c$.

> **INSTRUCTIONAL NOTE**
> A helpful notation from Number Theory can be used in Task 24. If a is a factor of b, then a divides b which can be written as $a \mid b$. That notation will be used in this sample proof.

Review

Just in Time

25
  a. 12 square units
  b. 40 cm^2
  c. 36 in^2
  d. 60 cm^2

26
  a. 30
  b. $\frac{6}{5}$
  c. 18
  d. $-\frac{1}{2}$

27
  a. Neither
  b. Neither
  c. Perpendicular

28 Rewrite each expression in simpler equivalent form.

   a. $7x - 2x$

   b. $3(2x + 5) - 7$

   c. $(4a - 9) - 3(5a + 1)$

   d. $\frac{15x}{3}$

   e. $\frac{10x + 15}{5}$

   f. $\frac{4t - 7}{4}$

29 Recall that the converse of an if-then statement reverses the order of the two parts of the statement. Consider this statement.

   If a polygon is a regular polygon, then all its sides
   are the same length.

   a. Is this a true statement?

   b. Write the converse of this statement.

   c. Is the converse a true statement?

30 Write each of these expressions in equivalent expanded form.

   a. $5(2x + 7)$

   b. $(x + 9)(x + 3)$

   c. $(x - 4)(x + 3)$

   d. $(x + 4)(x - 4)$

   e. $(x + 3)^2$

   f. $(x - 3)^2$

31 Is the information in each diagram below enough to completely determine the size and shape of the triangle? Explain your reasoning in each case.

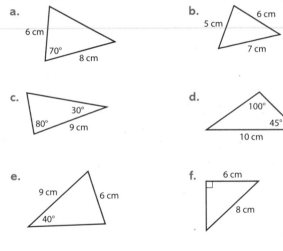

28 **a.** $5x$

    c. $-11a - 12$

    e. $2x + 3$

    b. $6x + 8$

    d. $5x$

    f. $t - \dfrac{7}{4}$

Just in Time

29 **a.** Yes, it is a true statement because the definition of regular polygon includes the condition that all sides are congruent.

    b. If a polygon has all sides the same length, then it is a regular polygon.

    c. The converse is not true. Consider a rhombus or the shape ⊹.

30 **a.** $10x + 35$

    b. $x^2 + 12x + 27$

    c. $x^2 - x - 12$

    d. $x^2 - 16$

    e. $x^2 + 6x + 9$

    f. $x^2 - 6x + 9$

31 **a.** Yes, by the SAS congruence condition

    b. Yes, by the SSS congruence condition

    c. Yes, by the ASA congruence condition

    d. Yes, by the AAS congruence condition

    e. No, SSA is not a congruence condition. A triangle like the obtuse one at the right could also be formed.

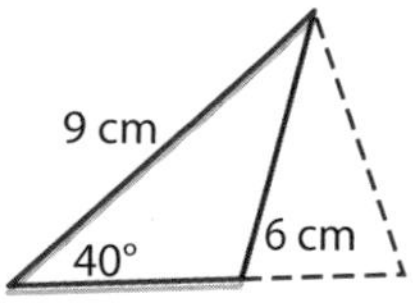

    f. Yes. Some students may recall the Hypotenuse-Leg Condition for right triangles. Others may use the SSS congruence condition noting that since this is a right triangle, the length of the third side is determined to be $\sqrt{28}$ and exactly one triangle is determined.

Unit 1

32 Using a compass and straightedge (no measuring), construct each of the following.

   a. A segment congruent to $\overline{AB}$

   b. A triangle congruent to $\triangle PQR$

   c. An angle congruent to $\angle FGH$

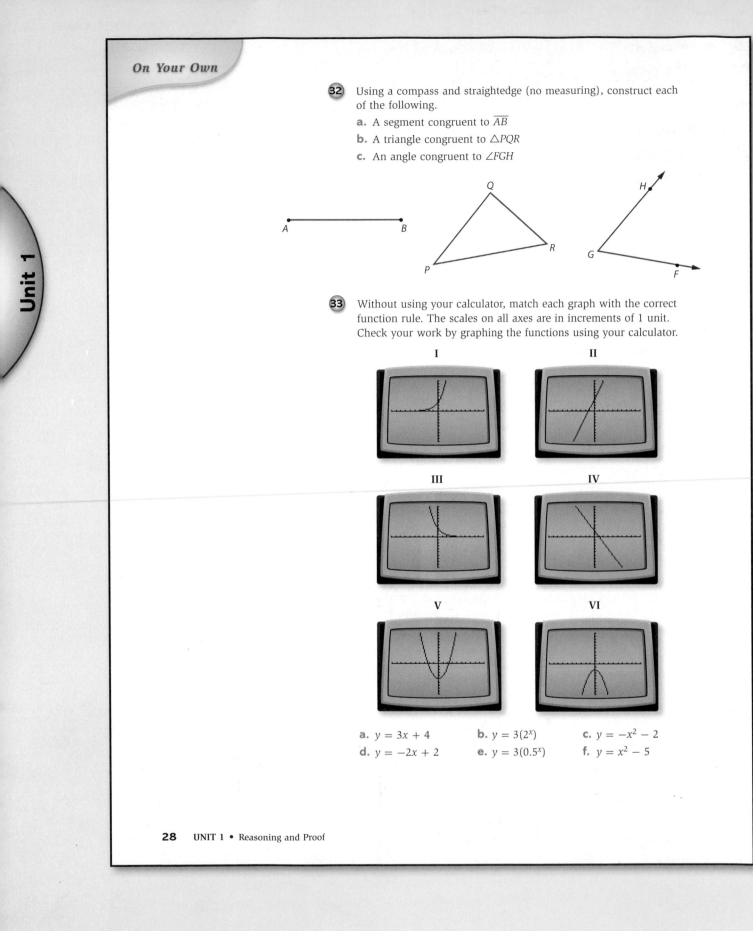

33 Without using your calculator, match each graph with the correct function rule. The scales on all axes are in increments of 1 unit. Check your work by graphing the functions using your calculator.

I   II

III   IV

V   VI

a. $y = 3x + 4$ **b.** $y = 3(2^x)$ **c.** $y = -x^2 - 2$

d. $y = -2x + 2$ **e.** $y = 3(0.5^x)$ **f.** $y = x^2 - 5$

Just in Time

32 **a–c.** See student constructions.

33 **a.** II   **b.** I   **c.** VI
    d. IV   **e.** III   **f.** V

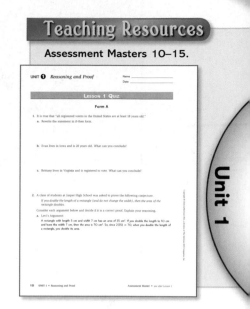

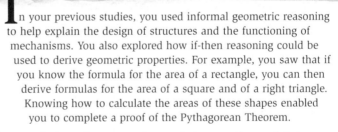

Geometric Reasoning and Proof

In your previous studies, you used informal geometric reasoning to help explain the design of structures and the functioning of mechanisms. You also explored how if-then reasoning could be used to derive geometric properties. For example, you saw that if you know the formula for the area of a rectangle, you can then derive formulas for the area of a square and of a right triangle. Knowing how to calculate the areas of these shapes enabled you to complete a proof of the Pythagorean Theorem.

The interplay among shapes, their properties, and their function is a recurring theme in geometry. The design of the lift-bed truck shown above is based on two of the most common figures in a plane, lines and angles.

LESSON 2 • Geometric Reasoning and Proof   **29**

Unit 1

Geometric Reasoning and Proof

In this lesson, students begin to develop an understanding of formal reasoning and proof in geometric contexts. Building on their understanding of desirable characteristics of a sound mathematical argument developed in Lesson 1, students apply deductive reasoning to familiar situations involving lines and angles. It is here that the need for certain assumptions (postulates) is introduced. The Linear Pair Postulate involves the special position of pairs of angles. The Parallel Lines Postulate involves equal measures of corresponding angles formed by two parallel lines and a transversal. (This postulate is equivalent to the assumption that "through a point not on a given line, there is exactly one line parallel to the given line.") This set of basic postulates is used to prove familiar relations involving vertical angles, perpendicular lines, and parallel lines cut by a transversal.

Local Deductive Systems In *Core-Plus Mathematics*, the intent is not to organize geometry as a complete deductive mathematical system. Rather, our approach is to enable students to experience the connectedness of geometry: how from a few undefined terms and some basic assumptions (postulates) they can deduce important properties of geometric figures.

Developing Proof-Writing Skills If you have not read the paragraph on page T1A related to developing these skills and the proof support masters in the Unit 1 Resource Masters, you may wish to do so at this point.

As students create their initial proofs, expect the forms to vary and the language used to be somewhat wordy or imprecise. Students may name specific angles or line segments rather than the general terms in their proofs. This is fine for now. Initially, the focus should be on looking for clear "if-then" reasoning that is structured in an appropriate sequence.

Lesson Objectives

- Know and be able to use the angle relationship theorems involving two intersecting lines
- Know and be able to use the theorems justifying the construction of a line perpendicular to a given line through a given point and the construction of a line parallel to a given line through a given point
- Know and be able to use the angle relationship theorems involving two parallel lines cut by a transversal and their converses
- Know and be able to use the angle sum theorem and the exterior angle theorem for triangles

Analyze the lift-bed truck mechanism shown on the previous page.

a How do you think the mechanism works?

b As the truck bed is raised or lowered, what elements change?

c As the truck bed is raised or lowered, what segment lengths and what angle measures remain unchanged?

d As the truck bed is raised or lowered, will it always remain parallel to the flat-bed frame of the truck? Explain your reasoning.

In this lesson, you will explore how from a few basic assumptions you can prove important properties of angles formed by intersecting lines and by two parallel lines intersected by a third line.

Investigation 1 — Reasoning about Intersecting Lines and Angles

Skill in reasoning, like skill in sculpting, playing a musical instrument, or playing a sport, comes from practicing that skill and reflecting on the process. In this lesson, you will sharpen your reasoning skills in geometric settings. As you progress through the lesson, pay particular attention to the assumptions you make to support your reasoning, as well as to the validity of your reasoning.

When two lines intersect at a single point, special pairs of angles are formed. For example, a pair of adjacent angles formed by two intersecting lines like ∠AEC and ∠CEB, shown at the right, are called a **linear pair** of angles. Pairs of angles like ∠AEC and ∠BED are called **vertical angles**. As you work on the problems in this investigation, make notes of answers to these questions:

How are linear pairs of angles related?

How are vertical angles related and why is that the case?

Think About
This Situation

a Student responses may vary but will likely focus on the large X component. They may raise their hands or pencils to model the change of size of the vertical angles of the X. The hydraulic cylinder, visible in the lower portion of the X in the diagram, pushes one arm of the X up (or down), causing the same change in the other arm of the X.

b As the truck bed is raised, the arm of the X from the top-right to the bottom-left goes up and the corresponding arm of the second X follows. (When the truck bed is raised, the length of the third side of each triangle along the bed and the frame decreases. This is the only length that changes.) The angles of the two triangles change: the angle formed by the two arms of the X decreases when the bed is raised and increases when the bed is lowered. The position of the bottom right "foot" of the X changes, sliding along the flatbed of the truck.

c It appears that the two arms of the X are the same length and joined at the midpoints. When the truck bed is raised or lowered, these lengths remain the same. The two triangles formed by the X appear to be isosceles triangles; their equal sides do not change. Students may note that the lengths of the truck bed and frame remain unchanged also. Students may also observe that pairs of angles that are congruent remain congruent (although they change their measure) as the truck bed is raised or lowered. This applies to the pair of vertical angles of the X, and the base angles of the isosceles triangles.

d Students will likely conjecture that the truck bed remains parallel to the frame. They may be thinking that the distance between the truck bed and the frame is uniform for any placement of congruent Xs joined at the midpoints. It may be helpful to have linkage strips available to help students visualize the movement of the lift. Ask students to explain why the bed and frame are parallel. From their work in Investigation 1, students should recognize that they are at this point making a conjecture about parallelism. Students will develop the necessary tools in this lesson to provide a convincing argument for this observation. (See Applications Task 8 page 43.)

INSTRUCTIONAL NOTE
In launching this lesson, use the photo of the lift-bed truck to remind students an important and recurring theme in geometry is the interplay among shapes, their properties, and their function—often in design and mechanics. Inquire if they have seen other situations involving a similar type of "scissors" lift mechanism.

Unit 1

COLLABORATION SKILL
Be a skeptic; respectfully challenge my own and others' thinking and look for alternative ideas. Ask for justification for assertions.

Teaching Resources

Student Masters 17–20.

Investigation 1 — Reasoning about Intersecting Lines and Angles

In this investigation, students will begin to develop the skills needed to create sound deductive arguments in the context of exploring and trying to understand relationships between angles created when two lines intersect. The approach used is to have students examine a given context, in this case two intersecting lines and the angles they form, and to make some conjectures about possible geometric relationships in that context (inductive reasoning). The next step is for students to learn to prove (deductive reasoning) or disprove (counterexample) their own conjectures. This approach will become commonplace in the geometry units of Course 3: explore, conjecture, and then prove or disprove. Using this process with confidence is important for students because it is not only relevant in the study of mathematics, but it is also generally applicable to all areas of knowledge acquisition.

This would be an appropriate time to distribute the student masters of key geometric ideas from Course 1 and Course 2.

Launch

You may want to launch this investigation by asking students, "How is the word 'argument' used differently in mathematics than in everyday life?" Then quickly review the key ideas of mathematical practice from the previous investigation, explore → conjecture → prove or disprove, letting students know that their mathematical attention will be pushed in two directions in the next two investigations. First, explain that they will be asked to explore the angle relationships that occur when two lines intersect. Second, they will focus on learning to create arguments to prove that the conjectures they made in their explorations are always true. It will help them if they understand that proof is a skill that they will develop over time and that during each investigation in this unit (and in lessons of subsequent units), they will have an opportunity to work on this skill.

It may be helpful to stop the small-group work periodically throughout this investigation in order to let groups share, compare, and revise their work. Revisiting the characteristics of a correct argument may help students evaluate their work. (See the Summarize the Mathematics following Investigation 1 of Lesson 1, page 9.) You might ask students to summarize what they have learned about the angle relationships they investigated and about creating sound arguments. As students see more proofs, the class may decide to add or reword characteristics of a correct argument from the Summarize the Mathematics on page 9. Since investigations will probably span more than one class period, a class discussion on the new vocabulary and the new theorems proven each day would provide closure to the class period.

Students will also have an opportunity to expand their list of techniques for creating an argument. Make sure that students appreciate the power they gain by recognizing that once they have proven a theorem, it can be used in many, varied ways to prove new statements (theorems).

Teacher Notes

1. In the diagram at the right, lines k and n intersect at the point shown, forming angles numbered 1, 2, 3, 4.

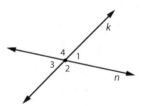

a. If $m\angle 1 = 72°$, what can you say about $m\angle 2$? About $m\angle 3$? About $m\angle 4$? What assumptions are you using to obtain your answers?

b. If $m\angle 2 = 130°$, what can you say about $m\angle 1$? About $m\angle 3$? About $m\angle 4$?

c. In general, what relationships between pairs of angles do you think are true? Make a list of them.

d. Will the general relationships you listed for Part c hold for any pair of intersecting lines? Test your conjectures using specific examples.

e. Write an if-then statement about linear pairs of angles that you think is *always* correct. You may want to begin as follows. If two angles are a linear pair, then … .

f. Write an if-then statement about vertical angles that you think is *always* correct. You may want to begin as follows. If two lines intersect, then … .

In the remainder of this lesson, you will continue to use inductive reasoning to discover possible relations among lines and angles, but you will also use deductive reasoning to prove your conjectures are always true. To reason deductively, you must first have some basic facts from which to reason. In mathematics, statements of basic facts that are accepted as true without proof are called **postulates** (or *axioms*). These assumed facts will be helpful in supporting your reasoning in the remainder of this unit and in future units. Begin by assuming the following postulate concerning linear pairs of angles.

Linear Pair Postulate If two angles are a linear pair, then the sum of their measures is 180°.

2. Study the attempt at the right by one group of students at Washington High School to prove the conjecture they made in Part f of Problem 1. Based on the labeling of the diagram, they set out to prove the following.

If lines n and k intersect at the point shown, then $m\angle 1 = m\angle 3$.

They reasoned as follows.

(1) Since lines n and k intersect, $\angle 1$ and $\angle 2$ are a linear pair. So, $m\angle 1 + m\angle 2 = 180°$.

(2) Since lines n and k intersect, $\angle 2$ and $\angle 3$ are a linear pair. So, $m\angle 2 + m\angle 3 = 180°$.

(3) If $m\angle 1 + m\angle 2 = 180°$ and $m\angle 2 + m\angle 3 = 180°$, then $m\angle 1 + m\angle 2 = m\angle 2 + m\angle 3$.

(4) If $m\angle 1 + m\angle 2 = m\angle 2 + m\angle 3$, then $m\angle 1 = m\angle 3$.

a. Explain why each of the statements in the students' reasoning is or is not correct.

b. Now write an argument to show the following: If lines n and k intersect at the point shown, then $m\angle 2 = m\angle 4$. Give reasons justifying each of your statements.

Math Toolkits As students prove conjectures in the investigations that follow, it is important for them to maintain a list of these theorems with labeled illustrations. Students' Math Toolkits would be a natural place for them to retain their theorems. These theorem lists should be kept with students' lists of new vocabulary, sample proofs, and techniques for proofs that can be applied to other conjectures. Some of the theorems will be proven while completing On Your Own assignments.

1   **a.** $m\angle 2 = 108°$, $m\angle 3 = 72°$, $m\angle 4 = 108°$
   It is assumed that linear pairs of angles and vertical angles are formed when the two lines intersect. It is assumed that the measure of a straight angle is 180° and that the measures of two adjacent angles sum to the measure of the angle formed by their union.

   b. $m\angle 1 = 50°$, $m\angle 3 = 50°$, $m\angle 4 = 130°$

   c.

Pairs that Sum to 180°	Pairs that are Congruent
$\angle 1$ and $\angle 4$	$\angle 2$ and $\angle 4$
$\angle 1$ and $\angle 2$	$\angle 1$ and $\angle 3$
$\angle 2$ and $\angle 3$	
$\angle 3$ and $\angle 4$	

   d. Yes, they will hold for all pairs of intersecting lines.

   e. If two angles are a linear pair, then the sum of their measures is 180°.

   f. If two lines intersect, then each pair of vertical angles formed will be equal in measure.

2   **a.** (1) This is correct. Since $\angle 1$ and $\angle 2$ are a linear pair, then by the Linear Pair Postulate, the sum of their measures is 180°.

   (2) This is correct. Since $\angle 2$ and $\angle 3$ are a linear pair, then by the Linear Pair Postulate, the sum of their measures is 180°.

   (3) This is correct. If both $m\angle 1 + m\angle 2$ and $m\angle 2 + m\angle 3$ equal 180°, then the two sums must be equal to each other.

   (4) This is correct because the Subtraction Property of Equality allows us to subtract $m\angle 2$ from each side of the equation.

   b. (1) Since lines n and k intersect, $\angle 2$ and $\angle 3$ are a linear pair. So, $m\angle 2 + m\angle 3 = 180°$ by the Linear Pair Postulate.

   (2) Since lines n and k intersect, $\angle 3$ and $\angle 4$ are a linear pair. So, $m\angle 3 + m\angle 4 = 180°$ by the Linear Pair Postulate.

   (3) If $m\angle 2 + m\angle 3 = 180°$ and $m\angle 3 + m\angle 4 = 180°$, then $m\angle 2 + m\angle 3 = m\angle 3 + m\angle 4$. They are both equal to 180°, so they are equal to each other.

   (4) If $m\angle 2 + m\angle 3 = m\angle 3 + m\angle 4$, then $m\angle 2 = m\angle 4$ by the Subtraction Property of Equality.

   Alternatively, students might use linear pairs $\angle 1$ and $\angle 4$, and $\angle 2$ and $\angle 3$, along with the conclusion in Part a that $m\angle 1 = m\angle 3$.

In mathematics, a statement that has been proved using deductive reasoning from definitions, accepted facts, and relations is called a **theorem**. The statement proved in Problem 2 is sometimes referred to as the **Vertical Angles Theorem**, *vertical angles have equal measure*.

In Course 1, you proved the Pythagorean Theorem. (Not all theorems are given names.) After a theorem has been proved, it may be used to prove other conjectures. As your geometric work in Course 3 progresses, you will want to know which theorems have been proved. Thus, you should prepare a geometry toolkit by listing assumptions, such as the Linear Pair Postulate, and proven theorems. Add each new theorem to your toolkit as it is proved.

3 Recall that two intersecting lines (line segments or rays) are **perpendicular** ($\perp$) if and only if they form a right angle.

a. Rewrite this definition as two if-then statements.

b. Claim: *Two perpendicular lines form four right angles.* Is this claim true or false? Explain your reasoning.

c. Study the following strategy that Juanita used to prove the claim in Part b.

- First, she drew and labeled the diagram at the right.

- Then she developed a *plan for proof* based on her diagram.

  I know that if $\ell \perp m$, they form a right angle, say $\angle 1$. A right angle has measure 90°. Use the fact that $\angle 1$ and $\angle 3$ are vertical angles to show m$\angle 3$ = 90°. Use the fact that $\angle 1$ and $\angle 2$ are a linear pair to show m$\angle 2$ = 90°. Then use the fact that $\angle 2$ and $\angle 4$ are vertical angles to show m$\angle 4$ = 90°.

- She then wrote her proof in a *two-column statement-reason form*.

Statements	Reasons
1. $\ell \perp m$	1. Given
2. ℓ and m form a right angle. Call it $\angle 1$.	2. Definition of perpendicular lines
3. m$\angle 1$ = 90°	3. Definition of right angle
4. $\angle 1$ and $\angle 3$ are vertical angles.	4. Definition of vertical angles
5. m$\angle 3$ = m$\angle 1$ = 90°	5. Vertical Angles Theorem
6. $\angle 1$ and $\angle 2$ are a linear pair.	6. Definition of linear pair
7. m$\angle 1$ + m$\angle 2$ = 180°	7. _____
8. m$\angle 2$ = 180° − m$\angle 1$ = 90°	8. _____
9. $\angle 2$ and $\angle 4$ are vertical angles.	9. _____
10. m$\angle 2$ = m$\angle 4$	10. _____
11. m$\angle 4$ = 90°	11. _____
12. $\angle 1$, $\angle 2$, $\angle 3$, and $\angle 4$ are right angles.	12. _____

3　**a.** If two intersecting lines (line segments or rays) are perpendicular, then they form a right angle. If two intersecting lines (line segments or rays) form a right angle, then they are perpendicular.

b. True. If lines ℓ and m are perpendicular, then one of the angles formed, say $\angle 1$, is a right angle. Because $\angle 1$ and $\angle 2$ form a linear pair, the Linear Pair Postulate implies $m\angle 1 + m\angle 2 = 180°$. It follows that $m\angle 2 = 90°$. Similar reasoning can be used to show $\angle 3$ and $\angle 4$ are right angles.

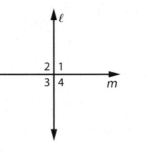

i. How does the diagram that Juanita drew show the information given in the claim?

ii. Why might it be helpful to develop a plan for a proof before starting to write the proof?

iii. Check the correctness of Juanita's reasoning and supply reasons for each of statements 7–12.

iv. Describe a *plan for proof* of the above claim that does *not* involve use of the Vertical Angles Theorem.

④ The design of buildings often involves perpendicular lines. In preparing a plan for a building like that below, an architect needs to draw lines perpendicular to given lines.

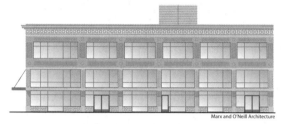

Marx and O'Neill Architecture

a. Draw a line ℓ on a sheet of paper. Describe how you would draw a line perpendicular to line ℓ through a point *P* in each case below.

i. *P* is a point on line ℓ.

ii. *P* is a point not on line ℓ.

b. Study the diagrams below which show a method for constructing a line perpendicular to a given line ℓ through a given point *P* on line ℓ. In the second step, the same compass opening is used to create both arcs.

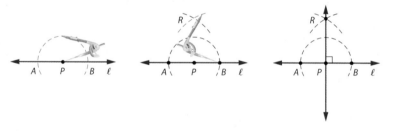

i. On a separate sheet of paper, draw a line ℓ and mark a point *P* on ℓ. Use a compass and straightedge to construct a line perpendicular to line ℓ at point *P*.

ii. Write an argument justifying that $\overleftrightarrow{PR} \perp \ell$ in the diagram above on the right. Start by showing that $\triangle APR \cong \triangle BPR$.

c. i. The given information says that the lines are perpendicular, so the definition of perpendicular lines tells Juanita that one right angle is formed, which is what her diagram shows.

  ii. It provides a "game plan" or reasoning strategy that connects information that is given (and other known facts) to the desired conclusion. With a strategy in mind, it is easier to then write the details of an argument.

 iii. (7) Linear Pair Postulate
   (8) Algebra (subtracting m$\angle$1 from both sides of the equation and substituting 90° for m$\angle$1)
   (9) Definition of vertical angles
   (10) Vertical Angles Theorem
   (11) Step 8 and Substitution Property of Equality
   (12) Steps 3, 5, 8, 11 and definition of right angle

  iv. Students may suggest a plan based on the Linear Pair Postulate. For example, I know that $\ell \perp m$, so they form a right angle, say $\angle 1$. Then m$\angle 1 = 90°$. Since $\angle 1$ and $\angle 2$ are linear pairs, m$\angle 1$ + m$\angle 2 = 180°$. It follows that m$\angle 2 = 90°$. $\angle 2$ and $\angle 3$ are linear pairs, so m$\angle 3 = 90°$; and $\angle 3$ and $\angle 4$ are linear pairs, so m$\angle 4 = 90°$. Thus, all four angles will be right angles.

4 **a. i.** Since the line through P on ℓ must form a 90° angle, students might suggest using a protractor. Place the point P at the vertex and locate the third point C to make a 90° angle. Then draw $\overleftrightarrow{PC}$. Students might also suggest using a corner of a paper placed at P along line ℓ to draw the line or folding the paper through point P so that ℓ is folded onto itself. The fold line will be the perpendicular line.

  ii. When point P is not on line ℓ, a protractor can be used to locate the vertex of a right angle on line ℓ through P. Alternatively, students might suggest aligning a corner of a paper so that the two adjacent sides of the page contain ℓ and P or folding the paper as described in part i.

b. i. Students should perform the construction as shown in the sequence of diagrams.

  ii. One possible argument is given:
   Since $AP = BP$ and $AR = BR$ (because radii of the same circle are equal in length) and $PR = PR$, $\triangle APR \cong \triangle BPR$ by the SSS congruence condition. Then $\angle APR \cong \angle BPR$ since they are corresponding angles in congruent triangles. But $\angle APR$ and $\angle BPR$ are also a linear pair, so they sum to 180°. Therefore, m$\angle APR$ = m$\angle BPR = 90°$. Since a right angle is formed, $\overleftrightarrow{PR} \perp \ell$.

Not Same Circle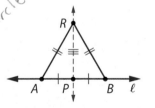

WRITING PROOFS Juanita's approach illustrates a method to writing proofs that students should emulate. In particular, always draw and label a diagram with the given information. Then identify what is to be proven in terms of the labeled diagram.

INSTRUCTIONAL NOTE It is important for students to see early on and understand that in mathematics, there is often more than one way to prove a statement. Watch for opportunities to compare students' arguments throughout this unit. If you have a document camera, this is easy to facilitate. If not, you may wish to have students complete proofs on transparencies or poster paper.

DIFFERENTIATION Depending on students' middle school experiences and experiences in the Course 1 *Patterns in Shape* unit, they may or may not have been exposed to constructions. In the latter case, you may wish to have them simply focus on the diagrams. The big idea here is the existence proofs, not construction. Constructions are the context for reasoning.

Unit 1

c. The following diagrams show a method for constructing a line perpendicular to a given line ℓ through a point P *not* on line ℓ. In the second step, the same compass opening is used to create both arcs.

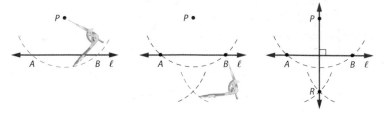

i. On a separate sheet of paper, draw a line ℓ and a point P not on ℓ. Construct a line perpendicular to line ℓ through point P.

ii. Write an argument justifying that $\overleftrightarrow{PR} \perp \ell$ in the diagram above on the right.

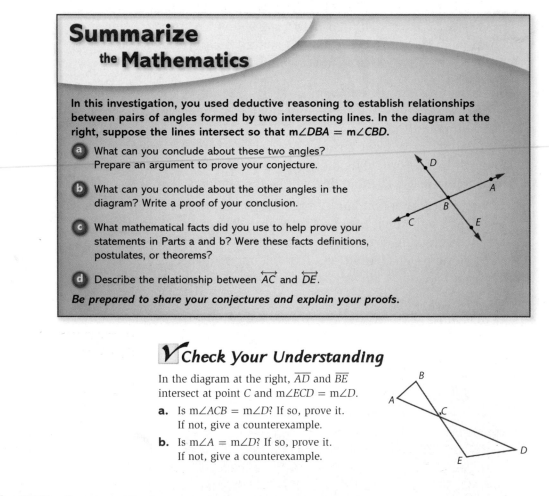

Summarize
the Mathematics

In this investigation, you used deductive reasoning to establish relationships between pairs of angles formed by two intersecting lines. In the diagram at the right, suppose the lines intersect so that m∠DBA = m∠CBD.

a What can you conclude about these two angles? Prepare an argument to prove your conjecture.

b What can you conclude about the other angles in the diagram? Write a proof of your conclusion.

c What mathematical facts did you use to help prove your statements in Parts a and b? Were these facts definitions, postulates, or theorems?

d Describe the relationship between $\overleftrightarrow{AC}$ and $\overleftrightarrow{DE}$.

Be prepared to share your conjectures and explain your proofs.

✔Check Your Understanding

In the diagram at the right, $\overline{AD}$ and $\overline{BE}$ intersect at point C and m∠ECD = m∠D.

a. Is m∠ACB = m∠D? If so, prove it. If not, give a counterexample.

b. Is m∠A = m∠D? If so, prove it. If not, give a counterexample.

c. i. Students should perform the construction as shown in the sequence of diagrams.

ii. One possible argument is given:

Label the point of intersection of ℓ and $\overleftrightarrow{PR}$, Q as shown. Draw $\overline{PA}$, $\overline{PB}$, $\overline{RA}$, and $\overline{RB}$. Label $\angle 1$ and $\angle 2$ as shown. $PA = PB$ and $RA = RB$ because they were constructed using the same radius, and $PR = PR$ (common side in two triangles). It follows that $\triangle PAR \cong \triangle PBR$ by the SSS congruence condition. So, $\angle 1 \cong \angle 2$ because they are corresponding angles in congruent triangles. Since $\overline{PA} \cong \overline{PB}$, $\angle 1 \cong \angle 2$, and $\overline{PQ} \cong \overline{PQ}$, $\triangle APQ \cong \triangle BPQ$ by the SAS congruence condition. $\angle AQP \cong \angle BQP$ because they are corresponding angles of congruent triangles. Since $\angle AQP$ and $\angle BQP$ are a linear pair, it follows that $m\angle AQR + m\angle BQP = 180°$ by the definition of a linear pair. It then follows that $m\angle AQP = 90°$. So, $\overleftrightarrow{PR} \perp \ell$ by the definition of perpendicular lines.

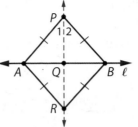

Teaching Resources

Student Master 21.

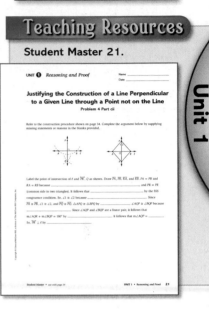

Unit 1

INSTRUCTIONAL NOTE In the sample response to Part a of the Summarize the Mathematics, note the use of the brackets in the *Reason* column. The numbers in the brackets refer to the statements in the *Statement* column. Each reference number shows where the hypothesis of the reason has been affirmed. For example, consider step 6. Statements 1 and 5 affirm the hypothesis of the Substitution Property of Equality. Teachers report that use of the bracket notations helps beginning students better see the logical flow of proofs reported in a two-column statement-reason format.

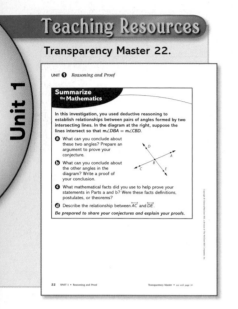
Summarize the Mathematics

a We can conclude that both ∠DBA and ∠CBD are right angles. See the diagram at the right. One proof might be:

Statement	Reason
1. $\overleftrightarrow{DE}$ and $\overleftrightarrow{AC}$ intersect at B and m∠DBA = m∠CBD.	1. Given
2. ∠DBA and ∠CBD are a linear pair.	2. Definition of a linear pair [1]
3. m∠DBA + m∠CBD = 180°	3. Linear Pair Postulate [2]
4. 2m∠CBD = 180°	4. Substitution [1,3]
5. m∠CBD = 90°	5. Divide both sides of the equation by 2. [4]
6. m∠DBA = 90°	6. Substitution Property of Equality [1,5]
7. ∠DBA and ∠CBD are right angles.	7. Definition of right angle [6]

b **Conclusion:** We can conclude that ∠CBE and ∠ABE also have measure 90°.

Proof: Since ∠DBA and ∠CBE are vertical angles (by the definition) and m∠DBA = 90°, the Vertical Angles Theorem says m∠CBE = 90°. Since m∠DBC = 90°, ∠ABE also measures 90° by the Vertical Angles Theorem. So, we can conclude that ∠CBE and ∠ABE have measure 90°.

c Students probably used some of the properties of equality, the Linear Pair Property, and the Vertical Angles Theorem. (Specific responses will depend on the proofs provided.) They used a combination of definitions, a postulate, properties, and a theorem.

d $\overleftrightarrow{AC} \perp \overleftrightarrow{DE}$

MATH TOOLKIT Students should record the Linear Pairs Postulate and Vertical Angle Theorem in their toolkit. Help students recognize that they have established another way to show that two lines are perpendicular: If two lines form a linear pair of angles having equal measure, then the lines are perpendicular.

COLLABORATION PROMPT During this investigation, I acted as a skeptic by … .

✓ Check Your Understanding

a. This conjecture is true.

   Proof: Since $\overline{AD}$ and $\overline{BE}$ intersect at point C, $\angle ECD$ and $\angle ACB$ are vertical angles. So, $m\angle ECD = m\angle ACB$. Since $m\angle D = m\angle ECD$, by substitution, $m\angle D = m\angle ACB$.

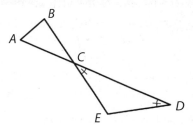

b. This conjecture will not always be true. As a counterexample, let $m\angle ECD = m\angle D = 35°$, then $m\angle ACB$ must also be $35°$. But $m\angle A$ does not have to equal $35°$; it could be any measure x, where $0° < x < 145°$. Therefore, $m\angle A$ is not always equal to $m\angle D$.

Unit 1

Investigation 2 · **Reasoning about Parallel Lines and Angles**

When a line intersects another line, four angles are formed. Some of the pairs of angles have equal measures, and some pairs are **supplementary angles**—they have measures that add to 180°. When a line intersects *two* lines, many more relationships are possible. Perhaps the most interesting case is when a line intersects two parallel lines, as with the various pairs of support beams on the faces of the John Hancock Center in Chicago, shown below.

Lines in a plane that do not intersect are called **parallel lines**. In the diagram below, line m is parallel to line n (written $m \parallel n$). Line t, which intersects the two lines, is called a **transversal**.

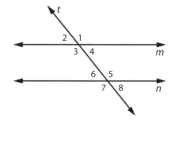

As you work on the problems of this investigation, look for answers to the following questions:

If two parallel lines are intersected by a transversal, what relations exist among the measures of the angles formed?

What relations among the angles formed when two lines are cut by a transversal allow you to conclude that the lines are parallel?

1. In the preceding diagram, the angles at each point of intersection are numbered so that they can be easily identified.

   a. What pairs of angles, if any, appear to be equal in measure?

   b. What angle pairs appear to be supplementary? (Supplementary angles need not be a linear pair.)

   c. Draw another pair of parallel lines and a transversal with a slope different from the one above. Number the angles as in the figure above.

      i. Do the same pairs of numbered angles appear equal in measure?

      ii. Do the same pairs of numbered angles appear to be supplementary?

Reasoning about Parallel Lines and Angles

In this investigation, students will continue working to develop the skills needed to create sound deductive arguments. The approach is the same as the one in the previous investigation; that is, students explore a given context, in this case, two parallel lines cut by a transversal, make some conjectures about angles in that context, and then prove or disprove their own conjectures.

Launch

You might want to launch this investigation by examining the context. What line-angle relationships can be seen on the face of the John Hancock Center?

After students consider the italicized questions in the text, you have a brief discussion of how the theorems in the previous investigation were developed. Students should note that, initially, they explored and discussed ideas about how the angles formed by intersecting lines might be related; then they made formal conjectures using previous knowledge and intuition. Finally, they confirmed the validity of their conjectures by proving (or disproving) that they were indeed true. Once they had proven a theorem, it could be utilized in the proof of another conjecture. This process resulted in a list of conditional statements called theorems that students knew for sure were true. Keep reinforcing the idea that this process of exploration, conjecture, and validation is the foundation for advancement of knowledge in most fields. It is critical that every student understand this process and become as skilled as possible in its use.

1 **INSTRUCTIONAL NOTE** Since this investigation builds on the exploration and conjectures that students generate in Problem 1, it is important that every student have a complete list of conjectures to prove and then use in later problems. Encourage groups to look carefully for as many relationships as they can find between the pairs of angles and to be prepared to share their lists with the entire class. Then develop a class list of possible angle relationships that can be used in the remainder of this investigation.

a. Pairs that appear equal:

∠1 and ∠3	∠1 and ∠5
∠1 and ∠7	∠2 and ∠4
∠2 and ∠6	∠2 and ∠8
∠3 and ∠5	∠3 and ∠7
∠4 and ∠6	∠4 and ∠8
∠5 and ∠7	∠6 and ∠8

b. Pairs that appear to be supplementary (in addition to the linear pairs):

∠1 and ∠6	∠1 and ∠8
∠2 and ∠5	∠2 and ∠7
∠3 and ∠6	∠3 and ∠8
∠4 and ∠5	∠4 and ∠7

c. **i.** Yes, the same pairs of angles in the new diagram appear to be the same measure.

ii. Yes, the same pairs of angles in the new diagram appear to be supplementary.

Angles that are in the same relative position with respect to each parallel line and the transversal are called **corresponding angles**. In the diagram on the previous page, angles 1 and 5 are corresponding angles; similarly, angles 3 and 7 are corresponding angles.

 Examine the diagram you drew for Part c of Problem 1.

    a. Name two pairs of corresponding angles, other than angles 1 and 5 or angles 3 and 7. Were those corresponding angles among the pairs of angles that you thought had equal measure?

    b. Suppose m∠1 = 123°. Find the measures of as many other angles as you can in your diagram.

3 Descriptive names are also given to other pairs of angles formed by a transversal and two parallel lines. In the diagram below, m ∥ n and t is a transversal intersecting m and n.

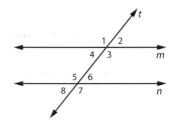

    a. For each pair of angles named below, describe how the pair can be identified in a diagram. Then give one more example of such a pair.

       i. **Interior angles on the same side of the transversal:** ∠4 and ∠5

       ii. **Exterior angles on the same side of the transversal:** ∠2 and ∠7

       iii. **Alternate interior angles:** ∠4 and ∠6

       iv. **Alternate exterior angles:** ∠1 and ∠7

    b. Identify a relationship that seems to exist for each type of angle pair named in Part a. Write your observations in if-then form, beginning each statement as follows. If two parallel lines are cut by a transversal, then … .

For Problems 4 and 5, assume the following statement as a known fact.

Corresponding Angles Assumption If two parallel lines are cut by a transversal, then corresponding angles have equal measure.

4 In completing Problem 3 Part b, one group of students at Brookwood High School made the following claim.

    If two parallel lines are cut by a transversal, then interior angles on the same side of the transversal are supplementary.

    a. Describe a plan for how you would prove this claim using the diagram in Problem 3 and the Corresponding Angles Assumption. Compare your plan for proof with that of others. Correct any errors in reasoning.

    b. The start of a proof given by the group of Brookwood students is on the next page.

       i. Supply a reason for each statement.

       ii. Continue the two-column statement-reason proof to show that ∠3 and ∠6 are supplementary.

2 **INSTRUCTIONAL NOTE** This problem sets the stage for assuming the equality of measures of corresponding angles when parallel lines are cut by a transversal. As you circulate among the groups, focus their thinking on this assumption. To help students identify corresponding angles, use language such as "corresponding" or "similar positions."

a. Other corresponding angles in the diagram are angles 4 and 8 and angles 2 and 6. The corresponding angles were among the pairs that appeared equal.

b.

57°	123°
m∠2	m∠3
m∠4	m∠5
m∠6	m∠7
m∠8	

3 **a.** **i.** Interior angles on the same side of the transversal are between the parallel lines and on the same side of the transversal: ∠3 and ∠6.

ii. Exterior angles on the same side of the transversal are not between the parallel lines and are on the same side of the transversal: ∠1 and ∠8.

iii. Alternate interior angles are between the two parallel lines and on opposite sides of the transversal: ∠3 and ∠5.

iv. Alternate exterior angles are not between the two parallel lines and are on opposite sides of the transversal: ∠2 and ∠8.

b. **i.** If two parallel lines are intersected by a transversal, then interior angles on the same side of the transversal are supplementary.

ii. If two parallel lines are intersected by a transversal, then exterior angles on the same side of the transversal are supplementary.

iii. If two parallel lines are intersected by a transversal, then alternate interior angles have equal measure.

iv. If two parallel lines are intersected by a transversal, then alternate exterior angles have equal measure.

> **DIFFERENTIATION** If some students seem to need more practice identifying pairs of angles by name, have them make a new diagram and label the angles with numbers not in consecutive order around the intersections. They could exchange diagrams with another student, identify angles by names, and check each other's work. They might also make diagrams in which the parallel lines are not horizontal.

4 **a. INSTRUCTIONAL NOTE** At this point, students should be making an effort to have complete, properly sequenced arguments with well-written statements. You will need to decide if you want students to write separate proofs for both pairs of the identified angles. If you decide to have them do only one, be sure you discuss with the class why a similar argument would prove the other part or how you could prove the other part using what was first proved as is done in Problem 4 Part bii.

If two parallel lines are cut by a transversal, then interior angles on the same side of the transversal are supplementary.

One possible plan is given:

Show that $m\angle 4 + m\angle 5 = 180°$ and $m\angle 3 + m\angle 6 = 180°$. To show that $m\angle 4 + m\angle 5 = 180°$, use the Linear Pair Postulate with $\angle 1$ and $\angle 4$ and the corresponding angles assumption with $\angle 1$ and $\angle 5$. Then use substitution. Use a similar argument to show $m\angle 3 + m\angle 6 = 180°$.

b. i.

Statements	Reasons
1. $\ell \parallel m$; t is a transversal cutting ℓ and m	1. Given
2. $m\angle 4 + m\angle 1 = 180°$	2. Linear Pair Postulate
3. $m\angle 1 = m\angle 5$	3. Corresponding Angles Assumption
4. $m\angle 4 + m\angle 5 = 180°$	4. Substitution ($m\angle 5$ for $m\angle 1$ in Step 2)
5. $\angle 4$ and $\angle 5$ are supplementary.	5. Definition of supplementary

ii.

Statements	Reasons
6. $m\angle 3 + m\angle 2 = 180°$	6. Linear Pair Postulate
7. $m\angle 2 = m\angle 6$	7. Corresponding Angles Assumption
8. $m\angle 3 + m\angle 6 = 180°$	8. Substitution; $m\angle 6$ for $m\angle 2$
9. $\angle 3$ and $\angle 6$ are supplementary	9. Definition of supplementary

Teacher Notes

Given: $\ell \parallel m$; t is a transversal
cutting ℓ and m

Prove: $\angle 4$ and $\angle 5$ are
supplementary.
$\angle 3$ and $\angle 6$ are
supplementary.

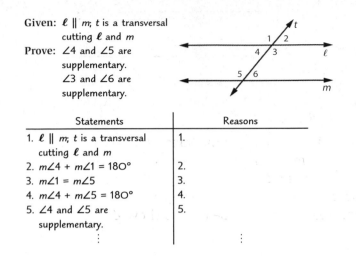

Statements	Reasons
1. $\ell \parallel m$; t is a transversal cutting ℓ and m	1.
2. $m\angle 4 + m\angle 1 = 180°$	2.
3. $m\angle 1 = m\angle 5$	3.
4. $m\angle 4 + m\angle 5 = 180°$	4.
5. $\angle 4$ and $\angle 5$ are supplementary.	5.
⋮	⋮

5 Describe plans for how you would prove that each of your three remaining conjectures in Part b of Problem 3 is correct. Share the task with others. Then discuss each other's plans for proof. Correct any errors in reasoning.

Using the Corresponding Angles Assumption, you can conclude that if two parallel lines are cut by a transversal, then certain relations among pairs of angles will always be true. In the next problem, you will consider the converse situation.

What relations among the angles formed when two lines are cut by a transversal allow you to conclude that the lines are parallel?

6 Conduct the following experiment.

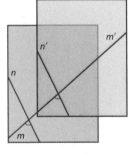

a. Draw and label two intersecting lines on a sheet of paper and mark an angle as shown.

b. Trace the lines and the angle marking on a second sheet of paper. Label the corresponding lines m' and n'. Slide the top copy so that line m' is a continuation of line m.

c. Why are the two marked angles congruent?

d. How is the pair of marked angles related to the two lines n and n' and transversal m? How do lines n and n' appear to be related? Check if those relationships hold when you slide the top copy to other positions, keeping line m' as a continuation of line m.

e. Write a conjecture in if-then form that generalizes the observations you made in the experiment.

5 Sample plans for proof are provided. The diagram at the right is used in all three proof plans.

If two parallel lines are cut by a transversal, then exterior angles on the same side of the transversal are supplementary.

Proof Plan:

Pick a pair of exterior angles on the same side of the transversal such as $\angle 2$ and $\angle 7$. Since the two lines are parallel, we can use a pair of congruent corresponding angles such as $\angle 3$ and $\angle 7$ along with a linear pair of angles such as $\angle 2$ and $\angle 3$ that add to $180°$ to show that $\angle 2$ and $\angle 7$ also add to $180°$. The same reasoning could be used to show $\angle 1$ and $\angle 8$ are supplementary.

If two parallel lines are cut by a transversal, then alternate interior angles have equal measure.

Proof Plan:

We want to show that alternate interior angles like $\angle 4$ and $\angle 6$ have equal measure. We could use the fact that $\angle 3$ and $\angle 4$ are a linear pair and so the measures sum to $180°$. Then also note that $m\angle 3$ and $m\angle 6$ add to $180°$ (interior angles on the same side of a transversal are supplementary—from Problem 4). So, $m\angle 3 = m\angle 4 = m\angle 3 + m\angle 6$ and by subtraction, $m\angle 4 = m\angle 6$. We could use similar reasoning to show $m\angle 3 = m\angle 5$.

If two parallel lines are cut by a transversal, then alternate exterior angles have equal measure.

Proof Plan:

We want to show that angles such as $\angle 1$ and $\angle 7$ have equal measure. Use congruent corresponding angles on the same side of the transversal ($\angle 1$ and $\angle 5$) and helpful congruent vertical angles ($\angle 5$ and $\angle 7$). Since $m\angle 1 = m\angle 5$ and $m\angle 5 = m\angle 7$, $m\angle 1 = m\angle 7$. The same reasoning could be used to show $m\angle 2 = m\angle 8$.

6 **a–b.** Students should follow the instructions indicated in the student text.

c. The angles have equal measure because one is a traced copy of the other.

d. The two angles are corresponding angles. The lines n and n' appear to be parallel. The relationship holds for other positions of n' when translated as instructed.

e. If two lines are cut by a transversal so that corresponding angles have equal measure, then the two lines are parallel.

Unit 1

In order to reason deductively about parallel lines and figures formed by parallel lines, you need to begin with some information about the conditions under which two lines are parallel. The conjecture you made in Problem 6 Part e could be stated this way.

If two lines are cut by a transversal so that corresponding angles have equal measure, then the lines are parallel.

This statement is the *converse* of the Corresponding Angles Assumption. There, you assumed that if two parallel lines are cut by a transversal, then corresponding angles have equal measure.

For the remainder of this unit and in future units, you can assume that both the Corresponding Angles Assumption and its converse are true. These two statements are combined as a single if-and-only-if statement called the *Parallel Lines Postulate*.

Parallel Lines Postulate In a plane, two lines cut by a transversal are parallel if and only if corresponding angles have equal measure.

7 It is reasonable to ask if there are other relations between two angles formed by a line intersecting two other lines that would allow you to conclude that the two lines are parallel. Consider the diagram below.

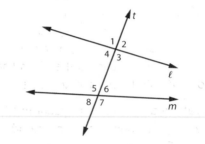

a. What condition on a pair of alternate interior angles would guarantee that line ℓ is parallel to line *m*? Write your conjecture in if-then form.

b. What condition on a pair of interior angles on the same side of the transversal *t* would guarantee that line ℓ is parallel to line *m*? Write your conjecture in if-then form.

c. What condition on a pair of exterior angles would guarantee that line ℓ is parallel to line *m*? Write your conjecture in if-then form.

d. Working with a classmate, write a proof for one of the statements in Parts a–c.

e. Be prepared to share and discuss the reasoning in your proof with the entire class. Correct any reasoning errors found.

EUCLIDEAN AND NONEUCLIDEAN GEOMETRIES When Euclid began building his rules of geometry, he started with five postulates. The postulate in the text, that corresponding angles have the same measure if and only if the two lines (in a plane) cut by the transversal are parallel, is functionally equivalent to Euclid's Fifth Postulate (also called the Parallel Lines Postulate):

If two lines L_1 and L_2 are cut by a transversal L, and the sum of two interior angles A and B on the same side of that transversal is less than two right angles, then lines L_1 and L_2 meet on the side of angles A and B.

The Parallel Lines Postulate is also equivalent to the following statement (called Playfair's Postulate): Given a line and a point not on the line, there is exactly one line parallel to the original line that passes through the point. (Part of the equivalence of this statement and the Parallel Lines Postulate is established in Extensions Task 25.) It seemed to many mathematicians that Playfair's Postulate should be provable from Euclid's first four postulates, but it was, in fact, a necessary postulate. Assuming one of the two negations of Playfair's Postulate will lead to other geometries, spherical or Riemannian geometry (there are no lines through the point that are parallel to the given line) and hyperbolic or Lobachevskian geometry (there are an infinite number of lines through the point that are parallel to the given line). Extensions Task 23 provides students the opportunity to investigate some aspects of spherical geometry.

The Parallel Lines Postulate in the text is equivalent to Euclid's parallel postulate and Playfair's Postulate because given one postulate, the other can be proved. Hence, by assuming the Parallel Lines Postulate in the text, students are studying Euclidean (plane) geometry. Some students may be interested in doing some research on the origins of spherical or hyperbolic geometry.

INSTRUCTIONAL NOTE To begin the next portion of this investigation, it would help if you facilitate a full-class discussion (see the student text, page 38) about the converse of a statement and connect it to the Parallel Lines Postulate. Emphasize that students will be assuming as fact both the statement (which is earlier called the Corresponding Angles Postulate) and its converse. In the discussion, be sure students understand the if-and-only-if statement.

(7) **a.** If two lines are cut by a transversal so that a pair of alternate interior angles have equal measure, then the lines are parallel.

b. If two lines are cut by a transversal so that a pair of interior angles on the same side of the transversal are supplementary, then the lines are parallel.

c. Two possible conjectures:

(1) If two lines are cut by a transversal so that a pair of alternate exterior angles have equal measure, then the lines are parallel.

(2) If two lines are cut by a transversal so that a pair of exterior angles on the same side of the transversal are supplementary, then the lines are parallel.

PROOF SUPPORT
A master for a proof of Problem 7 Part b is provided as un-numbered statement-reason strips. You may wish to provide each student with a set of strips so they can individually order the strips and then compare orderings with others.

Teaching Resources

Student Master 23.

INSTRUCTIONAL NOTE
Student proofs for Part d may
be in paragraph form, a chain
of if-then statements, or a
two-column format. Allow
students to use a variety of
formats so comparisons can
be made. Also, note the
brackets following the
reasons below. The brackets
reference the hypothesis that
has been affirmed. See also
page T34 for an example
and explanation.

INSTRUCTIONAL NOTE
The numbers in the brackets
refer to the statement(s) that
show where the hypothesis
of the reason has been
affirmed. See the note on
page T34.

INSTRUCTIONAL NOTE
It is important for students
to consider other students'
proofs carefully. This type of
critical reading and discussion
will improve their reasoning
and proof skills.

INSTRUCTIONAL NOTE
In Problem 8 Part b,
students have established this
important result: though a
point not on a given line, a line
can be drawn parallel to the
given line. Students will need
to cite this in later proofs.

d. Proofs of two of the conjectures in
Parts a–c are supplied here.

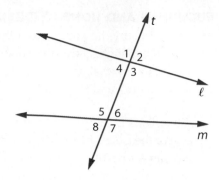

*If two lines are cut by a transversal so that interior angles on the same
side of the transversal are supplementary, then the lines are parallel.*

Statements	Reasons
1. t a transversal cutting ℓ and m; $\angle 4$ and $\angle 5$ are supplementary	1. Given
2. $m\angle 5 + m\angle 4 = 180°$	2. Definition of supplementary angles [1]
3. $m\angle 1 + m\angle 4 = 180°$	3. Linear Pair Postulate [1]
4. $m\angle 1 + m\angle 4 = m\angle 5 + m\angle 4$	4. Substitution [2,3]
5. $m\angle 1 = m\angle 5$	5. Subtraction Property of Equality [4]
6. $\ell \parallel m$	6. Parallel Lines Postulate using corresponding angles $\angle 1$ and $\angle 5$ [5]

*If two lines are cut by a transversal so that alternate interior angles
have equal measure, then the lines are parallel.*

Proof: Two lines ℓ and m are cut by a transversal t so that alternate
interior $\angle 4$ and $\angle 6$ have equal measure. Because $m\angle 4 = m\angle 2$
(vertical angles), we can say that $m\angle 2 = m\angle 6$. Angles 2 and 6 are
corresponding angles with equal measure, so $\ell \parallel m$ by the Parallel
Lines Postulate.

e. As a whole class, discuss proofs for each statement in Parts a–c.

8 **a–b.** See the diagrams below. Construct line t through point P
perpendicular to line ℓ. Construct line m through point P
perpendicular to line t. Line m is parallel to line ℓ since corresponding
angles 1 and 2 have equal measure (Parallel Lines Postulate).

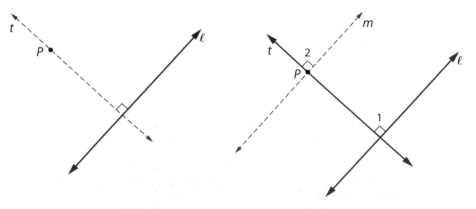

Teacher Notes

8 In designing buildings such as the John Hancock Center, architects need methods for constructing parallel lines. In Investigation 1 (page 34), you examined how to use a compass and straightedge to construct a line perpendicular to a given line through a point not on the line.

a. On a copy of the diagram below, show how you could use the constructions of perpendiculars (pages 33–34) to construct a line *m* through point *P* that is parallel to ℓ.

P •

ℓ

b. Write an argument that justifies that *m* ‖ ℓ.

Summarize
the Mathematics

In this investigation, you reasoned both inductively and deductively about angles formed by parallel lines and a transversal.

a What statements did you accept to be true without proof?

b What theorems and their converses were you able to prove about parallel lines and the angles they form with a transversal?

c Restate each theorem and its converse in Part b as a single if-and-only-if statement similar to the statement of the Parallel Lines Postulate.

Be prepared to compare your responses with those of others.

✓Check Your Understanding

Each of the following statements expresses a relationship between perpendicular and parallel lines. For each statement, draw and label a diagram. Then write an argument proving that the statement is true.

a. In a plane, if two lines are perpendicular to the same line, then they are parallel.

b. If a transversal is perpendicular to one of two parallel lines, then it is perpendicular to the other.

Summarize
the Mathematics

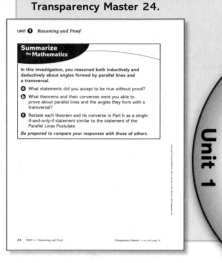

(a) In this investigation, one if and only if statement was accepted without proof:

> Parallel Lines Postulate: In a plane, two lines cut by a transversal are parallel if and only if corresponding angles have equal measure.

(b) If two parallel lines are cut by a transversal, then alternate interior angles have equal measure; and its converse, if two lines are cut by a transversal so that alternate interior angles have equal measure, then the lines are parallel.

If two parallel lines are cut by a transversal, then alternate exterior angles have equal measure; and its converse, if two lines are cut by a transversal so that alternate exterior angles have equal measure, then the lines are parallel.

If two parallel lines are cut by a transversal, then interior angles on the same side of the transversal are supplementary; and its converse, if two lines are cut by a transversal so that interior angles on the same side of the transversal are supplementary, then the lines are parallel.

If two parallel lines are cut by a transversal, then exterior angles on the same side of the transversal are supplementary; and its converse, if two lines are cut by a transversal so that exterior angles on the same side of the transversal are supplementary, then the lines are parallel.

(c) In a plane, two lines cut by a transversal are parallel if and only if alternate exterior angles have equal measure.

In a plane, two lines cut by a transversal are parallel if and only if alternate interior angles have equal measure.

In a plane, two lines cut by a transversal are parallel if and only if exterior angles on the same side of the transversal are supplementary.

MATH TOOLKIT Students should record the Parallel Lines Postulate and the theorems and converses about parallel lines and the angles they form with a transversal in their toolkits. Naming the theorems such as Interior Angles Theorem is helpful for referencing in arguments.

INSTRUCTIONAL NOTE Remind students that when something is to be proved, it is important to draw and label a diagram and identify what is to be proven in terms of the diagram.

✓Check Your Understanding

Student proofs can use postulates and statements proven in Investigations 1 and 2.

a. Given: Lines s, t, and ℓ, with $s \perp \ell$ and $t \perp \ell$

Prove: $s \parallel t$

Suppose that $s \perp \ell$ and $t \perp \ell$ as in the diagram. Since perpendicular lines form four right angles, $m\angle 1 = m\angle 3 = 90°$. Since $\angle 1$ and $\angle 3$ are corresponding angles, $s \parallel t$ by the Parallel Lines Postulate.

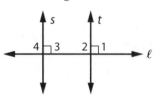

b. Given: Parallel lines ℓ, m with transversal $t \perp \ell$

Prove: $t \perp m$

Suppose $\ell \parallel m$ and that $t \perp \ell$ as in the diagram. By the Parallel Lines Postulate, $m\angle 1 = m\angle 2$. Since $m\angle 1 = 90°$, $m\angle 2 = 90°$. By the definition of perpendicular lines, $t \perp m$.

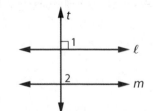

On Your Own

Applications

1 In the diagram at the right, the lines $\overleftrightarrow{AD}$, $\overleftrightarrow{EC}$, and $\overleftrightarrow{FG}$ intersect at point B. $\overleftrightarrow{AD} \perp \overleftrightarrow{EC}$.

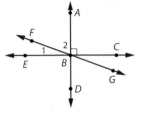

a. What is m∠DBC?

b. Suppose m∠1 = 27°. Find the measure of each angle.

  i. ∠2

  ii. ∠FBD

  iii. ∠EBG

c. Suppose m∠2 = 51°. Find m∠ABG and m∠1.

d. How would your answers to Part c change if m∠2 = p, where $0° < p < 90°$?

2 Computer-aided design (CAD) programs and interactive geometry software include tools for constructing perpendicular lines and parallel lines.

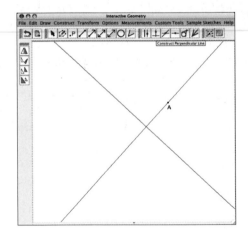

a. Use one of those tools to draw a line. Then construct a line through a point A perpendicular to the drawn line in each case below.

  i. A is a point on the line.

  ii. A is a point *not* on the line.

b. How do you think your software determines the perpendicular line in each case?

c. Use one of those tools to construct a line parallel to a drawn line through a point not on the line. How do you think the software determines the parallel line?

Applications

1 **a.** m∠DBC = 90°

  b. **i.** m∠2 = 90° − 27° = 63°

   ii. m∠FBD = 90° + 27° = 117°

   iii. m∠EBG = 180° − 27° = 153°

  c. m∠ABG = 180° − 51° = 129°
   m∠1 = 90° − 51° = 39°

  d. m∠ABG = 180° − p°
   m∠1 = 90° − p°

2 **a.** Students should use one of the tools suggested to carry out the construction.

  b. Responses may vary. Students might suggest that the technology tools rotate the line 90° or that the software uses the equation of the line and writes the equation of the line perpendicular to the given line using slopes that are negative reciprocals of each other (if the drawn line is not horizontal or vertical).

  c. Responses may vary. Students might suggest that the software finds the slope of the given line and uses that slope and the point to write the equation of the parallel line. They might also suggest that the drawn line is translated to the point, keeping the slope the same.

> **TECHNOLOGY NOTE**
> The interactive geometry software in *CPMP-Tools* uses slopes to produce these constructions. Specific instructions are available in the built-in help system. Use the A–Z Index (or Topic Selection) to quickly find the desired content.

3 Use the diagram below with separate assumptions for Part a and Part b.

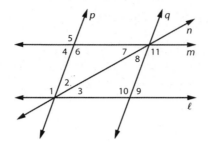

a. Assume $\ell \parallel m$, $p \parallel q$, $m\angle 2 = 40°$, and $m\angle 3 = 35°$.

   i. Find $m\angle 8$.   **ii.** Find $m\angle 10$.

   iii. Find $m\angle 4$.   **iv.** Find $m\angle 7$.

b. Do not assume any of the given lines are parallel. For each of the given conditions, which lines, if any, can you conclude are parallel?

   i. $m\angle 2 = m\angle 8$ **ii.** $m\angle 6 = m\angle 1$

   iii. $m\angle 1 = m\angle 10$ **iv.** $m\angle 2 = m\angle 7$

4 The photo below shows a carpenter's bevel, which is used to draw parallel lines.

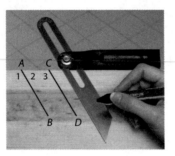

a. What part of the bevel guarantees that $\overleftrightarrow{AB} \parallel \overleftrightarrow{CD}$?

b. How are $\angle 2$ and $\angle 3$ related? How do you know?

5 In the diagram below, $\overleftrightarrow{AD}$ and $\overleftrightarrow{HE}$ are cut by transversal $\overleftrightarrow{GC}$. $\angle 1$ and $\angle 2$ are supplementary.

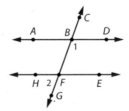

Can you conclude $\overleftrightarrow{AD} \parallel \overleftrightarrow{HE}$? If so, prove it. If not, find a counterexample.

LESSON 2 • Geometric Reasoning and Proof   **41**

3 **a.** **i.** $m\angle 2 = m\angle 8 = 40°$

    ii. $m\angle 10 = 180° - (m\angle 2 + m\angle 3) = 105°$

    iii. $m\angle 4 = m\angle 2 + m\angle 3 = 75°$

    iv. $m\angle 3 = m\angle 7 = 35°$

  b. **i.** $p \parallel q$

    ii. $\ell \parallel m$

    iii. $p \parallel q$

    iv. No conclusion possible

4 **a.** The fixed angle on the carpenter's bevel guarantees $\overleftrightarrow{AB} \parallel \overleftrightarrow{CD}$. The transversal is the top edge of the board. It is labeled $\overleftrightarrow{AC}$. Angles 1 and 3 are corresponding angles. Therefore, $\overleftrightarrow{AB} \parallel \overleftrightarrow{CD}$ by the Parallel Lines Postulate.

  b. Angles 2 and 3 are supplementary. We know that $\overleftrightarrow{AB} \parallel \overleftrightarrow{CD}$ and $\overleftrightarrow{AC}$ is a transversal. Since $\angle 2$ and $\angle 3$ are interior angles on the same side of the transversal, they are supplementary.

5 Yes, the lines must be parallel. The following proof is illustrative only, as there are other ways to proceed.

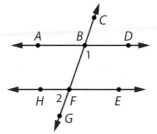

    Since $\overleftrightarrow{GC}$ and $\overleftrightarrow{HE}$ intersect, then $m\angle 2 = m\angle BFE$ (Vertical Angles Theorem). If $m\angle 1 + m\angle 2 = 180°$ (given) and $m\angle 2 = m\angle BFE$, then $m\angle 1 + m\angle BFE = 180°$.

If $m\angle 1 + m\angle BFE = 180°$, then by the theorem: $\overleftrightarrow{AD} \parallel \overleftrightarrow{HE}$. If two lines are cut by a transversal and interior angles on the same side of the transversal are supplementary, then the lines are parallel.

6 The sparkle of a diamond results from light being reflected from facet to facet of the jewel and then directly to the eye of the observer. When a light ray strikes a smooth surface, such as a facet of a jewel, the angle at which the ray strikes the surface is congruent to the angle at which the ray leaves the surface. A diamond can be cut in such a way that a light ray entering the top will be parallel to the same ray as it exits the top.

Examine the cross sections of the two diamonds shown below. The diamond at the left has been cut too deeply. The entering and exiting light rays are not parallel. The diamond on the right appears to be cut correctly. The entering and exiting light rays are parallel.

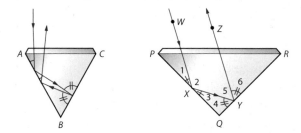

a. Use deductive reasoning to determine the measure of ∠Q at the base of the diamond to ensure that the entering and exiting light rays will be parallel.

b. Explain how you could use inductive reasoning to conjecture what the measure of ∠Q should be to ensure that the entering and exiting light rays will be parallel.

c. What are the advantages of deductive reasoning in this case?

d. As you have seen before, when modeling a situation it often helps to make simplifying assumptions. Consult with a science teacher about reflection and refraction of light and the modeling of the diamond cut. What simplifying assumptions were made in this situation?

7 Figure *PQRS* is a trapezoid with $\overline{PQ} \parallel \overline{SR}$.

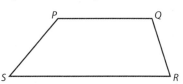

a. What can you conclude about ∠S and ∠P? About ∠Q and ∠R?

b. Write an if-then statement summarizing one of your observations in Part a. Prove your statement is correct.

c. Suppose m∠S = m∠R. What can you conclude about ∠P and ∠Q? Write an argument proving your claim.

6 **a.** In order for the exiting light rays to be parallel, we must have
$m\angle 2 + m\angle 5 = 180°$. From the diagram, $m\angle 1 + m\angle 2 + m\angle 3 = 180°$
and $m\angle 4 + m\angle 5 + m\angle 6 = 180°$. Combining these two equations,
we get $m\angle 1 + m\angle 2 + m\angle 3 + m\angle 4 + m\angle 5 + m\angle 6 = 360°$.
But if $m\angle 2 + m\angle 5 = 180°$, then this equation becomes
$m\angle 1 + m\angle 3 + m\angle 4 + m\angle 6 = 180°$. Since $m\angle 1 = m\angle 3$
and $m\angle 4 = m\angle 6$ (congruent angles from light reflection),
$2m\angle 3 + 2m\angle 4 = 180°$. Divide both sides of this equation
by 2 to get $m\angle 3 + m\angle 4 = 90°$. But in $\triangle XYQ$,
$m\angle 3 + m\angle 4 + m\angle Q = 180°$, so $m\angle Q = 90°$.

b. To use inductive reasoning, you could keep drawing diagrams by
hand or use an interactive geometry program and measure angles
until you got a diagram for which the entering and exiting light rays
were parallel.

c. It is very time-consuming to keep drawing diagrams and also very
difficult to draw the diagrams accurately. But deductive reasoning
leads us directly to the correct angle.

d. The simplifying assumption that was made in this situation is that
the light ray would not be refracted (bent) upon entering or leaving
the diamond.

7 **a.** Since $\overleftrightarrow{PQ} \parallel \overleftrightarrow{SR}$, both pairs of angles are supplementary because they
are interior angles on the same side of their respective transversals.

b. If *PQRS* is a trapezoid with $\overleftrightarrow{PQ} \parallel \overleftrightarrow{SR}$, then $\angle P$ and $\angle S$ are
supplementary.

Proof: If $\overleftrightarrow{PQ} \parallel \overleftrightarrow{SR}$, then $\angle P$ and $\angle S$ are interior angles on the same
side of the transversal $\overleftrightarrow{PS}$. By the interior angles theorem for parallel
lines, $\angle P$ and $\angle S$ are supplementary.

c. **Conclusion:** $m\angle P = m\angle Q$

Proof: If $\overleftrightarrow{PQ} \parallel \overleftrightarrow{SR}$, then $m\angle P + m\angle S = 180°$ and $m\angle Q + m\angle R = 180°$.
So, $m\angle P + m\angle S = m\angle Q + m\angle R$. Since $m\angle P + m\angle S = m\angle Q + m\angle R$
and $m\angle S = m\angle R$, then $m\angle P + m\angle S = m\angle Q + m\angle S$ by substitution.
It follows that $m\angle P = m\angle Q$ by subtracting.

8. Re-examine the mechanism of the lift-bed truck shown here. Assume the frame of the truck is parallel to the ground, and *E* is the midpoint of $\overline{AB}$ and $\overline{DC}$. You may want to make a simple model by attaching two linkage strips of the same length at their midpoints.

   a. How is ∠*AEC* related to ∠*BED*? Why?

   b. How is △*AEC* related to △*BED*? Why?

   c. How is ∠*BAC* related to ∠*ABD*? Why?

   d. As a hydraulic ram pushes point *B* in the direction of point *D*, what happens to the relations in Parts a–c? Explain your reasoning.

   e. Explain as precisely as you can why the truck bed $\overline{AC}$ remains parallel to the truck frame $\overline{BD}$ as the hydraulic ram is extended or contracted.

Connections

9. When two lines intersect, two pairs of vertical angles are formed.

   a. How many pairs of vertical angles are formed when three lines (in a plane) intersect at the same point?

   b. How many pairs of vertical angles are formed when four lines (in a plane) intersect at the same point?

   c. Suppose a fifth line was added to a diagram for Part b and the line intersected the other lines at the same point. How many *additional* pairs of vertical angles are formed? What is the total number of pairs of vertical angles formed by the five lines?

   d. Make a conjecture about the number of pairs of vertical angles formed by *n* lines (in a plane) that intersect at the same point. Assume $n \geq 2$.

10. In Investigation 2, you saw that if you *assume* the Parallel Lines Postulate, then it is possible to prove other conditions on angles that result when parallel lines are cut by a transversal. It is also possible to prove other conditions on angles that guarantee two lines are parallel.

    If the Parallel Lines Postulate is rewritten, replacing each occurrence of the phrase "corresponding angles" with "alternate interior angles," the new statement is often called the Alternate Interior Angles Theorem. You proved the two parts of this theorem in Problem 5 on page 37 and in Problem 7 on page 38 using the Parallel Lines Postulate.

8 **a.** m∠*AEC* = m∠*BED*; vertical angles theorem.

b. △*AEC* ≅ △*BED*; the segments $\overline{AB}$ and $\overline{CD}$ are connected at the midpoints; so, $\overline{AE}$ ≅ $\overline{EB}$ and $\overline{DE}$ ≅ $\overline{EC}$. These congruent segments and the vertical angles provide the necessary SAS corresponding pairs.

c. m∠*BAC* = m∠*ABD*; corresponding parts of congruent triangles

d. The relations remain the same since you can repeat the same line of reasoning because of the way the mechanism is constructed.

e. Since the alternate interior angles formed by $\overline{AB}$ with the truck bed and truck frame are the same measure, the bed and frame are parallel (Alternate Interior Angles Theorem).

Connections

9 **a.** 6; See diagram at the right.

b. 12

c. 8; 20; The new line makes an angle with each of the other four lines, and the supplements of these four new angles are also additional angles, giving 18 additional angles.

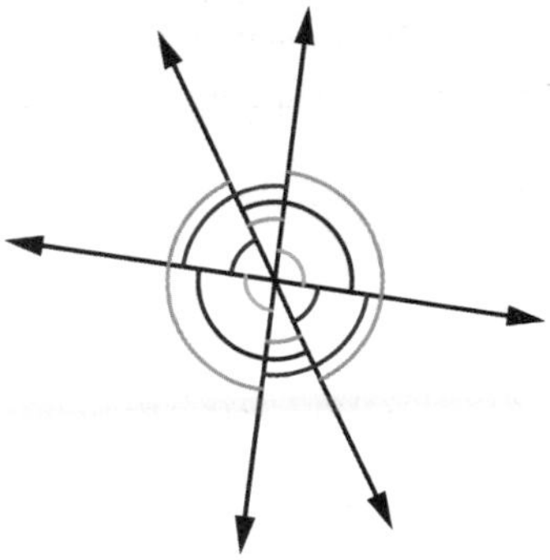

d. Students should consider the following pairs of (*n lines, vertical pairs*):

Number of Lines	2	3	4	5	...	*n*
Vertical Pairs	2	6	12	20	...	*n*(*n* − 1)

Suppose next year's math class *assumes* the Alternate Interior Angles Theorem as its Parallel Lines Postulate.

a. Could the class then *prove* the two parts of the Parallel Lines Postulate? Explain your reasoning.

b. Could the class also prove the relationships between parallelism of lines and angles on the same side of the transversal? Explain.

11 In the diagram below, $\ell \parallel m$ and $m \parallel n$. Line p intersects each of these lines.

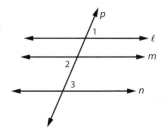

a. How are the measures of angles 1 and 2 related? Explain your reasoning.

b. How are the measures of angles 2 and 3 related? Explain your reasoning.

c. Using your deductions in Parts a and b, prove that lines ℓ and n are parallel.

d. Write an if-then statement that summarizes the theorem you have proved.

12 In the coordinate plane diagram below, lines ℓ, m, and n are parallel and contain the points shown.

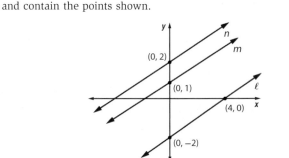

a. Write an equation for each line.

b. On a copy of this diagram, draw a line perpendicular to each line through its y-intercept.

c. How do the three lines you drew in Part b appear to be related to each other?

10 a. Yes, the class could prove both parts of the
Parallel Lines Postulate by assuming the
Alternate Interior Angles Theorem:

> In a plane, two lines cut by a
> transversal are parallel if and only
> if alternate interior angles have
> equal measure.

Student explanations might include a plan
for a proof as follows.

> Use the fact that alternate interior angles congruent implies
> that lines are parallel along with vertical angles to show
> that corresponding angles congruent also implies the lines
> are parallel.
>   For the converse, use the fact that if two lines are parallel, then
> alternate interior angles are congruent along with vertical angles to
> show that if two lines are parallel, then the corresponding angles
> are congruent.

b. Yes; once the relationship using corresponding angles has been
established in the previous item, all the other relationships follow.

11 a. $m\angle 1 = m\angle 2$. If two parallel lines ℓ and m are cut by a transversal,
then the alternate exterior angles have the same measure.

b. Angles 2 and 3 are the same measure because they are alternate
interior angles for parallel lines m and n cut by transversal p.

c. Since $m\angle 1 = m\angle 2$ and $m\angle 2 = m\angle 3$, $m\angle 1 = m\angle 3$. Angles 1 and 3 are
corresponding angles for lines ℓ and n cut by transversal p, so $\ell \parallel n$.

d. If two lines are each parallel to a third line, then they are parallel to
each other.

> **MATH TOOLKIT** Students
> should record the theorems
> proved in Connections
> Tasks 11, 12, and 15 in
> their toolkits.

12 a. Line ℓ has slope $\frac{0+2}{4-0}$, or $\frac{1}{2}$. Therefore, because the lines are
parallel, each line has slope $\frac{1}{2}$: ℓ has equation $y = \frac{1}{2}x - 2$, m has
equation $y = \frac{1}{2}x + 1$, and n has equation $y = \frac{1}{2}x + 2$.

b.

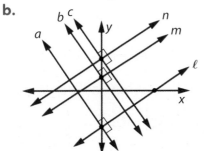

c. The lines a, b, and c appear to be parallel.

d. Prove your conjecture in Part c using postulates and/or theorems you proved in Investigation 2.

e. Prove your conjecture in Part c using the equations of the lines and coordinate methods.

⑬ In previous courses, you used the well-known fact that the sum of the measures of the angles of a triangle is 180°. That property was developed through experimentation and inductive reasoning based on several cases. One possible experiment is illustrated below. But how can you be sure this is true for *all* triangles?

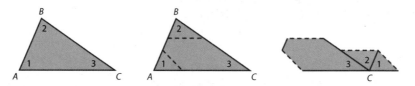

There is an important connection between the Triangle Angle Sum Property and the Alternate Interior Angles Theorem (Connections Task 10) that you proved using the Parallel Lines Postulate. To establish that connection, an additional assumption is needed.

Angle Addition Postulate If *P* is a point in the interior of ∠*ABC*, then m∠*ABP* + m∠*PBC* = m∠*ABC*.

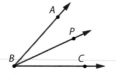

The diagram below shows a triangle *ABC* and a line *k* drawn parallel to $\overleftrightarrow{AC}$ through point *B*.

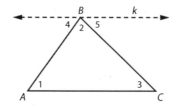

a. What construction did you carry out earlier that shows that line *k* can be drawn parallel to $\overleftrightarrow{AC}$ through point *B*?

b. How are ∠1 and ∠4 related? How are ∠3 and ∠5 related?

c. Write a deductive proof that m∠1 + m∠2 + m∠3 = 180°.

d. Prove: $a \parallel b$, $b \parallel c$, and $a \parallel c$

We know that $a \perp \ell$, $b \perp m$, $c \perp n$, and lines ℓ, m, and n are parallel. In the Check Your Understanding on page 39, we proved that if a transversal is perpendicular to one of two parallel lines, then it is perpendicular to the other. So, $a \perp m$ and $a \perp n$. Likewise, lines b and c are perpendicular to lines ℓ, m, and n. We also proved that in a plane, if two lines are perpendicular to the same line, they are parallel. So, $a \parallel b$, $b \parallel c$, and $a \parallel c$.

e. The slope of each of the new lines is -2 since each is perpendicular to a line with slope $\frac{1}{2}$. Thus, since all three of the new lines have the same slope, they must all be parallel to each other.

13

a. In Problem 8 page 39, students justified the construction of a line parallel to a given line from a point not on the line.

b. Since $k \parallel \overleftrightarrow{AC}$, $\angle 1$ and $\angle 4$ are alternate interior angles using transversal $\overleftrightarrow{AB}$. Similarly, $\angle 3$ and $\angle 5$ are alternate interior angles using transversal $\overleftrightarrow{BC}$. Thus, m$\angle 1$ = m$\angle 4$ and m$\angle 3$ = m$\angle 5$.

c.

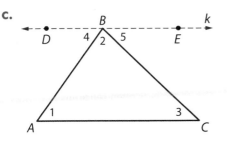

Proof: Since $k \parallel \overleftrightarrow{AC}$ with transversal $\overleftrightarrow{AB}$, m$\angle 1$ = m$\angle 4$ (alternate interior angles). Using $\overleftrightarrow{BC}$ as a transversal, m$\angle 3$ = m$\angle 5$ (alternate interior angles). By the Angle Addition Postulate, m$\angle 4$ + m$\angle 2$ = m$\angle DBC$ and m$\angle DBC$ + m$\angle 5$ = m$\angle DBE$. By substitution, m$\angle 4$ + m$\angle 2$ + m$\angle 5$ = m$\angle DBE$. So, m$\angle 4$ + m$\angle 2$ + m$\angle 5$ = 180° (the Linear Pair and Angle Addition Postulates). It follows by substitution that m$\angle 1$ + m$\angle 2$ + m$\angle 3$ = 180°.

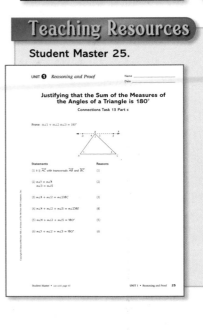

14 In Connections Task 13, you proved that the sum of the measures of the angles of a triangle is 180°. For each of the following statements, decide if it is true. If true, explain why. Otherwise, give a counterexample. (Recall that an acute angle is an angle whose measure is less than 90°.)

  a. If the measures of two angles of one triangle are equal to the measures of two angles of another triangle, then the measures of the third angles are equal.

  b. The sum of the measures of the acute angles of a right triangle is 90°.

  c. If two angles of a triangle are acute, then the third angle is not acute.

  d. If a triangle is equiangular (all angles have the same measure), then each angle has measure 60°.

15 Recall that an *exterior angle* of a triangle is formed when one side of the triangle is extended as shown at the right. ∠A and ∠B are called *remote interior angles* with respect to the exterior angle, ∠ACD.

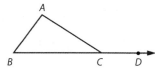

  a. How is m∠ACD related to m∠A and m∠B?

  b. Write an argument to support your claim.

  c. Using the term "remote interior angles," write a statement of the theorem you have proved. This theorem is often called the **Exterior Angle Theorem for a Triangle**.

Reflections

16 In this lesson, you proved mathematical statements in geometric settings. How do you decide where to start in constructing a proof? How do you know when the proof is completed?

17 In Investigation 1, you explored how to construct a line perpendicular to a given line through a point on the line and through a point not on the line. In Investigation 2, you discovered a method to construct a line parallel to a given line through a point not on the line. Think about these ideas algebraically in the context of a coordinate plane. Consider the line ℓ with equation $2x - y = 11$.

  a. Is $P(8, 5)$ on line ℓ? Write an equation of a line m perpendicular to line ℓ through point P.

  b. Write an equation of a line perpendicular to line ℓ through point $Q(8, 0)$.

  c. Compare your methods for answering Parts a and b.

  d. Write an equation of a line parallel to line ℓ through the point $Q(8, 0)$.

14 a. True. Suppose $\triangle ABC$ and $\triangle XYZ$ are such that $m\angle A = m\angle X$ and $m\angle B = m\angle Y$. In $\triangle ABC$, we know that $m\angle A + m\angle B + m\angle C = 180°$; and in $\triangle XYZ$, we know that $m\angle X + m\angle Y + m\angle Z = 180°$. It follows that, $m\angle A + m\angle B + m\angle C = m\angle X + m\angle Y + m\angle Z$. If $m\angle A = m\angle X$ and $m\angle B = m\angle Y$, then by the Subtraction Property of Equality, $m\angle C = m\angle Z$.

b. True. If $\triangle ABC$ is a right triangle with acute angles A and B and right angle C, then $m\angle A + m\angle B + m\angle C = 180°$. Since $m\angle C = 90°$, $m\angle A + m\angle B + 90° = 180°$. Thus, $m\angle A + m\angle B = 90°$ by the Subtraction Property of Equality.

c. This statement is not correct. Consider a triangle with angles of 50°, 60°, and 70°. All three angles are acute, which is a counterexample to the proposition.

d. If $\triangle ABC$ is equiangular, then $3m\angle A = 180°$. Thus, $m\angle A = 60°$. Since all the angles have equal measure, each has measure 60°.

15 a. $m\angle ACD = m\angle A + m\angle B$

b. $m\angle ACD + m\angle ACB = 180°$ by the Linear Pair Postulate. $m\angle A + m\angle B + m\angle ACB = 180°$ since the measures of the three angles in a triangle must sum to 180°. Therefore, $m\angle ACD + m\angle ACB = m\angle A + m\angle B + m\angle ACB$ by substitution. By the Subtraction Property of Equality, $m\angle ACD = m\angle A + m\angle B$.

c. *An exterior angle of a triangle has a measure equal to the sum of the measures of the two remote interior angles.*

> **TOOLKIT NOTE** The Exterior Angle Theorem for a triangle should be added to students' lists of theorems.

Reflections

16 You most often start with the information given. If the statement is expressed in if-then form, the given information is in the hypothesis. You then consider previous results you proved, postulates, and definitions that involve the given condition or conditions. From that inventory, select results that seem related to the conclusion you are trying to establish. You then use that information to reason to the conclusion of the if-then statement. The proof is complete when the conclusion of the statement has been deduced.

17 a. The line with equation $2x - y = 11$ does contain $P(8, 5)$ since $2 \cdot 8 - 5 = 11$. Line ℓ has slope 2 since $y = 2x - 11$. Line m must have slope $-\frac{1}{2}$ to be perpendicular to ℓ. $-\frac{1}{2} = \frac{y - 5}{x - 8}$, so the equation for m is $y - 5 = -\frac{1}{2}(x - 8)$, or an equivalent form of this equation.

b. $-\frac{1}{2} = \frac{y - 0}{x - 8}$; $-\frac{1}{2}(x - 8) = y$, or $y = -\frac{1}{2}x + 4$.

c. Methods above both use the definition of slope.

d. $2(x - 8) = y$, or $y = 2x - 16$.

18 Parallel lines were defined to be lines in a plane that do not intersect.

    a. Rewrite the definition of parallel lines as an if-and-only-if statement.

    b. Is it possible for two lines in three-dimensional space neither to be parallel nor to intersect? Illustrate your reasoning.

19 Determining if edges or lines are parallel is very important in design and construction.

    a. Describe at least three methods you could use to test if a pair of lines are parallel.

    b. Libby claimed that you could determine if two lines are parallel by measuring the perpendicular distance between the lines at two places. Describe how you would perform this test. Provide an argument that justifies Libby's claim.

20 On the John Hancock Center building, are angles of the type marked ∠*ABC* and ∠*BAC* congruent or not?

    a. Prove your claim.

    b. On what assumptions does your proof rely?

Extensions

21 What is the sum of the measures of ∠*A*, ∠*B*, ∠*C*, ∠*D*, and ∠*E*? What geometric assumptions and theorems did you use in answering this question?

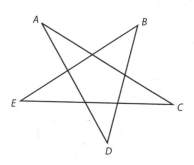

18 **a.** Two lines in a plane are parallel if and only if they do not intersect.

b. It is possible for two lines in three-dimensional space to be neither parallel nor intersecting. Lines with this relationship are called **skew lines**. See lines m and n at the right.

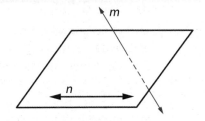

19 **a.** (1) Measure the perpendicular distance between the two lines at two places to see if they are equal.

(2) Draw a transversal and measure corresponding angles to see if they are congruent (or other appropriate angle pairs).

(3) Construct a perpendicular line to ℓ. Then check to see if the new line is perpendicular to m.

(4) On each line, mark off a segment, both segments the same length. Join the corresponding endpoints of the segments to make a quadrilateral and measure the two new segments. If they have equal length, then the figure is a parallelogram, and the original lines are parallel.

b. **Test Method:** Construct a line perpendicular to ℓ at point P, and let it intersect m at point Q. Construct a second line perpendicular to ℓ at point S, and let it intersect m at point R. Measure PQ and SR. If they are equal, then $\overleftrightarrow{PQ} \parallel \overleftrightarrow{SR}$ and hence, opposite sides are parallel; $\ell \parallel m$.

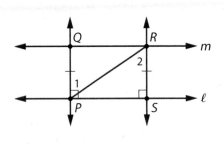

Argument: $\overline{QP} \parallel \overline{RS}$ because they are perpendicular to the same line ℓ or because interior angles on the same side of a transversal are supplementary. $\angle 1 \cong \angle 2$ (alternate interior angles), $\overline{QP} \cong \overline{RS}$ by measurement and $\overline{PR} \cong \overline{PR}$, so $\triangle PQR \cong \triangle RSP$ (SAS). It follows that $\overline{QR} \cong \overline{SP}$ (CPCTC). Since opposite sides of quadrilateral $PQRS$ are congruent, by definition it is a parallelogram. Thus, $\overleftrightarrow{QR} \parallel \overleftrightarrow{PS}$. (Alternatively, students could indicate that $\angle PQR$ is a right angle by CPCTC and use this with the fact that interior angles on the same side of transversal $\overleftrightarrow{QP}$ are supplementary to conclude that $\overleftrightarrow{QR} \parallel \overleftrightarrow{PS}$.)

20 ∠*ABC* is not congruent to ∠*BAC*. (Some students might conjecture that the angles are congruent.)

Unit 1

    a. Indirect reasoning to show that ∠*ABC* ≇ ∠*BAC*:
    If ∠*ABC* ≅ ∠*BAC*, then *AC* = *BC* and
    DC = *CE*. Since the diagonals of *AEDB*
    bisect each other and are congruent, *AEDB*
    is a rectangle. But it is not a rectangle
    because the building narrows as it goes up.
    So, ∠*ABC* is not congruent to ∠*BAC*.

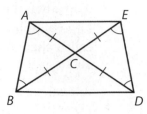

    b. Assumptions were: the building is not rectangular and ∠*ABC* ≅ ∠*BAC*. One proof that ∠*ABC* ≅ ∠*BAC* would incorrectly assume that *AEDB* is a rectangle and use the fact that the diagonals bisect each other to show that the angles are congruent.

Extensions

21 There are a variety of ways to prove that the sum of the angles is 180°. One follows:

The diagram at the right has angle numbers inserted for the angles of the five triangles that form the points of the star. Vertical angles are labeled with the same number since their measures are equal. The measures of the interior angles of the central pentagon are equal to the sum of the two angles of each adjacent triangle as shown (exterior angle theorem for triangles).

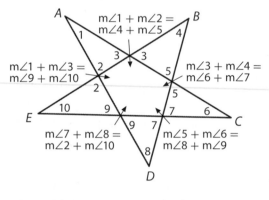

    The goal is to find: m∠1 + m∠4 + m∠6 + m∠8 + m∠10. We know that the sum of the angles of a pentagon is 540°. Adding the first expressions for the interior angles gives the first equation below; adding the second expressions gives the second equation.

$$(m\angle 1 + m\angle 2) + (m\angle 3 + m\angle 4) + (m\angle 5 + m\angle 6) + (m\angle 7 + m\angle 8) + (m\angle 1 + m\angle 3) = 540°$$
$$(m\angle 4 + m\angle 5) + (m\angle 6 + m\angle 7) + (m\angle 8 + m\angle 9) + (m\angle 2 + m\angle 10) + (m\angle 9 + m\angle 10) = 540°$$

The underlined groups of three angle measures above are angles that form triangles. So, subtracting those from the left side of each equation and 2 • 180° from 540° results in the following two equations.

$$m\angle 4 + m\angle 8 + m\angle 1 + m\angle 3 = 180°$$
$$m\angle 4 + m\angle 5 + m\angle 6 + m\angle 10 = 180°$$

Summing the two equations gives
$m\angle 4 + m\angle 4 + m\angle 8 + m\angle 5 + m\angle 1 + m\angle 6 + m\angle 3 + m\angle 10 = 360°$. Since
$m\angle 3 + m\angle 4 + m\angle 5 = 180°$, $m\angle 1 + m\angle 4 + m\angle 6 + m\angle 8 + m\angle 10 = 180°$.

For this proof, the following theorems were used:

Sum of angles of a triangle is 180°.

Sum of the measure of exterior angles of a triangle is the same as the sum of the measure of remote interior angles.

Vertical angles have the same measure.

Assuming a regular pentagon, students might provide a proof similar to the following:

The angle formed at each vertex of the pentagon measures 108°. So, each corresponding linear pair angle measures 72°. Each triangle outside the pentagon has two 72° angles and thus one 36° angle at the lettered vertex. So, $m\angle A + m\angle B + m\angle C + m\angle D + m\angle E = 5(36°) = 180°$.

22 If you look at a map of flight paths of an airline, you will see that the flight paths are not straight lines. Since the Earth is a *sphere*, the shortest path between cities, staying on or slightly above the Earth's surface, follows a **great circle**—a circle on the surface of a sphere formed by a plane passing through the center of the sphere. For example, the equator is a great circle.

Think about how the geometry of a sphere (called *spherical geometry*) differs from the Euclidean geometry of a plane. In spherical geometry, all "lines" (shortest paths on the surface) are great circles.

Consider the equator as line ℓ and the North Pole as point *P*. In spherical geometry:

a. How many "lines" can be drawn through point *P* perpendicular to ℓ?

b. How many "lines" can be drawn through point *P* parallel to ℓ?

c. In spherical geometry, "segments" are parts of great circles. Draw a diagram of a "triangle" *PAB* for which m∠*A* + m∠*B* + m∠*P* > 180°.

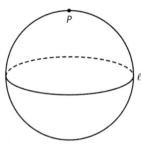

d. Draw a diagram to show that the Pythagorean Theorem is not true in spherical geometry.

e. Explain how a "triangle" in spherical geometry can have three right angles.

23 In the diagram below, ℓ ∥ *m*. Prove that m∠*BCD* = m∠1 + m∠2. (*Hint*: Introduce a new line in the diagram as was done in the proof of the Triangle Angle Sum Theorem (page 45). Such a line is called an *auxiliary line*. Its addition to the diagram must be justified by a postulate or previously proved theorem.)

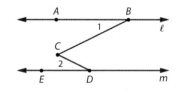

22 **a.** An infinite number

b. None

c.

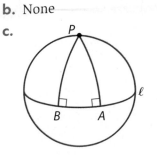

d. Using the diagram in Part c, $PA^2 + AB^2 \neq PB^2$ since $PA = PB$, but m∠$PAB = 90°$.

e. Triangle PAB would need to have a right angle at P as shown and intersect ℓ at two right angles.

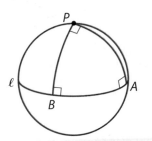

23 Introducing an auxiliary line parallel to ℓ and m containing the point C is helpful.

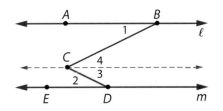

We know from the proof of the Triangle Angle Sum Theorem that through a point not on a line (in this case, point C not on line ℓ or line m), there is one line through the point parallel to the given lines. m∠2 = m∠3 (alternate interior angles) and m∠1 = m∠4 (alternate interior angles). m∠BCD = m∠4 + m∠3; therefore, m∠BCD = m∠1 + m∠2.

24 Drawing an altitude in a triangle or parallelogram to calculate its area rests on the following theorem.

> *Through a point not on a given line, there is exactly one line perpendicular to the given line.*

A proof of this theorem has two parts. First, establish there is one line n through P perpendicular to ℓ. Then establish there is no more than one line perpendicular to ℓ. You established the first part in Investigation 1, Problem 4 Part c.

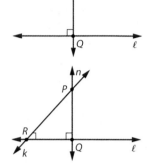

a. Study the following plan for proof of the second part. Give reasons that will support each proposed step.

Plan for Proof:
Use indirect reasoning. Suppose there is a second line k through P perpendicular to ℓ. Show that this will lead to a contradiction. Conclude there is only one line n through P perpendicular to ℓ.

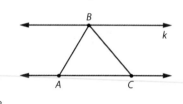

b. How does this theorem compare with the corresponding situation in spherical geometry (Extensions Task 22 Part a)?

25 In the process of proving the Triangle Angle Sum Theorem (Connections Task 13), you used the previously established fact: Through a point B not on a given line $\overleftrightarrow{AC}$, there is a line k through the point parallel to the given line.

a. Do you think there is more than one line through point B parallel to $\overleftrightarrow{AC}$? Compare your answer with that for Extensions Task 22 Part b.

b. To show there is no more than one parallel line in Part a, you can use *indirect reasoning*.

  i. *Assume* there is a second line, call it ℓ, through point B such that $\ell \parallel \overleftrightarrow{AC}$.

  - Why is m$\angle 4$ = m$\angle 1$?
  - Why is m$\angle 4$ = m$\angle 2$ + m$\angle 3$?
  - Why is m$\angle 1$ = m$\angle 2$?
  - Why is m$\angle 4$ = m$\angle 1$ + m$\angle 3$?

  ii. Identify a *contradiction* in part i.

  iii. That contradiction shows the assumption in part i is false. So, what must be true?

24 **a.** Assuming there is a second line perpendicular to ℓ means that ∠*QRP* is a right angle. So, △*QRP* will have two right angles. This is not possible since the sum of the three angle measures of a triangle is 180°. So, there cannot be a second line through *P* perpendicular to ℓ; there is exactly one line through *P* perpendicular to ℓ.

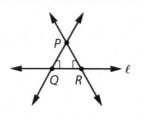

   b. In spherical geometry, there are infinitely many lines through point *P* perpendicular to line ℓ.

25 **a.** No, there is only one line through point *B* parallel to $\overleftrightarrow{AC}$. In spherical geometry, there are no parallel lines (since lines are great circles and intersect at two points).

   b. **i.** • ℓ ∥ $\overleftrightarrow{AC}$, so m∠4 = m∠1 since they are alternate interior angles.

   • m∠4 = m∠2 + m∠3 by the Angle Addition Postulate.

   • k ∥ $\overleftrightarrow{AC}$, so m∠1 = m∠2 since they are alternate interior angles.

   • Since m∠1 = m∠2 and m∠4 = m∠2 + m∠3, m∠4 = m∠1 + m∠3 (Substitution Property of Equality).

   ii. Since m∠4 = m∠1, m∠4 ≠ m∠1 + m∠3 unless m∠3 = 0°.

   iii. It must be true that there is no more than one line through point *B* parallel to $\overleftrightarrow{AC}$.

Review

26 When trying to solve real-world problems, it is often necessary to write symbolic expressions or rules that indicate relationships described in words. Write a symbolic rule that matches each description. Indicate what your letter symbols represent.

  a. There are 3 more cats than dogs in the veterinarian's waiting room.

  b. There are 25 students for each teacher on the field trip.

  c. There are 3 fewer calculators than there are students in the classroom.

  d. There are twice as many sophomores as there are juniors on the organizing committee.

27 The density of an object can be found by dividing the mass of the object by the volume of the object. Using symbols, this can be written $d = \frac{m}{V}$.

  a. Rock 1 and Rock 2 have the same volume. The density of Rock 1 is greater than the density of Rock 2. How do their masses compare?

  b. Two objects have the same mass but the volume of Object 1 is greater than the volume of Object 2. Compare the densities of the two objects.

  c. Rewrite the formula in the form $m = \ldots$.

  d. Rewrite the formula in the form $V = \ldots$.

28 Use properties of triangles and the right triangle trigonometric ratios to find an approximate value of z in each triangle.

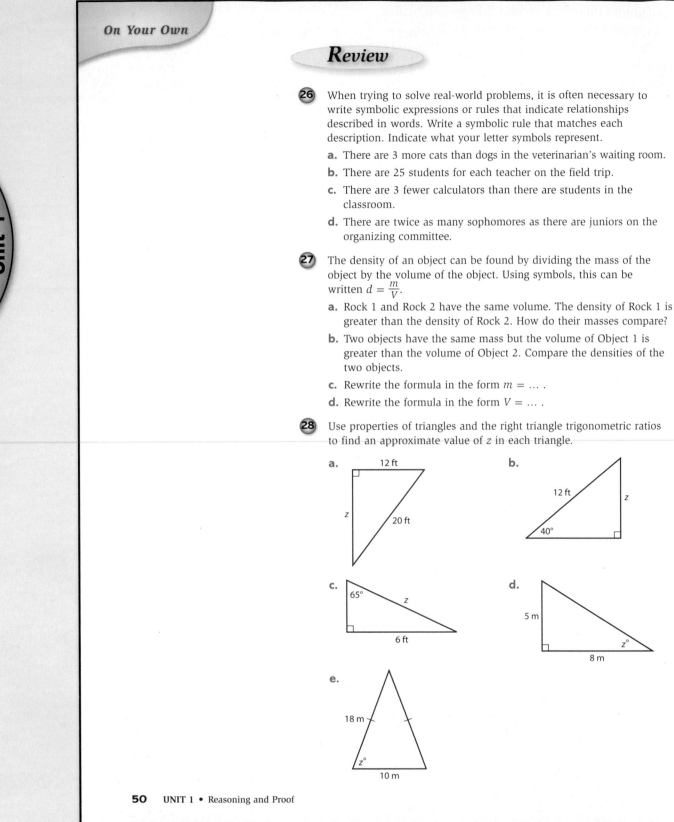

Review

26 a. $C = D + 3$, where D is the number of dogs and C is the number of cats.

b. $S = 25T$, where T is the number of teachers and S is the number of students.

c. $C = S - 3$, where S is the number of students and C is the number of calculators.

d. $S = 2J$, where J is the number of juniors and S is the number of sophomores.

27 a. The mass of Rock 1 is greater than the mass of Rock 2. Since $d_1 = \dfrac{m_1}{V}$ and $d_2 = \dfrac{m_2}{V}$, if $d_1 > d_2$, then $m_1 > m_2$.

b. The density of Object 1 is less than the density of Object 2. Since $d_1 = \dfrac{m}{V_1}$, and $d_2 = \dfrac{m}{V_2}$, if $V_1 > V_2$, then $d_1 < d_2$.

c. $m = dV$

d. $V = \dfrac{m}{d}$

28 a. $z = \sqrt{20^2 - 12^2} = 16$ feet

b. $\sin 40° = \dfrac{z}{12}$; $z \approx 7.71$ feet

c. $\sin 65° = \dfrac{6}{z}$; $z \approx 6.62$ feet

d. $\tan z = \dfrac{5}{8}$; $z \approx 32.0°$

e. The altitude from the vertex angle to the base bisects the base; so, $\cos z = \dfrac{5}{18}$ and $z \approx 73.9°$. Alternatively, students might use the Law of Cosines.

29 Write each of these expressions in equivalent factored form.

   a. $3x + 15$ **b.** $5x^2 + 15x$ **c.** $x^3 - x^2$

   d. $x^2 - 9$ **e.** $x^2 + 6x + 9$ **f.** $x^2 - 3x - 10$

30 There are 16 marbles in a bag. There are red and blue marbles. If a marble is randomly selected from the bag, the probability of selecting a red one is $\frac{1}{4}$.

   a. How many blue marbles are in the bag?

   b. Suppose that you reach into the bag, draw one marble, note the color, and return it to the bag. You then draw a second marble from the bag. What is the probability that the two marbles you draw are the same color? Explain your reasoning or show your work.

   c. How many yellow marbles would you need to add to the bag to make the probability of choosing a red or a yellow marble $\frac{1}{2}$? Explain your reasoning.

31 Write each of these expressions in different equivalent form.

   a. $(a^2)(a^5)$ **b.** $\dfrac{a^5}{a^3}$ **c.** $(a^2)^5$

   d. a^{-2} **e.** $(2a^2)^3$ **f.** $a^5(a) - a^5$

32 Refer to the coordinate diagram shown at the right.

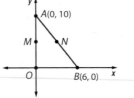

   a. Find the coordinates of the midpoint M of $\overline{AO}$. The midpoint N of $\overline{AB}$.

   b. Use coordinates to explain why $\overline{MN} \parallel \overline{OB}$.

   c. How does the length of $\overline{MN}$ compare to the length of $\overline{OB}$?

   d. How would your answers for Parts a–c change if point A has coordinates $(0, a)$ and point B has coordinates $(b, 0)$.

33 Solve each equation.

   a. $3(2x - 5) = 6 - 2x$ **b.** $5(3^x) = 45$

   c. $x(x + 6) = 0$ **d.** $(x + 3)(x - 2) = 6$

34 Determine if the relationship in each table is linear, exponential, or quadratic. Then write a rule that matches each table. Explain your reasoning or show your work.

   a.

x	2	3	4	5	6
y	6	11	18	27	38

   b.

x	4	6	8	10	12
y	2	4.5	7	9.5	12

   c.

x	1	2	3	4	5
y	200	100	50	25	12.5

29 **a.** $3(x + 5)$ **b.** $5x(x + 3)$

c. $x^2(x - 1)$ **d.** $(x + 3)(x - 3)$

e. $(x + 3)^2$ **f.** $(x - 5)(x + 2)$

30 **a.** There are 12 blue marbles in the bag.

b. $P(red)$ and $P(red)$ or $P(blue)$ and $P(blue) = \frac{1}{4} \cdot \frac{1}{4} + \frac{3}{4} \cdot \frac{3}{4} = \frac{1}{16} + \frac{9}{16} = \frac{10}{16}$

c. You need to add 8 yellow marbles. Student explanations will vary. They may use a guess-and-check method. Two ways to think about the situation follow.

(1) There are 12 blue marbles in the bag. Since we want the probability of choosing either a red or a yellow marble to be $\frac{1}{2}$, we would want the probability of choosing a blue marble to be $\frac{1}{2}$ also. So, we need 24 marbles in the bag. So, add 8 marbles to the 16 already in the bag.

(2) Symbolically, focusing on the red and yellow marbles:

$P(red) + P(yellow) = \frac{4}{16 + y} + \frac{y}{16 + y} = \frac{1}{2}$

$\frac{4 + y}{16 + y} = \frac{1}{2}$

$8 + 2y = 16 + y$

$y = 8$

31 **a.** a^7 **b.** a^2

c. a^{10} **d.** $\frac{1}{a^2}$

e. $8a^6$ **f.** $a^6 - a^5$, or $a^5(a - 1)$

32 **a.** M has coordinates $(0, 5)$ and N has coordinates $(3, 5)$.

b. The slope of $\overline{MN}$ is 0 since $\frac{5 - 5}{3 - 0} = 0$, and the slope of $\overline{OB}$ is 0 since $\frac{0 - 0}{6 - 0} = 0$. Therefore, $\overline{MN} \parallel \overline{OB}$.

c. The length of $\overline{MN}$ is 3 units and the length of $\overline{OB}$ is 6 units, so the length of $\overline{MN}$ is half the length of $\overline{OB}$.

d. Part a becomes: $\left(0, \frac{a}{2}\right)$ and $\left(\frac{b}{2}, \frac{a}{2}\right)$.

Part b becomes: The slope of $\overline{MN}$ is 0 since $\frac{\frac{a}{2} - \frac{a}{2}}{\frac{b}{2} - 0} = 0$, and the slope

of $\overline{OB}$ is 0 since $\frac{0 - 0}{b - 0} = 0$. Therefore, $\overline{MN} \parallel \overline{OB}$.

Part c becomes: The length of $\overline{MN}$ is $\frac{b}{2}$ units and the length of $\overline{OB}$ is b units, so the length of $\overline{MN}$ is half the length of $\overline{OB}$.

33 **a.** $x = \frac{21}{8}$ **b.** $x = 2$

c. $x = 0$ or $x = -6$ **d.** $x = 3$ or $x = -4$

34 **a.** Quadratic; $y = x^2 + 2$

b. Linear; $y = 1.25x - 3$

c. Exponential; $y = 400(0.5^x)$

Teaching Resources

Assessment Masters 26–31.

UNIT ❶ *Reasoning and Proof* Name
Date

LESSON 2 QUIZ

Form A

1. Emma wants to build two fence lines that are parallel to each other. They will intersect a straight private drive as shown below.

a. Identify three pairs of angles that she could make congruent in order to ensure that the fences are parallel.

b. If Emma found that $m\angle 3 + m\angle 4 = 180°$, could she conclude that the two fences are parallel? Explain your reasoning.

2. In the diagram at the right, if $m\angle 1 = m\angle 3$, prove that $m\angle 2 = m\angle 3$.

26 UNIT 1 • *Reasoning and Proof* Assessment Master • *see after Lesson 2*

LESSON 3

Algebraic Reasoning and Proof

Algebraic calculations and reasoning can be used to solve many kinds of practical problems. But they can also be used to perform some amazing magic tricks with numbers. For example, do these numerical operations.

> **Pick an integer between 0 and 20.**
>
> **Add 5 to your number.**
>
> **Multiply the result by 6.**
>
> **Divide that result by 3.**
>
> **Subtract 9 from that result.**

If each class member reports the final number that results from those operations, your teacher will be able to tell the starting number of each student.

If you believe that your teacher performs this number magic by memorizing all the possible starting and ending number combinations, you can increase the range of starting numbers to 0–50 and then 0–100. Your teacher will still be able to find each start number.

Data in the table at the right show some combinations of starting and ending numbers.

Start Number	End Number
4	9
11	23
17	35
33	67
45	91

Algebraic Reasoning and Proof

Algebraic notation and symbolic manipulation are essential tools for representing and reasoning about quantitative relationships in every branch of mathematics and its applications. The most common tasks to which algebraic methods are applied involve inference from some known data and conditions to determine values of unknown quantities or to demonstrate that some numerical pattern observed in a few situations actually holds in a wider variety of cases.

Elementary algebraic reasoning generally requires one to:

- *Recognize* a quantitative pattern or relationship that holds for some or all values of the independent and dependent variables involved.
- *Represent* the observed pattern or relationship in symbolic form—usually as an equation, inequality, or function rule/formula.
- Start with some given or assumed relational information (again, usually an equation, inequality, or formula), and *derive* a sequence of conclusions that lead to the conjectured pattern or relationship.

  The if-then steps in these chains of reasoning generally involve *replacing an expression* by one which is equivalent to it or *transforming an equation or inequality* by suitable operations on both sides.

This lesson highlights these features of algebraic reasoning through problems in two investigations. The first focuses on situations in which one wants to show that a numerical pattern observed to be true in several specific cases actually holds for all cases. The second focuses on situations in which one wants to establish a general relationship between two or more variables by proving that an equation or inequality holds for all x, y, z, ...

Developing Algebraic Reasoning Skills It is quite likely that students will explain and record their reasoning in a variety of ways. Using Problem 4 of Investigation 1 as an example, conventional mathematical writing of an algebraic argument might be

$$(n + 1)^2 - n^2 = (n^2 + 2n + 1) - n^2$$
$$= 2n + 1.$$

This argument does not make the logic of the argument particularly visible. While teaching this lesson, periodically have different students or groups display their work and talk about what they mean to say by the way they have recorded things.

The key point in many arguments is the fact that a chain of expressions connected by equals signs can be proven to be equivalent, so the first and the last must be equivalent.

The logic might be a bit clearer (without quantifiers) if the proof on the previous page were written like this:

$$(n + 1)^2 - n^2 = (n^2 + 2n + 1) - n^2 \text{ and}$$
$$(n^2 + 2n + 1) - n^2 = 2n + 1.$$
$$\text{So, } (n + 1)^2 - n^2 = 2n + 1.$$

You might want to abstract the pattern of inference to show the transitivity of equality that is invoked:

$$A = B$$
$$B = C$$
$$\text{So, } A = C.$$

Another issue that you will want to discuss with the class is how much detail should be offered in such a proof and where one should provide justifications for claims that expressions are equivalent. Despite common conceptions about the nature of mathematical proof, the standard of detail in proofs is relative—it depends on who is offering and who is to be hearing/reading the argument. In the proof given above, for instance, we have expanded the square binomial $(n + 1)^2$ in a single step (assuming that this is something that students have seen before, in both Courses 1 and 2, or could work out for themselves if they did not remember). We have also assumed that students could do the combining of like terms involved in the next step without elaborate detail using associative and commutative properties, as one might do if forced to provide all the details.

As for providing reasons that justify intermediate claims in an algebraic proof, it is possible to offer them alongside the various steps—much the way conventional two-column proofs are used in geometry. There are many other ways to record and present algebraic proofs. One might combine explanations/justifications and claims in a mixture of words and symbols like this:

(1) Consecutive integers can be represented by n and $n + 1$, so the difference of consecutive squares can be represented by $(n + 1)^2 - n^2$.

(2) Repeated application of the distributive property shows that the expression $(n + 1)^2$ is equivalent to $n^2 + 2n + 1$, so $(n + 1)^2 - n^2 = (n^2 + 2n + 1) - n^2$.

(3) Combining like terms in $(n^2 + 2n + 1) - n^2$ shows that this expression is equivalent to the simpler expression $2n + 1$, so $(n + 1)^2 - n^2 = 2n + 1$ for all n.

(4) Odd numbers are those that can be expressed in the form $2n + 1$, so the pattern is proven to hold for any n.

This sort of modified paragraph proof chunks the argument into pieces that seem to need justification, and it gives explanation/justification that the purely algebraic presentation omits. Since there is no widely agreed upon convention about how to present algebraic proofs, you will have to establish class norms (probably quite flexible at first) that satisfy you and your students.

It seems unlikely that students will become very proficient in creating algebraic proofs on their own in one short lesson. Thus, the investigations of the lesson begin with scaffolds for constructing algebraic arguments and, in some cases, sample arguments. The problems request that students complete and analyze the reasoning that seems to be involved in the arguments. Only later are students asked to formulate proofs independently. *There exists a real risk of expecting too much in this short introductory lesson on algebraic proof. We do not expect mastery of general algebraic proof strategies at this point.*

Lesson Objectives

- Use algebraic notation—letters, expressions, equations, and inequalities—to represent general patterns and relationships among variables
- Use algebraic transformations of expressions, equations, and inequalities to establish general propositions about quantitative relationships

Lesson Launch

One important use of algebraic reasoning is to explain why observed number patterns occur as they do. The introduction to this lesson asks students to think about one such situation—a number trick designed to amaze and amuse folks who do not know how the underlying structure of the procedure really makes it all quite clear. The aim of this launch is to pique student interest in the kinds of mathematical powers they can gain through learning more about algebraic reasoning.

You might choose to start the class by asking students to follow the directions in the box on page 52. Then ask students to tell you their final results, from which you can quickly tell them what their starting number must have been (by subtracting one from what they tell you and dividing that even number by two). If students suspect that you have simply memorized all possible (*start number, end number*) combinations, let them choose start numbers from a wider range.

After showing your prowess with this "mathematical mind-reading," you might ask if any students think that they could play the role of the person who figures out start numbers from reported ending numbers. If no one can, ask the class to study a list of sample (*start number, end number*) pairs like that given in the text.

When students seem to have figured out *how* the trick works, you can ask them if they can see *why* it works. This might lead to consideration of the Think About This Situation questions that follow in the student text.

We do not really expect many, if any, students to be able to formulate the kind of argument asked for in Part b of the Think About This Situation. In fact, a partially completed algebraic analysis of the trick is the first problem in the subsequent investigation. If students do solve this problem readily at the time of the TATS discussion, you can indicate that similar reasoning is used throughout algebra to verify such general patterns and relationships. If students are unable to resolve the puzzle, you can indicate that the investigations of the lesson will provide some ideas for work on this and similar problems.

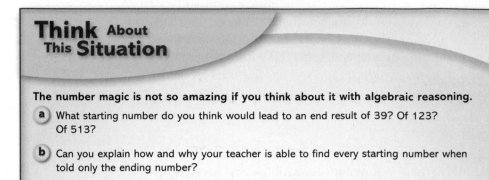

Think About This Situation

The number magic is not so amazing if you think about it with algebraic reasoning.

a What starting number do you think would lead to an end result of 39? Of 123? Of 513?

b Can you explain how and why your teacher is able to find every starting number when told only the ending number?

In this lesson, you will explore ways to use algebraic reasoning to discover and prove number patterns and relationships like the one used in the number trick. Then you will see how the same reasoning methods can be used to prove other important mathematical principles.

Investigation 1 — Reasoning with Algebraic Expressions

In earlier algebra units of *Core-Plus Mathematics*, you developed a toolkit of techniques for writing algebraic expressions in useful equivalent forms. As you work on the problems in this investigation, look for answers to this question:

> *How can strategies for manipulating algebraic expressions into equivalent forms be used to explain interesting number patterns?*

Algebra and Number Magic Algebraic reasoning skills can be used to create and explain many different number tricks.

1 There is a simple way to discover start numbers in the Think About This Situation number trick: *Subtract one from the end number and divide that result by two.* Explaining why that decoding strategy works and proving that it will *always* work requires some algebraic reasoning.

a. Use the letter n to represent the start number and build an algebraic expression that shows the steps for calculating the result that will be reported to the teacher.

   i. Adding 5 to your number is expressed by … .

   ii. Multiplying that result by 6 is expressed by … .

   iii. Dividing that result by 3 is expressed by … .

   iv. Subtracting 9 from that result is expressed by … .

b. Use what you know about algebra to write the final expression from Part a in simplest form. What relationship between starting and ending numbers is shown by the result?

Think About This Situation

a) The requested (*start number*, *end number*) pairs would be (19, 39), (61, 123), and (256, 513). To find the start number, subtract one from the end number and divide by two.

b) The trick works because for any starting number n, the ending number is calculated by the expression $\dfrac{6(n+5)}{3} - 9$ which is equivalent to $2n + 1$.

Investigation 1 — Reasoning with Algebraic Expressions

This investigation picks up from the lesson launch problem by examining the logic behind the number magic trick and asking students to analyze and develop some other similar ideas through algebraic reasoning. The first problem provides scaffolding to help students discover why the original magic trick works. The second problem describes another similar trick and asks students to discover the pattern involved, to represent it algebraically, and to show by algebraic manipulation why the trick works as it does. The third problem invites students to construct their own similar trick.

The second section of this investigation focuses on more standard mathematical sequences. Again, students are asked to recognize interesting patterns in those sequences, to represent the patterns in algebraic notation, and to use algebraic manipulation to show why the patterns unfold as they do. For one of the problems, students are asked to analyze a visual "proof without words" as an alternative to the more conventional algebraic reasoning.

The third section of the investigation shows how algebraic reasoning can be used to derive important properties of functions—in this case, an extension of previous work with the base 10 logarithm function. In this situation, as in the other examples of number tricks and number sequence patterns, the core argument involves a series of equivalent expressions.

> **COLLABORATION SKILL**
> Take turns proposing a way to approach a problem.

Launch

INSTRUCTIONAL NOTE If students have been unable to provide a convincing proof of the number trick in the lesson launch, suggest that they use the guiding questions in Problem 1 to work out a general argument.

There are several different ways to represent the directions in the number trick. The most conventional might be $\dfrac{6(n+5)}{3} - 9$. However, students might write $(n + 5) \times 6 \div 3 - 9$. You might want to have students work on Part a and then share their results immediately as a whole class to make sure that order of operation conventions are reviewed and clarified.

> **NOTE** Solutions to Problem 1 are on page T54.

c. How can the relationship between starting and ending numbers be used to find starting numbers when only ending numbers are known?

d. Suppose that the third step of the number trick, "Divide that result by 3," is replaced by "Divide that result by 2." How would that change in the procedure affect the decoding strategy?

2 Consider this different number trick.

> **Pick a number.**
>
> **Double it.**
>
> **Add 3 to the result.**
>
> **Multiply that result by 5.**
>
> **Subtract 7 from that result.**

a. Explore the way that this procedure transforms start numbers into final results. Find a decoding strategy that could be used to find the start number when only the final result is known.

b. Use algebraic reasoning to explain why your decoding strategy will always work.

3 Now that you have analyzed some number tricks with algebraic reasoning, you can adapt those arguments to design your own trick.

a. Create a similar number trick. Test it with other students to see if it works as intended.

b. Develop an algebraic argument to prove the trick that you created will work in every case.

Explaining Number Patterns Number patterns have fascinated amateur and professional mathematicians for thousands of years. It is easy to find interesting patterns, but usually more challenging to explain why the patterns work.

4 Consider the sequence of square numbers that begins 0, 1, 4, 9, 16, ...

a. Complete the following table to show how that sequence continues.

n	0	1	2	3	4	5	6	7	8	...	n
S_n	0	1	4	9	16					...	

b. Calculate the differences between consecutive terms in the sequence of square numbers (for example, $S_4 - S_3 = 16 - 9 = 7$). Then describe the pattern that develops in the sequence of differences.

1 **a. INSTRUCTIONAL NOTE** To highlight the importance of parentheses to keep order of operations as desired, in part ii, ask students whether $6 \times n + 5$ or $n + 5 \times 6$ are correct. To highlight the role of the fraction bar as a grouping symbol, it is probably important to have a class discussion about whether the two different forms offered in solution steps (iii) and (iv) are equivalent. It may be helpful to evaluate each expression for some specific values of n and point out how each expression produces the same result because each indicates the same sequence of calculations.

    i. $n + 5$ or $5 + n$

    ii. $6(n + 5)$ or $(n + 5)6$ or some equivalent form

    iii. $\dfrac{6(n + 5)}{3}$ or $6(n + 5) \div 3$ or some equivalent form

    iv. $\dfrac{6(n + 5)}{3} - 9$ or $6(n + 5) \div 3 - 9$ or some equivalent form

b. All correct expressions reduce to the simplest form of $2n + 1$. The simplified expression shows that every ending number is one more than twice the starting number.

c. To recover the start number, you need only subtract one from the end number and divide that intermediate result by 2 (easy to do in one's head).

d. If the third step is "divide by 2," the expression for the rule would become $\dfrac{6(n + 5)}{2} - 9$, which simplifies to $3n + 6$, and the decoding procedure would be "subtract 6 and divide by 3" (not so easy to do in one's head).

2 **a.** This procedure can be represented by $5(2n + 3) - 7$, which is equivalent to $10n + 8$. So, the decoding rule will be to subtract 8 from the end number and divide that intermediate result by 10 (always easy to do in decimal numeration).

b. To decode the final number and obtain the start number, you need to solve $10n + 8$ for n. So, take the final number, subtract 8, and then divide by 10. This gives the start number.

3 **a–b.** Number tricks and arguments will vary.

INSTRUCTIONAL NOTE The sequence of differences between successive square integers in Problem 4 is a fairly accessible and appealing pattern: 1, 3, 5, 7, 9, 11, 13. This problem gives students an opportunity to discover a generalization and to represent the result that they want to prove with only a little help in getting started on that proof.

> **INSTRUCTIONAL NOTE**
> It is not essential that students do Problem 3 before a class summary discussion takes place on the first two problems. In fact, you might want to have this problem be part of a lesson project due a few days later.

4 **a.** The table shows how sequences can be defined as functions with domain the whole numbers (or natural numbers if one prefers).

n	...	5	6	7	8	...	n
S_n	...	25	36	49	64	...	n^2

Thus, the whole numbers n provide an indexing scheme that shows where any particular term occurs in the sequence.

b. The differences between successive square integers form the sequence of positive odd numbers. (Students are not expected to represent this by saying something like, "The nth difference of squares is given by $2n + 1$." They will discover this in the proof in Part c.)

c. If n and $n + 1$ represent consecutive whole numbers, the difference between the squares of those numbers can be given by $S_{n+1} - S_n = (n + 1)^2 - n^2$. Use your ability to simplify algebraic expressions to prove that the pattern of differences you described in Part b is certain to continue as the sequence of square numbers is extended.

d. How would you describe the pattern of differences between successive square numbers as a proposition in the form *If ... , then ... ?*

5 The pattern that you analyzed in Problem 4 can also be justified with a visual proof.

a. The diagrams shown here have shaded and unshaded regions. Express the area of each unshaded region as a difference of two square numbers.

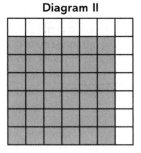

Diagram I   **Diagram II**

b. Explain how you could use the next diagram to justify the formula for the difference of any two consecutive square numbers that you found in work on Problem 4.

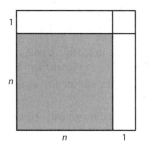

6 Consider the sequence of powers of two that begins 1, 2, 4, 8, 16, ...

a. Complete the following table to show how that sequence continues.

n	0	1	2	3	4	5	6	7	8	...	n
P_n	1	2	4	8	16					...	

b. Calculate the differences between consecutive terms in the sequence P_n. Describe the pattern that develops.

c. What algebraic expression shows how to calculate $P_{n+1} - P_n$?

c. $S_{n+1} - S_n = (n + 1)^2 - n^2$
$$= (n^2 + 2n + 1) - n^2$$
$$= 2n + 1$$

d. The given pattern can be described in *If ... , then ...* form using a variety of wordings or algebraic expressions, with various levels of mathematical sophistication. Some responses might be:

If you calculate differences between successive terms in the sequence of square numbers, then the result will be the sequence of odd numbers.

If one square number is subtracted from the next, then the result will be an odd number.

If you calculate $(n + 1)^2 - n^2$ for any whole number n, then the result will always be the odd number $2n + 1$.

5 **a.** **i.** $5^2 - 4^2 = 9$

ii. $7^2 - 6^2 = 13$

In each case, the difference is twice the smaller number (4 or 6) plus 1, or $2n + 1$.

b. The picture shows that $(n + 1)^2 - n^2 = 2n + 1$ because the area of the shaded region is n^2, the area of the large square is $(n + 1)^2$, and the area of the difference is the area of two $1 \times n$ rectangles plus a 1×1 square, $2n + 1$.

6 **a.** The sequence of powers of 2 as a function:

n	...	5	6	7	8	...	n
P_n	...	32	64	128	256	...	2^n

ASSIGNMENT NOTE Be sure students have completed Review Task 32 prior to doing Problem 6.

b. The difference of two consecutive terms in the sequence of powers of 2 equals the smaller term in the difference.

c. $P_{n+1} - P_n = 2^{n+1} - 2^n$

d. Use the result from Part c, what you know about writing exponential expressions in equivalent forms, and other algebraic manipulations to prove that the pattern observed in Part b is certain to continue as the sequence is extended.

e. How would you describe the pattern of differences between successive powers of 2 as a proposition in the form *If … , then … ?*

Proving Properties of Numbers and Functions In the Course 2 unit, *Nonlinear Functions and Equations*, you learned how to use *logarithms* to describe the intensity of sound and earthquakes and the pH of liquids. Historically, however, logarithms were first used as an aid to scientific calculation involving large numbers. That application of logarithms depends on a very useful property of the function $y = \log x$.

 Recall that $y = \log x$ means $10^y = x$. For example, $3 = \log 1{,}000$ because $10^3 = 1{,}000$. Use reasoning about powers of 10 or the **log** function on your calculator to complete the following table that compares $\log a$, $\log b$, and $\log ab$ for a sample of positive numbers a and b.

a	b	ab	log a	log b	log ab
100	1,000				
100	0.001				
0.1	0.001				
75	100				
75	0.01				
75	120				
50	20				

What pattern do you see that relates $\log a$, $\log b$, and $\log ab$? Describe the pattern in words and algebraically with symbols.

8 Rows in the table of Problem 7 illustrate a property of logarithms that connects multiplication and addition in a very useful way: For any a and $b > 0$, $\log ab = \log a + \log b$. Use what you know about logarithms and exponents to justify each step in the following algebraic proof of that property.

(1) Since $a > 0$ and $b > 0$, there are numbers x and y so that $x = \log a$ and $y = \log b$.
(2) So, $a = 10^x$ and $b = 10^y$.
(3) $\log ab = \log (10^x 10^y)$
(4) $\quad\quad\quad = \log 10^{x+y}$
(5) $\quad\quad\quad = x + y$
(6) $\quad\quad\quad = \log a + \log b$
(7) Therefore, $\log ab = \log a + \log b$.

This property of the logarithm function enabled mathematicians and scientists to use a table giving the logarithms of many numbers to convert any multiplication problem into an easier addition problem. This strategy was particularly useful for calculations involving very large numbers, such as those that occur in sciences, because it is much simpler to add logarithms of two large numbers than to find the product of the numbers.

d. $P_{n+1} - P_n = 2^{n+1} \quad 2^n$
$$= 2^n(2) - 2^n(1)$$
$$= 2^n(2-1)$$
$$= 2^n$$

The key justifications involve use of the exponent property $x^{a+b} = x^a x^b$ and the distributive property to factor out the common factor of 2^n.

e. Once again, the pattern can be described in a variety of *If ... , then ...* statement forms. Here are a couple:

If you calculate the differences of successive terms in the sequence of powers of 2, then those differences will themselves be a sequence of powers of 2.

If n is any whole number, then $2^{n+1} - 2^n = 2^n$.

INSTRUCTIONAL NOTE The next set of questions explore an important property of the logarithm function that students have met for the first time in Course 2 Unit 5. This is not material that the students will have used on a regular basis, and it is notoriously challenging. You might want to read through the introduction and the stem of Problem 7 and have the class fill in the first line or two of the table that is designed to produce examples of the general relationship $\log ab = \log a + \log b$ before that pattern is articulated and proven in Problem 8. Encourage students to do as much by reasoning with the definition of $\log x$ and to use their calculators only when stumped or to check their reasoning.

7 The completed table should look similar to the one below (depending on the number of decimal places that students track).

a	b	ab	log a	log b	log ab
100	1,000	100,000	2	3	5
100	0.001	0.1	2	−3	−1
0.1	0.001	0.0001	−1	−3	−4
75	100	7,500	1.875	2	3.875
75	0.01	0.75	1.875	−2	−0.125
75	120	9,000	1.875	2.079	3.954
50	20	1,000	1.699	1.301	3

The pattern is that the logarithm of the product of two numbers is the same as the sum of the logarithms of the two factors. Symbolically, $\log ab = \log a + \log b$.

8 (1) Previous study of logarithms showed that every positive number has a logarithm because the range of 10^x is all positive numbers

(2) Definition of logarithms applied to results in Step 1

(3) Substitution of results from Step 2

(4) Exponent of a product is sum of exponents of factors

(5) Definition of logarithms

(6) Substitution from Step 1

(7) Steps 3–6 form a chain of equivalent expressions or more formally, the Transitive Property of Equality.

9. The speed of light travels at about 186,000 miles per second, and there are 31,536,000 seconds in one year. To find the length in miles of a *light year*, you need to multiply $186,000 \times 31,536,000$.

a. To calculate, apply the standard multiplication algorithm.

$$31,536,000$$
$$\times\ 186,000$$

b. Use the facts $\log 186,000 \approx 5.26951$ and $\log 31,536,000 \approx 7.49881$ to find $\log (186,000 \times 31,536,000)$. Then use the definition $y = \log x$ when $10^y = x$ to find $186,000 \times 31,536,000$.

c. Which procedure for finding the product of large numbers involves the simplest arithmetic?

Summarize the Mathematics

In this investigation, you explored ways that algebraic reasoning explains interesting number patterns.

a What were the key steps in explaining the number tricks discovered in Problems 1 and 2?

b What overall strategy and algebraic properties were used to prove the generality of number patterns discovered in Problems 4 and 6?

c What overall strategy and algebraic properties were used to prove that $\log ab = \log a + \log b$ for all positive values of a and b?

Be prepared to explain your ideas to the class.

✓ Check Your Understanding

Use your understanding of equivalent expressions and algebraic reasoning to complete these tasks.

a. Prove that, whatever the starting number, the following calculations always lead to a result that is one greater than the starting number.

> **Think of a number.**
> **Double that number and add 7.**
> **Multiply that result by 5 and subtract 25.**
> **Divide that result by 10.**

9 **a.** The standard algorithm requires at least 15 partial products and a lot of bookkeeping to be sure that those results are placed correctly. The product is 5,865,696,000,000 or nearly 6 trillion miles in a light year.

b. log (186,000 × 31,536,000) ≈ 5.26951 + 7.49881 = 12.76832. This implies that $186{,}000 \times 31{,}536{,}000 \approx 10^{12.76832} \approx 5{,}865{,}702{,}062{,}000$.

c. When logarithms are readily available, it is certainly much easier to find the sum 5.26951 + 7.49881 = 12.76832 than the product. Of course, to get from log ab back to ab requires reading a table of logarithms in reverse order, using a table of anti-logs, or using technology to compute $10^{12.76832}$.

Summary

The answer for Part a of the Summarize the Mathematics highlights the key steps in explaining number tricks. This might not be what students have seen as their work on the problem, especially since we have twice offered scaffolding on this process. So, you may need to discuss the key steps by referring to Problems 1 and 2. Ask students to explain why they know that their transformations lead to equivalent expressions.

Summarize
the Mathematics

a The steps in explaining the number trick are: expressing a sequence of operations on a number in algebraic notation, rewriting that symbolic representation in simpler equivalent form, and then, solving that algebraic expression for the variable which is the starting number.

b In the proof that successive squares differ by successive odd numbers, the key principles were rules for expanding and simplifying quadratic expressions. Those depend on the distributive property in particular and the general rules for rearrangement of terms in an expression (which students may or may not recall to use commutative and associative properties).

In the proof that successive powers of 2 differ by a power of 2, the key principle was the product of powers exponent law. The distributive property was also used at a crucial step in the proof.

In both cases, the approach was to express a difference in one algebraic form and then show that this difference could be written in a sequence of simpler or more informative equivalent forms.

c To prove this basic property of logarithms, one had to use the definition of logarithm to express a and b in terms of exponents and then use a property of exponents to write an equivalent expression. Finally, use the definition of logarithm a second time to obtain the desired result.

HISTORICAL NOTE One of the early uses of logarithms was to aid in astronomical calculations. Large numbers could be written in scientific notation. Tables of logarithms were constructed for the numbers between 1 and 10, and the rules of logarithms were then used to accomplish multiplication. Today, this use of logarithms is not particularly important, but it does highlight a fundamental property of the logarithm function that turns out to have many continuing uses. This idea will come up again in Course 3 Unit 8, and in Course 4 Unit 5.

ROUND OFF ERROR Using the approximate values in the text, the answer in Part b is an approximate answer. Further, round-off error is introduced when calculating $10^{12.76832}$. This should be discussed.

Teaching Resources

Transparency Master 34.

UNIT ❶ *Reasoning and Proof*

Summarize
the Mathematics

In this investigation, you explored ways that algebraic reasoning explains interesting number patterns.
❶ What were the key steps in explaining the number tricks discovered in Problems 1 and 2?
❷ What overall strategy and algebraic properties were used to prove the generality of number patterns discovered in Problems 4 and 6?
❸ What overall strategy and algebraic properties were used to prove that log ab = log a + log b for all positive values of a and b?
Be prepared to explain your ideas to the class.

34   UNIT 1 • Reasoning and Proof   Transparency Master • *use with page 57*

COLLABORATION PROMPT I proposed a way to solve Problems ___ and ___.

NOTE The solution to CYU Part a is on page T58.

b. Consider the sequence $S_n = (n - 1)^2 + 1$.

  i. Write the first seven terms of this sequence.

  ii. Calculate the differences of consecutive terms in that sequence and describe the pattern that develops.

  iii. Use algebraic reasoning to prove that the pattern you described in part ii is certain to continue as the number sequence is extended.

Investigation 2 — Reasoning with Algebraic Equations

Many important mathematical facts are expressed in the form of equations or inequalities relating two or more variables. For example, the coordinates (x, y) of points on a line will always be related by an equation in the form $ax + by = c$. In this investigation, look for answers to this question:

> *How can strategies for reasoning with algebraic equations*
> *be used to explain and prove important principles*
> *in algebra, geometry, and trigonometry?*

① Mathematical work often requires solving linear equations, so it might be convenient to write a short calculator or computer program that will perform the necessary steps quickly when given only the equation coefficients and constants.

  a. What formula shows how to use the values of a, b, and c to find the solution for any linear equation in the form $ax + b = c$ with $a \neq 0$? Show the algebraic reasoning used to derive the formula. Check your work by asking a computer algebra system (CAS) to **solve(a*x+b=c,x)** and reconcile any apparent differences in results.

  b. What formula shows how to use the values of a, b, c, and d to find the solution for any linear equation in the form $ax + b = cx + d$ with $a \neq c$? Show the algebraic reasoning used to derive the formula. Check your work by asking a CAS to **solve(a*x+b=c*x+d,x)** and reconcile any apparent differences in results.

  c. What statements would express the formulas of Parts a and b in if-then form?

② When a problem requires analysis of a linear equation in two variables, it often helps to draw a graph of the equation. Information about x- and y-intercepts and slope can be used to make a quick sketch. For example, the diagram at the right shows the slope and intercepts of the graph for solutions of the equation $3x + 6y = 12$.

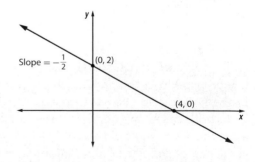

Slope $= -\frac{1}{2}$ (0, 2)   (4, 0)

a. $\dfrac{5(2n + 7) - 25}{10} = \dfrac{10n + 35 - 25}{10}$

$= \dfrac{10n + 10}{10}$

$= n + 1$

b. **i.** 1, 2, 5, 10, 17, 26, 37

    ii. The differences of consecutive terms in part i are 1, 3, 5, 7, 9, and 11. The differences of consecutive terms are consecutive odd positive numbers.

    iii. $S_{n+1} - S_n = (((n + 1) - 1)^2 + 1) - ((n - 1)^2 + 1)$

$= (n^2 + 1) - (n^2 - 2n + 2)$

$= 2n - 1$

Investigation ② Reasoning with Algebraic Equations

Proofs of the number puzzle, number pattern, and logarithm relationships that occur in Investigation 1 make frequent use of substitution to build chains of equivalent expressions. However, quite a few important algebraic and geometric relationships can only be verified by transforming given equations (or inequalities) into equivalent forms by operating on both sides in ways known to produce *equivalent equations or inequalities*. To highlight the value and logic of this sort of algebraic reasoning, this second investigation guides students to proofs of answers to questions like these:

> *What formula will provide the solution to any linear equation in the form $ax + b = c$? In the form $ax + b = cx + d$?*

> *What formulas will provide the slope and intercepts for any line with equation in the form $ax + by = c$?*

> *How can algebraic reasoning and the following diagram be used to provide another proof of the Pythagorean Theorem?*

Launch

You might launch the investigation by pointing out that the process of solving equations is really a kind of mathematical proof. For instance, to find the solution of the equation $3(4x + 7) = 5 - 2x$, we might typically proceed as follows:

$$\begin{aligned} \textit{If} \qquad 3(4x + 7) &= 5 - 2x \\ \textit{Then} \qquad 12x + 21 &= 5 - 2x \\ 14x &= -16 \\ x &= -\frac{8}{7} \end{aligned}$$

$$\textit{Check} \quad 3\left(4\left(-\frac{8}{7}\right) + 7\right) = 5 - 2\left(-\frac{8}{7}\right)$$

$$-\frac{96}{7} + \frac{147}{7} = \frac{35}{7} + \frac{16}{7},$$

> **INSTRUCTIONAL NOTE**
> For this investigation, different groups could be assigned different problems with whole-class presentation of the results.

Asking students to explain each if-then step in this solution should highlight the fact that what is going on is starting from an equation that is known or assumed to be true (in this case, we assume that there is an x that satisfies the equation) and deriving a sequence of other equations by performing identical operations on both sides of the equations.

DIFFERENTIATION Although students have been solving linear equations for many years prior to this more general look at the situation, a number of them might still need more practice on choosing the right moves and executing those moves accurately. To give this practice a fresh look, you might choose to use a special feature of most CAS software that makes it easy to "do the same thing to both sides of an equation."

With most CAS programs, this work can begin by entering an equation like $3x - 7 = 11$. Then type "$+7$" on the command line and press enter. The CAS will produce "$3*x = 18$". If you then type "$\div 3$" on the command line, the CAS will produce "$x = 6$".

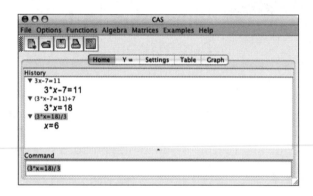

If a student happens to make a different move, the CAS will faithfully execute whatever he or she commanded. For example, if the first move had been "$\div 3$", the CAS would show "$\dfrac{3*x - 7}{3} = \dfrac{11}{3}$". It probably is not what the student wanted, but it is correct. Research has shown that use of the CAS in this way is very effective and efficient in helping students develop strategic sense and skill in by-hand solution of equations. They quickly learn which moves are most effective in solving equations.

1

a. For the case $ax + b = c$, derivation of a general solution formula might look like this:

   (1) If $ax + b = c$, then $ax = c - b$ (subtract b from both sides of the equation).

   (2) If $ax = c - b$, then $x = \dfrac{c - b}{a}$ (divide both sides of the equation by a).

b. For the case $ax + b = cx + d$, derivation of a general solution formula might look like this:

   (1) If $ax + b = cx + d$, then $ax = cx + (d - b)$ (subtract b from both sides of the equation).

   (2) If $ax = cx + (d - b)$, then $ax - cx = (d - b)$ (subtract cx from both sides of the equation).

   (3) If $ax - cx = (d - b)$, then $(a - c)x = (d - b)$ (distributive property).

   (4) If $(a - c)x = (d - b)$, then $x = \dfrac{d - b}{a - c}$ (divide both sides of the equation by $(a - c)$).

c. Part a: If $ax + b = c$ and $a \neq 0$, then $x = \dfrac{a - b}{c}$.

   Part b: If $ax + b = cx + d$ and $a \neq c$, then $x = \dfrac{d - b}{a - c}$.

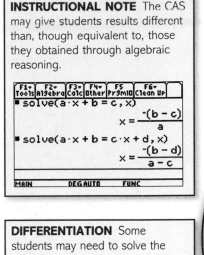

Unit 1

Find the *x*- and *y*-intercepts and the slopes for lines with equations given in Parts a–d. Use that information to *sketch* graphs of the equations, labeling the *x*- and *y*-intercepts with their coordinates.

a. $-6x + 4y = 12$ **b.** $6x + 3y = 15$

c. $5x - 3y = -5$ **d.** $4y + 5x = -8$

3 To find formulas that give intercepts and slope of any line with equation in the form $ax + by = c$, you might begin by reasoning as follows.

    (1) The *y*-intercept point has coordinates in the form $(0, y)$ for some value of *y*.

    (2) If $a(0) + by = c$, then $y = \dots$.

a. Complete the reasoning to find a formula for calculating coordinates of the *y*-intercept. Describe any constraints on *a* and *b*.

b. Use reasoning like that in Part a to find a formula for calculating coordinates of the *x*-intercept of any line with equation in the form $ax + by = c$. Describe any constraints on *a* and *b*.

c. Use reasoning about equations to find a formula for calculating the slope of any line with equation in the form $ax + by = c$ with $b \neq 0$.

d. Write CAS solve commands that could be used to check your work in Parts a, b, and c.

4 You probably recall the Pythagorean Theorem that relates lengths of the legs and the hypotenuse in any right triangle. It says, "If *a* and *b* are lengths of the legs and *c* the length of the hypotenuse of a right triangle, then $a^2 + b^2 = c^2$."

There are over 300 different proofs of the Pythagorean Theorem. In Course 1, you completed a proof of the Pythagorean Theorem that was based on a comparison of areas. The diagram at the right shows how to start on a proof that makes use of geometric and algebraic reasoning in important ways. It shows a large square divided into four triangles and a smaller quadrilateral inside that square.

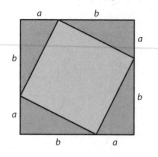

a. Use only the fact that the whole colored figure is a square and the division of its edges into lengths *a* and *b* to prove that the four triangles are congruent right triangles.

b. How can you use the fact that the outside figures are congruent right triangles to prove that the interior quadrilateral is a square?

c. Write two different algebraic expressions that show how to find the area of the large square.

    • In the first, use the fact that the sides of the large square are of length $(a + b)$.

    • In the second, label the edges of the inner square with length *c*. Use the fact that the large square is made up of four triangles, each with base *a* and height *b*, and an inner square with sides of length *c*.

d. Equate the two expressions from Part b and apply algebraic reasoning to that equation in order to show that $a^2 + b^2 = c^2$.

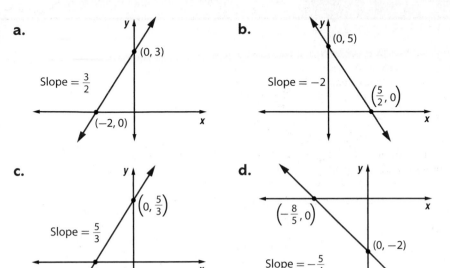

2 **a.** Slope $= \frac{3}{2}$, $(0, 3)$, $(-2, 0)$

b. Slope $= -2$, $(0, 5)$, $\left(\frac{5}{2}, 0\right)$

c. Slope $= \frac{5}{3}$, $\left(0, \frac{5}{3}\right)$, $(-1, 0)$

d. $\left(-\frac{8}{5}, 0\right)$, $(0, -2)$, Slope $= -\frac{5}{4}$

INSTRUCTIONAL NOTE
For Problem 2, it is more revealing to keep answers in fraction form and not to simplify them.

3 **a.** $y = \frac{c}{b}$, so the y-intercept of $ax + by = c$ is $\left(0, \frac{c}{b}\right)$, $b \neq 0$.

b. The x-intercept has coordinates $(x, 0)$, so $ax + b(0) = c$. Simplifying, $x = \frac{c}{a}$, so the x-intercept of $ax + by = c$ is $\left(\frac{c}{a}, 0\right)$, $a \neq 0$.

c. $y = \frac{c - ax}{b} = \frac{c}{b} - \frac{a}{b}x$, so the slope of $ax + by = c$ is $-\frac{a}{b}$.

d. `solve(a*0+b*y=c,y)`
`solve(a*x+b*0=c,x)`
`solve(a*x+b*y=c,y)`

INSTRUCTIONAL NOTE
While work on Problem 3 leads to formulas for intercepts and slope of any linear equation given in "standard form," do not expect students to memorize those formulas.

4 **a.** Since the figure is a square, its angles are all right angles. Each triangle has a 90° angle included between two sides, one of length a, and one of length b. So by the SAS congruence condition, all four triangles are congruent.

b. The two acute angles in each of the right triangles have angle sum 90°. The three angles formed where the interior quadrilateral meets the outer square have angle sum 180°, and two of those angles are congruent to the two acute angles of each right triangle. Thus, each angle of the small quadrilateral is 90°. This means the quadrilateral is a rectangle or a square. The four congruent right triangles have congruent hypotenuses of length c, and so the quadrilateral is a square.

c. • $(a + b)^2$

• $c^2 + 4\left(\frac{1}{2}ab\right)$, or $c^2 + 2ab$

d. $(a + b)^2 = c^2 + 2ab$
$a^2 + 2ab + b^2 = c^2 + 2ab$ (expand $(a + b)^2$)
$a^2 + b^2 = c^2$ (subtract $2ab$ from both sides)

Unit 1

5 The kind of algebraic reasoning used to prove the Pythagorean Theorem can be adapted to prove the very useful Law of Cosines, introduced in Course 2.

In any triangle ABC with sides of length a, b, and c opposite $\angle A$, $\angle B$, and $\angle C$, respectively,

$$c^2 = a^2 + b^2 - 2ab \cos C.$$

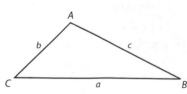

Analyze the following argument to identify and explain ways that algebraic principles (and a small amount of geometry and trigonometry) can be used to prove the special case pictured. Here $\angle C$ is an acute angle and $\overline{AD}$ is an altitude of the triangle with point D between points C and B.

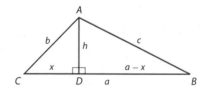

Step 1. In $\triangle ADC$: $\frac{x}{b} = \cos C$, so $x = b \cos C$.
Why are these relationships true?

Step 2. In $\triangle ABD$: $h^2 = c^2 - (a - x)^2$
$$= c^2 - (a^2 - 2ax + x^2)$$
$$= c^2 - a^2 + 2ax - x^2$$
Why are these equations true?

Step 3. In $\triangle ADC$: $h^2 = b^2 - x^2$
Why is this equation true?

Step 4. From Steps 2 and 3, we can conclude that
$$c^2 - a^2 + 2ax - x^2 = b^2 - x^2.$$
Why is this equation true?

Step 5. From the equation in Step 4, we can conclude that
$$c^2 = a^2 + b^2 - 2ax.$$
What rules of algebra justify this conclusion?

Step 6. Finally, combining Steps 1 and 5, we conclude that
$$c^2 = a^2 + b^2 - 2ab \cos C.$$
What property justifies this conclusion?

You can check that the same formula results in the cases where point D coincides with or is to the right of point B and that, as long as $\angle C$ is acute, point D cannot lie to the left of point C. A complete proof of the Law of Cosines requires considering cases when $\angle C$ is a right angle or an obtuse angle. See Reflections Task 24.

PROOF SUPPORT The Law of Cosines is a very important result in trigonometry and should not be omitted. To provide some scaffolding for students, you may choose to use the student masters developed for this task. The first master contains the problem as shown in the student text. The second master contains the reasons for the steps of the proof. Make copies of the page with the reasons. Then cut them out and place in envelopes for distribution and storage. Provide each student with a set of strips to tape to the page that lists the steps of the proof. Then students can compare their ordering of the reasons.

 Step 1. The definition of cosine $\left(\dfrac{\text{length of adjacent side}}{\text{length of hypotenuse}}\right)$ says that $\cos C = \dfrac{x}{b}$ and algebraic reasoning (multiplying both sides of the equation by b) gives the equivalent equation $x = b \cos C$.

Step 2. These equations are true by the Pythagorean Theorem, algebraic expansion of the square of a binomial, and the Distributive Property of Multiplication over Addition.

Step 3. This equation is true by the Pythagorean Theorem.

Step 4. Both sides of the equation are equal to h^2. So by substitution, they are equal to each other.

Step 5. The Addition and Subtraction Properties of Equality justify this conclusion.

Step 6. The Substitution Property of Equality justifies this conclusion.

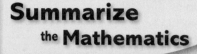

Summarize
the Mathematics

In this investigation, you explored ways that reasoning with equations can be used to prove important general principles in algebra, geometry, and trigonometry.

a What general properties of numbers, operations, and equations did you use to discover and prove a formula for solving equations in the form $ax + b = c$ with $a \neq 0$? In the form $ax + b = cx + d$ with $a \neq c$?

b What general properties of numbers, operations, and equations did you use to discover and prove formulas for slope and intercepts of graphs for linear equations in the form $ax + by = c$?

c What algebraic principles were used to justify steps in the proof of the Pythagorean Theorem?

d What is the main idea behind the proof of the Law of Cosines?

Be prepared to explain your ideas to the class.

✔ Check Your Understanding

Use your understanding of equations and algebraic reasoning to complete these tasks.

a. Consider linear equations that occur in the form $a(x - b) = c$.

   i. Solve the particular example $3(x - 7) = 12$.

   ii. Write a formula that will give solutions to any equation in the form $a(x - b) = c$ with $a \neq 0$, in terms of a, b, and c. Show the algebraic reasoning used to derive your formula. Check your work by using a computer algebra system to **solve(a*(x−b)=c,x)**.

b. Many problems in geometry require finding the length of one leg in a right triangle when given information about the lengths of the other leg and the hypotenuse.

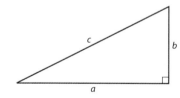

   i. If the hypotenuse of a right triangle is 20 inches long and one leg is 15 inches long, what is the length of the other leg? Show the reasoning that leads to your answer.

   ii. Starting with the algebraic statement of the Pythagorean Theorem $a^2 + b^2 = c^2$, use algebraic reasoning to derive a formula that shows how to calculate the length a when lengths b and c are known.

Summarize
the Mathematics

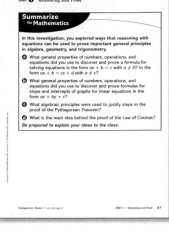

(a) Properties used included addition, subtraction, multiplication, and division of both sides of an equation by the same quantity, combining/rearranging terms in an expression, and often using the distributive property.

(b) Properties used included addition, subtraction, multiplication, and division of both sides of an equation by the same quantity. Definitions of x- and y-intercepts and the fact that slope of a line is given by the coefficient of x when a linear equation is written in the $y = mx + b$ form were also used.

(c) Properties used included expanding the square of a sum (using the distributive property), equating two expressions for the same area, and subtracting the same quantity from both sides of an equation.

(d) The main idea behind the proof of the Law of Cosines is the Pythagorean Theorem. It is used to generate two equivalent algebraic expressions. Then algebraic properties are used to derive an equation expressing the relationship between an angle and the sides of a triangle.

✔ Check Your Understanding

a. **i.** $3(x - 7) = 12$ or $3x - 21 = 12$
$x - 7 = 4$ $3x = 33$
$x = 11$ $x = 11$

ii. $a(x - b) = c$ or $ax - ab = c$
$x - b = \dfrac{c}{a}$ $ax = c + ab$

$x = \dfrac{c}{a} + b$ $x = \dfrac{c + ab}{a}$

Check with CAS.

b. **i.** The length of the other leg is $\sqrt{175}$ inches.
$15^2 + b^2 = 20^2$
$b^2 = 400 - 225$
$b = \sqrt{175}$ since $b > 0$.

ii. $a^2 + b^2 = c^2$
$a^2 = c^2 - b^2$
$a = \sqrt{c^2 - b^2}$ since $a > 0$.

> **INSTRUCTIONAL NOTE**
> In both parts i and ii, you may want to address the fact that in the context of a right triangle, the negative solution in each case is not relevant.

On Your Own

Applications

(1) Whenever three consecutive integers are added together, the sum is always equal to three times the middle number. For example, $7 + 8 + 9 = 3(8)$ and $-4 + -3 + -2 = 3(-3)$.

a. If n represents the smallest number in a sequence of three consecutive integers, what expressions represent:

    i. the other two numbers?

    ii. the sum of all three numbers?

b. Simplify the expression for the sum in Part a to prove that the pattern relating the sum and the middle number occurs whenever three consecutive integers are added.

c. What pattern will relate the sum of any five consecutive integers to one of the integer addends? Use algebraic reasoning to prove your idea.

(2) By definition, any odd number can be expressed in the form $2m + 1$ for some integer m. Any even number can be expressed in the form $2m$ for some integer m.

a. Express 5, 17, and 231 in the form $2m + 1$.

b. Express 6, 18, and 94 in the form $2m$.

c. Prove that the product of an odd number and an even number is always an even number. Begin by writing the odd number as $2m + 1$ and the even number as $2n$.

d. Prove that the product of any two odd numbers is always an odd number. Use different letters in representing the two numbers symbolically.

e. Why are different letters, m and n, used to represent integers in Parts c and d?

(3) The two-digit number 53 can be written in *expanded form* as $5(10) + 3$. In general, a two-digit number with tens digit a and ones digit b can be written as $a(10) + b$. Use this fact to prove the number patterns described below.

a. Pick any two-digit number and reverse the order of the digits. Then add the new number to the original number. The result will always be a multiple of 11.

b. Pick any two-digit number and reverse the order of the digits. Then find the difference between the new number and the original number. The result will always be a multiple of 9.

Applications

(1) **a.** **i.** The other numbers are represented by $n + 1$ and $n + 2$.

     ii. The sum is then $n + (n + 1) + (n + 2)$.

   b. The sum can be simplified to $3n + 3$ which can be rewritten as $3(n + 1)$ which, in words, is "three times the middle number."

   c. The sum of any five consecutive integers, beginning with n, will be $5n + 10$ which is equivalent to $5(n + 2)$ or 5 times the middle number in the sequence starting with n. This can be proven by reasoning as follows.

$$n + (n + 1) + (n + 2) + (n + 3) + (n + 4) = 5n + 10 = 5(n + 2)$$

(2) **a.** $5 = 2(2) + 1$
$17 = 2(8) + 1$
$231 = 2(115) + 1$

   b. $6 = 2(3)$
$18 = 2(9)$
$94 = 2(47)$

   c. $(2m + 1)(2n) = 4mn + 2n = 2(2mn + n)$, which is an even number. Therefore, the product of an odd and even number is always an even number.

   d. $(2m + 1)(2n + 1) = 4mn + 2m + 2n + 1 = 2(2mn + m + n) + 1$. This is an odd number since it is twice a number plus 1. Therefore, the product of any two odd numbers is always an odd number.

   e. In Part c, different letters are used to indicate *any* odd and even number, not just a consecutive pair represented by $2m$ and $2m + 1$. In Part d, $(2m + 1)(2m + 1)$ would represent an odd number squared, not the product of any two odd numbers.

(3) **a.** $(a(10) + b) + (b(10) + a) = (a + b)(10) + (a + b)$
$$= (a + b)(10 + 1)$$
$$= (a + b)(11)$$

   b. $(a(10) + b) - (b(10) + a) = (a - b)(10) + (b - a)$
$$= (a - b)(10) + (-1)(a - b)$$
$$= (a - b)(10 - 1)$$
$$= (a - b)(9)$$

(4) Consider the sequence 1, 3, 9, 27, 81, 243, 729, ... generated by powers of 3. Use reasoning similar to your work in Problem 6 of Investigation 1 to prove that the differences between successive terms of this sequence can be calculated using the expression $2(3^n)$.

(5) The beginnings of two number sequences are given here.

Sequence I   1, 4, 16, 64, 256, 1,024, 4,096, ...
Sequence II   1, 5, 25, 125, 625, 3,125, 15,625, ...

For each sequence:

a. Find an algebraic rule that shows how to calculate the nth term in the sequence.

b. Study the pattern of differences between successive terms and find a formula that gives the nth difference.

c. Prove that your formula is correct.

(6) If the logarithm of the product of two positive numbers is the sum of the logarithms of the individual numbers, you might expect that the logarithm of the quotient of the two numbers is the difference of their logarithms. Use reasoning about powers of 10 or the **log** function of your calculator to check the property $\log\left(\frac{a}{b}\right) = \log a - \log b$ for the sample of positive numbers a and b in this table.

a	b	$\frac{a}{b}$	$\log a$	$\log b$	$\log\left(\frac{a}{b}\right)$
1,000	10				
0.01	100.01				
0.001	0.1				
75	100				
75	0.01				
75	3				

(7) Adapt the reasoning in Problem 8 of Investigation 1 to prove that for any positive numbers a and b, $\log\left(\frac{a}{b}\right) = \log a - \log b$. (*Hint*: Recall that $\left(\frac{1}{10}\right)^y = 10^{-y}$.)

(8) Consider linear equations that occur in the form $a(x + b) = c$ with $a \neq 0$.

a. Solve the particular example $7(x + 3) = 49$.

b. Write a formula that will give solutions for any equation in the form $a(x + b) = c$ with $a \neq 0$, in terms of a, b, and c. Show the algebraic reasoning used to derive the formula.

4 $3^{n+1} - 3^n = 3^n(3) - 3^n(1)$
$$= 3^n(3 - 1)$$
$$= 2(3^n)$$

5 **a.** Rules are: (i) $f(n) = 4^n$ and (ii) $g(n) = 5^n$.

b. Differences are:

Sequence I	3	12	48	192	768	3,072
Sequence II	4	20	100	500	2,500	12,500

The nth difference for Sequence I is $3(4^n)$ and for Sequence II is $4(5^n)$.

c. Each term in Sequence I is a power of 4. The difference between the $(n + 1)$st term and the nth term is:
$$4^{n+1} - 4^n = 4^n(4 - 1)$$
$$= 3(4^n)$$

Each term in Sequence II is a power of 5. The difference between the $(n + 1)$st term and the nth term is:
$$5^{n+1} - 5^n = 5^n(5 - 1)$$
$$= 4(5^n)$$

6 The completed table will look like this:

a	b	$\dfrac{a}{b}$	$\log a$	$\log b$	$\log\left(\dfrac{a}{b}\right)$
1,000	10	100	3	1	2
0.01	100.01	0.0001	−2	2	−4
0.001	0.1	0.01	−3	−1	−2
75	100	0.75	1.875	2	−0.125
75	0.01	7,500	1.875	−2	3.875
75	3	25	1.875	0.477	1.398

7 **Proof:** (1) Since $a > 0$ and $b > 0$, there are numbers x and y so that $x = \log a$ and $y = \log b$.

(2) Therefore, $a = 10^x$
and $b = 10^y$. (definition of logarithm)

(3) $\log\left(\dfrac{a}{b}\right) = \log\left(\dfrac{10^x}{10^y}\right)$ (subtraction)

(4) $= \log 10^{x-y}$ (property of exponents $\dfrac{a^x}{a^y} = a^{x-y}$)

(5) $= x - y$ (definition of logarithm)

(6) $= \log a - \log b$ (substitution)

(7) Therefore, $\log\left(\dfrac{a}{b}\right) = \log a - \log b$.

8 **a.** $x = 4$

b. One form of the formula is $x = \dfrac{c}{a} - b$; another is $x = \dfrac{c - ab}{a}$.
The reasoning for the first form follows.

If $a(x + b) = c$,

then $x + b = \dfrac{c}{a}$, and (dividing both sides by a)

then $x = \dfrac{c}{a} - b$. (subtracting b from both sides)

(9) If a line has slope m and passes through the point (p, q), it is sometimes convenient to write the equation for that line in the form $(y - q) = m(x - p)$.

   a. Write an equation in this form for the line that has slope 2 and passes through the point $(4, 7)$.

     • Check that coordinates of the points $(4, 7)$ and $(5, 9)$ satisfy your equation.

     • Use the two points to check that the slope of the graph will be 2.

   b. Explain how you know that the point (p, q) is always on the graph of $(y - q) = m(x - p)$.

   c. Use algebraic reasoning to write the equation from Part a in $y = mx + b$ form.

   d. Show how any equation in the form $(y - q) = m(x - p)$ can be written in equivalent $y = mx + b$ form.

   e. Look back at your work in Part d. How is b related to p and q?

(10) You have seen in the problems of this lesson that algebraic reasoning usually involves writing symbolic expressions or equations in equivalent forms using rules for symbol manipulation. The most useful symbol manipulations are based on the list of algebraic properties of equality and operations shown in the following charts.

Algebraic Properties

Addition

For any numbers a, b, and c:

Commutative Property of Addition:	$a + b = b + a$
Associative Property of Addition:	$(a + b) + c = a + (b + c)$
Additive identity element (0):	$a + 0 = a$
Additive Inverse Property:	There is a number $-a$ such that $a + (-a) = 0$.

Multiplication

For any numbers a, b, and c:

Commutative Property of Multiplication:	$ab = ba$
Associative Property of Multiplication:	$(ab)c = a(bc)$
Multiplicative identity element (1):	$a1 = a$
Multiplicative Inverse Property:	For each $a \neq 0$, there is a number a^{-1} such that $a^{-1}a = 1$.

Distributive Property of Multiplication over Addition

For any numbers a, b, and c: $a(b + c) = ab + ac$

Properties of Equality

For any numbers a, b, and c:

Transitive Property of Equality:	If $a = b$ and $b = c$, then $a = c$.
Addition Property of Equality:	If $a = b$, then $a + c = b + c$.
Subtraction Property of Equality:	If $a = b$, then $a - c = b - c$.
Multiplication Property of Equality:	If $a = b$, then $ac = bc$.
Division Property of Equality:	If $a = b$, then $a \div c = b \div c$ (whenever $c \neq 0$).

9   **a.** Equation: $(y - 7) = 2(x - 4)$

     • Check: $(7 - 7) = 2(4 - 4); 0 = 0$

               $(9 - 7) = 2(5 - 4); 2 = 2(1)$

     • The slope is $\dfrac{9 - 7}{5 - 4} = 2$.

   b. The point (p, q) is on the graph because it satisfies the equation:
$(q - q) = 0 = m(p - p)$.

   c. If $(y - 7) = 2(x - 4)$,

     then $y - 7 = 2x - 8$, and   (distributive property)

     then $y = 2x - 1$.   (add 7 to both sides)

   d. If $(y - q) = m(x - p)$,

     then $y - q = mx - mp$,   (distributive property)

     then $y = mx - mp + q$, and   (add q to both sides)

     then $y = mx + (q - mp)$.   (commutative and associative
                                                 properties)

   e. $b = q - mp$

State the properties that justify steps in the following derivations of equivalent expressions. Some steps may involve more than one property. Arithmetic and substitution may also be used to justify steps.

a. For any x, $3x + 5x = (3 + 5)x$ (1)

$\qquad\qquad\qquad\quad = 8x$ (2)

b. For any x, $(3x + 5) + 7x = (5 + 3x) + 7x$ (1)

$\qquad\qquad\qquad\qquad = 5 + (3x + 7x)$ (2)

$\qquad\qquad\qquad\qquad = 5 + 10x$ (3)

c. If $7x + 5 = 5x + 14$, then $(7x + 5) + (-5) = (5x + 14) + (-5)$ (1)

$\qquad\qquad\qquad 7x + (5 + (-5)) = 5x + (14 + (-5))$ (2)

$\qquad\qquad\qquad\qquad\qquad 7x + 0 = 5x + 9$ (3)

$\qquad\qquad\qquad\qquad\qquad\quad 7x = 5x + 9$ (4)

$\qquad\qquad\qquad\quad -5x + 7x = -5x + (5x + 9)$ (5)

$\qquad\qquad\qquad\qquad\qquad\quad 2x = (-5x + 5x) + 9$ (6)

$\qquad\qquad\qquad\qquad\qquad\quad 2x = 0x + 9$ (7)

$\qquad\qquad\qquad\qquad\qquad\quad 2x = 9$ (8)

$\qquad\qquad\qquad\qquad \left(\tfrac{1}{2}\right)(2)x = \left(\tfrac{1}{2}\right)9$ (9)

$\qquad\qquad\qquad\qquad\qquad\quad 1x = 4.5$ (10)

$\qquad\qquad\qquad\qquad\qquad\qquad x = 4.5$ (11)

11 In your work on Task 10 Part c, you probably used a property of multiplication that seemed so obvious it did not need justification: For any n, $0n = 0$. While not stated as one of the basic number system properties, this result can be proven from the listed properties. Provide explanations for each step in the following proof.

$0 + 0 = 0$ (1)

$(0 + 0)n = 0n$ (2)

$0n + 0n = 0n$ (3)

$0n + 0n = 0n + 0$ (4)

$0n = 0$ (5)

12 In your previous coursework, you used the **Zero Product Property**:

$$\text{If } ab = 0, \text{ then } a = 0 \text{ or } b = 0.$$

a. Show how this property is used to solve $(x + 6)(2x - 8) = 0$.

b. Use properties listed in Tasks 10 and 11 to justify each step in the following proof of the Zero Product Property.

Suppose that $ab = 0$. If $a = 0$, the result is clearly true. Suppose $a \neq 0$.

(1) Then there is a number a^{-1} so that $a^{-1}a = 1$.

(2) $a^{-1}(ab) = a^{-1}0$

(3) $(a^{-1}a)b = 0$

(4) $1b = 0$

(5) $b = 0$

c. What is the logic of the argument given in Part b to prove the claim that "if $ab = 0$, then $a = 0$ or $b = 0$"?

10 **a.** (1) Distributive property

(2) Substitution using arithmetic

b. (1) Commutative Property of Addition

(2) Associative Property of Addition

(3) Distributive property and arithmetic

c. (1) Addition Property of Equality

(2) Associative Property of Addition

(3) Arithmetic

(4) Additive identity

(5) Addition Property of Equality

(6) Distributive property, arithmetic, and Associative Property of Addition

(7) Distributive property, arithmetic, and Additive Inverse Property

(8) Unstated property that 0 times any number is 0 (will be proven as a theorem in Task 11) and Additive Identity Property

(9) Multiplication Property of Equality

(10) Multiplicative Inverse Property and arithmetic

(11) Multiplicative Identity Property

11 (1) Additive identity

(2) Multiplication Property of Equality

(3) Distributive property

(4) Additive identity

(5) Subtraction Property of Equality

12 **a.** $x + 6 = 0$ or $2x - 8 = 0$

$x = -6$ $\qquad x = 4$

b. Suppose that $a \times b = 0$ and $a \neq 0$.

(1) Multiplicative Inverse Property

(2) Multiplication Property of Equality

(3) Associative Property of Multiplication and the property that any number times 0 is 0.

(4) Multiplicative Inverse Property

(5) Multiplicative Identity Property

c. The proof in Part b has a more subtle logic than in most of the other proofs that students will have encountered so far. The proposition claims that if a product of two numbers is 0, then at least one of the factors must be zero. The proof strategy is to consider the two possible cases: (1) both a and b are 0 and (2) at least one of a or b is nonzero. In the first case, the conclusion is satisfied, and in the second, it is shown that if one factor is nonzero, then the other factor must be zero. In both instances, the conclusion of the statement is proved, that is, $a = 0$ or $b = 0$.

INSTRUCTIONAL NOTE

The Transitive Property of Equality is introduced on page 64. You may wish to have students recognize its use in Task 10 Part b.

Teaching Resources

Student Masters 38–39.

INSTRUCTIONAL NOTE

The argument in Part c might be rather puzzling to students. So if you assign the problem, you will probably need to have some class discussion of the results.

Unit 1

13 An **isosceles trapezoid** is shown in the coordinate diagram below. It has a pair of nonparallel opposite sides the same length. Use ideas from geometry and trigonometry and algebraic reasoning to complete the following tasks.

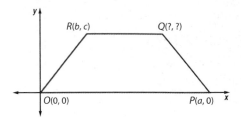

a. Draw and label a similar diagram on a coordinate grid. Determine the coordinates of point Q.

b. Prove that the *base angles*, $\angle O$ and $\angle P$, have the same measure.

c. Draw diagonals $\overline{OQ}$ and $\overline{PR}$. How do the diagonals appear to be related? Prove your conjecture.

d. Find the coordinates of the midpoint M of $\overline{OR}$ and the midpoint N of $\overline{PQ}$. Draw $\overline{MN}$. How does $\overline{MN}$ appear to be related to $\overline{OP}$? Prove your conjecture.

e. Write three general statements that summarize what you have proven about isosceles trapezoids.

14 Because proportional reasoning is required to solve many practical, scientific, and mathematical problems, it is important to be able to solve proportions in specific and general cases.

a. Solve these proportions for x.

   i. $\dfrac{3}{x} = \dfrac{9}{15}$ **ii.** $\dfrac{x}{12} = \dfrac{10}{30}$ **iii.** $\dfrac{4}{5} = \dfrac{10}{x}$

b. What algebraic reasoning justifies the fact that for any a, b, and c ($a \neq 0$, $b \neq 0$, and $x \neq 0$) if $\dfrac{a}{b} = \dfrac{c}{x}$, then $x = \dfrac{bc}{a}$?

Connections

15 The kind of algebraic reasoning you used to explain and create number tricks can also be used to explain some useful procedures for rewriting algebraic expressions in convenient equivalent forms. For example, you might impress friends or parents with your mental arithmetic skills by backing up the following claim.

> "Pick two numbers that are equidistant from 100, like 112 and 88, and I'll find their product almost immediately without using a calculator."

(13) **a.** Two possible methods follow. See the diagram in Part b.

(1) The y-coordinate for Q is c since $\overline{RQ} \parallel \overline{OP}$ and the slope of $\overline{OP}$ is 0. To find the x-coordinate for $Q(x, c)$, note that $OR = PQ$. $\sqrt{b^2 + c^2} = \sqrt{(a - x)^2 + c^2}$ (distance formula). So, $b^2 + c^2 = (a - x)^2 + c^2$, or $b^2 = (a - x)^2$. Since $a > x$, $b = a - x$. So, $x = a - b$.

(2) Some students may reason more visually with congruent triangles as follows. Vertical and horizontal lines are perpendicular in coordinate systems. Thus, $\triangle OSR$ and $\triangle PTQ$ are right triangles. (See the diagram below.) Either the Pythagorean Theorem (distance formula) and the SSS congruence condition, or if students recall it, the Hypotenuse-Leg congruence condition for right triangles can be used to get $TP = b$. From this, the x-coordinate for Q is $a - b$.

Students who use the second method above will likely use congruent triangles to answer Part b by CPCTC.

b. (1) Using ideas from trigonometry, students might reason as follows:

From Part a, we know that $TP = b$. So, $\tan O = \frac{c}{b}$ and $\tan P = \frac{c}{b}$. Since $\tan O = \tan P$ and both angles are acute, $m\angle O = m\angle P$.

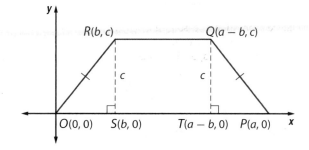

(2) Using ideas from geometry, students might reason as outlined in Part a above to determine that $\triangle OSR \cong \triangle PTQ$. So, $m\angle O = m\angle P$ since they are corresponding angles in congruent triangles.

c. Conjecture: The diagonals appear to be equal in length.

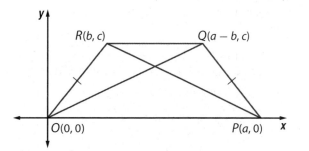

Proof: $OQ = \sqrt{(a - b - 0)^2 + (c - 0)^2} = \sqrt{a^2 - 2ab + b^2 + c^2}$

$PR = \sqrt{(a - b)^2 + (0 - c)^2} = \sqrt{a^2 - 2ab + b^2 + c^2}$

Since $OQ = PR$, the diagonals have the same length.

d. Midpoint M of $\overline{OR}$: $\left(\frac{b}{2}, \frac{c}{2}\right)$

Midpoint N of $\overline{PQ}$: $\left(\frac{2a - b}{2}, \frac{c}{2}\right)$

Conjecture: $\overline{MN}$ appears to be parallel to $\overline{PQ}$.

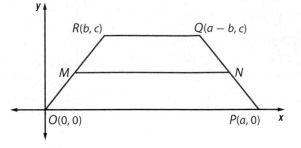

Proof: The slope of $\overline{MN} = \dfrac{\frac{c}{2} - \frac{c}{2}}{\frac{2a-b}{2} - \frac{b}{2}} = \dfrac{0}{a-b} = 0$. The slope of

$\overline{OP} = \dfrac{0-0}{a-0} = 0$. Therefore, $\overline{MN} \parallel \overline{OP}$ since they have the same slope. (This proof assumes $a \neq 0$ and $a \neq b$.)

e. (1) The base angles of an isosceles trapezoid have equal measure.

(2) The diagonals of an isosceles trapezoid have the same length.

(3) The segment connecting the midpoints of the two nonparallel sides of an isosceles trapezoid is parallel to the base of the trapezoid.

14 **a.** **i.** $x = 5$

ii. $x = 4$

iii. $x = 12.5$

b. Given $\dfrac{a}{b} = \dfrac{c}{x}$, $a \neq 0$, $b \neq 0$, and $x \neq 0$.

$\dfrac{ax}{b} = c$ (multiply by x)

$ax = bc$ (multiply by b)

$x = \dfrac{bc}{a}$ (divide by a)

Reasoning with proportions repeatedly uses the relationship between multiplication and division that $\dfrac{a}{b} = c$ if and only if $a = bc$. Another way to work with proportions and this reciprocal relationship is to think of multiplying both sides of the proportion by either the denominator of one of the fractions and simplifying using the principle $\dfrac{a}{a} = 1$ in various forms.

Teacher Notes

Do you know how to do this kind of calculation in your head quickly? You can use the fact that for any two numbers r and s, the product $(r + s)(r - s) = r^2 - s^2$.

a. Explain why each step in the following algebraic proof is justified.

$$(r + s)(r - s) = (r + s)r - (r + s)s \qquad (1)$$
$$= r^2 + sr - rs - s^2 \qquad (2)$$
$$= r^2 + rs - rs - s^2 \qquad (3)$$
$$= r^2 - s^2 \qquad (4)$$

b. How could the given algebraic relationship be used to calculate 105×95 or 112×88?

c. How could you quickly calculate products like $990 \times 1{,}010$ or $996 \times 1{,}004$?

16 The expanded form of any expression like $(x + p)^2$ is $x^2 + 2px + p^2$.

a. Check this relationship by calculating the value of each expression when:

  i. $x = 3$ and $p = 7$

  ii. $x = 3$ and $p = -7$

  iii. $x = -4$ and $p = -3$

b. Adapt the reasoning in Task 15 to develop an algebraic proof of expanding perfect squares, $(x + p)^2 = x^2 + 2px + p^2$.

17 Suppose that in one school term, you have five mathematics quiz scores x_1, x_2, x_3, x_4, and x_5.

a. What algebraic expression shows how to calculate the mean of those scores?

b. Use algebraic reasoning to show how the mean of your quiz scores is affected if each score is multiplied by some common factor p.

c. Use algebraic reasoning to show how the mean of your quiz scores is affected if a constant k is added to each score.

18 Suppose that $\bar{x}$ is the mean of five mathematics quiz scores x_1, x_2, x_3, x_4, and x_5.

a. Describe in words how to calculate the standard deviation

$s = \sqrt{\dfrac{\Sigma(x - \bar{x})^2}{n}}$ for this set of scores.

b. Use algebraic reasoning to show how the standard deviation is affected if each score is multiplied by some common factor p.

c. Use algebraic reasoning to show how the standard deviation is affected if a constant k is added to each score.

Connections

15 **a.** (1) Distributive property

(2) Distributive property

(3) Commutative Property of Multiplication

(4) Additive Inverse Property

b. $(105)(95) = (100 + 5)(100 - 5) = (100^2 - 5^2) = 10,000 - 25 = 9,975$

$(112)(88) = (100 + 12)(100 - 12) = (100^2 - 12^2) = 10,000 - 144 = 9,856$

c. Use the same reasoning as above: $(990)(1,010) = (1,000^2 - 10^2) = 999,900$

and $(996)(1,004) = (1,000^2 - 4^2) = 999,984$

16 **a.** **i.** $(3)^2 + 2(7)(3) + (7)^2 = 9 + 42 + 49 = 100 = 10^2 = (3 + 7)^2$

ii. $(3)^2 + 2(-7)(3) + (-7)^2 = 9 - 42 + 49 = 16 = (-4)^2 = (3 - 7)^2$

iii. $(-4)^2 + 2(-3)(-4) + (-3)^2 = 16 + 24 + 9 = 49 = (-7)^2 = (-4 - 3)^2$

b. $(x + p)^2 = (x + p)(x + p)$

$= (x + p)x + (x + p)p$

$= x^2 + px + xp + p^2$

$= x^2 + px + px + p^2$

$= x^2 + 2px + p^2$

17 **a.** $\dfrac{x_1 + x_2 + x_3 + x_4 + x_5}{5}$

b. $\dfrac{px_1 + px_2 + px_3 + px_4 + px_5}{5} = \dfrac{p(x_1 + x_2 + x_3 + x_4 + x_5)}{5}$

The mean will change by a factor of p.

c. $\dfrac{(x_1 + k) + (x_2 + k) + (x_3 + k) + (x_4 + k) + (x_5 + k)}{5} =$

$\dfrac{(x_1 + x_2 + x_3 + x_4 + x_5) + 5k}{5} = \dfrac{(x_1 + x_2 + x_3 + x_4 + x_5)}{5} + k$

k will be added to the mean.

18 **a.** Find the difference between each score and the mean; square those differences; find the mean of the squared differences; and then take the square root of the mean of square differences.

b. Multiplying each score by p also multiplies the mean by p.

$$\sqrt{\dfrac{(px_1 - p\bar{x})^2 + (px_2 - p\bar{x})^2 + (px_3 - p\bar{x})^2 + (px_4 - p\bar{x})^2 + (px_5 - p\bar{x})^2}{5}} =$$

$$\sqrt{\dfrac{p^2(x_1 - \bar{x})^2 + p^2(x_2 - \bar{x})^2 + p^2(x_3 - \bar{x})^2 + p^2(x_4 - \bar{x})^2 + p^2(x_5 - \bar{x})^2}{5}} =$$

$$\sqrt{\dfrac{p^2((x_1 - \bar{x})^2 + (x_2 - \bar{x})^2 + (x_3 - \bar{x})^2 + (x_4 - \bar{x})^2 + (x_5 - \bar{x})^2)}{5}} =$$

$$p\sqrt{\dfrac{(x_1 - \bar{x})^2 + (x_2 - \bar{x})^2 + (x_3 - \bar{x})^2 + (x_4 - \bar{x})^2 + (x_5 - \bar{x})^2}{5}}$$

As seen above, multiplying each score by p also multiplies the standard deviation by p. Intuitively what is happening is that by multiplying each score by p, we are effectively spreading the scores out by a scale factor of p.

NOTE The solution to Task 18 Part c is on page T68.

19 Recall that for any two points on a number line, the distance between them is the absolute value of the difference of their coordinates. For example, on the number line below, the distance between points A and B is given by $|5 - 2| = |2 - 5| = 3$, and the distance between points B and C is given by $|5 - (-4)| = |(-4) - 5| = 9$.

$$
\begin{array}{c}
\quad C \qquad\qquad\qquad\qquad\qquad A \qquad\quad B \\
\underset{\substack{| \\ -5}}{\vdash}\!\!\!\!\!\!\underset{\substack{ \\ -4}}{}\!\!\!\!\underset{\substack{ \\ -3}}{}\!\!\!\!\underset{\substack{ \\ -2}}{}\!\!\!\!\underset{\substack{ \\ -1}}{}\!\!\!\!\underset{\substack{ \\ 0}}{}\!\!\!\!\underset{\substack{ \\ 1}}{}\!\!\!\!\underset{\substack{ \\ 2}}{}\!\!\!\!\underset{\substack{ \\ 3}}{}\!\!\!\!\underset{\substack{ \\ 4}}{}\!\!\!\!\underset{\substack{ \\ 5}}{}
\end{array}
$$

a. Find the numbers represented by the following absolute value expressions.

  i. $|12 - 3|$ **ii.** $|3 - 12|$ **iii.** $|7 - (-4)|$

  iv. $|(-4) - 7|$ **v.** $|(-7) - (-3)|$ **vi.** $|(-3) - (-7)|$

b. What can you conclude about the relationship between numbers p and q in each case below?

  i. $|p - q| = p - q$ **ii.** $|p - q| = q - p$ **iii.** $|p - q| = 0$

c. Use your answers to Part b to prove that the following calculations can be used to compare any two distinct numbers p and q.

  i. The larger of numbers p and q will always be given by
  $$\frac{p + q + |p - q|}{2}.$$

  ii. The smaller of numbers p and q will always be given by
  $$\frac{p + q - |p - q|}{2}.$$

20 Algebraic reasoning can be used to prove one of the most useful relationships in trigonometry. Justify each step in the following proof that for any angle θ, $\sin^2 \theta + \cos^2 \theta = 1$. The notation $\sin^2 \theta$ means $(\sin \theta)^2$.

Proof: Suppose θ is an angle in standard position in the coordinate plane, and $P(a, b)$ is a point on the terminal side of θ. Let c be the distance from the origin to point P.

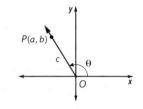

Then:
$$\sin \theta = \frac{b}{c} \text{ and } \cos \theta = \frac{a}{c} \qquad (1)$$

$$\sin^2 \theta = \frac{b^2}{c^2} \text{ and } \cos^2 \theta = \frac{a^2}{c^2} \qquad (2)$$

$$\sin^2 \theta + \cos^2 \theta = \frac{b^2}{c^2} + \frac{a^2}{c^2} \qquad (3)$$

$$\sin^2 \theta + \cos^2 \theta = \frac{b^2 + a^2}{c^2} \qquad (4)$$

$$\sin^2 \theta + \cos^2 \theta = \frac{c^2}{c^2} \qquad (5)$$

$$\sin^2 \theta + \cos^2 \theta = 1 \qquad (6)$$

c. Adding k to each term also adds k to the mean, so the terms in the standard deviation calculation will look like $((x_i + k) - (\bar{x} + k))^2 = (x_i - \bar{x})^2$. This implies that adding k to each term does not change the standard deviation. Intuitively, what is happening is that adding a constant to each score does not affect the spread of the distribution, it only shifts the whole distribution k units (right or left, depending on whether k is positive or negative).

19 **a.** **i.** 9   **ii.** 9   **iii.** 11

    iv. 11   **v.** 4   **vi.** 4

b. **i.** $|p - q| = p - q$ if $p \geq q$.

    ii. $|p - q| = q - p$ if $p \leq q$.

    iii. $|p - q| = 0$ if $p = q$.

c. **i.** If p is greater than q, $\dfrac{p + q + |p - q|}{2} = \dfrac{p + q + p - q}{2} = \dfrac{2p}{2} = p$.

    If q is greater than p, $\dfrac{p + q + |p - q|}{2} = \dfrac{p + q + q - p}{2} = \dfrac{2q}{2} = q$.

    ii. If p is greater than q, $\dfrac{p + q - |p - q|}{2} = \dfrac{p + q - (p - q)}{2} =$

    $\dfrac{p + q - p + q}{2} = \dfrac{2q}{2} = q$.

    If q is greater than p, $\dfrac{p + q - |p - q|}{2} = \dfrac{p + q - (q - p)}{2} =$

    $\dfrac{p + q - q + p}{2} = \dfrac{2p}{2} = p$.

20 (1) Definitions: $\sin \theta = \dfrac{b}{c}$ and $\cos \theta = \dfrac{a}{c}$

    (2) Squaring both sides and squaring a quotient

    (3) Adding the equations in (1) and (2) (If $a = b$ and $c = d$, then $a + c = b + d$.)

    (4) Simplifying the addition of fractions with a common denominator

    (5) Substitution using the distance formula $\sqrt{a^2 + b^2} = c$, so $a^2 + b^2 = c^2$.

    (6) Simplification of fraction

Reflections

21 Students in one Colorado school came up with a simple rule of thumb for deciding on the kinds of algebraic manipulations that would transform given expressions into forms that they could be sure were equivalent to the original. They reasoned, "You can do anything to algebraic expressions that you can do to expressions that involve only specific numbers." Does this seem like a safe guideline for symbol manipulation?

22 A mathematician once said that there are three stages in proving the truth of some mathematical proposition. First, you have to convince yourself. Second, you have to convince your friends. Third, you have to convince your enemies. The kinds of evidence that you find convincing for yourself might be different than the evidence that will convince someone else.

  a. What kinds of evidence do you find to be most persuasive: a collection of specific examples, a visual image of the pattern, or an algebraic argument that links given conditions to conclusions by a sequence of equivalent equations or expressions?

  b. Describe the value of each of these types of persuasive arguments.

   i. several specific illustrative examples

   ii. a visual image

   iii. formal algebraic reasoning

23 In Lesson 2, you used geometric reasoning to prove that if two lines in a plane are perpendicular to the same line, then they are parallel to each other. How could you prove that statement using algebraic reasoning? Assume ℓ, p, and m are lines with $\ell \perp p$, $m \perp p$, and the slope of ℓ is a where $a \neq 0$.

24 In Investigation 2, you completed a proof of the Law of Cosines for one case of an acute angle in a triangle.

  a. Why is the Law of Cosines true for the case where $\angle C$ is a right angle?

  b. Modify the diagram and its labeling on page 60 for the case where $\angle C$ is an obtuse angle. How would you modify the argument in the text for this case?

25 How is reasoning with algebraic properties as in Applications Tasks 10–12 similar to reasoning with postulates in geometry?

Reflections

21 Answers may vary. Many students will agree with the rule of thumb. Some students may note that squaring or taking square roots can introduce answers that have no meaning in problem situations. The way that operating on both sides can introduce extraneous roots for an equation will be dealt with more thoroughly in future units on rational expressions and equations.

22 **a.** Responses will vary. However, students who rely heavily on illustrative examples should be asked to examine the other methods in detail.

　　If you want an example that shows the risk of inductive reasoning alone, consider this conjecture: *Every even number has more factors than either of its neighboring odd numbers*. This conjecture holds until $n = 46$ which has factors $\{1, 2, 23, 46\}$, but $n = 45$ has factors $\{1, 3, 5, 9, 15, 45\}$.

　　b. **i.** Illustrative examples help to show the general pattern of what is happening in the situation, and specific numbers often feel "comfortable" or "friendly" in ways that abstract algebraic expressions may not. However, there may be counterexamples to the newly formulated rule. Specific illustrative examples (especially those that use arithmetic and algebraic operations) may indicate how a general argument can be constructed to prove a conjectured property.

　　　ii. A visual image may help to extend to more general cases but does not always show all cases. For some people, visual images are very easy to comprehend and remember.

　　　iii. Formal algebraic reasoning is usually the most precise and general way to provide support for a mathematical proposition that can be expressed in algebraic form. However, mistakes in algebra are easily made and results should be re-examined or tested when complete.

23 Since the slope of ℓ is a, the slope of p is $-\frac{1}{a}$. Since the slope of p is $-\frac{1}{a}$, the slope of m is a. Thus, $\ell \parallel m$ since they have the same slope. Therefore, two lines perpendicular to the same line are parallel to each other.

24 **a.** For the case of a right triangle ABC, students might reason as follows.

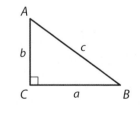

Since $\angle C$ is a right angle, $\cos C = 0$ and therefore, $2ab \cos C = 0$. By the Pythagorean Theorem, $c^2 = a^2 + b^2$. So, $c^2 = a^2 + b^2 - 2ab \cos C$.

b. For the case of $\triangle ABC$ with an obtuse angle at C, modify the diagram as shown. Use right triangles ABD and ACD to write two different expressions for h^2 and equate. Also, use the fact that $\cos ACD = -\cos C$.

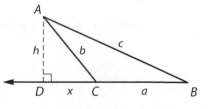

25 The reasoning with algebraic properties is similar to reasoning with postulates in geometry because the properties are assumed without proof and used to justify proceeding from one step to the next in an argument.

Extensions

26 A number trick found on the Web site www.flashpsychic.com begins with these directions.

Pick a two-digit number.

Find the sum of the digits.

Subtract that digit sum from the original number.

Then the program asks you to find your result in a table that pairs each two-digit number with a special symbol. The program proceeds to tell you the symbol corresponding to your ending number.

a. Visit the Web site and see if the program works as advertised for you.

b. Use algebraic reasoning to explain how the number trick works.

27 The following table shows days and dates for January 2010. Several sets of four related dates have been enclosed in boxes.

Sun	Mon	Tue	Wed	Thu	Fri	Sat
					1	2
3	4	5	6	7	8	9
10	11	12	13	14	15	16
17	18	19	20	21	22	23
24	25	26	27	28	29	30
31						

a. In each box, identify the pairs of date numbers that are at opposite corners. Find the products of those pairs, then find the differences of the products.

b. Describe the pattern relating all results of the calculations prescribed in Part a and check some more 2 × 2 boxes in the calendar page to test your pattern conjecture.

c. If the number in the upper-left corner of a box is x, how can the other three numbers in the box be expressed in terms of x?

d. Use the expressions in Part c and algebraic reasoning to prove the pattern that you described in Part b will hold for any such 2 × 2 box of dates on any calendar page arranged in rows like that above.

28 Explore the output of the following algorithm.

Start with the first three digits of your phone number (not the area code).

Multiply that entry by 80 and add 1.

Multiply that result by 250.

Double the number given by the last four digits of your phone number and add that number to your result from the previous step.

Subtract 250 from that result.

Divide that result by 2.

Extensions

26 **a–b.** Let the 2-digit number be represented by $a(10) + b$. The sum of the digits is $a + b$.

$$(a(10) + b) - (a + b) = a(10) + b - a - b$$
$$= a(10 - 1)$$
$$= 9a$$

The final number will always be 9 times the first digit.

Each time you play the *Vanilla Mind Reader* game on the Web site, all multiples of nine will correspond to the same symbol (a pattern that is not easy to notice when there are 100 numbers and many symbols displayed). The symbol corresponding to multiples of nine changes from play to play, making it even harder to detect what is happening.

27 **a.** $(1)(9) - (2)(8) = -7$ $(2)(8) - (1)(9) = 7$
$(10)(18) - (11)(17) = -7$ $(11)(17) - (10)(18) = 7$
$(21)(29) - (22)(28) = -7$ $(22)(28) - (21)(29) = 7$

b. The absolute value of the difference of the two products is 7. Test with $(12)(20) - (13)(19) = -7$.

c. Upper-left is x
Upper-right is $x + 1$
Lower-left is $x + 7$
Lower-right is $x + 8$

d. $(x)(x + 8) - (x + 1)(x + 7) = (x^2 + 8x) - (x^2 + 8x + 7) = -7$
(If the diagonal products are subtracted in reverse order, the difference will be positive 7.)

a. What does the algorithm seem to do with your phone number?

b. Use x to represent the number defined by the first three digits of a phone number and y to represent the number defined by the last four digits of a phone number and write an expression that shows how the algorithm operates.

c. Simplify the expression in Part b to explain the connection between the entry and result of the algorithm.

29 The largest planet in our solar system, Jupiter, has volume of about 333,000,000,000,000 cubic miles, while our Earth has volume of about 268,000,000,000 cubic miles.

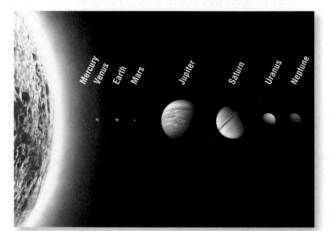

a. Explain why log 333,000,000,000,000 = 14 + log 3.33. Use a calculator or software **log** function to approximate this value.

b. Explain why log 268,000,000,000 = 11 + log 2.68. Use a calculator or software **log** function to approximate this value.

c. Use the results of Parts a and b to approximate log (333,000,000,000,000 ÷ 268,000,000,000).

d. Use the result of Part c and the fact that $y = \log x$ when $10^y = x$ to find an approximate value of the quotient 333,000,000,000,000 ÷ 268,000,000,000. Then explain what the result tells about the ratio of the volume of Jupiter to the volume of Earth.

e. Explain why 333,000,000,000,000 ÷ 268,000,000,000 = 333,000 ÷ 268. Find that quotient and compare the result to your answer in Part d.

f. The average radius of Jupiter is about 43,000 miles and that of Earth is about 4,000 miles. What do those figures imply about the ratio of the volumes of the two planets, and how does your answer compare to that in Part d?

28 **a.** The algorithm returns your phone number.

b. $\dfrac{250(80x + 1) + 2y - 250}{2}$

c. The reasoning which follows justifies the fact that the end result is your phone number.

$$\frac{250(80x + 1) + 2y - 250}{2} = \frac{20{,}000x + 250 + 2y - 250}{2}$$

$$= \frac{20{,}000x + 2y}{2}$$

$$= 10{,}000x + y$$

Since the phone number has 7 digits, $x = abc$ and $y = pqrs$,
$1{,}000x + y = abc0000 + pqrs = abcpqrs$.

29 Though Earth and (especially) Jupiter are not perfect spheres, we have assumed so in this problem that compares their sizes.

a. $333{,}000{,}000{,}000{,}000 = 3.33 \times 10^{14}$ and $\log(3.33 \times 10^{14}) =$
$\log 3.33 + \log 10^{14} = \log 3.33 + 14 \approx 14.5224$. This reasoning uses the basic property of logs developed in Investigation 1.

b. $268{,}000{,}000{,}000 = 2.68 \times 10^{11}$ and $\log(2.68 \times 10^{11}) =$
$\log 2.68 + \log 10^{11} = \log 2.68 + 11 \approx 11.4281$. This reasoning also uses the basic property of logs developed in Investigation 1.

c. $\log(333{,}000{,}000{,}000{,}000 \div 268{,}000{,}000{,}000) \approx 14.5224 - 11.4281 \approx$
3.0943.

d. $10^{3.0943} \approx 1{,}242.5$. This means that the volume of Jupiter is approximately 1,242.5 times that of Earth.

e. The quotient can be simplified by "canceling" 9 zeroes in each term, or describing it a bit more carefully, by dividing divisor and dividend by 1,000,000,000. The resulting simpler division is approximately 1,242.5, almost identical to what is reported in Part d.

f. The formula for volume of a cube is $V = \dfrac{4\pi r^3}{3}$, so its volume is proportional to r^3. The ratio of the radii of the two planets is 43,000 to 4,000, or about 10.75, and $10.75^3 \approx 1{,}242.3$, a number very close to what was produced in Part d.

30 Explain how the diagram below gives a visual "proof without words" of the fact that the product of two odd numbers is always an odd number.

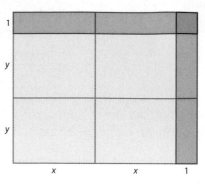

Review

31 Use algebraic reasoning to solve the following equations for x.

a. $12x - 9 = -7x + 6$ b. $3x^2 + 7 = 55$

c. $3x^2 + 7x = 0$ d. $x^2 + 5x - 14 = 0$

e. $4(x - 5) = 5 + 7x$

32 Use properties of exponents to write each of the following expressions in equivalent simplest form, using only positive exponents.

a. p^3p^7 b. $(p^3)^2$

c. $(p^2q^3)(p^{-1}q^2)$ d. $\dfrac{p^4q^3}{q^2p^2}$

e. $\left(\dfrac{p^2q}{pq^3}\right)^4$

33 A is the point with coordinates $(6, 3)$, B is the point $(-4, 8)$, and O is the origin $(0, 0)$.

a. Plot these points in the coordinate plane. Draw $\overleftrightarrow{OA}$ and $\overleftrightarrow{OB}$. How do these two lines appear to be related?

b. Justify your conjecture in Part a in two different ways.

   i. using slopes

   ii. using the distance formula

30 The diagram shows that the total area can be represented as $(2y + 1)(2x + 1)$ and as $4xy + 2y + 2x + 1$. The latter of these expressions is equivalent to $2(2xy + y + x) + 1$. This is in the form $2n + 1$ which is an even number plus 1 or an odd number.

Alternatively, some students may reason by noting that there are 4 lightly colored congruent blocks and 4 darker colored congruent blocks. These would represent two even quantities. Then there is a 1-unit block left that would make the total quantity odd.

Review

31 **a.** $x = \dfrac{15}{19}$ **b.** $x = \pm 4$

    c. $x = 0$ or $x = -\dfrac{7}{3}$ **d.** $x = 2$ or $x = -7$

    e. $x = -\dfrac{25}{3}$

🕐 Just in Time

32 **a.** p^{10} **b.** p^6

    c. pq^5 **d.** p^2q

    e. $\dfrac{p^4}{q^8}$

33 **a.**

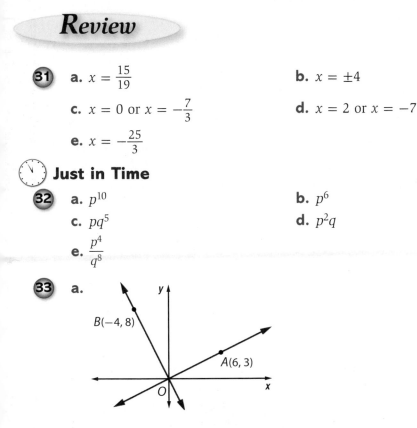

These lines appear to be perpendicular.

  b. **i.** The slope of $\overleftrightarrow{OA}$ is $\dfrac{3}{6}$ and the slope of $\overleftrightarrow{OB}$ is $\dfrac{8}{-4}$.

      Since $\dfrac{3}{6} \cdot \dfrac{8}{-4} = -1$, $\overleftrightarrow{OA} \perp \overleftrightarrow{OB}$.

    ii. $OA = \sqrt{(3 - 0)^2 + (6 - 0)^2} = \sqrt{45}$

      $OB = \sqrt{(8 - 0)^2 + (-4 - 0)^2} = \sqrt{80}$

      $AB = \sqrt{(6 - (-4))^2 + (3 - 8)^2} = \sqrt{125}$

      Since $(OA)^2 + (OB)^2 = (AB)^2$, $m\angle AOB = 90°$.

      Therefore, $\overleftrightarrow{OA} \perp \overleftrightarrow{OB}$.

34 In the diagram at the right, $\angle C$ is a right angle. Use information given to find the requested trigonometric function values. Express your answers as fractions in simplest form.

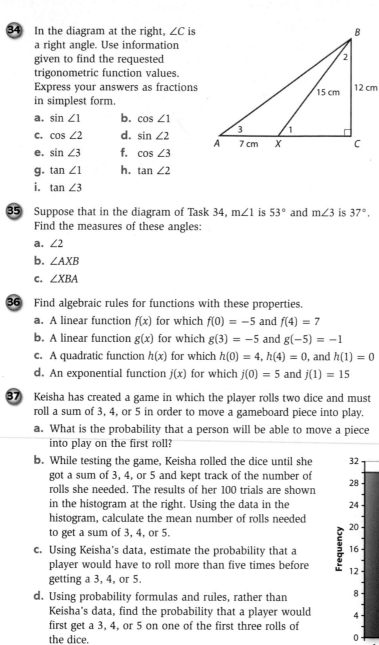

a. $\sin \angle 1$ b. $\cos \angle 1$

c. $\cos \angle 2$ d. $\sin \angle 2$

e. $\sin \angle 3$ f. $\cos \angle 3$

g. $\tan \angle 1$ h. $\tan \angle 2$

i. $\tan \angle 3$

35 Suppose that in the diagram of Task 34, $m\angle 1$ is 53° and $m\angle 3$ is 37°. Find the measures of these angles:

a. $\angle 2$

b. $\angle AXB$

c. $\angle XBA$

36 Find algebraic rules for functions with these properties.

a. A linear function $f(x)$ for which $f(0) = -5$ and $f(4) = 7$

b. A linear function $g(x)$ for which $g(3) = -5$ and $g(-5) = -1$

c. A quadratic function $h(x)$ for which $h(0) = 4$, $h(4) = 0$, and $h(1) = 0$

d. An exponential function $j(x)$ for which $j(0) = 5$ and $j(1) = 15$

37 Keisha has created a game in which the player rolls two dice and must roll a sum of 3, 4, or 5 in order to move a gameboard piece into play.

a. What is the probability that a person will be able to move a piece into play on the first roll?

b. While testing the game, Keisha rolled the dice until she got a sum of 3, 4, or 5 and kept track of the number of rolls she needed. The results of her 100 trials are shown in the histogram at the right. Using the data in the histogram, calculate the mean number of rolls needed to get a sum of 3, 4, or 5.

c. Using Keisha's data, estimate the probability that a player would have to roll more than five times before getting a 3, 4, or 5.

d. Using probability formulas and rules, rather than Keisha's data, find the probability that a player would first get a 3, 4, or 5 on one of the first three rolls of the dice.

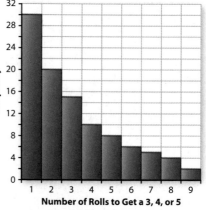

34 a. $\frac{12}{15} = \frac{4}{5}$ b. $\frac{9}{15} = \frac{3}{5}$

c. $\frac{12}{15} = \frac{4}{5}$ d. $\frac{9}{15} = \frac{3}{5}$

e. $\frac{12}{20} = \frac{3}{5}$ f. $\frac{16}{20} = \frac{4}{5}$

g. $\frac{12}{9} = \frac{4}{3}$ h. $\frac{9}{12} = \frac{3}{4}$

i. $\frac{12}{16} = \frac{3}{4}$

35 a. $37°$

b. $127°$

c. $16°$

36 a. $f(x) = 3x - 5$

b. $g(x) = -\frac{1}{2}x - \frac{7}{2}$

c. $h(x) = (x - 4)(x - 1) = x^2 - 5x + 4$

d. $j(x) = 5(3^x)$

Just in Time

37 a. $P(3) + P(4) + P(5) = \frac{2}{36} + \frac{3}{36} + \frac{4}{36} = \frac{9}{36} = \frac{1}{4}$

b. $\dfrac{\text{sum of the number of rolls}}{100} = \dfrac{316}{100} = 3.16$ rolls

c. $\dfrac{6 + 5 + 4 + 2}{100} = \dfrac{17}{100}$

d. $P(\textit{first 3, 4, or 5 on first roll}) = \frac{1}{4}$

$P(\textit{first 3, 4, or 5 on second roll}) = \frac{3}{4} \cdot \frac{1}{4} = \frac{3}{16}$

$P(\textit{first 3, 4, or 5 on third roll}) = \frac{3}{4} \cdot \frac{3}{4} \cdot \frac{1}{4} = \frac{9}{64}$

$P(\textit{first 3, 4, or 5 on first, second or third roll}) = \frac{1}{4} + \frac{3}{16} + \frac{9}{64} = \frac{37}{64}$

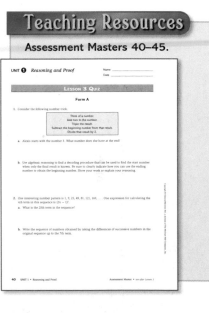

Teaching Resources

Assessment Masters 40–45.

Unit 1

LESSON 4

Statistical Reasoning

In the first three lessons of this unit, you explored how mathematical statements can be proved using algebraic and geometric reasoning. The reasoning was deductive—it involved showing that the conclusion followed logically from definitions, accepted postulates or properties, and theorems. If the reasoning was correct, you could be certain about the truth of the conclusion. However, problems in life that involve data also involve variability, randomness, or incomplete information. This means that you can never be completely certain that you have come to the correct conclusion. In such situations, statistical reasoning can help you come to a reasonable conclusion, backed by convincing evidence.

Advances in fields such as science, education, and medicine depend on determining whether a change in treatment causes better results.

Is a particular drug more effective against acne than doing nothing?

Does a sprain heal faster if the part is exercised or if it is rested?

Does listening to Mozart make people smarter?

You can get convincing evidence about such questions only by carrying out properly designed experiments.

Statistical Reasoning

T here are three main types of statistical studies. In surveys or polls, questions are asked of a sample from a larger population. In experiments, two or more treatments are randomly assigned to the available subjects in order to see which treatment is the most effective. In observational studies, conditions to be compared come already built into the subjects of the study.

If you want to establish that a treatment causes a particular response, you must use a controlled randomized experiment. In this lesson, students will learn how to design a good experiment to compare two different treatments and how to use a randomization test to determine if one of the treatments is more effective than the other. They learn the fundamental ideas behind tests of statistical significance (sometimes called *hypothesis testing*) in this setting of the design and analysis of experiments.

The first investigation teaches students the characteristics of a well-designed experiment. The primary example is the experiment to establish the efficacy of the Salk polio vaccine, which was conducted in 1954. A very large group of children was randomly divided into two treatment groups, one of which was given the Salk vaccine and the other was given a placebo injection.

The second investigation introduces students to the randomization test (sometimes called a *permutation test*), which is used to decide whether the results from an experiment are statistically significant or whether it is reasonable to attribute the results solely to the particular random assignment of subjects to treatments. An informal wording of this test is in the student text on pages 84 and 85. A more formal wording is on page T85.

In the third investigation, students learn to distinguish between the three types of statistical studies and learn what conclusions can be drawn from each type of study.

CPMP-Tools

The *CPMP-Tools* software includes a "Randomization Distribution" feature to quickly create an approximate distribution of possible differences in means of two treatments. See page T83 and corresponding Technology Tip for more information. The data sets included in the software are shown at the right.

Lesson Objectives

- Know the characteristics of a well-designed experiment
- Understand the importance of subject and evaluator blinding and the placebo effect
- Under the hypothesis of no treatment effect, construct an approximate sampling distribution for the difference of two means by rerandomizing; identify extreme events
- Use a randomization test to decide if an experiment provides statistically significant evidence that one treatment is more effective than another
- Distinguish between three types of statistical studies—sample surveys, experiments, and observational studies—and understand what inference can be made from each

Short Path in Course 2 Unit 8, *Probability Distributions*

If your students have not studied the probability unit in Course 2 of *Core-Plus Mathematics*, they should complete the following parts of that unit before beginning Unit 1 Lesson 4.

Course 2 Unit 8, *Probability Distributions*
Lesson 1
Investigation 1 OYO A1, C9, R14
Investigation 2 OYO A3, A4, C11
Investigation 3 OYO A6, C13, R17

Lesson 2
Investigation 1 omit
Investigation 2 A3, A6, C10, R15

Lesson 3
Investigation 1 omit
Investigation 2 OYO A5 and C10

Lesson Launch

First, ask students to agree on the rules (*protocol*) such as whether they can touch a penny again after they have stacked it. Then, randomly divide your class into two groups of about equal size. You can do this, for example, by counting out a playing card for each student in your class with about half of the cards red and half black. Students who draw a red card will use their dominant hand (the hand with which they write) to stack pennies, and students who draw a black card will use their nondominant hand. The score is the number of pennies the student is able to stack before any penny falls.

You can have students stack small wooden cubes, sugar cubes, or similar objects if you do not have a supply of pennies available.

Another way to design this experiment would be to have each student get both "treatments." Have each student stack pennies with one hand and then the other. Because people get better with practice, it is important to determine which hand goes first by a random method like a coin flip, so that about half of the students start with their dominant hand and half start with the other hand. Each student's response would be the difference in the number of pennies between the two hands: *number of pennies stacked by dominant hand − number stacked by nondominant hand*. In this design, each student belongs to each treatment group. This design, called a *repeated measures* design, is more powerful because (with a fixed number of subjects) you are more likely to pick up any difference in the two treatments. However, the analysis in Investigation 2 will not directly apply to this design.

With your class, perform an experiment to decide whether students can, on average, stack more pennies with their dominant hand (the hand with which they write) or with their nondominant hand. First, agree on the rules. Can you touch a penny again after you have stacked it? Can your elbow rest on the table? Then, randomly divide your class into two groups of about equal size. The students in one group will stack pennies using only their dominant hand. The students in the other group will use their nondominant hand. Each student will count the number of pennies he or she stacks before a penny falls.

Think About This Situation

Think about the design of this penny-stacking experiment and how you would interpret the results.

a Why is it important to agree on rules (a *protocol*) for how you must stack the pennies?

b Why is it important to divide your class into the two groups at random?

c Complete this experiment and then organize your data using plots and summary statistics. (Save the data, as you will need them in Investigation 2.)

d What can you conclude? Have you *proved* that, for students your age, one hand tends to be better than the other in stacking pennies? Why or why not?

In this lesson, you will learn how to design a good experiment and how to use statistical reasoning to decide whether one treatment (using the dominant hand) causes a better result (number of pennies stacked) than another treatment (using the nondominant hand). You will also explore reasoning from a sample to a population as in the case of predicting the results of an election from polling a sample of voters.

Investigation 1 Design of Experiments

Statistical reasoning involves these steps.

- Formulate a question that can be answered with data.
- Collect data.
- Display and summarize the data.
- Interpret the results and make generalizations.

Think About This Situation

a) Students who follow different protocols will be able to stack different numbers of pennies. For example, if students straighten the stack as they go along, they will be able to stack more pennies than students who do not straighten the stack. This could invalidate the experiment if, for example, those using their dominant hand decided to straighten the stack and those using their nondominant hand decided they would not. Even if the various methods of stacking occur equally often in the two treatment groups, the differences they cause can add to the unwanted variability within each treatment in the number of pennies stacked.

b) If subjects are not assigned at random to the treatment groups, then it is likely that some important characteristic will be overrepresented in one of the groups. For example, suppose all of the athletes in your class sit on one side of the room. If you establish the two treatment groups by dividing your class down the middle of the room, all of the athletes will be in one of the treatment groups. If athletes tend to be more coordinated than other students, you will not know whether it was the different treatments that caused any difference in the mean responses or whether it was the difference in coordination.

c) Summaries will vary. Results from one class are given in Problem 5 of Investigation 2.

d) Students are likely to find that, on average, they can stack more pennies with their dominant hand. (In some classes, students do better with the nondominant hand as they appear to be concentrating more when they use that less-often-used hand.) However, on a different day or with a different group of students, the results might have gone the other way. Further, it is possible that, just by chance, all of the students who are good penny-stackers, no matter which hand they use, all got in the same group. Thus, this experiment cannot provide a *proof* that one hand is better than the other for stacking pennies.

Unit 1

INSTRUCTIONAL NOTE
This TATS takes a bit longer than most because of the penny stacking activity. *Be sure to have pennies or similar objects to stack.* Some students stack more than 50 pennies. Consider entering the data in *CPMP-Tools* so that plots and summary statistics will be readily available.

Investigation 1   Design of Experiments

In this investigation, students learn the vocabulary of the design of experiments: *treatment, response variable, subjects* (sometimes called *experimental units*), *random assignment, comparison* or *control group, placebo, placebo effect, subject blind, evaluator blind, double blind,* and *lurking variable.* They learn that a well-designed experiment must have:

- random assignment of treatments to subjects,
- a sufficient number of subjects, and
- a comparison or control group.

POSSIBLE MISCONCEPTION
Note that science teachers may use the word "experiment" to mean any demonstration or lab activity. In this lesson, the word "experiment" means a designed experiment that has the three characteristics listed on page 77 of the student book (random assignment, treatments replicated on many subjects, and at least two treatment groups).

In earlier statistics units of *Core-Plus Mathematics*, you concentrated mostly on the third and fourth steps, plotting data that had already been collected, computing summary statistics, and interpreting the results. In this investigation, you will focus on the second step. As you work on the problems in this investigation, look for answers to this question:

How can you design an experiment that provides convincing evidence that one treatment causes a different response than another treatment?

 A common science experiment attempts to determine if mung bean seeds that are given a gentle zap in a microwave oven are more likely to sprout than mung bean seeds that are not given a zap.

Mung beans that were zapped in a microwave oven

a. In such an experiment, what are the **treatments** (conditions you want to compare)? What is the **response variable** (outcome you are measuring)?

b. For his experiment, Carlos zapped 10 mung bean seeds and 8 sprouted. Explain why Carlos should not conclude that mung bean seeds zapped in a microwave are more likely to sprout than if they had not been zapped.

c. For her experiment, Mia took 20 mung bean seeds, picked out 10 that looked healthy and zapped them. Of the 10 that were zapped, 8 sprouted. Of the 10 that were not zapped, 3 sprouted. Explain why Mia should not conclude that mung bean seeds zapped in a microwave are more likely to sprout than if they had not been zapped.

d. For her experiment, Julia took 4 mung bean seeds, selected 2 at random to be zapped, and zapped those 2. Both seeds that were zapped sprouted. The 2 seeds that were not zapped did not sprout. Explain why Julia should not conclude that mung bean seeds zapped in a microwave are more likely to sprout than if they had not been zapped.

e. Design an experiment to determine if mung bean seeds are more likely to sprout if they are zapped in a microwave.

Encourage students to bring to class the results of activities they do in their science classes. Discuss whether these "experiments" meet all of the criteria of experiments as defined in this lesson. In many cases, the science experiments will be measurements (such as the pH of various liquids, or the speed of a ball as it rolls down a ramp) with no random assignment of experimental units to treatments or random selection from a larger population (all things are treated as if they are all alike). Ask students whether they took into consideration the variability involved—that if they measured each object several times, the measurements would probably not all be the same.

1 a. One treatment is the seed is zapped, and the other treatment is the seed is not zapped. The response variable is whether the seed sprouted or not.

b. Carlos does not know the rate that his mung bean seeds sprout when they are not zapped. That rate could be the same or even higher than 80%.

c. The "healthy-looking" mung bean seeds may be more likely to sprout than the others with or without the zapping. In fact, the zapping may have made them *less* likely to sprout and Mia would not know that.

d. Julia used so few seeds that she cannot tell whether it was the zapping that caused the two seeds to sprout or whether these two seeds were the only ones that were going to sprout anyway, no matter whether they were zapped or not.

INSTRUCTIONAL NOTE To help students understand this, you may wish to use the following example.

Suppose that two particular seeds will sprout (S_1 and S_2) and the other two will not (N_1 and N_2), no matter whether they are zapped or not. There are six ways to randomly divide the four seeds into two treatment groups, as shown in the table. Note that the probability of getting both seeds that are going to sprout in the same treatment group is $\frac{2}{6} = \frac{1}{3}$. Thus, when zapping makes no difference, Julia has a $\frac{1}{3}$ chance of wrongly concluding that zapping makes a difference.

Random Assignment	Zapped	Not Zapped
1	S_1 S_2	N_1 N_2
2	S_1 N_1	S_2 N_2
3	S_1 N_2	S_2 N_1
4	S_2 N_1	S_1 N_2
5	S_2 N_2	S_1 N_1
6	N_1 N_2	S_1 S_2

e. Take as large a quantity of mung bean seeds as practical. Randomly divide them into two groups, preferably by using a random digit table. Zap the ones in one group, and do not zap the ones in the second group. Plant them; and again, randomly decide which seed gets planted where (but keep track of which got zapped and which did not), treat them all alike with respect to watering, quality of soil, amount of light, amount of fertilizer, temperature, and so on, and then count the number in each group that sprouted.

Unit 1

2 In a typical experiment, two or more treatments are randomly assigned to an available group of people (or animals, plants, or objects) called **subjects**. The purpose of an experiment is to establish cause and effect. Does one treatment cause a different response than the other treatment? A well-designed experiment must have three characteristics.

- *Random assignment*: Treatments are assigned randomly to the subjects.

- *Sufficient number of subjects*: Subjects will vary in their responses, even when they are treated alike. If there are not enough subjects, this variability within each treatment may obscure any difference between the effects of the treatments. Deciding how many subjects are sufficient is one of the more difficult tasks that statisticians do.

- *Comparison group or control group*: Either the group that gets the treatment is compared to a group that gets no treatment (a **control group**) or two groups that get different treatments are compared.

a. Which characteristic(s) of a well-designed experiment was (were) missing in Problem 1 in the mung bean seed study of:

i. Carlos?   **ii.** Mia?   **iii.** Julia?

b. Which characteristics of a well-designed experiment, if any, were missing from your penny-stacking experiment?

c. What can go wrong if treatments are not assigned randomly to the subjects?

3 In 1954, a huge medical experiment was carried out to test whether a newly developed vaccine by Jonas Salk was effective in preventing polio. Over 400,000 children participated in the portion of the study described here. Children were randomly assigned to one of two treatments. One group received a *placebo* (an injection that looked—and felt!—like a regular immunization but contained only salt water). The other group received an injection of the Salk vaccine. (Source: Paul Meier, "The Biggest Public Health Experiment Ever," in *Statistics: A Guide to the Unknown*, 3rd ed. Edited by Judith Tanur, *et al*. Pacific Grove, CA: Wadsworth and Brooks/Cole Advanced Books and Software, 1989, pp. 3–14.)

a. What are the treatments in the Salk experiment? What is the response variable?

b. Did the test of the Salk vaccine have the three characteristics of a well-designed experiment?

Jonas Salk examining vials of polio vaccine

HISTORICAL NOTE Before it was understood why it is important to randomly assign treatments to subjects, many experiments came to erroneous conclusions. For example, in a famous experiment in Scotland in 1930 to determine whether giving milk to schoolchildren caused greater growth, some teachers chose to give the milk to the students who they felt needed it. These children tended to be smaller than those who were not given milk. Thus, at the end of the experiment, it appeared that receiving milk did not cause greater growth. (Source: Student. "The Lanarkshire Milk Experiment." *Biometrika*, Vol. 23, 1931, pp. 398–404.) If the children had been randomly assigned to the treatment groups, the smaller children should have been somewhat evenly divided between the milk and no-milk treatments. There are many possible variables that might affect a child's growth, and it is impossible to think of all of them when making assignments to treatments. So, it is best to let randomization spread them evenly between the treatments.

(2) **NOTE** Deciding whether there is a sufficient number of subjects is the most uncertain part of designing an experiment. Statisticians say that the question they are asked most frequently is, "How many subjects do I need?" At this stage, students will not be able to give a definite answer as to whether there is a sufficient number of subjects. As they progress through this lesson, students should come to understand that the answer depends on three things.

- How far apart the means will be: the farther apart, the fewer subjects needed to establish statistical significance (if a difference really does exist)

- How big the spread in the responses from each treatment will be: the smaller the spread, the fewer subjects needed to establish statistical significance (if a difference really does exist)

- How important it is to establish statistical significance (if a difference really does exist) and not make the error of concluding that the difference can reasonably be attributed to chance alone: the more important, the more subjects you will want

Statisticians consult with their client when designing the experiment in order to make estimates of these three things. They then can compute the needed number of subjects. Students will see a simplified version of such a formula in an Extensions task of Lesson 2 in Unit 4, *Samples and Variation*.

a. **i.** Comparison or control group
   ii. Random assignment
   iii. Sufficient number of subjects

b. Unless the class was very small, all characteristics should have been met.

c. If treatments are not assigned at random to the subjects, you might end up in a situation like Mia's, where the healthiest seeds got the microwave treatment. At the end of her experiment, Mia could not tell whether it was the zapping or the fact that they were healthier seeds to begin with that resulted in a higher proportion sprouting than in the nonzapped group. Even if Mia had not made such an obvious mistake, but she had just used her judgment to assign the seeds to the treatments, something similar might have happened. It is best to trust that the randomization make the treatment groups as similar as possible before the treatments are applied.

POLIO BACKGROUND Polio (or poliomyelitis) is a viral infection that can invade the nervous system and cause paralysis. Before a vaccine was developed, most victims were children; although, adults were affected as well. Two famous people who contracted polio and suffered paralysis that prevented them from walking without assistance are President Franklin D. Roosevelt (1882–1945) and the violinist Itzhak Perlman (1945–). A great success story of modern medicine is the near eradication of this much-feared disease. The first effective vaccine was developed by Jonas Salk (1914–1995). An oral vaccine developed by Albert Sabin (1906–1993) was approved soon afterward.

Alternatively, you may show students the 49-second video, "Jonas Edward Salk," at: www.britannica.com/eb/art-18529/Archival-footage-showing-children-afflicted-with-polio-Jonas-Edward-Salk?articleTypeId=1

ADDITIONAL RESOURCES For more information about this experiment, see Paul Meier's article, "The Biggest Public Health Experiment Ever: The 1954 Field Trial of the Salk Poliomyelitis Vaccine," which may be found in *Statistics: A Guide to the Unknown* (1st, 2nd, and 3rd editions), edited by Judith Tanur or at www.stat.luc.edu/StatisticsfortheSciences/MeierPolio.htm.

The United States Center for Disease Control recommends that most people get four doses of polio vaccine between ages 2 months and 4–6 years. No additional vaccinations are usually necessary.
(Source: www.cdc.gov/vaccines/pubs/vis/downloads/vis-IPV.pdf)

 a. The treatments were injections with the Salk vaccine and injections with salt water. The response variable was whether the child was later diagnosed with polio or not. (Problem 5 contains more information on diagnosing polio.)

b. Yes. Treatments were assigned randomly to subjects. There was a sufficient number of subjects (see Connections Task 10 Part c). There was a treatment group who got the Salk vaccine and a control group who got salt water.

Teacher Notes

4 Many difficulties in testing the Salk vaccine had been anticipated. Which of the three characteristics of a well-designed experiment helped overcome each difficulty described below? Explain.

a. The incidence of polio was very low, even without immunization.

b. The vaccine was not expected to be 100% effective.

c. One possible approach would have been to immunize all children in the study and compare the incidence of polio to that of children the same age the previous year. However, the incidence of polio varied widely from year to year.

d. One possible experimental design would have been to let parents decide whether their child was vaccinated and compare the rates of polio of the vaccinated and unvaccinated children. In the United States, polio was primarily a disease of children from middle- and upper-income families and so those children's parents were especially anxious to get them vaccinated.

5 Many studies have shown that people tend to do better when they are given special attention or when they believe they are getting competent medical care. This is called the **placebo effect**. Even people with post-surgical pain report less discomfort if they are given a pill that is actually a placebo (a pill containing no medicine) but which they believe contains a painkiller.

One way to control for the placebo effect is to make the experiment **subject blind**, the person receiving the treatment does not know which treatment he or she is getting. That is, subjects in both treatment groups appear to be treated exactly the same way.

In an **evaluator-blind** experiment, the person who evaluates how well the treatment works does not know which treatment the subject received. If an experiment is both subject blind and evaluator blind, it is called **double blind**.

a. The Salk experiment was double blind. One reason this was necessary was because the diagnosis of polio is not clear-cut. Cases that cause paralysis are obvious, but they are the exception. Sometimes polio looks like a bad cold, and so professional judgment is needed. How might a doctor's knowledge of whether or not a child had been immunized affect his or her diagnosis? How might this lead to the wrong conclusion about how well the vaccine works?

b. Could you make the penny-stacking experiment in the Think About This Situation subject blind? Evaluator blind? Double blind? Explain.

4 **a.** This difficulty was overcome by having a sufficient number of subjects. A low incidence of polio meant that a large number of children was necessary. If a small group had been used, polio cases might not have developed even in the placebo group. (This is explored further in Connections Task 10.)

b. This difficulty was overcome by having a control group. If the vaccine had been expected to be 100% effective, the researchers would not have needed a control group. They would need only to give the vaccine to a very large number of children. If there were no cases of polio in that group, they would be sure the vaccine worked. (This assumes that polio can be diagnosed with certainty.) However, because the vaccine was expected to reduce the incidence of polio but not eliminate it, a control group was needed.

c. This difficulty was overcome by randomly assigning treatments to subjects. Like most infectious diseases, the incidence of polio varied widely from year to year. This made it impossible to use the unvaccinated children from the previous year as controls. Thus, the researchers had to have a control group and a treatment group during the same year, randomly assigning the children to the two treatments.

d. As in Part c, this difficulty also was overcome by random assignment of treatments to subjects. Without random assignment, the children more likely to get polio (children of affluent parents) would have been in the vaccine group and the children less likely to get polio would have been in the placebo group. In this case, even though the vaccine was effective in reducing polio in each group, the conclusion might have been that the vaccine was not effective because the children of affluent parents that had been given the vaccine still had higher rates of polio than the other children who did not receive the vaccine.

> **NOTE** Even before the availability of a polio vaccine, polio was virtually unknown in countries with poor hygiene. In these countries, it is thought that the virus was common, in fact, so common that virtually everyone got it as an infant while still having some protection from the mother's immunity. Thus, everyone established his or her own immunity by getting the disease in a very mild form.

5 **a.** A doctor would be less likely to diagnose polio in a borderline case if he or she knew the child had been vaccinated and more likely to diagnose polio if the child had not been vaccinated. (This is a reasonable medical decision because if the vaccine had not been expected to work, such a large experiment could not have been carried out!) However, this bias would invalidate the experiment. It would result in a smaller proportion of diagnosed polio cases in the vaccinated group than there should have been and a higher proportion of cases in the placebo group, making the vaccine look better than it was.

> **NOTE** In the Salk experiment, only a code number identified each vial as the vaccine or the placebo, so no one close to the child or the doctor knew which children received the vaccine and which received the placebo.

b. You could not make the penny-stacking experiment subject blind as subjects must know which hand they were using. It would be possible to make the experiment evaluator blind by, say, making a film of the person stacking the pennies and have the evaluator count the number successfully stacked. The film could be reversed at random so the evaluator would not know which hand the person was using. Because the experiment cannot be made subject blind, it cannot be double blind.

⑥ A **lurking variable** helps to explain the association between the treatments and the response but is not the explanation that the study was designed to test. Treatments are assigned randomly to subjects to equalize the effects of possible lurking variables among the treatment groups as much as possible. Analyze each of the following reports of studies with particular attention to possible lurking variables.

a. Researchers from the Minnesota Antibiotic Resistance Collaborative reported an attempt to deal with the problem that bacteria are becoming resistant to antibiotics. One reason for increasing resistance is that some people want antibiotics when they have a cold, even though cold viruses do not respond to antibiotics.

　　Five medical clinics distributed colorful kits containing Tylenol®, decongestant, cough syrup, lozenges, powdered chicken soup, and a tea bag to patients with cold symptoms. At five other medical clinics, patients with similar symptoms were not given these kits. Patients with colds who visited clinics that made the kits available were less likely to fill prescriptions for antibiotics than patients with colds who visited clinics where the kits were not available. This study involved nearly 11,000 patients. (Source: sciencedaily.com/releases/2004/02/040229231510.htm; *The Los Angeles Times*, March 8, 2004.)

　i. What are the treatments in the study? What is the response variable?

　ii. Why is this not a well-designed experiment? How could you improve it?

　iii. What lurking variable might account for the difference in response?

b. Researchers supplied 238 New York City households with hand-washing soaps, laundry detergents, and kitchen cleansers. Half of the households, selected at random, were given antibacterial products, and the other half received products that were identically packaged but without the antibacterial ingredient.

　　The participants were asked weekly about any disease in the household. The researchers found no difference in frequency of infectious disease symptoms over one year. (Source: Elaine L. Larson *et al.* "Effect of Antibacterial Home Cleaning and Handwashing Products on Infectious Disease Symptoms," *Annals of Internal Medicine*, Vol. 140, No. 5, March 2, 2004.)

　i. Does this study have the three characteristics of a well-designed experiment?

　ii. This study was double blind. Explain how that must have been done.

　iii. Suppose that instead of assigning the treatments at random to the households, the researchers simply compare the frequency of infectious disease symptoms over a year in households that use antibacterial products and those that do not. Describe lurking variables that might invalidate the conclusion of the study.

6 a. i. The treatments are getting the kit and not getting the kit. The response variable is whether the person filled a prescription for antibiotics in the next three days or not.

ii. This is not a well-designed experiment because the treatments were not randomly assigned to the subjects. It would have been better to randomize the treatments to individual patients. (The treatments might have been randomly assigned to the medical clinics, which is also a legitimate design. Because the response variable must match the randomization, the response variable would be the proportion of people at each clinic who filled prescriptions in the next three days. However, this design might have an insufficient number of experimental units—each treatment would have only five experimental units.)

iii. There is no mention of randomization, so a lurking variable might be the fact that some clinics are more likely to give prescriptions than other clinics; and for some reason, these clinics were less likely to be assigned to give out the kits. It is also possible that having the kits available changed the behavior of the doctors rather than the behavior of the patients. For example, doctors who had the kits available became less likely to prescribe antibiotics. But apparently, it was patient behavior that was being investigated rather than doctor behavior (as the number of prescriptions filled was the response variable, not the number of prescriptions written).

b. i. Yes. Treatments were assigned at random to the households. The number of households given each treatment, 119, probably was sufficient. Two groups were being compared, one with the antibacterial products and one without.

ii. Each of the two treatment groups got identical-looking products. Further, the evaluators who asked about any disease must not have been told which product the household received.

iii. Households that use antibacterial products may be more careful in other ways about avoiding sickness, such as always washing hands before eating and staying away from people who are sick. (On the other hand, trying to avoid sickness in these ways ultimately may result in more disease, as with polio.)

c. i. The treatments are taking an AP exam and not taking an AP exam in high school. The response variable is whether the person graduates from college in five years.

ii. No, it would be unethical to randomly assign students to take an AP course in high school or not.

iii. Students who enroll in an AP course (even those who fail the AP exam) may be more ambitious than those who do not and so more likely to graduate from college. Or, students who enroll in an AP course in high school must have taken the prerequisites for a college course before their twelfth-grade year and so simply may be more accelerated than students who do not. Thus, they are more likely to graduate from college in five years than students who were less accelerated through high school.

c. A December 2004 article on washingtonpost.com entitled "In AP-vs.-IB Debate, A Win for the Students" reports on a study by the National Center for Educational Accountability that shows that "even students who fail AP examinations in high school are twice as likely to graduate from college in five years as students who never try AP." This study followed 78,079 students in Texas.

   i. What are the treatments? What is the response variable?

   ii. Do you think that the conclusion came from a well-designed experiment?

   iii. What lurking variables could account for the difference in responses for the two groups?

   iv. Can you design an experiment to establish that taking an AP course, even if you fail the exam, means you are more likely to graduate from college in five years?

Summarize the Mathematics

In this investigation, you examined characteristics of well-designed experiments.

a What are the three characteristics of a well-designed experiment? Why is each necessary?

b Why are subject blinding and evaluator blinding desirable in an experiment?

c What is the placebo effect? How can you account for it when designing an experiment?

Be prepared to share your ideas with the class.

✔ Check Your Understanding

To find out if students do better on exams where the easier problems come first, a teacher wrote two versions of an exam. One had the more difficult problems first, and a second contained the same problems only with the easier ones first. He gave the first version to his first-period class and the second version to his second-period class. He will compare the scores on the first version with the scores on the second version.

a. What are the treatments? What is the response variable?

b. Does this study have the three characteristics of a well-designed experiment?

c. Is this study subject blind? Is it evaluator blind?

d. Name at least one lurking variable for this study.

e. Describe how the teacher could improve the design of his study.

iv. Because it is unethical to randomly assign students to these two treatments, you would have to search for high schools that do not offer AP courses and try to match them with similar high schools that do offer AP courses. Then you would try to match each student taking an AP course in the high schools that offer them to a similar student who attends the matching high school where AP courses are not offered. The matching of students might be done by variables such as state test scores, financial ability of parents to send children to college, specific courses taken, and grades in those courses. Then you would compare the college graduation rates of the students in five years. This is not perfect, as it leaves room for lots of lurking variables. (How can you know that a high school that does not offer AP is similar in all other respects to a high school that does?) But it is about the best you can do.

NOTE Solutions to Part c are on page T79.

Summarize
the Mathematics

ⓐ The three characteristics are random assignment, using a sufficient number of subjects, and a control or comparison group. Random assignment is needed because it is the best way to "average out" between the treatments any characteristics of the subjects (lurking variables) that might affect the results and obscure the effect of the treatments. (As students will see in the next investigation, it also gives you justification for constructing a sampling distribution under the supposition that the treatments do not cause different effects.) A sufficient number of subjects is necessary so that you have enough subjects to determine whether a difference in the responses can be reasonably attributed to chance or whether you should attribute it to the treatment. A small or moderate difference, even if it reflects a real difference in the effects of the treatments, will not be statistically significant if the number of subjects is small. A control or comparison group is needed so that you know if the treatment in which you are interested works better than another and so that you can eliminate the placebo effect as the cause of any improvement.

ⓑ If people expect something to work, it is more likely to work (the placebo effect). Thus, if you want to separate people's expectations from the actual effect of the treatment, you should, if possible, not let them know which treatment they are getting or evaluating.

ⓒ The placebo effect is the phenomenon that people tend to do better when given a treatment, even if it is just a placebo. The way to deal with this is to give the treatments in such a way that they look exactly the same to the subjects even though one treatment may be a placebo.

COLLABORATION PROMPT
On a scale of 1 to 5 with 5 best, my listening skills deserve a __ because ... .

✔ Check Your Understanding

a. The two treatments are an exam with the easier problems first and an exam with the harder problems first. The response variable is the score on the exam.

b. No, the treatments were not randomly assigned to the students.

c. The study may be subject blind as the students do not even know they are in an experiment (which may not be acceptable at some schools). However, the first-period students may have noticed that their exam was different from the usual type and this knowledge alone could affect their scores. The study is not evaluator blind as the teacher grades the exams and knows which class got which treatment.

d. The two classes may be different in a way that affects the scores on the exam, regardless of the treatment. For example, the first-period class may have better students. Perhaps first-period students are more (or less) alert. Perhaps some particular group of students enrolled in first period to avoid conflict with another course that meets during second period. A final lurking variable may be that students who had the harder questions first simply ran out of time and were unable to complete as many questions.

e. The teacher could do two things. First, he could distribute the two types of exams randomly in both periods. Second, he could have the exams graded by someone who does not know what he is trying to establish.

Test on Factoring into Primes

Circle the correct answer. There is no penalty for guessing, so if you do not know, guess.

1. The largest known prime is $2^{30,402,457} - 1$. How many digits does it have?

   A 9,152,051   **B** 9,152,052

2. Twin primes are a pair of primes that differ by 2, such as 3 and 5 or 29 and 31. How many pairs of twin primes exist where both numbers are less than one million?

   A 137   **B** 8,169

3. If you factor 17,422,457,186,352,049,329,324,779,900,065,324,265,471 into primes, how many different primes are there?

   A 1   **B** 2

4. If you factor 5,439,042,183,600,204,290,159 into primes, how many different primes are there?

   A 1   **B** 2

5. What is the 1,000th prime?

   A 7,919   **B** 7,927

6. What do you get if you add up the reciprocals of all of the primes?

   $$\frac{1}{2} + \frac{1}{3} + \frac{1}{5} + \frac{1}{7} + \frac{1}{11} + \cdots$$

   A about 10   **B** about 50   **C** neither of these

7. Suppose you factor 26! into primes. How many times does 5 appear as a factor?

   A 5   **B** 6

8. How many perfect squares evenly divide $7,200 = 2^5 3^2 5^2$?

   A 10   **B** 12

NUMBER CORRECT _____

Student Master • *use with page 81*

Statistical Reasoning **T80B**

Investigation 2 — By Chance or from Cause?

In the previous investigation, you learned the importance of randomly assigning treatments to the subjects in an experiment. With randomization, you trust that any initial differences among the subjects get spread out fairly evenly between the two treatment groups. Consequently, you feel justified in concluding that any large difference in response between the two groups is due to the effect of the treatments. In this investigation, you will learn a technique for making *inferences* (drawing valid conclusions) from an experiment.

As you work on the problems in this investigation, look for answers to this question:

How can you decide whether the difference in the mean responses for the two groups in your experiment happened just by chance or was caused by the treatments?

1 To illustrate what happens when treatments are equally effective, your class will perform a simple but well-designed experiment to determine whether a calculator helps students perform better, on average, on a test about factoring numbers into primes.

- Each student should write his or her name on a small card.

- Divide your class at random into two groups of about equal size by having one person shuffle the name cards and deal them alternatively into two piles. One group will get the "calculator" treatment and the other group will get the "pencil-and-paper" treatment.

- Using the treatment assigned to you, answer the questions on the test provided by your teacher. If you do not know an answer for sure, make the best guess you can so that you have an answer for all eight questions.

- Grade your test from the answers provided by your teacher. Report the number of questions that you got correct as your response.

  a. Was a calculator any help on this test? Should the treatment you received make any difference in your response?

  b. Make a list of the responses for each treatment. Then, for each treatment, prepare a plot of the number correct and calculate appropriate summary statistics.

  c. To the nearest hundredth, compute the difference:
  mean of calculator group − mean of pencil-and-paper group.
  Is there a difference in the mean response from the two treatment groups?

  d. Why did you get a difference that is not zero even though which treatment you received should not matter?

In this investigation, students will learn how to perform a randomization test to determine if one treatment is more effective than another. The randomization test developed in this investigation is due to R. A. Fisher, perhaps the greatest statistician of all time. Fisher first described the test in his 1935 book *The Design of Experiments* in the context of an agricultural experiment. (The 8th edition of this book was published in 1966 by Macmillan.) The advantage of the randomization test is that no assumptions of normality or minimum sample sizes are needed, only that treatments are randomly assigned to subjects. The far more well-known *t*-test for the difference of two means can be considered an approximation to the randomization test. Such an approximation was necessary until recently because computers were not powerful enough to do randomization tests. Fisher wrote in 1936 about randomization tests:

> "Actually, the statistician does not carry out this very simple and very tedious process, but his conclusions have no justification beyond the fact that they agree with those which could have been arrived at by this elementary method."

1 **INSTRUCTIONAL NOTE** The test on factoring into primes may be found in the *Unit 1 Resource Masters*. (Also, see page T80B for the contents of the test.) Be sure that all students answer all questions, even if they have to guess (which they will have to do on most questions).

In Problem 1, there is a 5% chance that the difference in means for your class will turn out to be statistically significant (in the outer 5% of the randomization distribution). If that turns out to be the case, you will have a different lesson. Students should realize that the calculator makes no difference whatsoever, but the results of your experiment showed that it did. To conclude that two treatments cause a difference, when, in fact, they do not is called a Type I error. Your students have just discovered that a Type I error happens occasionally (5% of the time) when the treatments cause no difference at all in the responses. The only way to minimize the probability of a Type I error is to require that the difference of the two means be in, say, the outer 1% of the randomization distribution. However, now you are more likely to make a Type II error, which is failing to conclude that the treatments make a difference when, in fact, they do.

INSTRUCTIONAL NOTE
In this investigation, students use two-tailed significance tests. See the note on page T82.

Teaching Resources

Student Masters 48–49.

Unit 1

Answers to Test on Factoring into Primes

1. B

2. B

3. B   17,422,457,186,352,049,329,324,779,900,065,324,265,471 = 32,032,215,596,496,435,569 • 5,439,042,183,600,204,290,159

4. A   This number is prime.

5. A   The other number also is prime.

6. C   The sum of the reciprocals of the primes does not converge but grows larger and larger.

7. B   This is a problem that students can actually do. The number $26! = 26 • 25 • 24 • \cdots • 3 • 2 • 1$ has one factor each of 5, 10, 15, 20, and 25. So, the prime factorization must contain the factor 5 six times.

8. B   Students may be able to do this problem, too. In a perfect square, each prime factor must occur an even number of times. There can be zero, two, or four 2s, zero or two 3s, and zero or two 5s. So, there are $(3)(2)(2) = 12$ ways to build a square number from these factors.

a. No, the score on this factoring test should be the same no matter what treatment was used. Further, most students will simply be guessing on all questions.

b. The difference will almost always be nonzero. The responses, summary statistics, and dot plots from a class of 16 students appear below.

Treatment	Number Correct
C	4
C	4
C	3
C	4
C	6
C	2
C	3
C	3
P	3
P	2
P	5
P	2
P	2
P	6
P	3
P	3

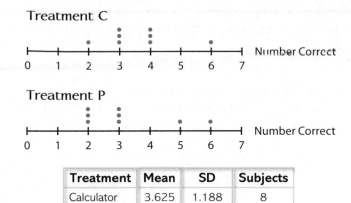

Treatment C

0 1 2 3 4 5 6 7   Number Correct

Treatment P

0 1 2 3 4 5 6 7   Number Correct

Treatment	Mean	SD	Subjects
Calculator	3.625	1.188	8
Pencil/Paper	3.250	1.488	8

c. In our example of the class of 16 students, there is a nonzero difference in the means:

mean of calculator group − mean of pencil-and-paper group
$= 3.625 - 3.25 = 0.375$

d. It would be incredibly lucky to get a difference of exactly 0 when you randomly divide the students into two groups. However, the larger the class, the closer to 0 the difference is likely to be.

Now, explore what the size of the difference in the mean responses in Problem 1 Part c would have been if the randomization had placed different students in the two treatment groups, but each student's response was exactly the same.

a. On each name card, record the number of correct responses for that student.

   i. Divide your class at random once again by shuffling the name cards and dealing them into two piles representing the calculator treatment and the pencil-and-paper treatment. To the nearest hundredth, what is the difference: *mean of calculator group − mean of pencil-and-paper group*?

   ii. Construct an approximate distribution of the possible differences of means by repeating the above process. Do this, sharing the work, until you have generated a total of at least 50 differences.

b. Where is your distribution centered? Why does this make sense?

c. Is the difference in the means from the original experiment (Problem 1 Part c) so extreme that it falls in the outer 5% of the distribution? In other words, would the difference be a rare event if it had been generated by chance alone?

d. If so, what can you conclude? If not, what can you conclude?

③ Researchers at the Smell & Taste Foundation were interested in the following question.

Can pleasant aromas improve ability to complete a task?

They randomly assigned volunteers to wear an unscented mask or to wear a floral-scented mask. The subjects then completed two pencil-and-paper mazes. The time to complete the two mazes was recorded. Data were recorded separately for smokers and nonsmokers as smoking affects the sense of smell. Results for the 13 nonsmokers are given in the table below.

Unscented Mask (in seconds)	Scented Mask (in seconds)
38.4	38.0
72.5	35.0
82.8	60.1
50.4	44.3
32.8	47.9
40.9	46.2
56.3	

Source: Hirsch, A. R., and Johnston, L. H. "Odors and Learning," Smell & Taste Treatment and Research Foundation, Chicago. DASL library, lib.stat.cmu.edu/ DASL/Datafiles/Scents.html

② **NOTE** In statistical practice, how "extreme" a result has to be before you believe the treatments have different effects depends on the situation. Often, the result from the experiment must be in the outer 5% of the randomization distribution. Whether the 5% is defined to be in just one of the tails (called a *one-sided* or *one-tailed* test) or split into 2.5% in each tail (called a *two-sided* or *two-tailed* test) depends on the situation.

The selection of the particular percentage also depends on the situation. This percentage, typically 5%, is called the "significance level" and has the symbol alpha, α.

We call a difference "statistically significant" if it is in the outer 2.5% of either tail. This is fairly standard practice and consistent with the "rare event" language used for outcomes that fall in the outer 5% of their probability distribution.

a. **i.** The difference probably will not be the same as in Problem 1 Part c.

   ii. The histogram of 50 differences, *mean of calculator group − mean of pencil-and-paper group*, using the data from the class of 16 students in Problem 1 appears at the right.

Calculators vs. Pencil-and-Paper

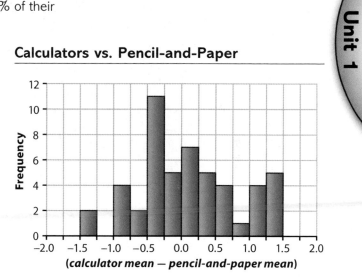

(calculator mean − pencil-and-paper mean)

b. The distribution is centered at 0. This makes sense because of the symmetry in the random allocation of subjects to treatments. For example, you are just as likely to get the 8 highest scores in the calculator treatment group and the 8 lowest scores in the pencil-and-paper group as you are to get the reverse. Consequently, the difference is just as likely to be +1.875 as −1.875. (This is not very likely as the probability of getting the 8 highest scores in one group and the 8 lowest scores in the other is only $2 \cdot \binom{16}{8} \approx \frac{1}{6,435}$.)

c. Answers will vary, but it is likely that the actual difference will not be in the tails of the distribution.

d. If the difference in the means from the actual experiment is not in the tails, then the difference is about what you would expect if the treatments were equally effective. That is, the difference in means is relatively small and can reasonably be attributed solely to the particular random assignment of treatments to students. You should conclude that there is no evidence that one of the treatments is more effective than the other.

If the difference in the means from the actual experiment is in a tail of the distribution, conclude that one treatment is more effective than the other in causing a larger mean.

The actual difference in means of 0.375 from the class of 16 students is near the middle of the distribution, not in the tails, and so is about what you would expect if the treatment made no difference whatsoever.

INSTRUCTIONAL NOTE
You may want to discuss what treatments might have made a difference on this test. Possibilities include access to Internet versus no access to Internet and use of computer software versus no use of computer software.

a. Does this study have the three characteristics of a well-designed experiment?

b. Why did some subjects have to wear an unscented mask?

c. Compute summary statistics and make plots to help you decide whether one type of mask results in shorter times to complete the mazes.

d. From your summaries, you found that people who wore the unscented mask took an average of 8.19 seconds longer to complete the mazes than people who wore the scented mask. Do you think that the scented mask causes a shorter mean time to complete the mazes or do you think that the difference of 8.19 seconds is no more extreme than you would expect just by chance?

④ Assume that the type of mask in Problem 3 makes absolutely no difference in how long it takes a person to complete the mazes.

a. Why would you expect there to be a nonzero difference anyway in the mean times for the two treatments?

b. How long should it take the people who wore the unscented masks to complete the mazes if they had worn scented masks instead?

c. Now suppose that you are the researcher beginning this experiment and need to pick 7 of the 13 nonsmokers to wear the unscented mask.

- Write, on identical slips of paper, the 13 maze-completing times given in the table on page 82.

- Mix them up well. Draw 7 of them to represent the 7 people who will wear the unscented mask. Compute their mean time. Compute the mean time of the remaining 6 people.

- Subtract: *unscented mean − scented mean*.

Compare your result with that of others.

INSTRUCTIONAL NOTE Students may ask why there are not equal sample sizes in the mask experiment. Equal sample sizes are somewhat better when it comes to the analysis, but people often drop out of experiments after the randomization is done. In this particular case, there happened to be 13 nonsmokers among the larger number of volunteers.

a. Maybe. Subjects were randomly assigned to treatments, and there is a treatment group (scented masks) and a control group (unscented masks). However, the number of subjects may be too small for any effect to show up as statistically significant.

b. Perhaps just wearing a mask makes people work mazes faster or slower. So to isolate the effect of the scent, which was the point of the experiment, all subjects must be treated the same except for the scent. Thus, the "control group" must also wear a mask even though it has no scent.

c.

Treatment	Mean	SD	Subjects
Unscented	53.44	18.49	7
Scented	45.25	8.80	6

Unscented Mask

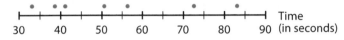

Scented Mask

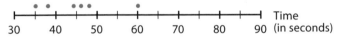

The difference in the means is 8.19 seconds.

d. The difference is fairly large, but there is a lot of overlap in the distributions. The sample sizes are small, so it is difficult to decide.

④ **INSTRUCTIONAL NOTE** CPMP-Tools software is available for download at www.wmich.edu/cpmp/CPMP-Tools/. The "Randomization Distribution" feature of CPMP-Tools is in the Statistics strand. The times for the mask experiment are built into the software. Before starting the resampling of the times to complete the mazes, students should look at either the display in the text or the opening screen of the "Randomization Distribution." Ask them to study the display to note the red and blue scented and unscented times to complete the mazes and the histogram settings in the lower left-hand corner. Then ask students what the display in their textbooks shows. Once this discussion occurs, students will be ready to watch "Randomization Distribution" create a histogram of the difference in means of the random assignments of subjects to treatments. A Technology Tip for this feature of CPMP-Tools is included in the Unit 1 Resource Masters.

a. It would be incredibly lucky to get a difference of *exactly* 0 from real data, especially with this small sample.

b. It should take the same amount of time as it did when they wore the scented masks because that is what we are supposing.

c. The results from the runs will vary.

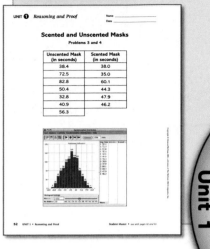
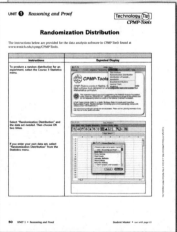
TECHNOLOGY NOTE
These data are in CPMP-Tools. When using CPMP-Tools, it is best to adjust the width of the bars of the histogram using the box rather than the slider.

Unit 1

d. A faster way to construct an approximate distribution from many randomizations is to use statistical software to randomly select groups. The "Randomization Distribution" feature of *CPMP-Tools* created this approximate distribution of possible differences (*unscented mean − scented mean*).

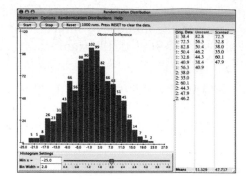

The display shows 1,000 runs of randomly assigning the 13 times required to complete the mazes to either the unscented mask treatment (7 times) or the scented mask treatment (6 times). Out of these 1,000 differences, about how many times is the difference at least as extreme as 8.19 seconds? If the scent made absolutely no difference, estimate the probability that you would get a difference as extreme as 8.19 seconds just by random chance.

e. Which of the following is the best conclusion?

- The difference of 8.19 from the actual experiment is extreme, so you should abandon your supposition that the scent made no difference.

- It is quite plausible that the scent does not affect the time to complete the maze. In other words, a difference of 8.19 seconds would not be unusual if the scent made no difference and you randomly divide the subjects into two groups.

 Look back at the results of your penny-stacking experiment in the Think About This Situation on page 75.

a. Compute the difference for your class: *mean number of pennies stacked by those using their dominant hand − mean for those using their nondominant hand*. Suppose that the hand people use makes absolutely no difference in how many pennies they can stack. Why, then, would there almost always be a nonzero difference in every class that does this experiment?

d. From the randomization distribution in the student text, at least 147 of the 1,000 runs produced a difference larger than 8.19. At least 141 runs produced a difference smaller than −8.19, so the estimated probability is 0.288.

e. The second conclusion is best. The difference of 8.19 from the actual experiment is not in the tails of the distribution. So, there is no reason to abandon your supposition that the type of mask made no difference. You should conclude that it is quite plausible that the scent did not affect the response and that the difference of 8.19 seconds can be reasonably attributed to the random assignment alone.

5 The number of pennies stacked by 54 students are given in the table below.

a.

Number of Pennies Stacked

Dominant Hand	Nondominant Hand	Dominant Hand	Nondominant Hand
27	6	16	36
52	12	42	45
39	14	47	45
25	26	18	46
25	26	35	51
22	26	30	7
32	27	27	17
52	29	29	17
29	31	37	18
26	32	54	19
35	33	54	12
16	34	18	30
41	35	30	28
30	36	Mean ≈ 32.89	Mean ≈ 27.33

Here, *dominant mean − nondominant mean* ≈ 5.56.

Because of the chance involved in stacking pennies, it would be very unusual to get the same mean number of pennies stacked by the two groups. Even if the same person stacks pennies twice with the same hand, he or she is unlikely to end up with the same number.

TECHNOLOGY NOTE
These data are in *CPMP-Tools* but it would be best to use data from your students.

Unit 1

Statistical Reasoning **T84**

b. If which hand you used made absolutely no difference, how many pennies would you have been able to stack if you had used your other hand?

c. Use the "Randomization Distribution" feature of *CPMP-Tools* to create an approximate distribution of the possible differences (*dominant hand mean − nondominant hand mean*). Run at least 500 random assignments, continuing until the shape of the distribution stabilizes.

d. How many times did you get a simulated difference as extreme as what you got in your experiment? If which hand you use makes no difference, estimate the probability that you would get a difference as extreme as what you got in your experiment just by random chance.

e. Should you conclude that the hand you used made a difference?

The reasoning that you followed in Problems 1–5 to decide whether the results of an experiment provide convincing evidence that different treatments cause a different mean response is called a **randomization test** (or, sometimes, **permutation test**). The steps below summarize this reasoning.

Step 1. Assume that which treatment each subject gets makes absolutely no difference in his or her response. In other words, assume the subjects in the experiment would give the same response no matter which treatment they receive. In the next two steps, you will see if this assumption is plausible.

Step 2. Simulate the experiment.
- Write the name of each subject along with his or her response on a card.
- Randomly divide the cards into two treatment groups.
- Compute the mean for each treatment group.
- Find the difference of these means.
- Repeat this many times until you can see the shape of the distribution of differences.

Step 3. Locate the difference from the actual experiment on the distribution you generated in Step 2.

Step 4. If the difference from the actual experiment is in the outer 5% of the distribution, conclude that the results are **statistically significant**. That is, you have evidence that the treatments caused the difference in the mean response. If the difference is not in the outer 5% of the distribution, conclude that your original assumption was plausible. The difference can be reasonably attributed solely to the particular random assignment of treatments to subjects.

b. If which hand was used made no difference, students would expect to stack about the same number of pennies with either hand.

c–d. INSTRUCTIONAL NOTE Responses will vary depending on your class results. If the randomization distribution shows a probability of 0.05 or less of getting a difference as extreme or even more extreme as the actual difference from your class, then you should conclude that the hand used made a difference.

For the sample data, using 1,000 runs in the "Randomization Distribution" feature of *CPMP-Tools* resulted in about 70 of the 1,000 differences being above 5.56 or below −5.56. So, the probability of getting a difference as extreme as 5.56 just by chance is about 0.070.

e. For the data above, conclude that you do not have evidence that the hand used made any difference.

TECHNOLOGY NOTE If the software is not available, write the numbers of pennies stacked by the members of your class on identical small slips of paper. Mix them up well. Draw out half of them to represent the students who used their dominant hand. Compute the mean number of pennies stacked. Compute the mean for the remaining slips of paper (that represent those using their nondominant hand). Subtract *dominant mean − nondominant mean*. Repeat until you have 100 differences.

FORMAL WORDING OF THE LOGIC OF RANDOMIZATION TESTS

- Suppose that each subject will respond the same way no matter which treatment he or she gets. Call this the *null hypothesis*.

- Randomly divide the available subjects into the two treatment groups, give the treatments, and record the responses.

- Generate a *randomization* distribution that shows the difference in the mean response from many different possible randomizations of the subjects to the treatments, still assuming that the null hypothesis is true.

- Decide if the difference from the actual experiment would be extreme (a rare event) if the null hypothesis is true.

- If not, you cannot reject the null hypothesis. If so, you can reject the null hypothesis and conclude that the treatments did make a difference in the mean response.

Unit 1

Chrysanthemums with long stems are likely to have smaller flowers than chrysanthemums with shorter stems. An experiment was conducted at the University of Florida to compare growth inhibitors designed to reduce the length of the stems, and so, increase the size of the flowers. Growth inhibitor A was given to 10 randomly selected plants. Growth inhibitor B was given to the remaining 10 plants. The plants were grown under nearly identical conditions, except for the growth inhibitor used. The table below gives the amount of growth during the subsequent 10 weeks.

Growth by Plants Given A (in cm)	Growth by Plants Given B (in cm)
46	51
41.5	55
45	57
44	57.5
41.5	53
50	45.5
45	53
43	54.5
44	55.5
30.5	45.5

Source: Ann E. Watkins, Richard L. Scheaffer, and George W. Cobb, *Statistics in Action*, 2nd Ed. Key Curriculum Press, 2008, p. 802.

a. Does this experiment have the three characteristics of a well-designed experiment?

b. Examine the following summary statistics and plots. Which growth inhibitor treatment appears to be better?

Treatment	Mean	Standard Deviation	Number of Plants
A	43.05	5.04	10
B	52.75	4.28	10

Inhibitor A

Inhibitor B

c. Describe how to use a randomization test to decide whether, on average, one growth inhibitor works better than the other.

6 **a.** Yes. The treatments were assigned randomly to the plants. Ten plants turns out to be enough per treatment to see a statistically significant effect (but students will not know that until Part d). There are two treatments being compared.

b. Treatment A appears to be better because there is less growth, on average, and there is not a lot of overlap between the two distributions.

c. Begin by making the assumption that the particular treatment each plant got made no difference in its growth. Write the 20 measurements representing the 20 plants on 20 slips of paper. Mix them thoroughly and deal out 10 to be "given" treatment A. The rest of the plants will be "given" treatment B. Because we are assuming that the treatment makes no difference in the growth, the response for each plant will be the same as in the actual experiment. Compute the mean for each treatment group and subtract: *mean for A − mean for B*. Repeat this many times until you see the shape of the distribution. Alternatively, you could use the "Randomization Distribution" feature of the data analysis software in *CPMP-Tools*.

d. The distribution of 500 runs of random assignment using *CPMP-Tools* gave no difference as extreme as −9.70. (Adding five new means to the histogram on the student master will not change its general shape.)

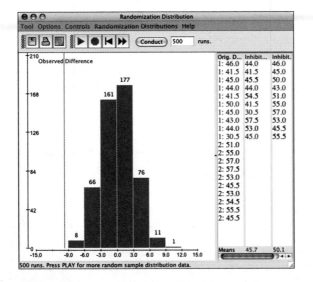

e. The difference from the actual experiment is *mean for A − mean for B* = 43.05 − 52.75 = −9.70. There is almost no chance of getting a difference at least as extreme as −9.70 if the type of growth inhibitor makes no difference.

f. Conclude that the difference from the actual experiment is so large that it must be a result of the growth inhibitors and not just a result of the particular random assignment of treatments to plants. The difference is statistically significant.

INSTRUCTIONAL NOTE
Be sure that students understand that the table in the student text gives the amount of *growth* during the subsequent 10 weeks. That is, each response is the difference *final height − initial height*. Thus, smaller numbers are better.

NOTE The probability of getting a difference as extreme or even more extreme than that from the actual experiment, under the assumption that the treatments have the same effect, is called the *P-value*.

NOTE Treatment A works better but notice that there is more variability in the results from treatment A. That is common in experiments. When a treatment works, it is common for the experimental units given that treatment to show more variability than experimental units given a less effective treament. When a treatment is not effective, similar experimental units tend to behave the same way.

Unit 1

d. Use the "Randomization Distribution" feature of *CPMP-Tools* to create an approximate distribution of possible differences (*growth inhibitor A mean − growth inhibitor B mean*). Run at least 500 random assignments.

e. If the type of growth inhibitor makes no difference, what is your estimate of the probability of getting a difference at least as extreme as the difference from the actual experiment?

f. What is your conclusion? Is the difference statistically significant?

Summarize the Mathematics

In this investigation, you explored the randomization test. This test is one method of determining whether a difference between two treatment groups can be reasonably attributed to the random assignment of treatments to subjects or whether you should believe that the treatments caused the difference.

a Explain why this statement is true: Even if the response for each subject would be the same no matter which treatment he or she receives, there is almost always a nonzero difference in the means of the actual responses from the two treatments.

b What does it mean if the results of an experiment are called "statistically significant"?

c Explain the reasoning behind the steps of a randomization test.

d Explain how this statement applies to the reasoning in this unit: Statistical reasoning is different from mathematical proof because in statistics, you can never say you are certain.

Be prepared to share your responses and thinking with the class.

✔ Check Your Understanding

Forty-nine volunteer college students were randomly assigned to two treatments. Twenty-five students were told that they would view a video of a teacher who other students thought was "charismatic": lively, stimulating, and encouraging. The remaining twenty-four students were told that the instructor they would view was thought to be "punitive": not helpful, not interested in students, and a hard grader. Then all students watched the same twenty-minute lecture given by the same instructor. Following the lecture, subjects rated the lecturer. The students' summary ratings are given below. Higher ratings are better.

Charismatic: $1\frac{2}{3}$, 3, $1\frac{2}{3}$, $2\frac{1}{3}$, 4, $2\frac{1}{3}$, 2, $2\frac{2}{3}$, $2\frac{2}{3}$, $2\frac{1}{3}$, $3\frac{1}{3}$, $2\frac{1}{3}$,

$2\frac{1}{3}$, $2\frac{2}{3}$, 3, $2\frac{2}{3}$, 3, 2, $2\frac{1}{3}$, $2\frac{2}{3}$, 3, $3\frac{1}{3}$, 3, $2\frac{2}{3}$, $2\frac{1}{3}$

Punitive: $2\frac{2}{3}$, 2, 2, $1\frac{1}{3}$, $1\frac{2}{3}$, $2\frac{1}{3}$, $2\frac{2}{3}$, 2, $1\frac{2}{3}$, $1\frac{1}{3}$, $2\frac{1}{3}$, 2,

$2\frac{1}{3}$, $2\frac{1}{3}$, $2\frac{1}{3}$, $2\frac{1}{3}$, $1\frac{2}{3}$, $3\frac{1}{3}$, $2\frac{1}{3}$, $2\frac{2}{3}$, 2, $2\frac{1}{3}$, $2\frac{1}{3}$, $3\frac{1}{3}$

Summarize
the Mathematics

NOTE Solutions to Problem 6 Parts d f are on page T86.

Unit 1

ⓐ Even if the two treatments would not differ in their effect on a given subject, there will almost always be a nonzero difference in the means of the responses because (1) the subjects in the two treatment groups were not exactly alike before the treatment was applied and (2) it is very unusual in any situation involving chance for things to work out exactly as expected (for example, it would be very unusual to flip a coin 1,000 times and get exactly 500 heads).

ⓑ "Statistically significant" means that it is unreasonable to attribute the results from the experiment solely to the random assignment of treatments to subjects. In other words, the researcher is saying that he or she believes that the results of the experiment establish that one treatment causes a larger mean response than the other.

ⓒ Begin by making the assumption that the particular treatment each subject received made no difference in its response. You have to make this assumption in order to create the randomization distribution, but you may reject it later as not plausible. Write the name of each subject on a slip of paper, mix the slips thoroughly, and deal out the same number as received in the first treatment. The rest of the subjects will be "given" the second treatment. Because you are assuming that the treatment makes no difference in the response, the response for each subject will be the same as in the actual experiment. Compute the mean for each treatment group and subtract *mean for first treatment − mean for second treatment*. Repeat this many times until you see the shape of the distribution. If the difference from the actual experiment is not in a tail of the distribution, then there is no reason to abandon the assumption that the treatments made no difference. If the difference from the actual experiment is in a tail of the randomization distribution, the assumption that the treatments made no difference is not plausible. Conclude that the treatments caused the difference in the mean response. The reasoning is similar to that of proof by contradiction. If you suspect something is true, assume the opposite and then look for evidence that this assumption leads to something that is not plausible.

ⓓ No matter which conclusion you come to after an experiment, you could be wrong. For example, it is possible that if there were more subjects in the scented masks experiment, then the difference in the means would be statistically significant. On the other hand, it is possible that the two treatments in the chrysanthemum experiment really do not have a different effect on the plants, but the ones that were going to grow less just happened to be assigned to treatment A. The probability of that is very small, however, as shown by the randomization distribution.

Treatment	Mean	Standard Deviation	Number of Students
Charismatic	2.61	0.53	25
Punitive	2.24	0.54	24

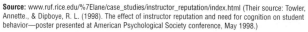

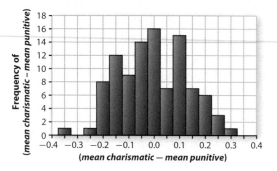

Source: www.ruf.rice.edu/%7Elane/case_studies/instructor_reputation/index.html (Their source: Towler, Annette., & Dipboye, R. L. (1998). The effect of instructor reputation and need for cognition on student behavior—poster presented at American Psychological Society conference, May 1998.)

a. What are the two treatments?

b. From the box plots and summary statistics, does it look like the two treatments cause different responses? Explain.

c. Describe how to perform one run for a randomization test to decide whether the two different treatments result in different mean ratings.

d. The randomization distribution below shows *mean charismatic − mean punitive* for 100 runs. Use the histogram to estimate the probability of getting a difference as extreme as that from the actual experiment if the treatment makes no difference.

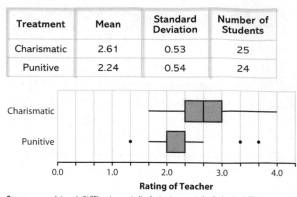

e. What is your conclusion? Is the difference statistically significant?

✔ Check Your Understanding

a. The two treatments are (1) being told before seeing the lecture that the instructor was thought to be charismatic and (2) being told that the instructor was thought to be punitive.

b. Although there is some overlap in the distributions of the responses, it looks like it would be unreasonable to attribute the difference in the means of the distributions to chance alone.

c. Begin by making the assumption that the particular treatment each subject received made no difference in his or her response. Write the 49 measurements representing the 49 subjects on 49 slips of paper. Mix them thoroughly and deal out 25 to represent the students who will get the "charismatic" treatment. The remaining 24 subjects will be "given" the "punitive" treatment. Because we are assuming that the treatment makes no difference in the response, the response for each subject will be the same as in the actual experiment. Compute the mean for each treatment group and subtract *mean for charismatic treatment − mean for punitive treatment*.

d. The difference from the actual experiment is *mean for charismatic treatment − mean for punitive treatment* = 2.61 − 2.24 = 0.37. This difference does not seem large, but a difference this extreme happened only once in 100 runs. The estimated probability is 0.01.

e. Conclude that the difference from the actual experiment is so large that it must be caused by the difference in the two treatments and is not just a result of the particular random assignment of treatments to students. The difference is statistically significant.

INSTRUCTIONAL NOTE

These data are in *CPMP-Tools*. Students may wish to create a distribution that has 500 or more runs to answer this Check Your Understanding.

Teaching Resources

Student Master 55.

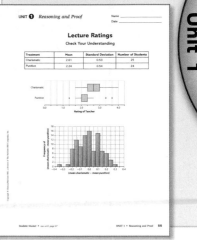

Unit 1

Investigation 3 — Statistical Studies

Experiments are one of the three major types of statistical studies. The other two are *sample surveys* and *observational studies*. As you work on the problems in this investigation, look for answers to these questions:

> *What are the differences between sample surveys, experiments, and observational studies?*

> *What kind of conclusions can be made from each?*

The three main types of statistical studies are described below.

- **sample survey or poll**: You observe a random sample in order to estimate a characteristic of the larger population from which the sample was taken. Getting a **random sample of size *n*** is equivalent to writing the name of every member of the population on a card, mixing the cards well, and drawing *n* cards.

- **experiment**: You randomly assign two (or more) treatments to the available subjects in order to see which treatment is the most effective.

- **observational study**: The conditions you want to compare come already built into the subjects that are observed. Typically, no randomization is involved.

1 Suppose you want to investigate the effects of exercise on the blood pressure of students in your school. You have thought about three different study designs. Classify each design as a sample survey, an experiment, or an observational study.

Study 1: You ask for volunteers from the students in your school and get 30 students willing to participate in your study. You randomly divide them into two groups of 15 students. You ask one group not to exercise at all for the next week, and you ask the other group to do at least 30 minutes of exercise each day. At the end of the week, you find that everyone complied with your instructions. You then take each student's blood pressure. You find that the mean blood pressure of the students who exercised is lower than the mean blood pressure of the students who did not exercise.

Study 2: You get a list of all students in your school and use a random digit table to select 30 of them for your study. You take these students' blood pressure and then have them fill out a questionnaire about how much exercise they get. You divide them into those who exercise a lot and those who exercise less. You find that the mean blood pressure of the students who exercise more is lower than the mean blood pressure of the students who exercise less.

In this investigation, students learn to distinguish between the three types of statistical studies: surveys or polls in which questions are asked of a sample from a larger population, experiments where treatments are randomly assigned to the available subjects, and observational studies in which no randomization is involved. They learn what conclusions can be drawn from each type of study.

Three Main Types of Statistical Studies Experiments are one method used to compare two groups. Surveys and observational studies provide two other methods. The results must be interpreted differently, however, depending on which type of study is used to collect the data.

In a sample survey to compare two groups, a random sample is taken from each of two populations. The purpose of a survey is to generalize from a difference in the samples to a difference in the population from which they were drawn.

In an observational study, random selection is not involved in the data collection. An observational study can sometimes establish that two variables are associated—more of one tends to be associated with more (or less) of the other—but an observational study cannot establish cause and effect. Generalization to a larger population is often difficult from an observational study. Both observational studies and experiments should be repeated a number of times on different populations before results become generally accepted.

(1) For more information about exercise and blood pressure, see:
www.kidshealth.org/teen/diseases_conditions/heart/hypertension.html,
www.mayoclinic.com/health/high-blood-pressure/Hl00024, or
www.massgeneral.org/children/adolescenthealth/articles/
aa_high_blood_pressure.aspx

Study 1: Experiment since you randomly divided the available subjects into two groups that received different treatments

Study 2: Sample survey since you took a random sample from a larger population

Study 3: You discover that the nurse in the health office at your school has taken the blood pressure of 157 students who have visited the health office over the past year for a variety of reasons. In some cases, they felt sick; and in other cases, they had to turn in routine paperwork. You get the names of these students and have them fill out a questionnaire about how much exercise they get. You find that the mean blood pressure of the students who exercise more is lower than the mean blood pressure of the students who exercise less.

2 In each study in Problem 1, there was an association between amount of exercise and blood pressure. Assume that in each case the difference in mean blood pressure was statistically significant. Answer the following questions for each study in Problem 1.

a. Is it reasonable to conclude that it was the exercise that caused the lower blood pressure? Explain your thinking.

b. Can you generalize the results of this study to all of the students in your school? Explain your thinking.

c. Exactly what can you conclude from this study?

3 Refer to Problem 6 Part c on page 80 about students who take AP examinations in high school.

a. What type of study is this?

b. State the conclusion that can be drawn.

4 Every four years, the Gallup organization tries to predict the winner of the U.S. presidential election. They do this by first creating a list of all possible household phone numbers in the United States. They then phone several thousand households using random digit dialing, calling back if no one answers. An adult is selected at random from each household and interviewed about whether he or she intends to vote and for whom. (Source: Frank Newport, Lydia Saad, David Moore "How are polls conducted?" *Where America Stands*, Wiley, 1997, media.gallup.com/PDF/FAQ/HowArePolls.pdf)

a. What type of study is this?

b. Explain why households cannot be selected from phone books.

c. Are all adults in the United States equally likely to be in the sample? Explain.

Study 3: Observational study since there was no randomization

(2) Study 1

a. Yes. Although many things other than exercise can cause lower blood pressure, these variables should have been spread out about equally between the two treatments by the random assignment. The only major difference in the two groups, therefore, should have been the amount of exercise the students did during the week.

b. No. The students who volunteered for this experiment may have been different in some important way from the other students in your school. You can generalize the results of the experiment only to those who participated. (This is a common potential difficulty with a typical medical experiment. Volunteers can be different from other patients and so the results of the experiment cannot be generalized to the population at large.)

c. In this group of 30 students, students who exercised over a week tended to have lower blood pressure than students who did not exercise during the week. It is reasonable to conclude that the exercise caused the lower blood pressure.

Study 2

a. No. It is possible that students with lower blood pressure feel more like exercising and so do it more than students with higher blood pressure. That is, it is the lower blood pressure that causes the exercise. Alternatively, a lurking variable such as stress or weight causes both higher blood pressure and less tendency to exercise.

b. Yes. Because the students in your study were a random sample from the students in your school, there is no reason to think they should be any different from the other students. Thus, the results should generalize to all students in your school.

c. You have reason to believe that if you were to check the blood pressure of all students in your school and how much exercise each student does, you would find that those who exercise more have lower blood pressure, on average, than those who exercise less.

Study 3

a. No. As in Part b, it is possible that students with lower blood pressure feel more like exercising and so do it more than students with higher blood pressure. That is, it is the lower blood pressure that causes the exercise. Alternatively, a lurking variable such as stress or weight causes both higher blood pressure and less tendency to exercise.

b. No. Although some students who visit the health center do so just to turn in routine paperwork, many students will be those who do not feel well. You should not assume that these students are typical of the other students in your school with respect to blood pressure and exercise.

c. You can conclude only that among students who have visited the health center and had their blood pressure taken, those who exercise more have lower blood pressure on average than those who exercise less. You do not know whether exercise causes lower blood pressure or whether this result can be generalized to all students in your school.

a. Unless the students were randomly assigned to try an AP exam or not (which is unlikely), this is an observational study.

b. You can conclude only that among the 78,079 students in Texas who were studied, students who failed AP exams are twice as likely to graduate from college as those students who did not try AP exams. You cannot generalize to any larger group of students. You cannot conclude that it was trying an AP exam that caused a higher college graduation rate.

 a. This is a sample survey. Participants are selected at random from the U.S. households that have phones, which is almost all households.

b. Households cannot be selected from phone books because a lot (around 30%) of household phone numbers are unlisted. These people might have different political preferences than people who list their phone numbers.

c. No. Adults without phones cannot be in the sample. People who are never at home cannot be in the sample. An adult who lives in the same household with many other adults is less likely to be in the sample than an adult who lives by himself or herself. (Gallup weights the results to balance the latter problem.)

Teacher Notes

Summarize the Mathematics

In this investigation, you examined the three main types of statistical studies.

a What is a random sample?

b How is randomization used in a sample survey? In an experiment? In an observational study?

c What kind of conclusion can you draw from a sample survey? From an experiment? From an observational study?

Be prepared to share your responses with the class.

✔ Check Your Understanding

The British Doctors Study was one of the earliest studies to establish a link between smoking and lung cancer. In 1951, all male doctors in the United Kingdom were contacted. About two-thirds, or 34,439 doctors, agreed to participate. Eventually, researchers found that the doctors who smoked were more likely to get lung cancer than doctors who did not smoke. The difference was statistically significant. (Source: Richard Doll, *et al.* "Mortality in Relation to Smoking: 50 Years' Observations on Male British Doctors," *British Medical Journal*, Vol. 22, June 2004, www.bmj.com/cgi/reprint/bmj.38142.554479.AEv1)

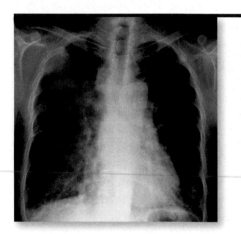

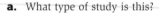

a. What type of study is this?

b. Can you conclude from this study that smoking causes lung cancer? Explain your thinking.

c. Can you generalize the results of this study to some larger population? Explain your thinking.

d. Describe exactly what you can conclude from this study.

Summarize
the Mathematics

Teaching Resources

Transparency Master 56.

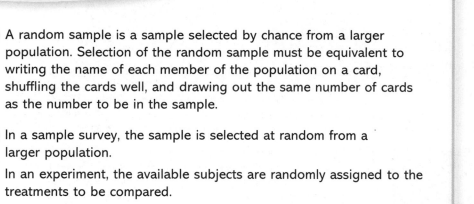

UNIT **1** *Reasoning and Proof*

Summarize
the Mathematics

In this investigation, you examined the three main types of statistical studies.

a What is a random sample?

b How is randomization used in a sample survey? In an experiment? In an observational study?

c What kind of conclusion can you draw from a sample survey? From an experiment? From an observational study?

Be prepared to share your responses with the class.

56   UNIT I • Reasoning and Proof   Transparency Master • see unit page 91

Unit 1

a A random sample is a sample selected by chance from a larger population. Selection of the random sample must be equivalent to writing the name of each member of the population on a card, shuffling the cards well, and drawing out the same number of cards as the number to be in the sample.

b In a sample survey, the sample is selected at random from a larger population.

In an experiment, the available subjects are randomly assigned to the treatments to be compared.

In an observational study, typically there is no random selection or random assignment.

c You can generalize the results of a sample survey, where the sample is selected randomly, to the larger population.

From an experiment, you can determine whether one treatment causes a different effect than another treatment, at least among the subjects used in the experiment.

From an observational study, you can determine that two variables are associated but only for the group you observed. You cannot generalize to a larger population or infer that a change in one variable causes a change in another variable.

✓ Check Your Understanding

a. This was an observational study. There was no random selection of doctors from a larger group, so it was not a sample survey. Smoking or not smoking were not randomly assigned to the doctors, so this was not an experiment.

b. No. Doctors who smoke might have associated behaviors that cause the lung cancer. For example, they may be more stressed, or live more often in urban areas, or drink more alcohol than doctors who do not smoke.

c. No. The doctors who participated were not selected at random from some larger population.

d. All you can conclude is that, among the 34,439 doctors who participated in this study, the ones who smoked were more likely to get lung cancer than the ones who did not smoke.

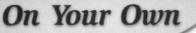

On Your Own

Applications

1 Suppose that the manufacturer of a cough medicine wants to conduct a randomized, double-blind experiment to determine if adding a new ingredient results in a reduction in the mean number of coughs per hour. Fifty adult volunteers with persistent coughs are available. Describe how the manufacturer should conduct this experiment.

2 The table below gives the overall driver death rate for various sizes of four-door cars. There is a strong association between the weight of a car and driver death rate. However, there are many advantages to lighter cars. They tend to be easier to park, to get better gas mileage, to be less polluting, to have cheaper insurance, and to be less expensive to buy. So, it is worth carefully considering whether they are really less safe.

Weight of Car (in lbs)	Overall Driver Death Rate (per million registered vehicle years)
2,500 or less	115
2,501–3,000	102
3,001–3,500	84
3,501–4,000	56
4,001–4,500	47

Source: *The Risk Of Dying In One Vehicle Versus Another: Driver Death Rates By Make And Model,* Insurance Institute for Highway Safety, Status Report special issue: March 19, 2005.

a. Describe the association between the weight of a car and driver death rate.

b. Suppose that 4,000,000 of a certain model of car are registered, and there were 467 driver deaths over a three-year period. What would be the overall driver death rate per million registered vehicle years for that particular model of car?

c. Name a possible lurking variable. Describe how it could account for the association between the weight of a car and driver death rate.

d. How could you design an experiment to provide convincing evidence that lighter cars cause a larger overall driver death rate than heavier cars? Would this be ethical?

Applications

1. Make up 50 bottles of cough syrup that look and taste identical, except that 25 bottles contain the new ingredient and 25 do not. Assign the bottles at random to the 50 volunteer subjects. Give each person a predetermined amount of cough syrup. Preferably, keep the people in the same environment for the next few hours (or however long the medicine is expected to be effective). Have evaluators who do not know which treatment the subjects received count the number of coughs. Compare the mean number of coughs per hour for the two groups.

2. **a.** The larger the weight of the car, the lower the overall driver death rate.

   b. $\dfrac{467 \text{ deaths}}{(4 \text{ million registered vehicles})(3 \text{ years})} \approx 38.92$ deaths per million registered vehicle years

   c. First, note that the possibility that there may be fewer larger cars cannot be a lurking variable because overall driver deaths are measured as a rate, in million registered vehicle years. A lurking variable may be that larger cars tend to be driven fewer miles per year than smaller cars (possibly because they use more gas), subjecting the drivers to less risk. Another possible lurking variable is that safer drivers buy larger cars because they expect them to be safer. A likely lurking variable is the age of the drivers. Older drivers tend to like larger cars, and they also tend to be safer, more careful drivers.

   d. You would have to randomly assign cars to the drivers. Even if drivers volunteered for this experiment, it would probably not be ethical because there is little doubt, from the crash-test dummy experiments, that larger cars are indeed, in general, safer. However, it might be ethical if you selected only drivers of small cars and randomly assigned half of them to larger cars.

3 Psychrotrophic bacteria cause meat to spoil. Six beef steaks were randomly assigned to be packaged using commercial plastic wrap or to be vacuum packaged. The following table gives the logarithm (log) of the number of psychrotrophic bacteria per square centimeter on the meat after nine days of storage at controlled temperature.

Commercial Plastic Wrap log (count/cm²)	Vacuum Packaged log (count/cm²)
7.66	5.26
6.98	5.44
7.80	5.80

Source: Robert O. Kuehl, *Statistical Principles of Research Design and Analysis*, Duxbury Press, Belmont, CA, 1994, p. 31. Original source: B. Nichols, *Comparison of Grain-Fed and Grass-Fed Beef for Quality Changes When Packaged in Various Gas Atmospheres and Vacuum*, M.S. thesis, Department of Animal Science, University of Arizona, 1980.

a. How many bacteria per square centimeter were on the steak with a log of 7.66?

b. Does this study have the three characteristics of a well-designed experiment? What else would you like to know about how it was conducted?

c. What is the difference *mean (log) response for commercial plastic wrap − mean (log) response for vacuum packaged*?

d. Describe how to conduct a randomization test to decide whether the different packaging causes different numbers of bacteria. Perform 10 runs and add them to a copy of the randomization distribution below, which shows the results of 90 runs.

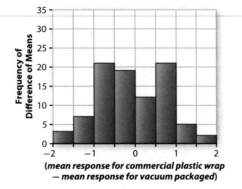

(*mean response for commercial plastic wrap − mean response for vacuum packaged*)

e. Use the randomization distribution to estimate the probability that random assignment alone will give you a difference that is at least as extreme as that from the real experiment. Do you have evidence from this experiment that one type of packaging is better than the other?

3   **a.** $10^{7.66} \approx 45,708,800$ bacteria per square centimeter

     b. Two treatments were being compared. The two treatments were randomly assigned to the six steaks. The sample size seems much too small for there to be a statistically significant difference, no matter how the experiment turns out. We would like to know why only six steaks were used.

     c. *mean response for commercial plastic wrap − mean response for vacuum packaged* = $7.48 - 5.5 = 1.98$

     d. Begin by making the assumption that the particular packaging of each steak made no difference in the log of the number of bacteria. Write the 6 measurements representing the 6 steaks on 6 slips of paper. Mix them thoroughly and deal out 3 to be "given" the plastic wrap. The remaining 3 steaks will be "given" the vacuum packaging. Because we are assuming that the treatment makes no difference in the response, the response for each steak will be the same as in the actual experiment. Compute the mean for each treatment group and subtract: *mean for commercial plastic wrap − mean for vacuum packaging.* Repeat this many times until you see the shape of the distribution. If the difference from the actual experiment is not in a tail of the distribution, there is no reason to abandon the assumption that the packaging made no difference. If the difference from the actual experiment is in a tail of the distribution, the assumption that the packaging made no difference is not plausible. So, you should conclude that the different packaging caused the difference in the means of the logs of bacteria count.

     e. Answers will depend on the student's 10 runs. Adding 10 runs to the distribution in the student text will probably not change its basic shape. For the 90 runs given, the difference from the randomization was more extreme (larger in absolute value) than that from the actual experiment at most 6 times out of 90, or about 0.067. So, you do not have convincing evidence from this experiment that the vacuum packaging causes a different mean log (bacteria count) than the commercial plastic wrap, but it is close.

Unit 1

4 For a science project, Brian wanted to determine whether eleventh-graders did better when they took a math test in silence or when Mozart was being played. Twenty-six students were randomly divided into the two treatment groups. Part of Brian's results are in the table below.

Mozart (percentage correct)	Silence (percentage correct)
65	44
80	70
72	68
68	58
38	58
58	47
45	54
42	44
58	61
81	61
40	9
41	52
27	30
Mean = 55	**Mean ≈ 50.46**

a. What is the difference *mean response for Mozart group − mean response for silence group*?

b. Describe how to conduct a randomization test to decide whether the different treatments cause different performance on the math test.

c. Use the "Randomization Distribution" feature of your data analysis software to create an approximate distribution of the possible differences (*mean response for Mozart group − mean response for silence group*). Run at least 500 random assignments.

d. Use the randomization distribution to estimate the probability that you could get a difference, just by the random assignment, that is as extreme as that from the real experiment.

e. Brian concluded that students who listen to Mozart during a test tend to do better. Do you agree with this conclusion or do you think the difference can reasonably be attributed to the random assignment alone?

(4) **NOTE** This task is based on a real science experiment done by a middle school student. See www.selah.k12.wa.us/SOAR/SciProj2003/BrianV.html.

a. The difference in means is 55 − 50.46 = 4.54.

b. Begin by making the assumption that the particular treatment each sixth-grader received made no difference in his or her percentage correct. Write the 26 percentages representing the responses for the 26 subjects on 26 slips of paper. Mix them thoroughly and deal out 13 to receive the Mozart treatment. The rest of the students will receive the silence treatment. Because we are assuming that the treatment makes no difference in the percentage correct on the test, the percentage correct for each student will be the same as in the actual experiment. Compute the mean for each treatment group and subtract: *mean for Mozart treatment − mean for silence treatment.* Repeat this many times until you see the shape of the distribution. If the difference from the actual experiment, 4.54, is not in a tail of the distribution, there is no reason to abandon the assumption that the treatments made no difference. If the difference from the actual experiment is in a tail of the distribution, the assumption that the treatments made no difference is not plausible. So, you should conclude that the treatments caused the difference in the mean response.

c. The screen below shows 500 runs of the "Randomization Distribution."

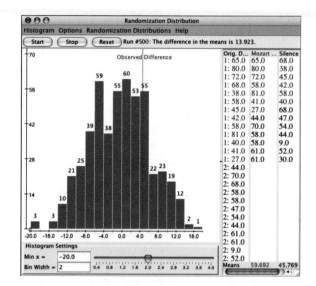

d. Using the distribution above, the probability that, just by the random assignment, you could get a difference that is at least as extreme as that from Brian's experiment is quite large, about $\frac{232}{500}$, or 0.464. (1 + 3 + 11 + 12 + 20 + 37 + 32 + 43 + 36 + 18 + 5 + 7 + 4 + 3 = 232) Using the distribution on the student master without 5 additional runs, the probability is also quite large, about $\frac{82}{195}$, or 0.42.

e. Although the mean percentage correct for the students who listened to Mozart during the test was larger, the difference is not statistically significant. The difference can reasonably be attributed to the random assignment alone. There is no reason to believe in a "Mozart effect."

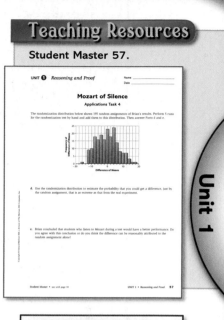

Teaching Resources

Student Master 57.

INSTRUCTIONAL NOTE
These data are in the *CPMP-Tools* software. Alternatively, a distribution of 195 runs and a version of Task 4 are shown on the Student Master for this task.

Unit 1

5. You conduct a test to see if an inexperienced person gets a bigger geyser if he or she drops Mentos® candy into a liter bottle of cola by hand or by using a paper funnel. You find ten friends who have never done this demonstration and are willing to participate. You write "by hand" on five slips of paper and "funnel" on five slips of paper. Each person draws a slip and is shown how to use that method. Then, each person drops Mentos® into his or her bottle of cola using the method assigned. The maximum height of each geyser is measured.

You find that the difference between the mean heights of the geysers produced by your friends who used their hand and your friends who used a paper funnel is not statistically significant.

a. What type of study is this?

b. What are the treatments? What are the subjects?

c. Can you generalize the results of this study to some larger population? Explain your thinking.

d. Describe exactly what you can conclude from this study.

6. Researchers wanted to determine whether social class is related to smoking behavior. They conducted telephone interviews with 1,308 Massachusetts adolescents aged 12 to 17, selected by dialing at random. They found a statistically significant association between whether the adolescent smoked or not and the household income. Adolescents from households with less income were more likely to smoke, and this was true across all ages, for both sexes, for all races, and for all amounts of disposable income the adolescent had. (Source: Elpidoforos S. Soteriades and Joseph R. DiFranza. "Parent's Socioeconomic Status, Adolescents' Disposable Income, and Adolescents' Smoking Status in Massachusetts," *Journal of Public Health*, Vol. 93, July 2003, pp. 1155–1160, www.pubmedcentral.nih.gov/articlerender.fcgi?artid=1447926)

a. What type of study is this?

b. Can you conclude from this study that smoking is caused by an adolescent's social class? Can you think of a lurking variable that might be responsible for both?

c. Can you generalize the results of this study to some larger population? Explain your thinking.

d. Describe exactly what you can conclude from this study.

⑤ For more information about the science of cola and Mentos®, see www.stevespanglerscience.com/experiment/00000109.

    a. This is an experiment.

    b. Dropping in the Mentos by hand is one treatment. The other treatment is dropping in the Mentos using a paper funnel. The subjects are your ten friends.

    c. No. The subjects, your friends, were the people available and not selected from a larger population.

    d. For your ten friends, it does not matter whether they use their hands or a paper funnel, the mean height of the geyser produced will not be much different.

⑥   **a.** This is a sample survey. The participants were selected at random from adolescents in Massachusetts.

    b. No. A lurking variable, such as a parent smoking, could be responsible for the association. If a parent smokes, the adolescent would more likely to smoke, and the poorer health of the parent might be responsible for the lower household income.

    c. Yes. Because these adolescents were selected at random (almost every household has a telephone), you can generalize the results to all adolescents aged 12 to 17 in Massachusetts.

    d. You can conclude that if you asked all adolescents aged 12 to 17 in Massachusetts, those from households with less income would be more likely to smoke (or, at least, admit to smoking) than adolescents from households with more income.

Unit 1

Connections

7 In mathematics, if you have one counterexample, it disproves a conjecture. For example, in Lesson 1, you disproved the conjecture that all numbers of the form $n^2 - n + 41$ are prime, where n is a whole number 0, 1, 2, 3, … . To disprove it, all you had to do was find one value of n for which this conjecture is not true.

However, anecdotal evidence, looking at just one counterexample, is the *worst* kind of statistical reasoning. For example, you should not conclude that smoking does not cause lung cancer just because you know someone who smoked all his life and died at age 98 in a traffic accident. Even though not everyone who smokes gets lung cancer, explain in what sense it is valid to say that smoking causes lung cancer.

8 Look back at Applications Task 3. Because the sample sizes are so small, you can list all possible randomizations.

   a. List all 20 of the possible selections of three of the six steaks to get the commercial plastic wrap and three to get vacuum packaging. Assuming that the type of packaging did not affect the response, compute the 20 possible differences *mean response for commercial plastic wrap − mean response for vacuum packaged.*

   b. What is the probability that you get a difference just through a random assignment of steaks to packaging that is as extreme as that from the real experiment?

   c. Do you have evidence from this experiment that one type of packaging is better than the other? Explain.

   d. Is your conclusion consistent with that from the randomization test in Applications Task 3?

9 The reasoning of a randomization test in statistics is similar to a special form of indirect reasoning in mathematics called *proof by contradiction*. (See Extensions Tasks 25 and 26 on page 49.) To prove that a statement is not true using proof by contradiction, you follow these steps.

   • Assume the statement is true.

   • Show that this assumption leads to a contradiction.

   • Conclude that the statement is not true.

It is a theorem (proven fact) that if a number p is a prime, then when you divide $2^p - 2$ by p, the remainder is 0.

   a. Show that this theorem holds for the primes 5, 7, and 11.

   b. Use this theorem and the three steps above to prove by contradiction that 21 is not a prime. Begin by assuming that 21 is a prime.

   c. Explain how using the reasoning of a randomization test to conclude that two treatments cause different mean responses is similar to proof by contradiction.

Connections

(7) People who smoke are more likely to get lung cancer than similar people who do not smoke. Another way to say this is: Some of the smokers who get lung cancer would not have gotten lung cancer if they had not smoked. While a randomized, controlled experiment with humans is definitely unethical, there is no doubt left about this conclusion. Randomized, controlled experiments have been done with rats, which develop lung cancer at alarming rates when subjected to the chemicals in cigarette smoke. Possible lurking variables, such as smokers may be more likely to live in polluted cities or more likely to drink alcohol, have been eliminated as the cause of the strong association between smoking and lung cancer. This is done by finding pairs of smokers and nonsmokers who drink the same amount of alcohol, for example. Further, the more a person smokes, the more likely he or she is to get lung cancer.

According to the National Institutes of Health, "Smoking cigarettes causes lung cancer. Harmful substances, called *carcinogens*, in tobacco damage the cells in the lungs. Over time, the damaged cells may become cancerous. The likelihood that a smoker will develop lung cancer is affected by the age at which smoking began, how long the person has smoked, the number of cigarettes smoked per day, and how deeply the smoker inhales. Stopping smoking greatly reduces a person's risk for developing lung cancer." (Source: www.nci.nih.gov/cancertopics/wyntk/lung/page5)

Also, see information from the American Lung Association: www.lungusa.org/site/pp.asp?c=dvLUK9O0E&b=39853

Teaching Resources

Student Master 58.

Unit 1

8 **a. INSTRUCTIONAL NOTE** A student master of the table below with two lines missing is provided for optional use.

Commercial Plastic Wrap	Mean of Plastic Wrap	Vacuum Wrap	Mean of Vacuum Wrap	Difference of Means
7.66, 6.98, 7.80	7.48	5.26, 5.44, 5.80	5.50	1.98
7.66, 6.98, 5.80	6.81	5.26, 5.44, 7.80	6.17	0.64
7.66, 6.98, 5.44	6.69	5.26, 5.80, 7.80	6.29	0.40
7.66, 6.98, 5.26	6.63	5.44, 5.80, 7.80	6.35	0.28
7.66, 7.80, 5.80	7.09	5.26, 5.44, 6.98	5.89	1.20
7.66, 7.80, 5.44	6.97	5.26, 5.80, 6.98	6.01	0.96
7.66, 7.80, 5.26	6.91	5.44, 5.80, 6.98	6.07	0.84
7.66, 5.26, 5.44	6.12	5.80, 6.98, 7.80	6.86	−0.74
7.66, 5.26, 5.80	6.24	5.44, 6.98, 7.80	6.74	−0.50
7.66, 5.44, 5.80	6.30	5.26, 6.98, 7.80	6.68	−0.38
5.26, 5.44, 5.80	5.50	7.66, 6.98, 7.80	7.48	−1.98
5.26, 5.44, 7.80	6.17	7.66, 6.98, 5.80	6.81	−0.64
5.26, 5.80, 7.80	6.29	7.66, 6.98, 5.44	6.69	−0.40
5.44, 5.80, 7.80	6.35	7.66, 6.98, 5.26	6.63	−0.28
5.26, 5.44, 6.98	5.89	7.66, 7.80, 5.80	7.09	−1.20
5.26, 5.80, 6.98	6.01	7.66, 7.80, 5.44	6.97	−0.96
5.44, 5.80, 6.98	6.07	7.66, 7.80, 5.26	6.91	−0.84
5.80, 6.98, 7.80	6.86	7.66, 5.26, 5.44	6.12	0.74
5.44, 6.98, 7.80	6.74	7.66, 5.26, 5.80	6.24	0.50
5.26, 6.98, 7.80	6.68	7.66, 5.44, 5.80	6.30	0.38

b. The probability that you get a difference just through a random assignment of steaks to packaging that is as extreme as that from the real experiment (equal to or larger in absolute value than 1.98) is 2 chances out of 20, or 0.10.

c. There is not convincing evidence that the type of packaging makes a difference in the means of the log of the counts of bacteria. It is too easy to get a difference of 1.98 in absolute value by chance alone.

d. The two conclusions are consistent.

NOTE This task demonstrates the idea that if your sample size is too small, you will not have enough power to conclude that the treatments must be causing the difference in the means, even if that is the case. If you use both tails of this distribution, which contains only 20 possible differences, it is impossible for the difference from the actual experiment to be in the outer 2.5% of one tail.

9 **a.** $\dfrac{2^5 - 2}{5} = 6$ with no remainder.

$\dfrac{2^7 - 2}{7} = 18$ with no remainder.

$\dfrac{2^{11} - 2}{11} = 186$ with no remainder.

b. • Assume that 21 is a prime.

• Then according to the theorem, there is no remainder when you divide $2^{21} - 2$ by 21. But, $2^{21} - 2 = 2{,}097{,}150$. When you divide 2,097,150 by 21, you get a remainder.

• Thus, it cannot be the case that 21 is prime.

c. In a randomization test, you:

• assume that the response of each subject would have been the same even if they had received the other treatment.

• resample using the assumption above and create a distribution of differences of the two mean responses that allows you to see the possible results of the experiment if the treatments had been assigned using different randomizations. If the difference of the mean responses from the actual experiment would be unusually large (in absolute value), that is, in the tail of the distribution under the assumption above, then you have a "contradiction."

• conclude that it is not reasonable to assume that the response of each subject would have been the same even if they had received the other treatment. (If your result from the actual experiment would not be unusually large under the assumption above, then you have no reason to abandon that assumption.)

Unit 1

10 In the Salk experiment, 82 of the 200,745 children who received the Salk vaccine were diagnosed with polio. Of the 201,229 children who received the placebo, 162 were diagnosed with polio.

a. What proportion of children who received the Salk vaccine were diagnosed with polio? What proportion who received the placebo were diagnosed with polio?

b. Do you think the result of this experiment is statistically significant or do you think the difference in the proportions is about the size that you would expect just by chance?

c. The number of children in the Salk experiment may seem excessive, but it was necessary. In the 1950s, before the Salk vaccine, the rate of polio in the U.S. was about 50 per 100,000 children. Suppose the experiment had "only" 4,000 children in the placebo injection group and 4,000 children in the Salk vaccine group. Also, suppose the vaccine is 50% effective; that is, it eliminates half of the cases of polio.

   i. How many children in the placebo group would you expect to get polio?

   ii. How many children in the Salk vaccine group would you expect to get polio?

   iii. Does the difference now appear to be statistically significant?

d. As another part of the Salk experiment, in some schools, parents of second-grade children decided whether the child would be vaccinated or not. Among the 123,605 second-grade children whose parents did not give permission for them to receive the Salk vaccine, there were 66 cases of polio. In other schools, children were selected at random to receive the vaccine or the placebo from among those children whose parents gave permission for them to be in the experiment. In those schools, there were 162 cases of polio among the 201,229 children who received the placebo. How do you explain this result? (You may want to reread Problem 4 on page 78.)

Reflections

11 You may have seen a child fall and skin his knee, and his mother picks him up and says she will "kiss it and make it well." On what is the mother depending?

12 Mathematical arguments frequently use sentences beginning with the phrase *it follows that …* . They also often involve sentences connected with words like *because, therefore, so,* and *consequently.* Statistical arguments often involve phrases like *it is reasonable to conclude that …, there is strong evidence that … ,* and *the data strongly suggest that … .* What is it about mathematical reasoning and statistical reasoning that explains the difference in choice of words and phrases?

10 **a.** The proportion of children who received the Salk vaccine who were diagnosed with polio is $\frac{82}{200,745}$, or about 0.0004. The proportion who received the placebo who were diagnosed with polio is $\frac{162}{201,229}$, or about 0.0008. The vaccine appears to cut the risk about in half.

b. Answers will vary, but this difference is statistically significant. A difference this large is unlikely to occur just by chance unless the vaccine makes a difference.

c. **i.** A rate of 50 per 100,000 is 0.0005. You would expect 0.0005(4,000), or only 2 cases in the placebo group.

    ii. If the vaccine eliminates half of the cases, you would expect 1 case in the vaccine group.

    iii. This difference of only one case of polio is not statistically significant.

d. In this part of the experiment, the proportion of children whose parents refused vaccination who got polio was $\frac{66}{123,605}$, or about 0.0005. The proportion of second-grade children randomly selected to get the placebo who got polio was $\frac{162}{201,229}$, or about 0.0008. In this second group, the parents must have given permission for their children to receive the Salk vaccine (even though the children did not end up being selected to get it). Because their rate of polio was lower than that of unvaccinated children whose parents did give permission, the children of parents who would not give permission for them to receive the Salk vaccine perhaps tended to already be more immune to polio.

    In Investigation 1 of this lesson, students read that the more affluent parents were the most worried about polio since their children were more likely to get it. Thus, they would tend to be the ones more likely to give permission for their children to receive this (uncertain) vaccine. If the other children were left as the controls, that group would be expected to have fewer cases of polio, even with no Salk vaccine. If their rate was quite a bit less, it might make it appear that the vaccine is not very effective. This verifies the importance of randomly assigning treatments to available subjects.

Reflections

11 The mother is counting on the placebo effect. The child will feel better just because the skinned knee has been "treated" by the mother's attention.

12 Mathematical reasoning is based on deductive reasoning where theorems are logically deduced from postulates, definitions, and previously proven theorems. So, there is no doubt about the validity of a conclusion if you assume that the postulates on which the reasoning is based are correct. Statistical reasoning, when based on properly-designed experiments with treatments randomly assigned to subjects and/or on a random sample taken from a population, allows you to come to a reasonable conclusion. However, due to the variability involved, you cannot be 100% certain that the conclusion applies even to the subjects in the experiment or to the entire population in the case of a survey.

13 How are the experiments as described in this lesson similar to and different from experiments you have conducted in your previous mathematical studies?

14 Why is it the case that an experiment can never *prove* without any doubt that two treatments cause different responses?

Extensions

15 Joseph Lister (1827–1912), surgeon at the Glasgow Royal Infirmary, was one of the first to believe in the theory of Louis Pasteur (1822–1895) that germs cause infection. In an early medical experiment, Lister disinfected the operating room with carbolic acid before 40 operations. He did not disinfect the operating room before another 35 operations. Of the 40 operations in which carbolic acid was used, 34 patients lived. Of the 35 operations in which carbolic acid was not used, 19 patients lived.

a. Why did Lister need to have one group of patients for whom he did not disinfect the operating room?

b. What is the difference in the proportion who lived if carbolic acid was used and the proportion who lived if carbolic acid was not used?

c. Does Lister's study provide convincing evidence that disinfecting operating rooms with carbolic acid results in fewer deaths than not disinfecting? Explain your thinking. Is there anything else you would like to know about how Lister conducted his experiment before you decide?

d. To begin a randomization test, you can let 0 represent a response of "died" and 1 represent a response of "lived." Describe how to finish the randomization test.

e. The randomization distribution below shows the results of 200 runs of the randomization. It records *proportion who survived when carbolic acid used − proportion who survived when carbolic acid not used*. Are the results of Lister's experiment statistically significant? Explain.

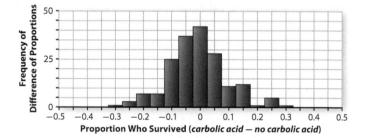

Proportion Who Survived (*carbolic acid − no carbolic acid*)

13 Other experiments often generated or gathered data to look for a trend or generalization. The experiments in this lesson were designed to compare the effects of two different treatments.

14 The reason is that we can never eliminate the randomness inherent in any experiment. The treatments were randomly assigned to the subjects. So, it is possible that all of the subjects who were going to do well, regardless of which treatment they received, were disproportionately in one of the groups.

Further, the subjects who were available or who volunteered for the experiment may be different in some fundamental way from the rest of the population. All we can say as a result of the experiment is whether the treatments seemed to cause different responses in this particular group of subjects.

Extensions

15 **a.** Lister needed a control group or he could not demonstrate that using carbolic acid caused a reduction in the death rate.

b. *proportion who survived if carbolic acid was used − proportion who survived if carbolic acid was not used* $= \frac{34}{40} - \frac{19}{35} = 0.85 - 0.54 = 0.31$

c. Most students will believe that the difference in success rates (85% vs. 54%) is statistically significant. Students will see in Part e that their intuition is correct. It is almost impossible to get a difference of $85\% - 54\% = 31\%$ in success rates just by chance. Thus, you should look for an explanation other than chance variation. Perhaps carbolic acid is that explanation. However, you first need to know whether the people who got carbolic acid were selected randomly from the 75 patients. If, for example, Lister did the 35 operations without carbolic acid, noted his low success rate, and then started using carbolic acid, you would not know if his higher success rate in the later operations was due to the carbolic acid or his additional experience as a surgeon. You might also want to know if the operations were of the same type or equally risky.

Unit 1

d. To begin a randomization test, you can let 0 represent a response of "died" and 1 represent a response of "survived." Begin by making the assumption that the carbolic acid made no difference whether a person survived or died. Write the 75 responses (0 or 1) representing the 75 subjects on 75 slips of paper. Mix them thoroughly and deal out 40 to be "given" the carbolic acid. The rest of the subjects will be given no carbolic acid. Because you are assuming that the treatment makes no difference in whether a person survived or died, the response for each subject will be the same as in the actual experiment. Compute the proportion for each treatment group and subtract *proportion for carbolic acid − proportion for no carbolic acid*. Repeat this many times until you see the shape of the distribution. If the difference of 31% from the actual experiment is not in a tail of the distribution, there is no reason to abandon the assumption that the carbolic acid made no difference. If the difference from the actual experiment is in a tail of the distribution, the assumption that the carbolic acid made no difference is not plausible. You can conclude that the carbolic acid caused the difference in the survival rate.

e. The results from Lister's experiment are statistically significant. The difference of 0.31 is in the tail of the distribution. It would be highly unusual to get a difference as extreme as 31% in the death rates if the carbolic acid made no difference. Such an extreme difference happened only a couple of times out of 200 randomizations.

HISTORICAL NOTE At the time of Lister's experiment, about half of all operations ended in death from infection of the patient several days later. Some types of operations are less dangerous than others, so it would be best to do a study like this with one particular type of surgery. In fact, Lister's operations were all of the same type, amputations. You can be fairly certain that Lister did not conduct his experiment in a way that would be acceptable today either scientifically or ethically.

The information in the student text about Joseph Lister comes from the following source: Larsen, Richard J. and Donna Fox Stroup. *Statistics in the Real World: A Book of Examples.* New York: Macmillan, 1976, pp. 205–207. Further information can be found in the source: Winslow, Charles-Edward A. *The Conquest of Disease.* Madison: University of Wisconsin Press, 1980.

Lister gave a speech in 1876 in Philadelphia about the importance of antiseptics, which was heard by Missouri physician Joseph Lawrence. Lawrence went back to his laboratory and developed an antibacterial liquid, which he called Listerine®.

Teacher Notes

16 In a psychology experiment, a group of 17 female college students were told that they would be subjected to some painful electric shocks. A group of 13 female college students were told they would be subjected to some painless electric shocks. The subjects were given the choice of waiting with others or alone. (In fact, no one received any shocks.) Of the 17 students who were told they would get painful shocks, 12 chose to wait with others. Of the 13 students told they would get painless shocks, 4 chose to wait with others. (Source: Stanley Schachter. *The Psychology of Affiliation*, Stanford, CA: Stanford University Press, 1959, pp. 44–45.)

a. Describe how to use a randomization test to see if the difference in the proportions of students who choose to wait together is statistically significant. You can let 0 represent a response of waiting alone and 1 represent waiting with others.

b. Conduct 5 runs for your test and add them to a copy of the randomization distribution below, which shows 195 runs.

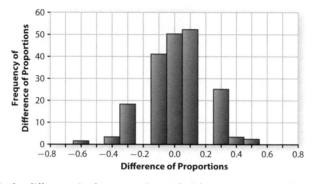

c. Is the difference in the proportions who choose to wait together statistically significant?

d. Why are there no differences between 0.15 and 0.25?

17 A market research experiment was designed to determine how much a subtle color change in white tennis shoes mattered to people who wore them. Twenty people who volunteered to try a new brand of tennis shoe were randomly assigned to get one of two colors of the same shoe. They wore the shoes for a month and then were told they could buy the pair of tennis shoes at a greatly reduced price or return them. Of the 10 people who got color A, 9 decided to buy them. Of the 10 people who got color B, 4 decided to buy them.

a. What kind of a study was this?

b. Describe the logic of a randomization test to determine if the difference is statistically significant and how to do such a test. You can let 0 represent a response of not buying the tennis shoes and 1 represent a response of buying the shoes.

c. Use the "Randomization Distribution" feature of your data analysis software to create an approximate distribution of the differences *mean number deciding to buy in group A − mean number deciding to buy in group B*. You will need to enter the data in a data sheet. Run at least 1,000 random assignments. What is your conclusion?

LESSON 4 • Statistical Reasoning   **99**

16

a. Begin by making the assumption that the particular treatment each subject received made no difference in whether they chose to wait alone or with others. Write the 30 responses (0 for waiting alone and 1 for waiting with others) on slips of paper. Mix them thoroughly and deal out 17 to represent students who were told they would get painful shocks. The rest of the slips represent the 13 students who were told they would get painless shocks. Because you are assuming that the treatment makes no difference in whether the subject wants to wait with others, the response for each subject will be the same as in the actual experiment. Compute the proportion who choose to wait with others for each treatment group and subtract *proportion for painful shocks − proportion for painless shocks*. Repeat this many times until you see the shape of the distribution. If the difference from the actual experiment, $\frac{12}{17} - \frac{4}{13} \approx 0.40$, is not in a tail of the distribution, there is no reason to abandon the assumption that the treatments made no difference. If the difference from the actual experiment is in a tail of the distribution, the assumption that the treatments made no difference is not plausible. Conclude that the treatments caused the difference in the proportions who chose to wait together.

b. Adding 5 runs will not make much change in the shape of the histogram.

c. Yes, the difference is statistically significant. The actual difference in proportions for this experiment was $0.706 - 0.308 = 0.398$, which is in the tail of the distribution shown. Since this outcome would be quite extreme (probability about 0.035) if students were picking which way to wait without regard to their treatment, you can conclude that the larger number who chose to wait together if promised painful shocks cannot reasonably be attributed to chance. Apparently, students are more likely to prefer to wait with others when faced with the prospect of pain.

d. Certain differences are impossible to get. You can show this by solving an inequality. To get a difference in the interval [0.15, 0.25), you would have to randomly assign x of the 16 students who chose to wait with others to the painful shocks treatment and the remaining $(16 - x)$ students who chose to wait with others to the painless shocks treatment so that

$$0.15 \le \frac{x}{17} - \frac{16 - x}{13} < 0.25.$$

Simplifying,

$$33.15 \le 13x - 17(16 - x) < 55.25$$
$$33.15 \le 30x - 272 < 55.25$$
$$305.15 \le 30x < 327.25$$
$$10.17 \le x < 10.91$$

But x must be an integer and there are no integers between 10.17 and 10.91.

Teaching Resources

Student Master 59.

Unit 1

INSTRUCTIONAL NOTE
These data are in the
CPMP-Tools software.
Alternatively, a distribution of
195 runs and a version of
Task 17 are shown on the
Student Master for this task.

Teaching Resources

Student Master 60.

17

a. This was an experiment. The subjects were randomly assigned to the two colors of tennis shoes. It looks like there were sufficient numbers of subjects to pick up the difference in proportions. The two colors were the two treatments.

b. Begin by making the assumption that the color of tennis shoes each subject received made no difference in whether they chose to buy them. Write the 20 responses (0 for did not buy or 1 for bought) on slips of paper. Mix them thoroughly and deal out 10 for each color of tennis shoes. Because you are assuming that the color makes no difference in the response, the response for each subject will be the same as in the actual experiment. Compute the proportion buying the shoes for each treatment group and subtract *proportion buying for first color − proportion buying for second color*. Repeat this many times until you see the shape of the distribution. If the difference from the actual experiment is not in a tail of the distribution, there is no reason to abandon the assumption that the colors made no difference in whether the person bought the tennis shoes. If the difference from the actual experiment is in a tail of the distribution, the assumption that the colors made no difference is not plausible. Conclude that the colors caused the difference in the proportion buying the tennis shoes.

c. A difference as extreme as that from the actual experiment, $0.9 − 0.4 = 0.5$, occurred in 35 of 1,000 runs in the distribution below. Conclude that it is not reasonable to assume that the color caused a difference in the proportion buying the tennis shoes.

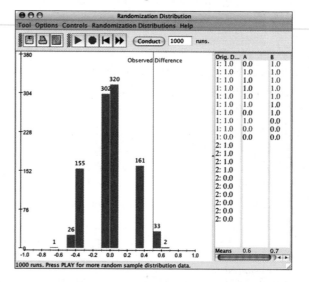

NOTE Theoretically, a difference as extreme as that from the actual experiment, $0.9 − 0.4 = 0.5$ or greater, or $−0.05$ or less, happens around 5.7% of the time. Thus, results from a simulation may not be conclusive. If the student runs a simulation and gets a probability more than 0.05, the conclusion should be that a difference as extreme as that from the experiment is likely to happen even if color made no difference. Conclude that there is no statistically significant evidence that the color caused a difference in the proportion buying the tennis shoes. If the student runs a simulation and gets a probability less than 0.05, the conclusion should be that a difference as extreme as that from the experiment would be unlikely to happen if color made no difference. Conclude that the color did cause a difference in the proportion buying the tennis shoes.

Review

Just in Time

18

a. $3x + 4y = 12$ **b.** $x - 5y = 7$

c. $y = -x$ **d.** $x = 5$

e. $y = 3$

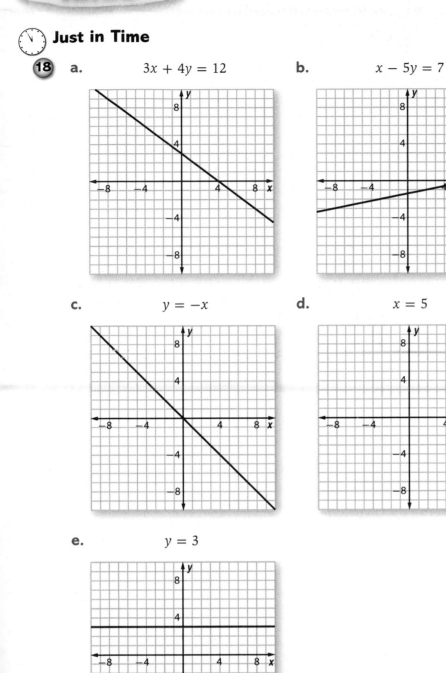

Review

18 Draw the graph of each equation.

a. $3x + 4y = 12$

b. $x - 5y = 7$

c. $x + y = 0$

d. $x = 5$

e. $y = 3$

19 Triangle ABC has vertex matrix $\begin{bmatrix} 0 & 5 & 10 \\ 2 & 6 & 2 \end{bmatrix}$.

a. Is $\triangle ABC$ an isosceles triangle? Explain your reasoning.

b. The transformation $(x, y) \rightarrow (-x, y)$ is applied to $\triangle ABC$. Find the vertex matrix for the image $\triangle A'B'C'$ and describe this transformation.

c. Give a vertex matrix for a triangle that has an area 9 times the area of $\triangle ABC$.

20 The Venn diagram below indicates the number of seniors who have taken Drama and Public Speaking. There are 178 seniors.

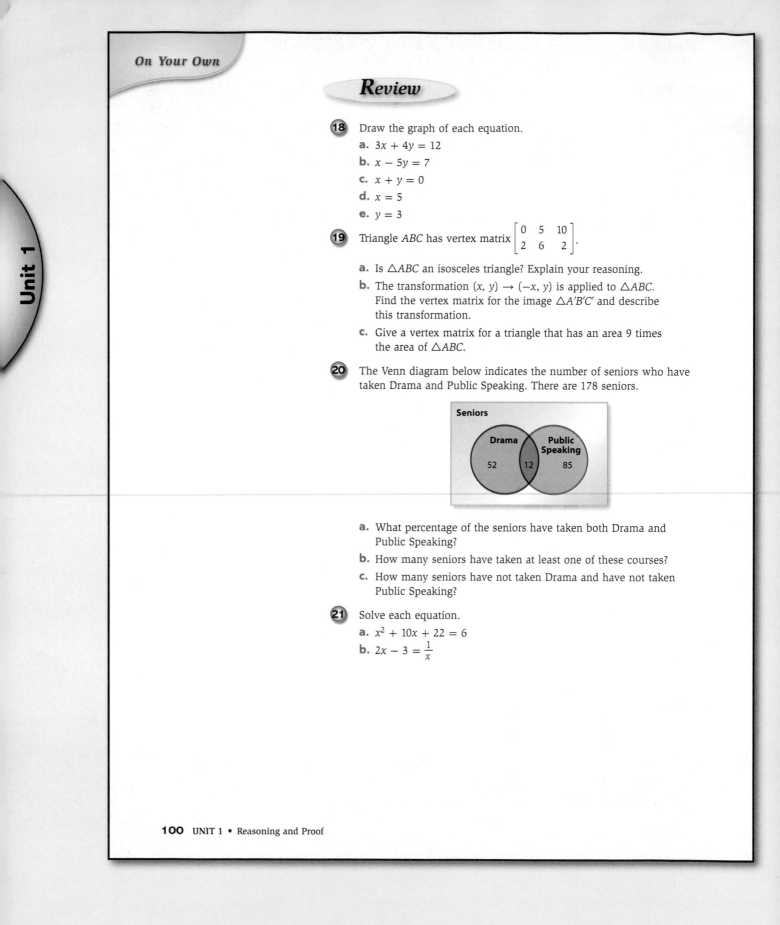

a. What percentage of the seniors have taken both Drama and Public Speaking?

b. How many seniors have taken at least one of these courses?

c. How many seniors have not taken Drama and have not taken Public Speaking?

21 Solve each equation.

a. $x^2 + 10x + 22 = 6$

b. $2x - 3 = \frac{1}{x}$

19 **a.** Triangle *ABC* is isosceles since $AB = \sqrt{5^2 + 4^2} = \sqrt{5^2 + (-4)^2} = BC$.

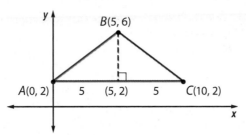

NOTE Solutions to Task 18 are on page T99B.

b. $\begin{bmatrix} 0 & -5 & -10 \\ 2 & 6 & 2 \end{bmatrix}$. The transformation is a reflection across the *y*-axis.

c. Answers may vary. One possible triangle is found by applying a size transformation of magnitude three, centered at the origin. The vertex matrix for that triangle is $\begin{bmatrix} 0 & 15 & 30 \\ 6 & 18 & 6 \end{bmatrix}$. Other common solutions might involve making the base of the isosceles triangle 9 times as long and keeping the same height or increasing the height by a factor of 9 and keeping the same base.

20 **a.** $\frac{12}{178} = 0.067 = 6.7\%$

b. 149 seniors

c. 29 seniors

Just in Time

21 **a.** $x = -2$ or $x = -8$

b. $x = \frac{3 + \sqrt{17}}{4} \approx 1.78$ or $x = \frac{3 - \sqrt{17}}{4} \approx -0.28$

Unit 1

22 Solve each inequality and graph the solution on a number line.

   a. $3(x + 5) \geq 3$

   b. $7x + 3 < 11x - 5$

   c. $4x + 2(3 - 5x) > -12$

   d. $10 - 2x \leq 6(x - 3) + 10$

23 Achmed kept track of the number of miles n he drove for several consecutive weeks and the amount of gas g in gallons he purchased each week. He found the linear regression equation relating these two variables to be $g = 0.035n + 0.4$.

   a. Is the correlation for these two variables positive or negative? Explain your reasoning.

   b. Explain the meaning of the slope of the regression equation in terms of these two variables.

   c. During one week, Achmed drove 228 miles and bought 7.36 gallons of gas. Find the residual for that week.

24 Without using a calculator or computer graphing tool, sketch graphs of these quadratic functions. Then, for each, use the graph to determine the number of solutions for the related quadratic equation $f(x) = 0$.

   a. $f(x) = x^2 - 4$

   b. $f(x) = x^2$

   c. $f(x) = x^2 + 4$

   d. $f(x) = -x^2 - 5$

   e. $f(x) = -x^2$

   f. $f(x) = -x^2 + 4$

25 The height h in feet of a thrown basketball is a function of the time t in seconds since it was released. Suppose that Samuel shoots a free throw for which the height of the ball can be approximated by the function $h(t) = 6 + 40t - 16t^2$.

   a. Find the value of $h(2)$ and explain what it tells you about the path of the basketball.

   b. How high above the floor was the basketball when it was released?

   c. For what values of t is $h(t) = 27$?

   d. When was the basketball at its highest point and how high was it?

LESSON 4 • Statistical Reasoning **101**

101 UNIT 1 • Reasoning and Proof

22 a. $x \geq -4$

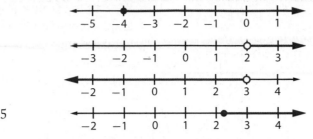

b. $x > 2$

c. $x < 3$

d. $x \geq 2.25$

23 a. The correlation is positive because the slope of the regression line is positive. Alternatively, students may say the slope is positive because the more miles you drive, the more gas you use.

b. If in one week Achmed drove one mile more than he did in a second week, we would expect him to purchase 0.035 gallons more gas in the second week than he did in the first week.

c. The regression equation gives the expected number of gallons of gas for 228 miles to be 8.38 gallons. So, the residual for this week is $7.36 - 8.38 = -1.02$.

Just in Time

24 a.

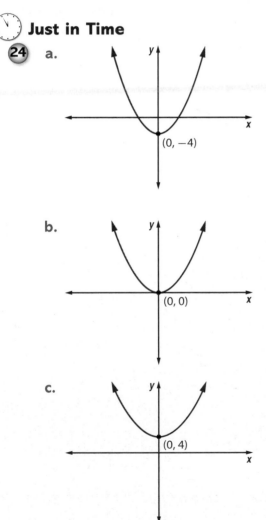

(0, −4)

We can tell from the rule that the parabola opens upward, and the y-intercept is $(0, -4)$. Since there is no linear term ($b = 0$), the y-axis is the symmetry line. Alternatively, students might recognize this function as a vertical shift of $y = x^2$. So, the graph has two x-intercepts, and the equation $f(x) = 0$ has two solutions.

b.

(0, 0)

We can tell from the rule that the graph opens upward, and the vertex is $(0, 0)$. So, the graph has one x-intercept, and the equation $f(x) = 0$ has one solution.

c.

(0, 4)

We can tell from the rule that the graph opens upward, and the vertex is $(0, 4)$. So, the graph has no x-intercepts, and the equation $f(x) = 0$ has no (real) solutions.

d.

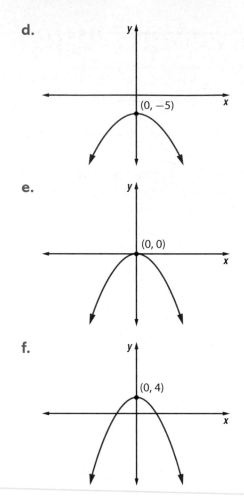

$(0, -5)$

We can tell from the rule that the graph opens downward, and the vertex is $(0, -5)$. So, the graph has no x-intercepts, and the equation $f(x) = 0$ has no (real) solutions.

e.

$(0, 0)$

We can tell from the rule that the graph opens downward, and the vertex is $(0, 0)$. So, the graph has one x-intercept, and the equation $f(x) = 0$ has one solution.

f.

$(0, 4)$

We can tell from the rule that the graph opens downward, and the vertex is $(0, 4)$. So, the graph has two x-intercepts, and the equation $f(x) = 0$ has two solutions.

Teaching Resources

Assessment Masters 61–68.

UNIT ❶ *Reasoning and Proof*

Name _____
Date _____

LESSON 4 QUIZ

Form A

1. Acupuncture is an important part of traditional Chinese medicine. This treatment is becoming more widely available throughout the United States.
   In England, a study was conducted to determine if acupuncture was an effective means of reducing chronic headache pain. In the study, 401 adults were randomly assigned to receive acupuncture treatments or to continue with their usual treatment for headaches. Acupuncture treatment was found to be more effective than usual care in decreasing headache severity. *(Source: American Family Physician, Vol. 70, No. 3, August 1, 2004, pp. 574–5.)*

   a. Does this study have the three characteristics of an experiment? Explain your reasoning.

   b. Was the experiment subject blind? Explain your reasoning.

   c. What were the treatments?

   d. What was the response?

2. Kayla conducted a study of how the color of water affects its evaporation rate. She filled each of ten identical containers to a height of 6.5 inches and then placed the containers on a windowsill. She then added red food coloring to the water in five randomly chosen containers. After one week, she measured the height of the water left in each of the containers. Her measurements are given below.

   Height (in inches) of Water Left in Containers

Clear Water	Red Water
5.4	5.2
5.6	5.5
5.8	5.4
6.0	4.8
6.3	5.1

   a. What are the treatments for this experiment?

Assessment Master • use after Lesson 4   UNIT 1 • Reasoning and Proof   **61**

⏱ Just in Time

25

a. $h(2) = 6 + 40(2) - 16(4) = 22$
Two seconds after the ball was released, it was 22 feet above the floor.

b. $h(0) = 6$; so, the basketball was released 6 feet above the floor.

c. $h(t) = 27$ when $t = 0.75$ or when $t = 1.75$.

d. The basketball was at its highest point after 1.25 seconds and it was 31 feet above the floor.

Looking Back

In this unit, you examined and practiced reasoning principles and strategies that mathematicians and statisticians use to prove or justify their claims. In particular, you learned how to use definitions and assumed geometric facts to prove important properties of perpendicular and parallel lines. You learned how to use operations on algebraic expressions to prove patterns in number sequences, prove properties of real numbers, write equivalent expressions, and solve equations. You also learned how statisticians design experiments and use reasoning like the randomization test to determine whether one treatment causes a different outcome than another treatment.

The following tasks will help you to review and apply some of the key ideas involved in geometric, algebraic, and statistical reasoning.

1. **Reasoning about Shapes** In your earlier coursework, you saw that there were at least two different, but equivalent, definitions of a parallelogram. One of those definitions was: A **parallelogram** is a quadrilateral with two pairs of opposite sides parallel.

   a. Write two if-then statements that together mean the same thing as that definition.

   b. Suppose you are told that in the case of quadrilateral $PQRS$, $\overline{PQ} \parallel \overline{SR}$ and $\overline{QR} \parallel \overline{PS}$. What can you conclude? Which of the two if-then statements in Part a was used in your reasoning?

   c. A definition of trapezoid was given in Lesson 1. A **trapezoid** is a quadrilateral with a pair of opposite sides parallel.

      i. Why is every parallelogram a trapezoid but not every trapezoid a parallelogram?

      ii. Use a Venn diagram to illustrate the relationship of parallelograms, trapezoids, and quadrilaterals.

1 **a.** (1) If a quadrilateral is a parallelogram, then it has two pairs of opposite sides parallel.

　　(2) If a quadrilateral has two pairs of opposite sides parallel, then it is a parallelogram.

b. Quadrilateral *PQRS* is a parallelogram using the statement: If a quadrilateral has two pairs of opposite sides parallel, then it is a parallelogram.

c. **i.** Since every parallelogram has a pair of opposite sides parallel, every parallelogram satisfies the definition of a trapezoid. However, a quadrilateral with exactly one pair of parallel sides is a trapezoid and does not satisfy the definition of a parallelogram.

　　ii.

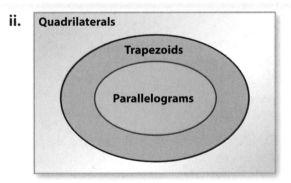

② In a parallelogram *ABCD*, angles that share a common side, like ∠*A* and ∠*B*, are called *consecutive angles*. Angles that do not share a common side, like ∠*A* and ∠*C*, are called *opposite angles*.

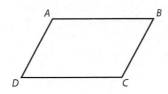

a. Using the definition of a parallelogram and properties of parallel lines, prove that in □*ABCD*, ∠*A* and ∠*B* are supplementary. Could you use a similar argument to prove other pairs of consecutive angles are supplementary? Explain your reasoning.

b. Use what you proved in Part a to help you prove that in □*ABCD*, m∠*A* = m∠*C*. Does the other pair of opposite angles have equal measure? Explain your reasoning.

c. You have seen that there is often more than one correct way to prove a statement. Use the numbered angles in the diagram below to provide a different proof that m∠*A* = m∠*C*.

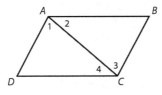

d. Write two statements summarizing what you proved in Parts a and b.

e. Give counterexamples to show the statements in Part d are not necessarily true for trapezoids.

③ **Reasoning about Patterns in Sequences** In Lesson 3, you discovered and proved an interesting pattern in the sequence of square numbers 1, 4, 9, 16, 25, 36, ... You found that the differences of successive terms in that sequence create the sequence of odd numbers 3, 5, 7, 9, 11, ... The *n*th number in that sequence of differences is given by the expression $2n + 1$.

a. Look again at the sequence of square numbers and study the pattern formed by calculating the differences that begins $9 - 1 = 8$, $16 - 4 = 12$, $25 - 9 = 16$, ...

  i. What are the next several terms in this sequence of differences?

  ii. What expression in the form "$an + b$" shows how to calculate the *n*th term in the sequence of differences?

  iii. Use algebraic reasoning to prove that the expression $(n + 2)^2 - n^2$ is equivalent to the simpler expression you proposed in part ii.

2 **a.** In □$ABCD$, $\overline{AB} \parallel \overline{CD}$ and $\overline{AD} \parallel \overline{BC}$, by the definition of a parallelogram. Then ∠A and ∠B are supplementary since they are interior angles on the same side of transversal $\overleftrightarrow{AB}$.

Yes, similar arguments can be made to prove the other pairs of consecutive angles are supplementary since both pairs of opposite sides are parallel and the common side for the two consecutive angles can be viewed as the transversal.

b. From Part a, we know that m∠A + m∠B = 180° and m∠B + m∠C = 180°, since they are both pairs of supplementary angles. Therefore, m∠A + m∠B = m∠B + m∠C (Substitution Property). So, m∠A = m∠C (Subtraction Property of Equality).

Yes, m∠B = m∠D. Using similar reasoning, we know that m∠A + m∠D = m∠A + m∠B. Thus, m∠B = m∠D.

c. A two-column statement-reason form is included here. However, students may choose to write their proof in a different form.

Given: □$ABCD$ is a parallelogram.

Prove: m∠A = m∠C

Statements	Reasons
1. □$ABCD$ is a parallelogram.	1. Given
2. $\overline{AD} \parallel \overline{BC}$, $\overline{AB} \parallel \overline{CD}$	2. Definition of parallelogram
3. m∠1 = m∠3, m∠2 = m∠4	3. If two parallel lines are cut by a transversal, then alternate interior angles have equal measure.
4. m∠1 + m∠2 = m∠3 + m∠4	4. Addition Property of Equality [3]
5. m∠1 + m∠2 = m∠A m∠3 + m∠4 = m∠C	5. Angle Addition Postulate
6. m∠A = m∠C	6. Substitution Property of Equality [5] into [4]

Alternatively, students might use the fact (proven in Course 2) that opposite sides of a parallelogram are congruent to show △ACD ≅ △CAB.

d. *In a parallelogram, consecutive angles are supplementary. In a parallelogram, opposite angles are equal in measure.*

e. Students' counterexamples will vary. One counterexample is given.

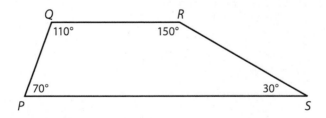

In the given trapezoid, each pair of consecutive angles is not supplementary and opposite angles are not equal in measure.

3 **a.** **i.** $36 - 16 = 20$, $49 - 25 = 24$, $64 - 36 = 28$, ...

ii. The nth term is given by $4n + 4$.

iii. $(n + 2)^2 - n^2 = (n^2 + 4n + 4) - n^2$
$$= 4n + 4$$

Teaching Resources

Student Master 69.

b. Now consider the sequence of differences that begins $16 - 1 = 15$, $25 - 4 = 21$, $36 - 9 = 27$, $49 - 16 = 33$, ...

   i. What are the next several terms in this sequence?

   ii. What simple expression shows how to calculate the nth term in this sequence of differences?

   iii. Use algebraic reasoning to prove that the expression proposed in part ii will give the nth term in the sequence of differences.

c. **i.** Try to generalize the patterns you examined in Parts a and b. What simple expression will give the nth term in the sequence formed by calculating the differences of numbers that are k steps apart in the sequence of square numbers?

   ii. Use algebraic reasoning to show that your idea is correct.

4 **Reasoning about Data** An experiment was designed to see whether a program of special stepping and foot-placing exercises for 12 minutes each day could speed up the process of babies learning to walk. As part of this study, 12 baby boys were randomly assigned to the special exercise group or to the "exercise control" group. For the control group, parents were told to make sure their infant sons exercised at least 12 minutes per day. But they were not given any special exercises to use, and they were not given any other instructions about exercise.

The researchers recorded the age, in months, when each baby first walked without help.

Age that Baby Boys Learned to Walk

Special Exercise (in months)	Exercise Control (in months)
9	11
9.5	10
9.75	10
10	11.75
13	10.5
9.5	15

Source: Phillip R. Zelazo, Nancy Ann Zelazo, and Sarah Kolb. "Walking in the Newborn," Science 176, 1972, pp. 314–315.

a. What are the treatments? What is the response?

b. Does this study have the three characteristics of a well-designed experiment? Could it have been double blind? Is the placebo effect a possible issue here?

b. i. $64 - 25 = 39$, $81 - 36 = 45$, $100 - 49 = 51$, ...

  ii. The nth term is given by $6n + 9$.

  iii. $(n + 3)^2 - n^2 = (n^2 + 6n + 9) - n^2$
  $$= 6n + 9$$

c. i. $(n + k)^2 - n^2$

  ii. $(n + k)^2 - n^2 = (n^2 + 2kn + k^2) - n^2$
  $$= 2kn + k^2$$

4

a. One treatment is that the baby receives special stepping and foot-placing exercises for 12 minutes each day. The other treatment is that the baby receives exercise (but no special exercises) for 12 minutes each day. The response is the age when the baby boy learned to walk.

> **TECHNOLOGY NOTE**
> These data are in *CPMP-Tools*.

b. Possibly. Treatments were randomly assigned to the babies, and there are two treatment groups. However, if there is a small difference between the two treatments in the age at which babies learn to walk, having only six babies in each treatment group may not be sufficiently large enough to detect this difference.

  This experiment cannot be double blind since the evaluators, in this case the baby's parents, are aware of the treatment received by the baby.

  The placebo effect may be a possible issue in this experiment because parents using the stepping and foot-placing exercises may expect this special treatment to speed up the process of learning to walk and thus give more encouragement to the child to learn to walk.

c. What is the difference: *mean walking age for exercise control group − mean walking age for special exercise group*?

d. Suppose that the treatment makes no difference in the age that baby boys learn to walk. Would you expect there to be a nonzero difference in *mean walking age for exercise control − mean walking age for special exercise* for almost any two groups of six baby boys? Explain.

e. Describe how to conduct a randomization test to determine if the different treatments cause a difference in the mean age that baby boys learn to walk. Perform 10 runs and add them to the randomization distribution below, which shows the results of 990 runs.

Baby Boys Walking

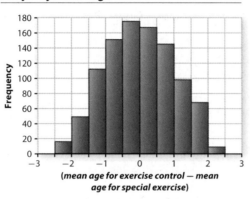

(*mean age for exercise control − mean age for special exercise*)

f. What is your estimate of the probability that just by the random assignment of treatments to subjects, you get a difference that is as least as extreme as that from the real experiment? What is your conclusion about whether you have evidence from this experiment that the special exercises are better than just reminding parents to be sure their baby boys exercise at least 12 minutes per day?

c. *mean walking age for exercise control group − mean walking age for special exercise group* = 11.375 − 10.125 = 1.25 months

d. Yes. If the treatment made no difference, we expect the difference in the mean walking ages to be fairly close, but not necessarily equal to, zero.

e. Get 12 identical slips of paper and write one of the 12 ages on each of them. Mix them up and draw 6 of them to represent the babies who received special exercises. Compute their mean walking age. Compute the mean walking age of the remaining 6 babies. Subtract *mean walking age for exercise control group − mean walking age for special exercise group*.

f. The estimated probability is at least 0.18 when you count above 1 month and below −1 month. The difference in the means of 1.25 months is not extreme because it is not in a tail of the randomization distribution. Therefore, there is no evidence that the special exercises are better than just reminding parents to be sure their babies exercise 12 minutes per day in lowering the age that walking begins.

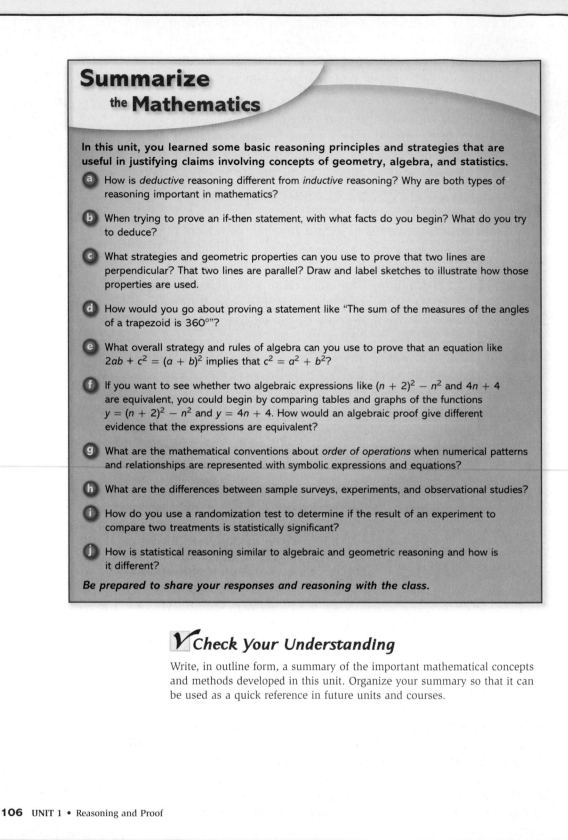

Summarize
the Mathematics

In this unit, you learned some basic reasoning principles and strategies that are useful in justifying claims involving concepts of geometry, algebra, and statistics.

a How is *deductive* reasoning different from *inductive* reasoning? Why are both types of reasoning important in mathematics?

b When trying to prove an if-then statement, with what facts do you begin? What do you try to deduce?

c What strategies and geometric properties can you use to prove that two lines are perpendicular? That two lines are parallel? Draw and label sketches to illustrate how those properties are used.

d How would you go about proving a statement like "The sum of the measures of the angles of a trapezoid is 360°"?

e What overall strategy and rules of algebra can you use to prove that an equation like $2ab + c^2 = (a + b)^2$ implies that $c^2 = a^2 + b^2$?

f If you want to see whether two algebraic expressions like $(n + 2)^2 - n^2$ and $4n + 4$ are equivalent, you could begin by comparing tables and graphs of the functions $y = (n + 2)^2 - n^2$ and $y = 4n + 4$. How would an algebraic proof give different evidence that the expressions are equivalent?

g What are the mathematical conventions about *order of operations* when numerical patterns and relationships are represented with symbolic expressions and equations?

h What are the differences between sample surveys, experiments, and observational studies?

i How do you use a randomization test to determine if the result of an experiment to compare two treatments is statistically significant?

j How is statistical reasoning similar to algebraic and geometric reasoning and how is it different?

Be prepared to share your responses and reasoning with the class.

✓Check Your Understanding

Write, in outline form, a summary of the important mathematical concepts and methods developed in this unit. Organize your summary so that it can be used as a quick reference in future units and courses.

Summarize
the Mathematics

a Inductive reasoning is based on examining possible patterns emerging in specific cases. Inductive reasoning is based on observations and is helpful for developing conjectures or questions about the continuing nature of the patterns. Deductive reasoning involves reasoning from definitions, assumptions (accepted properties), and theorems to new statements. If the assumption(s) is true and the reasoning is correct, the conclusion is true. Principles of logic are used to reach conclusions that are certain, not just possible.

b When trying to prove an if-then statement, begin with the facts given in the *if* part of the if-then statement (the hypothesis). Then try to deduce the *then* part of the if-then statement (the conclusion).

c To show that two lines are perpendicular, you would show that one of the angles formed is a right angle. You might also use information from other angles in the diagram, supplementary angles, the Triangle Sum Theorem, or the Linear Pairs Postulate. For example, if you know that the two angles forming the linear pair are the same measure, you could conclude that these angles measure 90° and so the lines are perpendicular. Additionally, you can conclude that a transversal is perpendicular to one of two parallel lines, it is perpendicular to the other line. (See page 39. Students should include labeled sketches to illustrate how the properties are used.)

To show that two lines are parallel, draw a transversal cutting through both lines ℓ and m. Use facts about the angles formed by the intersections of the transversal and the parallel lines. If corresponding angles are equal in measure, then $\ell \parallel m$. If alternate interior angles are equal in measure, then $\ell \parallel m$. If alternate exterior angles are equal in measure, then $\ell \parallel m$. If interior angles on the same side of the transversal are supplementary, then $\ell \parallel m$. If exterior angles on the same side of the transversal are supplementary, then $\ell \parallel m$. Two lines are also parallel if they are both perpendicular to the same line. (See page 39.)

d Students might suggest a variety of ways to prove that the sum of the angles of a trapezoid is 360°. One way is to use the fact that one pair of sides in the trapezoid is parallel making interior angles on the same side of a transversal ($\angle 1$ and $\angle 2$, and $\angle 3$ and $\angle 4$) supplementary. Therefore, the trapezoid has two sets of supplementary angles. Since supplementary angles sum to 180°, the angles in the trapezoid sum to $2(180°) = 360°$.

Another way would be to draw a diagonal to form two triangles. Since the angles of the triangles form the angles of the trapezoid, the sum of the measures of the angles of the trapezoid is $2(180°) = 360°$.

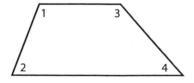

e To derive one equation from another, apply substitution of equivalent expressions where appropriate and also perform the same operation on both sides of a given equation to get one that follows logically from it.

f Comparing tables and graphs often gives a strong intuitive and visual sense that two expressions might be equivalent. However, such checking of cases (even though there are many cases "checked") will not provide proof in general. (If one knows the fact that two linear expressions are equivalent if they agree in at least two points and quadratic expressions are equivalent if they agree in at least three points, and so on, checks of specific cases can be sufficient. However, in the examples of this Looking Back task and the earlier problems, it was not always obvious that the two expressions being compared were of the same degree.) An algebraic proof would show that equivalence exists for all numbers n.

g Order of operation conventions are essential in expressing patterns so that the calculating rule turns out to produce the sequence of operations that one has in mind. These include operating inside of parentheses first and precedence to powers, then multiplication and division, and finally addition and subtraction. With this in mind, one operates from left to right. The most common and tempting error is to simply write down the numbers or variable symbols and operation symbols in left-to-right order following the intended sequence of operational steps. Without careful use of parentheses (to indicate when a next operation applies to the previous result, not simply the most recently entered number), errors are very likely to creep in when the formula is entered into a machine that follows the order of operation conventions and not what the user intended. For example, "$5 - x \wedge 2$" is not the same as "$(5 - x)^2$" and "$5 - x \div 3$" is not the same as "$(5 - x) \div 3$."

h With a sample survey or poll, you observe a random sample in order to estimate a characteristic of the larger population from which the sample was taken. The results can be generalized to the larger population. No randomization is involved in an observational study. From an observational study, you cannot generalize to a larger population or infer that a change in one variable causes a change in another variable. You can determine only that two variables are associated within the group you observed. As with a sample survey, an experiment involves randomization. Two or more treatments are randomly assigned to available subjects. You can determine whether one treatment causes a different effect than another treatment, at least among the subjects in the experiment. Both observational studies and experiments should be repeated a number of times on different populations before results become generally accepted.

(i) To use a randomization test to compare two treatments, you assume that each subject's response would have been the same no matter which treatment he or she received. Then you randomly divide the responses into two treatment groups and compute the difference of the means for each treatment. If the actual difference of means is in the outer 5% of the randomization distribution difference of means, you conclude that the difference is statistically significant.

(j) Both mathematical and statistical reasoning involve reasoning from assumptions. Statistical reasoning is inductive reasoning. Mathematical reasoning may also involve inductive reasoning. However, in deductive mathematical reasoning, you can use definitions, properties, and theorems to prove with certainty what you believe is true. In statistical reasoning, you gather data from experiments. You then use a test such as the randomization test to see if differences are statistically significant, usually at a significance level of 0.05. When using valid mathematical reasoning, you are certain of your conclusions. When using statistical reasoning, you are never certain of your conclusions.

✔ Check Your Understanding

You may wish to have students use the Teaching Master, *Reasoning and Proof* Unit Summary, to help them organize the information. Above all, this should be something that is useful to the individual student.

Practicing for Standardized Tests

Each Practicing for Standardized Tests master presents 10 questions in the multiple-choice format of test items similar to how they often appear in standardized tests. Answers are provided below.

Answers to Practice Set 1

1. (b) **2.** (e) **3.** (d) **4.** (c) **5.** (c)
6. (d) **7.** (e) **8.** (b) **9.** (e) **10.** (d)

Student Masters 72–74.

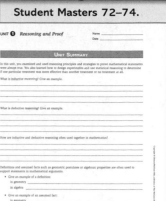

Assessment Masters 75–86.

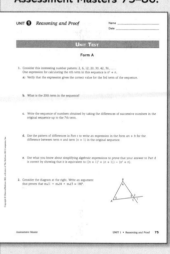

Student Masters 87–89.

Unit 1

UNIT 2

Inequalities and Linear Programming

For some people, athletes and astronauts in particular, selection of a good diet is a carefully planned scientific process. Each person wants maximum performance for minimum cost. The search for an optimum solution is usually constrained by available resources and outcome requirements.

The mathematics needed to solve these and other similar optimization problems involves work with *inequalities* and a technique called *linear programming*. The essential understandings and skills required for this work are developed in two lessons of this unit.

Lessons

1 Inequalities in One Variable

Use numeric and graphic estimation methods and algebraic reasoning to solve problems that involve linear and quadratic inequalities in one variable.

2 Inequalities with Two Variables

Use graphic and algebraic methods to determine solution sets for systems of linear inequalities in two variables. Recognize problems in which the goal is to find optimum values of a linear objective function, subject to linear constraints on the independent variables. Represent both objective and constraints in graphic and algebraic form, and use linear programming techniques to solve the optimization problems.

INEQUALITIES AND LINEAR PROGRAMMING

Unit Overview

In the Course 1 unit *Linear Functions*, students developed skill in solving linear inequalities in one variable. In subsequent units, students developed and solved a broader range of inequalities in one variable using tables and graphs. This unit reviews and extends students' understanding of and their ability to solve inequalities in one and two variables.

The unit reviews and pulls together students' prior work with graphing of linear, quadratic, and inverse variation functions; solving inequalities graphically; solving quadratic equations algebraically; graphing linear equations in two variables; and solving systems of linear equations in two variables. The understanding and skill needed to solve and apply inequalities is developed in three lessons.

Lesson 1 *Inequalities in One Variable* Lesson 1 develops students' ability to combine algebraic and graphical reasoning to solve quadratic inequalities in one variable.

Lesson 2 *Inequalities with Two Variables* Lesson 2 builds their skills with graphing linear inequalities and systems of linear inequalities and applies that knowledge to determining the feasible regions for linear programming problems. Students also discover that the optimal solution for a linear programming problem is generally at or near a vertex of the feasible region. The final lesson takes a look back and reviews the key concepts and skills of the unit.

In this unit, students are encouraged to reason graphically without the use of a graphing calculator; however, some students may still find it useful to check their reasoning with a graphing calculator or computer. Practice for the skills developed in this unit is incorporated in the On Your Own tasks of this and subsequent units.

- Write inequalities to express questions about functions of one or two variables
- Solve quadratic inequalities in one variable, and describe the solution set symbolically, as a number line graph, and using interval notation
- Solve and graph the solution set of a linear inequality in two variables
- Solve and graph the solution set of a system of inequalities in two variables
- Solve linear programming problems involving two independent variables

CPMP-Tools *CPMP-Tools* includes CAS software that can be used to solve and graph inequalities and systems of inequalities. You may wish to have students explore or check solutions using the software.

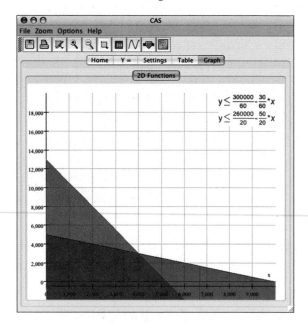

Lesson Objectives	On Your Own Assignments*	Suggested Pacing	Materials
Lesson 1 *Inequalities in One Variable* • Write inequalities to express questions about functions of one or two variables • Given a graph of one or more functions, solve inequalities related to the function(s) • Solve quadratic inequalities in one variable by solving the corresponding equation algebraically and reasoning about the graph of the related function(s) • Describe the solution set of an inequality in one variable symbolically, as a graph on a number line, and using interval notation	**After Investigation 1:** A1–A3, C12, C14, R18, R19, Rv25–Rv27 **After Investigation 2:** A4–A6, C13, C15, C16, R20, Rv28–Rv30 **After Investigation 3:** A6 or A7, A8–A10, C17, choose one of E21–E24, Rv30, Rv31	6 days (including assessment)	• Unit Resources • *CPMP-Tools* CAS or other CAS
Lesson 2 *Inequalities with Two Variables* • Graph the solution set of a linear inequality in two variables • Graph the solution set of a system of inequalities in two variables • Solve linear programming problems involving two independent variables	**After Investigation 1:** A1–A5, C15 or C16, R20, E26 or E27, Rv34–Rv36 **After Investigation 2:** Choose one of A6–A8, C17, E28, Rv37–Rv39 **After Investigation 3:** Choose one of A9–A11 corresponding to choice from A6–A8, A13 or A14, C18, C19, choose two of R21–R25, choose two of E29–E33, Rv40–Rv42	8 days (including assessment)	• Unit Resources • *CPMP-Tools* CAS or other CAS
Lesson 3 *Looking Back* • Review and synthesize the major objectives of the unit		3 days (including assessment)	• Unit Resources

* When choice is indicated, it is important to leave the choice to the student.

Note: It is best if Connections tasks are discussed as a whole class after they have been assigned as homework.

Unit 2

LESSON 1

Inequalities in One Variable

In previous courses, you learned how to solve a variety of problems by representing and reasoning about them with algebraic equations and inequalities. For example, suppose that plans for a fundraising raffle show that profit P will depend on ticket price x according to the function $P(x) = -2,500 + 5,000x - 750x^2$. A graph of profit as a function of ticket price is shown here.

Raffle Fundraiser Profit

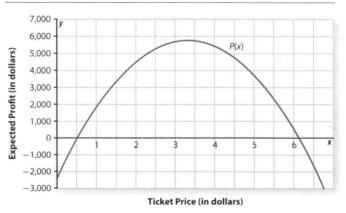

Ticket Price (in dollars)

Inequalities in One Variable

This lesson focuses on the formulation and solution of inequalities in one variable with special emphasis on quadratic inequalities.

The lesson material is organized into three investigations. The first develops students' ability to solve inequalities in one variable using graphical reasoning and asks students to represent solution sets symbolically and using number line graphs. The second investigation develops algebraic methods for solving quadratic inequalities. The third investigation develops graphic and algebraic methods for solving inequalities involving two functions of one variable and introduces interval notation for recording the solutions.

Lesson Objectives

- Write inequalities to express questions about functions of one or two variables
- Given a graph of one or more functions, solve inequalities related to the function(s)
- Solve quadratic inequalities in one variable by solving the corresponding equation algebraically and reasoning about the graph of the related function(s)
- Describe the solution set of an inequality in one variable symbolically, as a graph on a number line, and using interval notation

Lesson Launch

We do not expect students to be familiar with all of the ways of describing solution sets of inequalities listed in Part c. This is an opportunity for you to assess their prior knowledge. Various ways of representing solution sets will be discussed in this lesson.

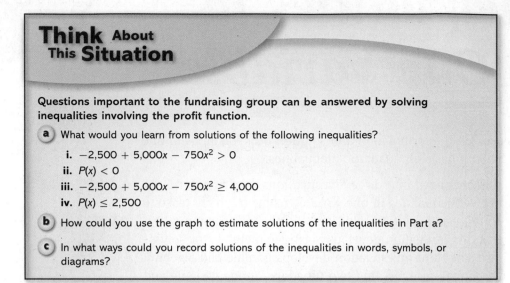

Think About This Situation

Questions important to the fundraising group can be answered by solving inequalities involving the profit function.

a What would you learn from solutions of the following inequalities?

  i. $-2{,}500 + 5{,}000x - 750x^2 > 0$

  ii. $P(x) < 0$

  iii. $-2{,}500 + 5{,}000x - 750x^2 \geq 4{,}000$

  iv. $P(x) \leq 2{,}500$

b How could you use the graph to estimate solutions of the inequalities in Part a?

c In what ways could you record solutions of the inequalities in words, symbols, or diagrams?

In this lesson, you will learn how to use graphical reasoning and algebraic methods to solve inequalities in one and two variables. You will also learn how to represent the solutions symbolically and graphically and how to interpret them in the contexts of the questions that they help to answer.

Investigation 1 — Getting the Picture

You learned in earlier work with inequalities that solutions can be found by first solving related equations. For example, in the raffle fundraiser situation, the solutions of the equation

$$-2{,}500 + 5{,}000x - 750x^2 = 2{,}500$$

are approximately $1.23 and $5.44. The reasonableness of these solutions can be seen by scanning the graph of the profit function and the constant function $y = 2{,}500$.

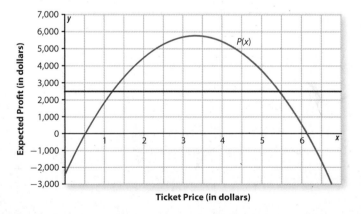

Ticket Price (in dollars)

Think About This Situation

a Solving each inequality gives the ticket prices for which:

  i. the fundraiser is predicted to give a positive profit.

  ii. the fundraiser is predicted to lose money.

  iii. the fundraiser is predicted to raise at least $4,000 in profit.

  iv. the fundraiser is predicted to raise at most $2,500 in profit.

b Estimating solutions from the graph involves finding the values of x that correspond to the portions of the graph that are

  i. above the x-axis,

  ii. below the x-axis,

  iii. on or above the line $y = 4,000$, and

  iv. on or below the line $y = 2,500$.

c **INSTRUCTIONAL NOTE** Solution descriptions in this lesson are given here. See the Lesson Launch above.

Solutions estimated from the graph may be described
(1) in words: when x is greater than $0.50 and less than about $6.10,
(2) as a number line graph:

(3) symbolically: $0.5 < x < 6.1$, or
(4) using interval notation introduced in Investigation 3: $(0.5, 6.1)$.

Unit 2

Investigation 1 Getting the Picture

This investigation lays a conceptual foundation for graphic thinking about inequalities that will be a useful complement to algebraic methods that are developed in the next two investigations. Students solve inequalities in one variable by appropriate estimation strategies using inspection of graphs or the function rule and graphing technology when available. Then they represent the solution sets of inequalities using words, number line graphs, and symbolic inequality sentences.

Think About This Situation, *page 109*

Teacher: In earlier courses, you learned how to solve a variety of problems by representing and reasoning about them with algebraic equations and inequalities. Let's consider a raffle fundraising situation as shown on page 109 of your book. Suppose that plans for the raffle show profit P is predicted to depend on ticket price x by the function rule $P(x) = -2,500 + 5,000x - 750x^2$. Let's consider questions important to the fundraising raffle that can be answered by solving inequalities involving this profit function. There are four inequalities in Part a of the Think About This Situation. What would you learn from the solution to each inequality? Think individually for a minute. Consider both the graph and the inequalities as you decide what you can learn from each inequality. *(The teacher wants each student to have time to consider Part a before ideas are shared in the whole group.)*

Teacher: Does anyone need more time to think about the inequalities and the graph? *(Since a few students indicate the need for more time, the teacher adds another task for those who are ready.)* Okay, let's take one more minute. If you do not need more time to think about Part a, then think of other questions about the fundraising effort that we might want answered about this situation and their corresponding inequalities. *(The teacher recognizes that this task is different from the task in Part a but is interested in what students can do with it.)* Okay, let's look at the first inequality in Part a. What would you learn from solving that inequality?

Anica: You find out when the profit is greater than 0? *(The teacher realizes that Anica has used the vague word "when" instead of "at what ticket price"; she makes a mental note to follow up to be sure students begin to connect the solution to the x values of the points that meet the inequality.)*

Carey: Yeah, but doesn't profit *mean* greater than 0? Aren't you really answering the question, "When will the fundraiser make a profit?"

Anica: I see what Carey is saying and I agree. I guess you either have a profit or no profit. Maybe we could think of it as a profit or a loss, not as a profit greater than zero.

Jeremiah: Or, having no profit might mean that you just break even.

Aston: That was one of my new questions. When will the fundraiser break even?

Teacher: Aston's question seems like an important one. How could the break-even question be built into one of the existing inequalities?

Julie: Just use a greater-than-or-equal-to sign for the first inequality. That covers both cases—when profit is zero (breaks even) and when a profit is made (positive profit).

Inua: That works!

Teacher: Are the rest of you okay with Julie's suggestion? *(Students indicate agreement.)* Then, let's think back to Anica's earlier statement. Anica suggested that solving the first inequality would tell us *when* the profit is greater than zero. What does the word "when" refer to?

Jonathan: "When" means finding the ticket price that gives a profit. Wait; there are lots of prices that do that. So, "when" means finding all the ticket prices that make money (rather than lose money).

Teacher: What do the rest of you think? *(Students indicate agreement with Jonathan but also reference the variable x representing ticket price.)* So, our solutions will involve x values that represent ticket prices. When you formulate your questions for the next three inequalities, include language that tells others that you are looking for *ticket prices* that solve the inequality.

Teacher: What about the second inequality in Part a; what question would be answered by $P(x) < 0$?

Ping: What ticket prices would make the fundraiser lose money?

Teacher: Does anyone disagree with Ping? *(No students indicate disagreement.)* What about the third inequality? What important question could be answered by solving it?

Carlos: What ticket prices would make $4,000 or more? We really get two answers at once with this one.

Teacher: Carlos, tell us a bit more about what you are thinking.

Carlos: I just mean that solving this inequality tells us both the ticket prices when the profit will be exactly $4,000 and the prices that will make a profit greater than $4,000. It's different than the first two inequalities.

Teacher: The next inequality also includes an equal sign. What might we learn about the fundraising effort by solving $P(x) \leq 2,500$?

Carmichael: When the profit is less than or equal to $2,500. I mean, "What ticket prices make a profit of $2,500 or less?"

Teacher: So, solving inequalities about particular situations like the fundraising event can answer some important and interesting questions. Earlier, I asked you to generate other questions about the fundraising raffle that might be answered by solving an inequality. Let's hear a few of the questions you came up with.

Susan: I said, "What ticket price will make the most profit?" And I did not know how to write an inequality or equation for this question. I just estimated from the graph that the maximum profit would be a little under $6,000 when the ticket price is somewhere between $3 and $3.50. *(The teacher chooses not to follow this line of thinking.)*

Mia: Mine was, "What ticket price should the fundraiser charge to have at least $1,000?" The inequality would be $P(x) \geq 1,000$.

Teacher: Thank you for sharing those. Let's think about Part b. How could you use the graph to estimate solutions of the inequalities in Part a?

Aston: Well, for the first two inequalities, you can look at the profit graph and the x-axis. Where they cross tells us the ticket price that makes the fundraiser break even, like I talked about earlier.

Nate: I agree with Aston. The goal is to find where the profit is greater than zero and less than zero. Above the x-axis the profit is positive and below it is negative. So, the places where the graph crosses the x-axis are what you need to answer the question.

Jarvis: Right, look for where the parabola is above the x-axis. That is where the profit is greater than zero. Then look where the graph is below the x-axis for when there is a loss.

(Here again, the use of "where" is a vague way to identify solutions, but the teacher recognizes that the inequality and number line representations of solutions in the investigation will help students solidify their understanding of solutions to inequalities. The teacher has planned to incorporate the discussion of ways to record solutions from Part c in this discussion and not treat it as a separate part of the TATS. But since Magdalene wishes to offer her thoughts, she waits and calls on Magdalene.)

Magdalene: You could use vertical lines to help.

Teacher: Can you tell us more about how that might help?

Magdalene: I need to show you on that graph. Here, set a paper along the y-axis covering the x-axis. Then pull it to the right—keep it vertical. Then you can see what Aston, Nate, and Jarvis are talking about. If you stop at the first break-even point, you see that the fundraiser is losing money until the ticket price is 50¢. If you keep pulling the paper to the right, you can find the other break-even price at about $6.25.

Teacher: Interesting! Thinking about the inequality $P(x) < 0$, how might we record the solutions to this inequality in words, symbols, or diagrams?

Sonja: We are looking for the x values that make the graph be below the x-axis. These are values from 0 to just less than 0.5 (50¢) and from about 6.25 and more. We could use inequalities to write this. *(She goes to the board.)* $0 < x < 0.5$ and $x > 6.25$.

Melissa: Magdalene's idea of moving the paper reminds me of how we colored the x-axis for inequalities. Pick a color to start a 0 and color along the x-axis until we get to 0.5. This would be the ticket prices that would make a loss because the profit is negative. Then switch colors ... *(The teacher interrupts Melissa to ask her to show her thinking on the class-displayed graph. Melissa colors x values between the x-intercepts a different color and then returns to red for the x values to the right of the largest x-intercept.)*

Teacher: Does anyone have other ways to record the solutions? *(No suggestions are offered. Since number lines are described in the investigation, if Melissa had not offered the coloring idea, the teacher would not have suggested that approach at this time. But she will connect to Melissa's idea at the STM discussion. The teacher asks for ways to use the graph to estimate solutions for Part aiii before concluding the discussion. If students do not offer the horizontal line for $y = 4,000$, she does not introduce it since students have much more time to consider how to read solutions from graphs and represent them in the upcoming investigation.)*

Teacher: Okay. We have lots of ideas generated from this TATS. In this lesson, we will learn more about how to use graphical reasoning and algebraic methods to solve inequalities in one and two variables. We will also learn more ways to represent our solutions symbolically and graphically, and then how to interpret our solutions to help answer questions that arise from the context at hand.

The solutions of the inequality $-2{,}500 + 5{,}000x - 750x^2 \geq 2{,}500$ are all values of x between \$1.23 and \$5.44. Those solutions to the inequality can be represented using symbols or a *number line graph*.

$$1.23 \leq x \leq 5.44$$

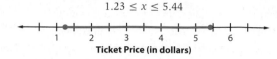
Ticket Price (in dollars)

Similarly, the solutions of the inequality $-2{,}500 + 5{,}000x - 750x^2 < 2{,}500$ are all values of x that are either less than \$1.23 or greater than \$5.44. Those solutions can also be represented using symbols or a number line graph.

$$x < 1.23 \text{ or } x > 5.44$$

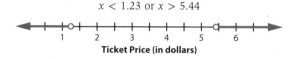
Ticket Price (in dollars)

As you work on problems of this investigation, look for answers to these questions:

> *How can you solve inequalities in one variable?*
>
> *How can you record the solutions in symbolic and graphic form?*

1 The next graph shows the height of the main support cable on a suspension bridge. The function defining the curve is $h(x) = 0.04x^2 - 3.5x + 100$, where x is horizontal distance (in feet) from the left end of the bridge and $h(x)$ is the height (in feet) of the cable above the bridge surface.

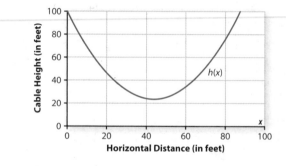

For the questions in Parts a–d:

- Write an algebraic calculation, equation, or inequality whose solution will provide an answer to the question.
- Then use the graph above to estimate the solution and calculator- or computer-generated tables and graphs of $h(x)$ to sharpen the accuracy to the nearest tenth.
- Express your answer with a symbolic expression and (where appropriate) a number line graph.

a. Where is the bridge cable less than 40 feet above the bridge surface?

b. Where is the bridge cable at least 60 feet above the bridge surface?

Refer back to the TATS questions to help students connect the problem context and language to the graphic, symbolic, and number line notation introduced prior to Problem 1. Ask students to identify the line $y = 2{,}500$ on the TATS graphic. Then identify the x values for the intersection of $y = 2{,}500$ and $P(x)$. Students should recognize that the solutions to

$$-2{,}500 + 5{,}000x - 750x^2 \geq 2{,}500$$

are all values between \$1.23 and \$5.44, an answer with precision that can be attained by inspecting tables or graphs of the function $y = -2{,}500 + 5{,}000x - 750x^2$. You could then sketch a number line to represent the solutions. The meaning of the open and closed circles could also be discussed. Finally, refer to the focus questions for Investigation 1 in the student text.

1 **a.** $0.04x^2 - 3.5x + 100 < 40$ has approximate solution $25 < x < 65$. More precise estimates would be $23.4 < x < 64.1$.

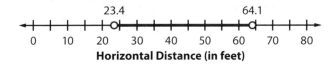

Horizontal Distance (in feet)

EXTENSION You may wish to have students recognize that the compound inequality $2 < x < 8$ includes the same values of x as the statement $x < 8$ and $x > 2$.

b. $0.04x^2 - 3.5x + 100 \geq 60$ has approximate solution $x \leq 15$ or $70 \leq x$. More precise estimates would be $x \leq 13.5$ or $74 \leq x$.

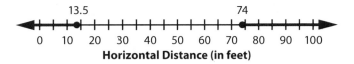

Horizontal Distance (in feet)

Unit 2

c. How far is the cable above the bridge surface at a point 45 feet from the left end?

d. Where is the cable 80 feet above the bridge surface?

(2) The graph below shows the height of a bungee jumper's head above the ground at various times during her ride on the elastic bungee cord. Suppose that $h(t)$ gives height in feet as a function of time in seconds.

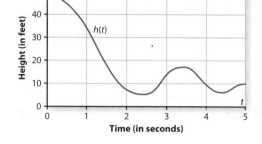

For each Part a–d:

- Write a question about the bungee jump that can be answered by the indicated mathematical operation.
- Use the graph to estimate the answer.
- Express your answer (where appropriate) with a number line graph.

a. Evaluate $h(2)$.

b. Solve $h(t) = 10$.

c. Solve $h(t) \geq 10$.

d. Solve $h(t) < 10$.

Summarize
the Mathematics

In this investigation, you developed strategies for solving problems by estimating solutions for equations and inequalities in one variable. You also used symbols and number line graphs to record the solutions.

a Describe strategies for solving inequalities in the form $f(x) \leq c$ and $f(x) \geq c$ when given a graph of the function $f(x)$.

b If the solution of an inequality is described by $2 \leq x$ and $x < 5$, what will a number line graph of that solution look like?

c What inequality statement(s) describe the numbers represented in this number line graph?

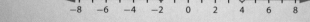

Be prepared to share your ideas and reasoning with the class.

c. $0.04(45)^2 - 3.5(45) + 100 = 23.5$. In this case, a number line graph does not really make any sense because what is asked is the value of $h(x)$ corresponding to the given $x = 45$.

d. $0.04x^2 - 3.5x + 100 = 80$ has two solutions $x \approx 6$ and $x \approx 80$. More precisely, $x \approx 6.1$ and $x \approx 81.4$.

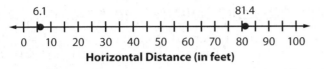

Horizontal Distance (in feet)

2 **a.** $h(2)$ will tell the height of the jumper's head above the ground at a time 2 seconds after he or she jumps. The graph suggests that this height will be about 8 feet. In this case, a number line graph does not really make any sense because we are given the value of t and asked to find the corresponding value of $h(t)$.

b. $h(t) = 10$ asks us to find time(s) when the bungee jumper's head is 10 feet above the ground. The solutions are approximately $t \approx 1.8$, 2.8, 3.9, and 5.0.

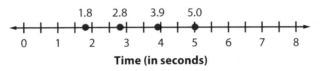

Time (in seconds)

c. $h(t) \geq 10$ asks us to find times when the jumper's head is at least 10 feet above the ground. The solutions are approximately $t \leq 1.8$, $2.8 \leq t \leq 3.9$, or $t = 5$.

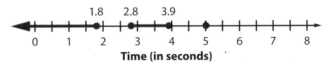

Time (in seconds)

d. $h(t) < 10$ asks us to find times when the jumper's head is less than 10 feet from the ground (during the first 5 seconds of the ride). The solutions are approximately $1.8 < t < 2.8$ or $3.9 < t < 5.0$.

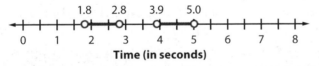

Time (in seconds)

Summarize
the Mathematics

a In general, to solve the inequality $f(x) \leq c$, look for points on the graph of $f(x)$ lying on or below the line $y = c$. To solve $f(x) \geq c$, look for points on or above that horizontal line. Then identify the x values associated with those points.

b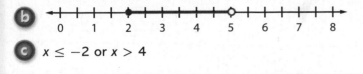

c $x \leq -2$ or $x > 4$

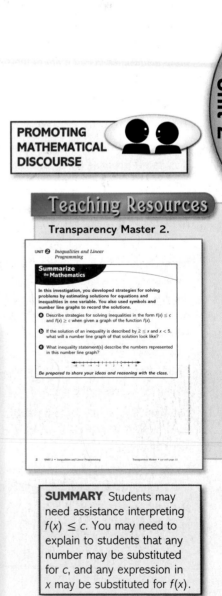

Summarize the Mathematics, *page 111*

Teacher: Let's discuss the summarizing questions for Investigation 1. We developed some strategies for solving problems by estimating solutions for equations and inequalities. We also used both symbols and line graphs to record the solutions. Our first summarizing question to think about is: What are some strategies for solving inequalities in the form $f(x) \leq c$ and $f(x) \geq c$ when the graph of the function is given to you? Are there any clarifying questions before we take a few seconds to think individually? *(The teacher is concerned that the formal function language may need clarification for some learners.)*

Antonina: Are they just talking about any function so they just call it $f(x)$? Like could $f(x)$ be the fundraiser profit function?

Teacher: Sure. You can think about the profit function if it is helpful. Let's look back to the Think About This Situation on page 109. What profit inequalities in Part a are of the same form we are now thinking about in the STM?

Jackson: Parts iii and iv

Teacher: Can you say more about that Jackson?

Jackson: If we think of the profit as $f(x)$, like Antonina was saying, then part iii would be the greater than or equal kind of inequality where $f(x) \geq c$ because it is $P(x) \geq 4,000$. And part iv is $P(x) \leq 2,500$ so it is like $f(x) \leq c$.

Antonina: That helps me.

Teacher: Other clarifying questions? *(None surface.)* Okay, take a few seconds to think about the strategies one might use to solve inequalities of the form $f(x) \leq c$ and $f(x) \geq c$ when the graph of the function is given to you. *(Although some students raise their hands, the teacher waits until all students have some individual thinking time before calling on anyone.)* Charles, what strategy would you offer?

Charles: Since the graph is given, I would draw the line $y = c$ and see where it crosses the graph of $f(x)$.

Teacher: Who would like to build off what Charles has offered as a strategy? What might students using Charles' strategy do next, Tonya?

Tonya: They would probably look for all the points on the graph that are below the horizontal line that they drew.

Jori: Or above the line, depending on which inequality they are solving.

Charles: Right. If I were solving the greater than or equal to inequality, I would look for points above the points of intersection, and if I were solving the less than or equal to, then I would look for the points below the points of intersection.

Juanita: Actually, we should also include the points of intersection because the inequalities are greater than or equal to and less than or equal to. We have to include the points where $f(x)$ is equal to c.

Teacher: Anything else we should add to Charles' strategy?

Yasu: Well, we aren't really done when we find the points above or below the line. We need to decide what the x-coordinates of those points are. I think of it as dropping down to the x-axis. Can I show this on an example? *(She goes to the board, sketches an upside-down parabola and a horizontal line not at the x-axis. Then she draws two dashed lines from the intersection points to the x-axis.)* Now the x-axis is split into sections from which I can read the solutions I need.

Teacher: Any questions or comments?

Melissa: That is kinda what I was doing when I colored the x-axis. I split it up into sections. These sections helped me figure out what x values were the solutions to the inequality.

Teacher: Wow! It looks like you are connecting the number line graphs of solutions to inequalities to the x-axis of the coordinate graph representation.

Dion: Yeah, and if c is 0, you don't need to draw a line. Just use the x-axis.

Teacher: Okay, then lets think about Part b. If the solution to an inequality is described by $2 \leq x$ and $x < 5$, what will the number line graph of the solution look like? Let's each individually draw a quick graph of the solution then we will compare. *(The teacher allows time for students to record a rough sketch of the number line graph of the solution and jots one down on scrap paper herself.)* Okay, everyone now share your sketch with someone near you. *(wait time)* Any discrepancies?

Marti: We had different graphs, but Tonya convinced me that her thinking was right. I read the inequalities the wrong way.

Tonya: Marti was thinking of the inequalities as $x \leq 2$ and $x < 5$, so she had all points less than 5.

George: Peter and I disagreed, too. Peter had a solid dot at 2 and I didn't. But when we talked about how our number lines were different, we agreed that 2 is part of the solution so there should be a solid dot at 2.

Teacher: Any other discrepancies? *(None are offered.)* So, Marti, would you sketch a number line graph of solutions for the inequalities in Part b on the board? *(The correct number line graph is presented.)* Notice that in Part c, we are given a graph and asked to write the inequality statement or statements that describe the numbers represented by the graph. Discuss and reach consensus as a group on an inequality statement or statements that match the number line graph. *(The teacher then asks one group to write the inequalities where all can see and reach agreement.)* Okay, please work on the Check Your Understanding task for the next few minutes by yourself. I'll be circulating to see if you have any questions.

✔Check Your Understanding

Use information from this graph of the function $f(x)$ to answer the questions that follow.

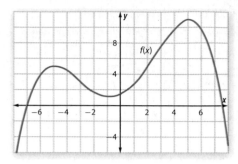

a. Estimate the values of x for which $f(x) = 5$.

b. Describe the values of x for which $f(x) \geq 5$ using the following.

    i. words   **ii.** symbols   **iii.** a number line graph

c. Explain how your answers to Part b would change if you were asked to consider the values of x for which $f(x) > 5$?

Investigation 2 · Quadratic Inequalities

Inequalities that involve functions with familiar rules can often be solved by algebraic reasoning. As you work on the problems of this investigation, look for answers to these questions:

> *What are the solution possibilities for quadratic inequalities?*
>
> *How can solution strategies for quadratic equations be applied to solution of inequalities?*

1 Consider the inequality $t^2 - t - 6 \leq 0$.

    a. Which of these diagrams is most like what you would expect for a graph of the function $g(t) = t^2 - t - 6$? How can you decide without using a graphing tool?

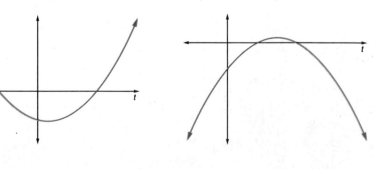

Graph I   Graph II

✓ Check Your Understanding

a. $f(x) = 5$ when $x = -5$, 2, or 7.

b. $f(x) \geq 5$ when:

   i. x is equal to -5 or when x is between 2 and 7, including 2 and 7

   ii. $x = -5$ or $2 \leq x \leq 7$

   iii.

c. If the inequality changed to a strict greater than symbol, then the solution $x = -5$ would be lost. The points 2 and 7 would be graphed as open circles to indicate that those boundaries are not part of the solution interval.

INSTRUCTIONAL NOTE
There is an implicit assumption that the graph of $f(x)$ will continue without any further "turns."

PROCESSING PROMPT
We helped our group stay focused on the mathematics by … .

Investigation 2   Quadratic Inequalities

The problems of this investigation focus on the solution of quadratic inequalities by algebraic reasoning with the conceptual support of graphic images. The key to solving standard quadratic inequalities is to use algebraic reasoning to express them in the form $ax^2 + bx + c < 0$ or $ax^2 + bx + c < d$, to solve the related quadratic equation, and to use those boundary points to determine the interval solutions to the inequality.

While there are some common algebraic strategies for determining the inequality solutions directly from knowledge of the equality solutions, we strongly recommend making the graphic connection as well. It gives an image of the pattern of change for the function(s) involved and a more robust understanding of the inequality solution. The first two problems of the investigation emphasize that kind of visual reasoning, so we recommend a whole class discussion (mini-summary) following Problem 2.

Problems 3–5 provide just-in-time review of techniques that are needed for solving quadratic inequalities. Then Problem 6 asks students to combine algebraic and graphing reasoning to solve quadratic inequalities.

1   a. The first graph is most like what one would expect for a graph of $g(t)$. Since the coefficient of t^2 is positive, the graph will open upward, and the constant term indicates a negative y-intercept.

b. The expression $t^2 - t - 6$ can be written in equivalent factored form as $(t - 3)(t + 2)$. How can this fact be used to solve the equation $t^2 - t - 6 = 0$? What do those solutions tell about the graph of $g(t)$?

c. Use your answers from Parts a and b to solve the inequality $t^2 - t - 6 \leq 0$. Describe the solution using symbols and a number line graph.

d. Use similar reasoning to solve the inequality $t^2 - t - 6 > 0$ and record the solutions using symbols and a number line graph.

② Your answers to the questions in Problem 1 show how two key ideas reveal solutions to any quadratic inequality in the form $ax^2 + bx + c \leq 0$ or $ax^2 + bx + c > 0$.

a. How does sketching the graph of $f(x) = ax^2 + bx + c$ help in solving a quadratic inequality in the form above?

b. How does solving the equation $ax^2 + bx + c = 0$ help in solving a quadratic inequality like those shown?

To use these strategies effectively, you need to recall the cues that tell shape and location of a quadratic function graph and the techniques for solving quadratic equations. Problems 3–5 provide review of the ideas required by those tasks.

③ For each of these quadratic functions, use the coefficients of the terms to help determine the shape and location of the graph.

- whether the graph has a maximum or minimum point
- the location of the line of symmetry
- where the graph will cross the y-axis

a. $f(x) = x^2 - 4x - 5$ **b.** $g(x) = -x^2 + 2x + 8$

c. $h(x) = x^2 + 6x + 9$ **d.** $j(x) = 2x^2 + 2x + 1$

④ What are the possible numbers of x-intercepts for the graph of a quadratic function? Sketch graphs to illustrate each possibility.

⑤ Solutions for quadratic equations can be estimated by scanning tables or graphs of the related quadratic functions. Solutions can also be found exactly by factoring the quadratic expression or by use of the quadratic formula. Practice using those exact solution strategies to solve these quadratic equations. Be prepared to explain your choice of strategy.

a. $x^2 + 5x + 4 = 0$ **b.** $x^2 + 2x - 8 = 0$

c. $-x^2 + 6x - 9 = 0$ **d.** $2x^2 + 2x + 1 = 0$

e. $x^2 - 6x + 11 = 2$ **f.** $x^2 + 1 = -3x$

b. $t - 3 = 0$ or $t + 2 = 0$, so $t = 3$ or $t = -2$. This indicates that the coordinates of the t-intercepts of the graph are $(-2, 0)$ and $(3, 0)$.

c. Since the graph is below the t-axis between the t values -2 and 3, the solution is $-2 \le t \le 3$.

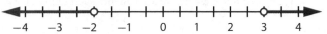

d. Since the graph is above the t-axis for t values to the left of -2 and to the right of 3, the solution is $t < -2$ or $t > 3$.

2 **a.** Sketching the graph of $f(x) = ax^2 + bx + c$ provides a visual representation to help locate the x values for which the expression is positive and negative.

b. Solving $ax^2 + bx + c = 0$ gives the x-intercept(s) that are boundaries of the intervals for which the expression is positive and negative.

3 **a.** • $a = 1$ is positive, so the graph has a minimum point.
 • $-\frac{b}{2a} = 2$, so the line of symmetry is $x = 2$.
 • $c = -5$, so the y-intercept is $(0, -5)$.

b. • $a = -1$ is negative, so the graph has a maximum point.
 • $-\frac{b}{2a} = 1$, so the line of symmetry is $x = 1$.
 • $c = 8$, so the y-intercept is $(0, 8)$.

c. • $a = 1$ is positive, so the graph has a minimum point.
 • $-\frac{b}{2a} = -3$, so the line of symmetry is $x = -3$.
 • $c = 9$, so the y-intercept is $(0, 9)$.

d. • $a = 2$ is positive, so the graph has a minimum point.
 • $-\frac{b}{2a} = -\frac{1}{2}$, so the line of symmetry is $x = -\frac{1}{2}$.
 • $c = 1$, so the y-intercept is $(0, 1)$.

4 A quadratic function may have 2, 1, or 0 x-intercepts as illustrated in the sketches of graphs at the right.

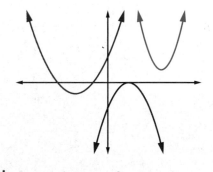

5 **a.** $x = -1$ or $x = -4$ **b.** $x = -4$ or $x = 2$

c. $x = 3$ **d.** no real solutions

e. $x = 3$ **f.** $x = \dfrac{-3 \pm \sqrt{5}}{2}$

6 Combine algebraic and graphic reasoning to solve the following inequalities. For each inequality:

- sketch a graph showing the pattern of change you expect for the function involved.
- use algebraic reasoning to locate key intersection points.
- combine what you learn from your sketch and algebraic reasoning to solve the inequality.
- record the solution using symbols and number line graphs.

a. $x^2 + 2x > 0$ **b.** $x^2 + 2x < 0$

c. $n^2 + 2n - 24 \leq 0$ **d.** $n^2 + 2n - 24 > 0$

e. $-s^2 + 4s - 6 < 0$ **f.** $-s^2 + 4s - 6 > 0$

g. $8r - r^2 \geq 15$ **h.** $3x^2 - 5x > 8$

i. $z^2 - 6z + 7 < 2$ **j.** $-p^2 + 10p - 7 \leq 14$

Summarize the Mathematics

In this investigation, you developed strategies for solving quadratic inequalities.

a Describe strategies for solving inequalities in the form $ax^2 + bx + c \leq d$ and $ax^2 + bx + c \geq d$ by algebraic and graphic reasoning.

b What are possible solutions for quadratic inequalities, and how can each form be expressed in algebraic and number line graph form?

Be prepared to share your ideas and reasoning with the class.

✓ Check Your Understanding

For each inequality: (1) sketch a graph of the function involved in the inequality, (2) use algebraic reasoning to locate x-intercepts of the graph, (3) combine what you learn from your sketch and algebraic reasoning to solve the inequality, and (4) record the solution using symbols and a number line graph.

a. $k^2 - 3k - 4 > 0$ **b.** $-b^2 + 8b - 10 \geq 0$

6 **INSTRUCTIONAL NOTE** Students may be confused about the direction of inequality solutions. To help avoid this, encourage students to *sketch* a rough graph of the function defined by the quadratic expression in the *original* inequality to help visualize the values of the independent variable for which the function is above or below the given function value (constant function on the right side of the inequality). Students should reason about the graph of the function defined by the quadratic expression in the *original* inequality and its relation to the given function value rather than manipulate the inequality or its related equation and then reason about the zeros of a quadratic expression obtained through manipulation.

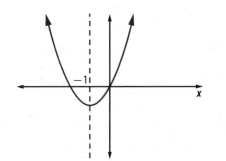
a. The graph of $f(x) = x^2 + 2x$ opens upwards and has y-intercept at 0. (Students may incorrectly sketch a graph that has a positive x-intercept at first unless they use the symmetry line $x = -1$. If so, they can adjust their graph after solving algebraically.)

$$x^2 + 2x = 0$$
$$x(x + 2) = 0$$
$$x = -2 \text{ or } x = 0:$$

Since $f(x) > 0$ when $x < -2$ or $x > 0$, $x^2 + 2x > 0$ over the same intervals.

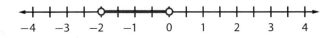

b. The function from Part a will be below 0 when $-2 < x < 0$. So, $x^2 + 2x < 0$ on that interval.

c. The graph opens upward, has y-intercept at -24, and has symmetry line $n = -1$.

$$n^2 + 2n - 24 = 0$$
$$(n + 6)(n - 4) = 0$$
$$n = -6 \text{ or } n = 4$$

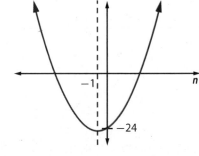

The function will be at or below 0 when $-6 \leq n \leq 4$. So, $n^2 + 2n - 24 \leq 0$ on that interval.

d. The function from Part c will be above 0 when $n < -6$ or $n > 4$. So, $n^2 + 2n - 24 > 0$ on those intervals.

e.

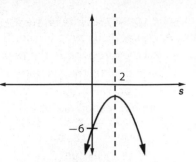

The graph opens downward, has a y-intercept of -6, and has symmetry line $s = 2$. (Students may sketch a graph that intersects the s-axis. They can adjust their sketch after solving algebraically.)

$$-s^2 + 4s - 6 \neq 0$$

Using the quadratic formula to solve $-s^2 + 4s - 6 = 0$:

$$s = \frac{-4}{-2} \pm \frac{\sqrt{16 - 4(-1)(-6)}}{-2} = 2 \pm \frac{\sqrt{-8}}{-2}$$

So, $-s^2 + 4s - 6 = 0$ has no real solutions.

The function is below 0. So, $-s^2 + 4s - 6 < 0$ for all real values of s.

f. The function from Part e is not above 0 for any real values of s. So, $-s^2 + 4s - 6 > 0$ has no real solutions.

g.

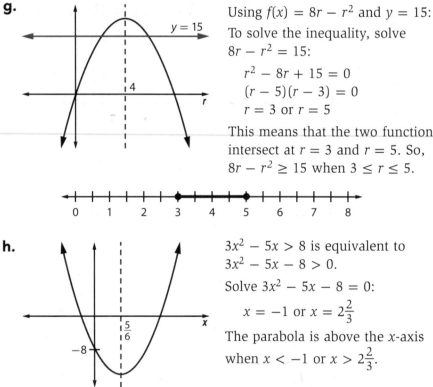

Using $f(x) = 8r - r^2$ and $y = 15$:
To solve the inequality, solve $8r - r^2 = 15$:

$$r^2 - 8r + 15 = 0$$
$$(r - 5)(r - 3) = 0$$
$$r = 3 \text{ or } r = 5$$

This means that the two functions intersect at $r = 3$ and $r = 5$. So, $8r - r^2 \geq 15$ when $3 \leq r \leq 5$.

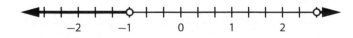

h.

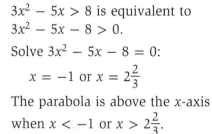

$3x^2 - 5x > 8$ is equivalent to $3x^2 - 5x - 8 > 0$.

Solve $3x^2 - 5x - 8 = 0$:

$$x = -1 \text{ or } x = 2\tfrac{2}{3}$$

The parabola is above the x-axis when $x < -1$ or $x > 2\tfrac{2}{3}$.

So, the solution to $3x^2 - 5x > 8$ is the union of the intervals $x < -1$ and $x > 2\tfrac{2}{3}$.

i.

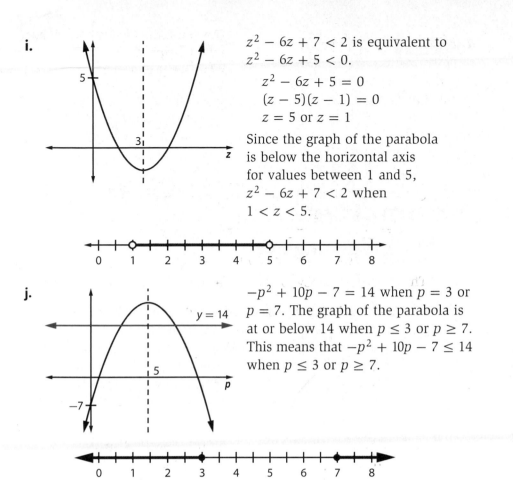

$z^2 - 6z + 7 < 2$ is equivalent to $z^2 - 6z + 5 < 0$.

$$z^2 - 6z + 5 = 0$$
$$(z - 5)(z - 1) = 0$$
$$z = 5 \text{ or } z = 1$$

Since the graph of the parabola is below the horizontal axis for values between 1 and 5, $z^2 - 6z + 7 < 2$ when $1 < z < 5$.

j.

$-p^2 + 10p - 7 = 14$ when $p = 3$ or $p = 7$. The graph of the parabola is at or below 14 when $p \le 3$ or $p \ge 7$. This means that $-p^2 + 10p - 7 \le 14$ when $p \le 3$ or $p \ge 7$.

When discussing both strategies outlined in Part a, help students recognize that this function $y = ax^2 + bx + (c - d)$ is simply a vertical translation of $y = ax^2 + bx + c$. The two functions have the same axis of symmetry. Knowing this helps to understand why the x boundary values using either approach are the same.

Unit 2

Summarize
the Mathematics

a One effective strategy for solving inequalities in the form $ax^2 + bx + c \le d$ and $ax^2 + bx + c \ge d$ would be to rewrite the inequality in less-than-or-equal-to-0 or greater-than-or-equal-to-0 form. Then solve the equation $ax^2 + bx + (c - d) = 0$ to identify values of x (x-intercepts) that bound the solution intervals for the inequalities, and use cues from the graph to decide which interval(s) satisfy each inequality. The x values at which the graph $y = ax^2 + bx + (c - d)$ is at or below the x-axis will be solutions of the $\le$ inequality. The x values at which the graph of $y = ax^2 + bx + (c - d)$ is at or above the x-axis will be solutions of the $\ge$ inequality. This strategy also applies when $d = 0$.

Another strategy would be to begin with a graph of the functions $y = ax^2 + bx + c$ and $y = d$. Then solve the equation $ax^2 + bx + c = d$ to identify the values of x that bound the solution intervals. The x values at which the graph of $y = ax^2 + bx + c$ is at or below the graph of $y = d$ will be solutions of the inequality $ax^2 + bx + c \le d$. The values of x at which the graph of $y = ax^2 + bx + c$ is at or above that of $y = d$ will be solutions of $ax^2 + bx + c \ge d$.

b Solutions for a quadratic inequality may be of the form "$x \le m$ or $x \ge n$" or "$m \le x \le n$." The corresponding number line graphs will look like these:

It is also possible to have no real solutions or a solution of one value as seen in Problem 5. Also, if the inequality is a strict inequality, the number lines above would have open dots on m and n.

✔ Check Your Understanding

a. $y = k^2 - 3k - 4$

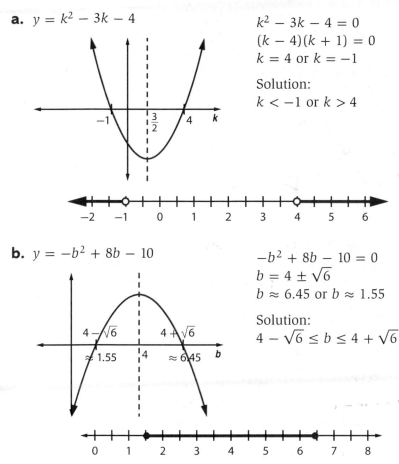

$k^2 - 3k - 4 = 0$
$(k - 4)(k + 1) = 0$
$k = 4$ or $k = -1$

Solution:
$k < -1$ or $k > 4$

b. $y = -b^2 + 8b - 10$

$-b^2 + 8b - 10 = 0$
$b = 4 \pm \sqrt{6}$
$b \approx 6.45$ or $b \approx 1.55$

Solution:
$4 - \sqrt{6} \leq b \leq 4 + \sqrt{6}$

Unit 2

Investigation 3   Complex Inequalities

Many problems require comparison of two functions to find when values of one are greater or less than values of the other. As you work on the problems of this investigation, look for answers to this question:

How can the reasoning developed to deal with inequalities involving a single function be adapted to find solutions for more complex cases?

1 The diagram below shows the graphs of functions $h(x)$ and $k(x)$. Assume that all points of intersection are shown and that the functions have no breaks in their graphs.

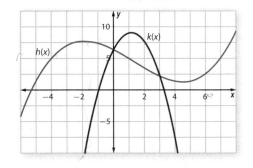

a. What are the approximate values of x for which $h(x) = k(x)$?

b. What are the values of x for which $h(x) \leq k(x)$? Express your answer using symbols and a number line graph.

c. What are the values of x for which $h(x) > k(x)$? Express your answer using symbols and a number line graph.

2 Harriet Tubman Elementary School needs to hire staff for a new after-school program. The program has a budget of $1,000 per week to pay staff salaries.

The function $h(p) = \dfrac{1,000}{p}$ shows how the number of staff that can be hired depends on the weekly pay per staff member p. Research suggested that the number of job applicants depends on the weekly pay offered according to the function $a(p) = -5 + 0.1p$.

a. Without using a graphing calculator, sketch a graph showing how $h(p)$ and $a(p)$ depend on p.

Complex Inequalities

The aim of this investigation is to generalize students' graphic and algebraic understanding and technique for solving inequalities to somewhat more complex situations and algebraic expressions. The aim is to use algebraic methods (where viable) to locate intersection points of graphs and to use the visual images provided by the graphs to inform solution of the related inequalities. Interval notation is introduced in Problem 4.

1   **a.** $h(x) = k(x)$ when $x = 0$ or $x = 3$.

   b. $h(x) \leq k(x)$ when $0 \leq x \leq 3$.

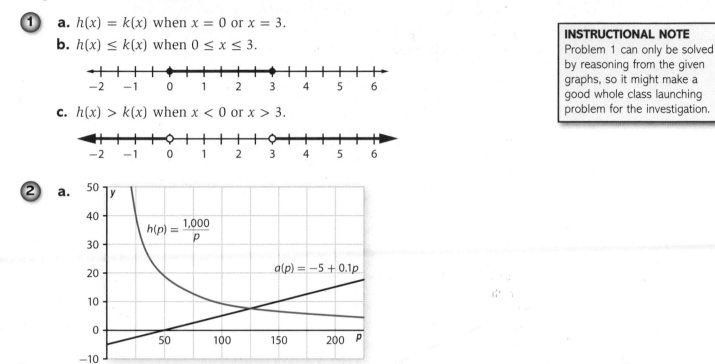

   c. $h(x) > k(x)$ when $x < 0$ or $x > 3$.

2   **a.**

Unit 2

b. Solve the equation $\frac{1{,}000}{p} = -5 + 0.1p$ algebraically. Then explain what the solution tells about the staffing situation for the after-school program at Harriet Tubman Elementary.

c. The program director wants to ensure that she will be able to choose her staff from a large enough pool of applicants.

    i. Write an inequality that can be solved to determine the weekly pay per staff member for which the number of applicants will be more than the number of staff that can be hired.

    ii. Use your responses to Parts a and b to solve the inequality.

(3) For each inequality given below:

- sketch a graph showing how you expect the two component functions to be related.
- use algebraic reasoning, a computer algebra system (CAS), or estimation using function tables or graphs to locate the points of intersection of the graphs.
- apply what you learn about the relationship of the functions to solve the inequality.
- record the solution using symbols and number line graphs.

a. $q^2 + 3q - 6 \le q + 2$ **b.** $c^2 - 4c - 5 \ge 2c + 2$

c. $v^2 - v + 3 > 2v - 1$ **d.** $2m + 3 > 4 - m^2$

e. $7 - x < \frac{10}{x}$ **f.** $\sqrt{d} > 2d - 1$

Interval Notation The solution of an inequality in one variable is generally composed of one or more intervals on a number line. Mathematicians use *interval notation* as a kind of shorthand to describe those solutions. For example, consider your response to Problem 1 Part b.

$$h(x) \le k(x) \text{ when } 0 \le x \le 3.$$

Using interval notation,

$$0 \le x \le 3 \text{ can be written as } [0, 3].$$

The square brackets [,] indicate that the endpoints 0 and 3 are included in the solution set as well as all points between those end points. On the other hand, in Part c of Problem 1, you found that:

$$h(x) > k(x) \text{ when } x < 0 \text{ or } x > 3.$$

Using interval notation,

$$x < 0 \text{ or } x > 3 \text{ can be written as } (-\infty, 0) \cup (3, +\infty).$$

Here, the round brackets (,) indicate that the end points are not included in the solution set. The symbol ∞ represents infinity. Round brackets are always used with $-\infty$ and $+\infty$. The symbol $\cup$ indicates the *union* of the two intervals, that is, the numbers that are in one interval *or* the other. If an inequality has no real number solutions, the solution set is the *empty set*, denoted by the symbol $\varnothing$.

b. $1{,}000 = -5p + 0.1p^2$

$0.1p^2 - 5p - 1{,}000 = 0$

Using the quadratic formula, the equation has two solutions, approximately 128 and -78. The first solution tells us that the number of applicants will be equal to the number of staff that can be hired if the weekly pay per staff member is about \$128. The other solution does not make sense in the problem situation.

c. **i.** $-5 + 0.1p > \dfrac{1{,}000}{p}$

ii. $p > 128$; the number of applicants will exceed the number of staff that can be hired when the weekly pay is greater than \$128.

③ **INSTRUCTIONAL NOTE** Emphasis here is in equalities as comparisons of two functions. Students should make a rough sketch of the two functions *before beginning any manipulations*. Students should use information from each expression that is quickly recognizable as helpful for sketching graphs, such as whether the slope of a line is positive or negative and whether a parabola opens upward or downward. After locating the points of intersection algebraically, students should consider the *original* inequality and ask themselves questions like, "For which *x* values will one function be above (or below) the other function?" For example, in Part a, students might ask, "For which *q* values is the line above the parabola?"

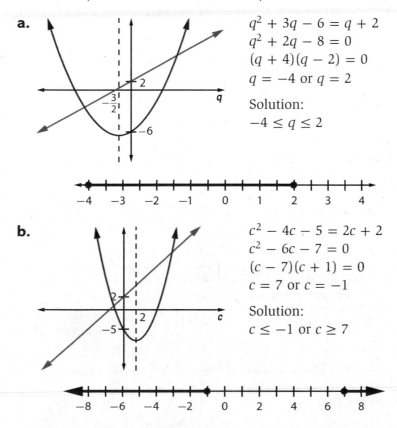

a.

$q^2 + 3q - 6 = q + 2$

$q^2 + 2q - 8 = 0$

$(q + 4)(q - 2) = 0$

$q = -4$ or $q = 2$

Solution:

$-4 \le q \le 2$

b.

$c^2 - 4c - 5 = 2c + 2$

$c^2 - 6c - 7 = 0$

$(c - 7)(c + 1) = 0$

$c = 7$ or $c = -1$

Solution:

$c \le -1$ or $c \ge 7$

Unit 2

c. INSTRUCTIONAL NOTE For this inequality, students may not be certain about whether the parabola and line have 0, 1, or 2 points of intersection. It is not necessary that their initial sketch accurately reflects the solution. Solving the inequality algebraically will allow them to determine how many intersections exist. This problem also provides another opportunity to discuss the fact that when the solution to an equation is "no solutions," the corresponding inequality may have no solutions or all real numbers as solutions.

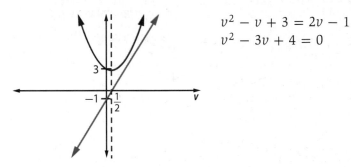

$$v^2 - v + 3 = 2v - 1$$
$$v^2 - 3v + 4 = 0$$

Since $b^2 - 4ac = -7$, there are no real solutions. This means that there are no intersection points for the two graphs. Since the inequality is $v^2 - v + 3 > 2v - 1$ and the line is below the parabola, the solution to the inequality is all real numbers.

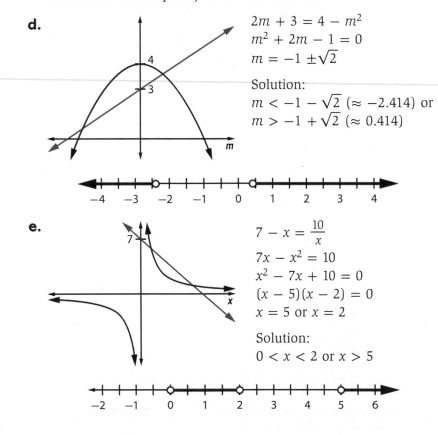

d.

$$2m + 3 = 4 - m^2$$
$$m^2 + 2m - 1 = 0$$
$$m = -1 \pm \sqrt{2}$$

Solution:
$$m < -1 - \sqrt{2} \ (\approx -2.414) \text{ or}$$
$$m > -1 + \sqrt{2} \ (\approx 0.414)$$

INSTRUCTIONAL NOTE
Here again, students may sketch the two graphs with 0, 1, or 2 points of intersection.

e.

$$7 - x = \frac{10}{x}$$
$$7x - x^2 = 10$$
$$x^2 - 7x + 10 = 0$$
$$(x - 5)(x - 2) = 0$$
$$x = 5 \text{ or } x = 2$$

Solution:
$$0 < x < 2 \text{ or } x > 5$$

f. Students can solve this problem graphically or using a CAS. The algebraic solution is provided here.

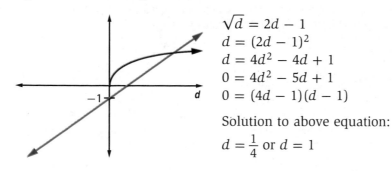

$$\sqrt{d} = 2d - 1$$
$$d = (2d - 1)^2$$
$$d = 4d^2 - 4d + 1$$
$$0 = 4d^2 - 5d + 1$$
$$0 = (4d - 1)(d - 1)$$

Solution to above equation:

$$d = \frac{1}{4} \text{ or } d = 1$$

But $d = \frac{1}{4}$ is *not* a solution to the equation $\sqrt{d} = 2d - 1$. Using the graph to inform the solution to $\sqrt{d} > 2d - 1$ gives the solution $0 \leq d < 1$.

Unit 2

4 Here are descriptions of solutions for several inequalities. Describe each solution using interval notation.

a. $x < -2$ or $x > 0$

b.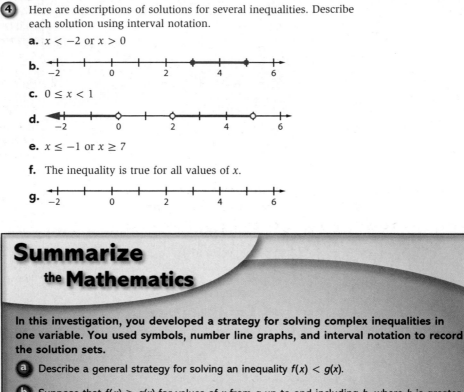

c. $0 \le x < 1$

d.

e. $x \le -1$ or $x \ge 7$

f. The inequality is true for all values of x.

g.

Summarize
the Mathematics

In this investigation, you developed a strategy for solving complex inequalities in one variable. You used symbols, number line graphs, and interval notation to record the solution sets.

a Describe a general strategy for solving an inequality $f(x) < g(x)$.

b Suppose that $f(x) \ge g(x)$ for values of x from a up to and including b, where b is greater than a. Represent the solution using symbols, a number line graph, and interval notation.

c Suppose that $h(t) < j(t)$ for values of t less than c or greater than d where d is greater than c. Represent the solution using symbols, a number line graph, and interval notation.

Be prepared to share your ideas and reasoning with the class.

✓Check Your Understanding

For each inequality: (1) sketch a graph of the functions involved in the inequality, (2) use algebraic reasoning to locate intersection points of the graphs, (3) combine what you learn from your sketch and algebraic reasoning to solve the inequality, and (4) record the solution using symbols, a number line graph, and interval notation.

a. $2 - w \le w^2 - 2w$

b. $\frac{6}{x} < x + 5$

4　**a.** $(-\infty, -2) \cup (0, \infty)$　　　**b.** $[3, 5]$

　　c. $[0, 1)$　　　　　　　　　　**d.** $(-\infty, 0) \cup (2, 5)$

　　e. $(-\infty, -1] \cup [7, \infty)$　　　**f.** $(-\infty, \infty)$

　　g. $\varnothing$

Summarize the Mathematics

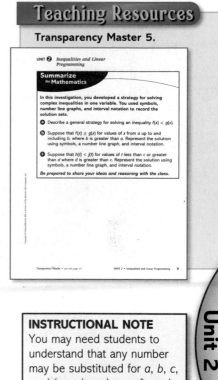
a In general, to solve an inequality $f(x) < g(x)$, determine the solution of the equation $f(x) = g(x)$. This divides the x-axis into intervals. Then reason using the graphs of $f(x)$ and $g(x)$ to determine the intervals on which the graph of $f(x)$ is below the graph of $g(x)$. (Students may wish to sketch a graph with their explanation.)

b $a \leq x \leq b$; $[a, b]$

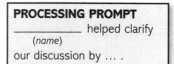

c $t < c$ or $t > d$; $(-\infty, c) \cup (d, \infty)$

✔ Check Your Understanding

a.

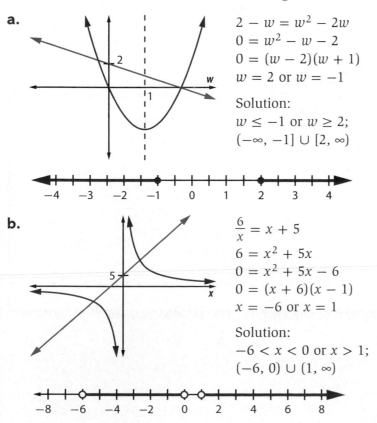

$$2 - w = w^2 - 2w$$
$$0 = w^2 - w - 2$$
$$0 = (w - 2)(w + 1)$$
$$w = 2 \text{ or } w = -1$$

Solution:
$$w \leq -1 \text{ or } w \geq 2;$$
$$(-\infty, -1] \cup [2, \infty)$$

b.

$$\frac{6}{x} = x + 5$$
$$6 = x^2 + 5x$$
$$0 = x^2 + 5x - 6$$
$$0 = (x + 6)(x - 1)$$
$$x = -6 \text{ or } x = 1$$

Solution:
$$-6 < x < 0 \text{ or } x > 1;$$
$$(-6, 0) \cup (1, \infty)$$

Inequalities in One Variable **T117**

On Your Own

Applications

(1) The graph below shows the path of a football kick, with height above the ground a function of horizontal distance traveled, both measured in yards. The function defining the path is $h(x) = -0.02x^2 + 1.3x + 1$.

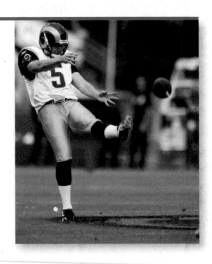

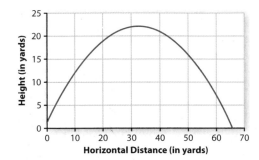

For each of the questions in Parts a–d:

- Write an algebraic calculation, equation, or inequality whose solution will provide an answer to the question.
- Use the graph above to estimate the solution and calculator-generated tables and graphs of $h(x)$ to sharpen the accuracy to the nearest tenth.
- Express your answer with a symbolic expression and a number line graph.

a. When is the kicked ball 20 yards above the field?

b. When is the ball less than 10 yards above the playing field?

c. How far is the ball above the field when it has traveled horizontally 40 yards?

d. When is the ball at least 15 yards above the field?

(2) The next graph shows the depth of water alongside a ship pier in a tidal ocean harbor between 12 A.M. and 12 P.M. on one day. Suppose that $d(t)$ gives depth in feet as a function of time in hours.

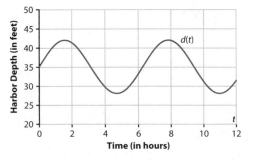

On Your Own

Applications

① **a.** $h(x) = 20$ when $20 = -0.02x^2 + 1.3x + 1$. The solutions are approximately $x = 22.2$ and $x = 42.8$.

```
          22.2        42.8
  +--+--+--+--●--+--+--●--+--+--+--+--+--+--+-->
  0    10   20   30   40   50   60   70   80
```

b. $h(x) < 10$ when $-0.02x^2 + 1.3x + 1 < 10$. The solutions are approximately $x < 7.9$ or $x > 57.1$.

```
        7.9                  57.1
 <--+--○--+--+--+--+--+--+--+--○--+--+--+--+-->
  0    10   20   30   40   50   60   70   80
```

c. $h(40) = 21$; A number line graph makes no sense here because the calculation required produces a y value or height.

d. $h(x) \geq 15$ when $-0.02x^2 + 1.3x + 1 \geq 15$. The solutions are approximately $13.6 \leq x \leq 51.4$.

```
         13.6             51.4
  +--+--+--●--+--+--+--+--●--+--+--+--+--+-->
  0    10   20   30   40   50   60   70   80
```

Unit 2

Inequalities in One Variable **T118**

For each Part a–d:

- Write a question about the water depth that can be answered by the indicated mathematical operation.
- Use the graph to estimate the answer.
- Express your answer (where appropriate) with a number line graph.

a. Evaluate $h(2)$. **b.** Solve $h(t) = 40$.

c. Solve $h(t) \geq 40$. **d.** Solve $h(t) < 30$.

3 Use this graph of a function $S(n)$ to estimate the values of n that satisfy each inequality below. Describe those values using words, symbols, and number line graphs.

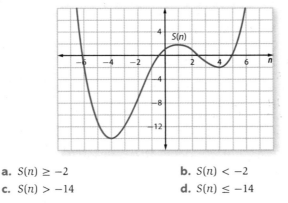

a. $S(n) \geq -2$ **b.** $S(n) < -2$

c. $S(n) > -14$ **d.** $S(n) \leq -14$

4 Describe the solutions of these inequalities using symbols and number line graphs.

a. $7t - t^2 < 0$ **b.** $a^2 + 4a \geq 0$

c. $h^2 + 2h - 3 \leq 0$ **d.** $x^2 + 0.5x - 3 > 0$

e. $-d^2 - 12d - 20 > 0$ **f.** $3 + 2r - r^2 \geq 0$

5 Describe the solutions of these inequalities using symbols and number line graphs.

a. $7t - t^2 < 10$ **b.** $a^2 + 4a \geq 12$

c. $5h^2 + 14h < 3$ **d.** $-x^2 + 6x - 8 < 1$

e. $-d^2 - 11d - 20 > 4$ **f.** $3 + 2r - r^2 \geq 8$

6 Describe the solutions of these inequalities using symbols and a number line graph.

a. $k + 10 \geq \dfrac{24}{k}$ **b.** $w - 1 < \dfrac{20}{w}$

c. $x + 6 < \dfrac{7}{x}$ **d.** $u + 1 \leq \dfrac{12}{u}$

2 **a.** How deep was the water at 2 A.M.? $h(2) \approx 41$ means that at 2 A.M., the depth of water in the harbor was approximately 41 feet. This answer does not make sense on a number line graph.

b. When was the water 40 feet deep? $h(t) = 40$ asks for the time(s) when the water depth is 40 feet. The solutions are approximately $t = 1, 2.5, 7,$ and 8.5.

c. When was the water depth at least 40 feet? The solutions are approximately when $1 \leq t \leq 2.5$ or when $7 \leq t \leq 8.5$.

d. When was the water depth less than 30 feet? Solutions are roughly when $4 < t < 5.5$ or $10.2 < t < 11.5$.

3 **a.** Values less than or equal to -6 and greater than or equal to -1
$n \leq -6$ or $n \geq -1$.

b. Values between -6 and -1 but not -6 and -1
$-6 < n < -1$.

c. All values except -4
$n < -4$ or $n > -4$ (or $n \neq -4$)

d. The only value is -4.
$n = -4$

4 **a.** $t < 0$ or $t > 7$

b. $a \leq -4$ or $a \geq 0$

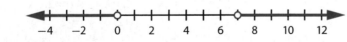

c. $-3 \leq h \leq 1$

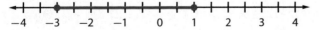

INSTRUCTIONAL NOTE
Students should solve Tasks 4–6 using the strategies they developed in Investigation 2.

Unit 2

d. $x < -2$ or $x > 1.5$

e. $-10 < d < -2$

f. $-1 \leq r \leq 3$

⑤ a. $t < 2$ or $t > 5$

b. $a \leq -6$ or $a \geq 2$

c. $-3 < h < 0.2$

d. $x < 3$ or $x > 3$ (or $x \neq 3$)

e. $-8 < d < -3$

f. No real solutions

⑥ a.

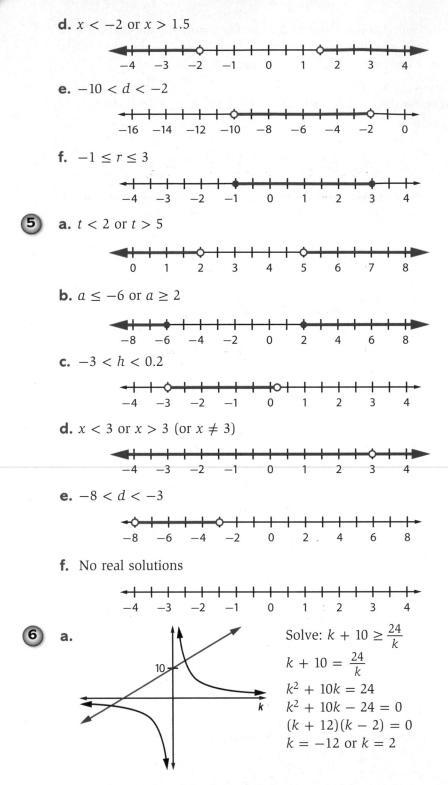

Solve: $k + 10 \geq \dfrac{24}{k}$

$k + 10 = \dfrac{24}{k}$

$k^2 + 10k = 24$

$k^2 + 10k - 24 = 0$

$(k + 12)(k - 2) = 0$

$k = -12$ or $k = 2$

So, the graphs of the line and the inverse function intersect when $k = 2$ and when $k = -12$. Use the graphs to identify the values of k where the graph of the line is at or above the graph of the inverse function, $k + 10 \geq \dfrac{24}{k}$.

Solution: $-12 \leq k < 0$ or $k \geq 2$; $[-12, 0) \cup [2, \infty)$

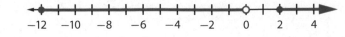

b.

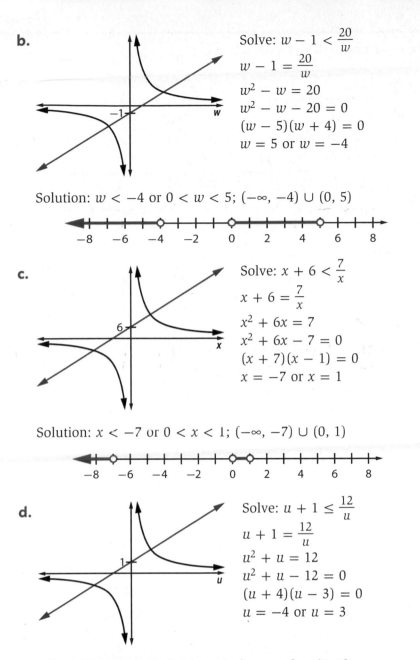

Solve: $w - 1 < \dfrac{20}{w}$

$w - 1 = \dfrac{20}{w}$

$w^2 - w = 20$

$w^2 - w - 20 = 0$

$(w - 5)(w + 4) = 0$

$w = 5$ or $w = -4$

Solution: $w < -4$ or $0 < w < 5$; $(-\infty, -4) \cup (0, 5)$

c.

Solve: $x + 6 < \dfrac{7}{x}$

$x + 6 = \dfrac{7}{x}$

$x^2 + 6x = 7$

$x^2 + 6x - 7 = 0$

$(x + 7)(x - 1) = 0$

$x = -7$ or $x = 1$

Solution: $x < -7$ or $0 < x < 1$; $(-\infty, -7) \cup (0, 1)$

d.

Solve: $u + 1 \leq \dfrac{12}{u}$

$u + 1 = \dfrac{12}{u}$

$u^2 + u = 12$

$u^2 + u - 12 = 0$

$(u + 4)(u - 3) = 0$

$u = -4$ or $u = 3$

Solution: $u \leq -4$ or $0 < u \leq 3$; $(-\infty, -4] \cup (0, 3]$

Unit 2

7 Shown below are the graphs of two functions $P(n)$ and $Q(n)$. Assume that the graph shows all points of intersection of $P(n)$ and $Q(n)$.

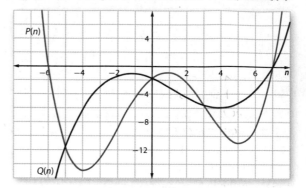

a. Describe the values of n for which $P(n) < Q(n)$ using symbols and a number line graph.

b. Describe the values of n for which $P(n) > Q(n)$ using symbols and a number line graph.

8 The Riverdale Adventure Club has planned a skydiving lesson and first jump for new members. They plan to make and sell videos of each jump.

Income from sale of videos of the jump and expenses for producing the videos will depend on price p charged according to these rules.

$$I(p) = p(118 - p)$$

$$E(p) = 6,400 - 50p$$

a. Sketch graphs showing how you expect the functions $I(p)$ and $E(p)$ to be related.

b. Find coordinates of the intersection points algebraically.

c. Describe the solution of the inequality $I(p) \geq E(p)$ using symbols and a number line graph.

d. Explain what your work suggests about how much the club should charge for videos of the jump.

9 For each of the following inequalities:

- sketch graphs showing how you expect the two functions in the inequality to be related.

- use algebraic reasoning, a CAS, or estimation using tables and graphs of the functions to locate the points of intersection of the graphs.

- use what you learn about the relationship of the functions to solve the inequality.

- record the solution using symbols and a number line graph.

a. $2n^2 + 3n < 8n + 3$ **b.** $9 + 6x - x^2 \leq x - 5$

c. $d^2 - 5d + 10 \geq 1 - 2d$ **d.** $j^2 + 7j + 20 < -j^2 - 5j$

e. $5 - u^2 \geq u^2 - 3$ **f.** $\sqrt{b} > 6 - b$

7 **a.** $P(n) < Q(n)$ when $-5 < n < 0$ or $3 < n < 7$.

(number line from −8 to 8, open circles at −5, 0, 3, 7)

b. $P(n) > Q(n)$ when $n < -5$ or $0 < n < 3$ or $n > 7$.

(number line from −8 to 8, open circles at −5, 0, 3, 7)

8 **a. INSTRUCTIONAL NOTE** When students make their initial sketches, they should know that the graph of $I(p)$ is a parabola that opens down and contains the origin and that the graph of $E(p)$ is a line with positive y-intercept and negative slope. They will not know with any certainty whether or how many times the line intersects the parabola until after Part c.

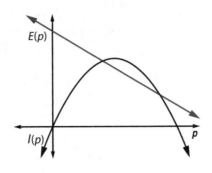

b. $E(p) = I(p)$ when:

$$6{,}400 - 50p = 118p - p^2$$
$$p^2 - 168p + 6{,}400 = 0$$
$$p \approx 58.39 \text{ or } p \approx 109.61$$

c. $58.39 \leq p \leq 109.61$

(number line from 40 to 120, filled circles at ~58 and ~110)

d. Responses will vary. Income from sale of the videos will exceed expenses for the videos as long as the club charges between $58.39 and $109.61. The greatest difference between income and expenses (or profit) occurs halfway between these two prices, at $84. So, the club would make the most money by charging $84 per video. However, if the club is interested in allowing the greatest number of members to purchase a video without losing money, rather than in making a profit, they should charge $58.39 per video. It would make sense to charge any amount between $58.39 and $84.

9 **a.**

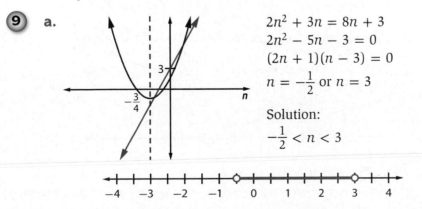

$$2n^2 + 3n = 8n + 3$$
$$2n^2 - 5n - 3 = 0$$
$$(2n + 1)(n - 3) = 0$$
$$n = -\frac{1}{2} \text{ or } n = 3$$

Solution:
$$-\frac{1}{2} < n < 3$$

(number line from −4 to 4, open circles at −½ and 3)

Unit 2

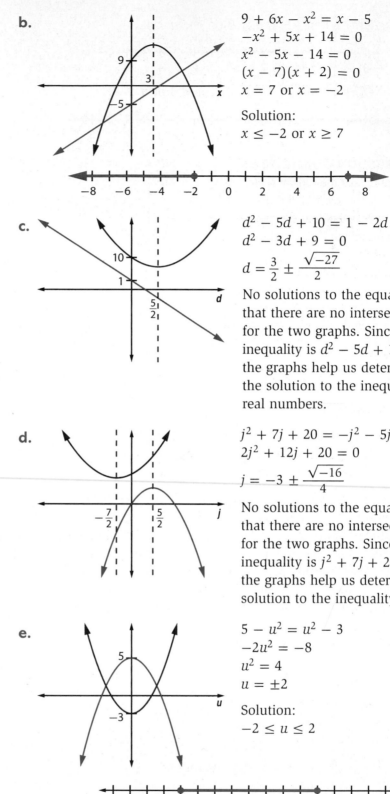

b.

$$9 + 6x - x^2 = x - 5$$
$$-x^2 + 5x + 14 = 0$$
$$x^2 - 5x - 14 = 0$$
$$(x - 7)(x + 2) = 0$$
$$x = 7 \text{ or } x = -2$$

Solution:
$$x \leq -2 \text{ or } x \geq 7$$

c.

$$d^2 - 5d + 10 = 1 - 2d$$
$$d^2 - 3d + 9 = 0$$
$$d = \frac{3}{2} \pm \frac{\sqrt{-27}}{2}$$

No solutions to the equation means that there are no intersection points for the two graphs. Since the inequality is $d^2 - 5d + 10 \geq 1 - 2d$, the graphs help us determine that the solution to the inequality is all real numbers.

d.

$$j^2 + 7j + 20 = -j^2 - 5j$$
$$2j^2 + 12j + 20 = 0$$
$$j = -3 \pm \frac{\sqrt{-16}}{4}$$

No solutions to the equation means that there are no intersection points for the two graphs. Since the inequality is $j^2 + 7j + 20 < -j^2 - 5j$, the graphs help us determine that the solution to the inequality is $\varnothing$.

e.

$$5 - u^2 = u^2 - 3$$
$$-2u^2 = -8$$
$$u^2 = 4$$
$$u = \pm 2$$

Solution:
$$-2 \leq u \leq 2$$

f.

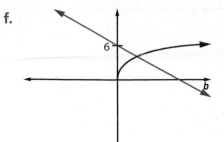

$\sqrt{b} = 6 - b$

$b = (6 - b)^2$

$b = 36 - 12b + b^2$

$0 = 36 - 13b + b^2$

$0 = (9 - b)(4 - b)$

$b = 9$ or $b = 4$

$b = 9$ is not a solution to the original equation.

Solution:

$b > 4$

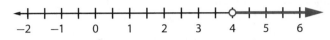

10 Graph these intervals on number lines. Write inequalities that express the same information.

  a. $[-2, 5)$ **b.** $(-\infty, 0) \cup [4, \infty)$

  c. $[3, 7]$ **d.** $(-4, -1) \cup (1, \infty)$

11 Below are descriptions of the solutions for six inequalities. Describe each solution using interval notation.

  a. $k \le -3$ or $k > -1$

  b. All numbers between negative 1 and positive 3.5

  c.

  d. $2 < g < 6$

  e. All numbers less than 4 or greater than 7

  f.

Connections

12 A firework contains a time-delay fuse that burns as the firework soars upward. The length of this fuse must be made so that the firework does not explode too close to the ground.

  The height (in feet) of a firework t seconds after it is launched is given by $h(t) = 3 + 180t - 16t^2$.

  a. The firework is to explode at a height of at least 450 feet. Write an inequality whose solution gives the possible explosion times for the firework.

  b. Draw a graph of the height of the firework over time, indicating the times when the firework is at a height of at least 450 feet.

13 The diagram at the right shows an angle in standard position whose terminal side lies in Quadrant II.

  a. Suppose the measure of the angle is θ. Explain why $\cos \theta < 0$, $\sin \theta > 0$, and $\tan \theta < 0$.

  b. For each of the following conditions, state the quadrant in which the terminal side of the angle in standard position must lie.

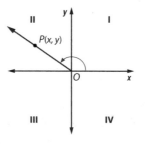

    i. $\cos \theta > 0$, $\sin \theta > 0$ **ii.** $\cos \theta > 0$, $\sin \theta < 0$

    iii. $\cos \theta < 0$, $\tan \theta > 0$ **iv.** $\sin \theta < 0$, $\tan \theta < 0$

LESSON 1 • Inequalities in One Variable   **121**

10 a.

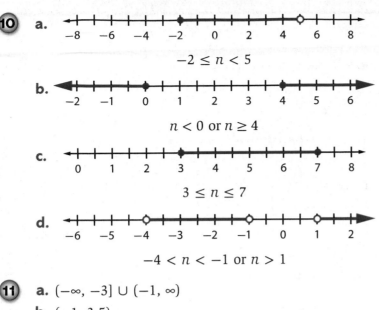

$-2 \le n < 5$

b.

$n < 0$ or $n \ge 4$

c.

$3 \le n \le 7$

d.

$-4 < n < -1$ or $n > 1$

11 a. $(-\infty, -3] \cup (-1, \infty)$

   b. $(-1, 3.5)$

   c. $[-2, 0]$

   d. $(2, 6)$

   e. $(-\infty, 4) \cup (7, \infty)$

   f. $(-\infty, -2] \cup (0, 3]$

Connections

12 a. $3 + 180t - 16t^2 \ge 450$

   b. $h(t)$ has values that are greater than or equal to 450 when $3.7 \le t \le 7.5$. The fuse should burn for at least 3.7 seconds and at most 7.5 seconds after the firework is launched.

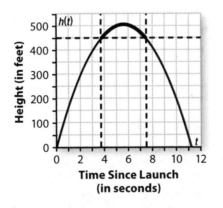

Time Since Launch (in seconds)

13 a. $\cos \theta = \frac{x}{r}$, $\sin \theta = \frac{y}{r}$, and $\tan \theta = \frac{y}{x}$. Since the terminal side of the angle is in Quadrant II, $x < 0$ and $y > 0$. $OP = r = \sqrt{x^2 + y^2}$ is positive. So, $\cos \theta < 0$, $\sin \theta > 0$, and $\tan \theta < 0$.

   b. i. Quadrant I   **ii.** Quadrant IV

       iii. Quadrant III   **iv.** Quadrant IV

Unit 2

The graphs below show the way two different variables depend on x. One function is given by $f(x) = \frac{50}{x^2}$. The other function is given by $g(x) = x^2 - 5x$.

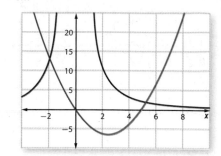

a. Make a copy of these graphs. Identify and label the graphs of $f(x)$ and $g(x)$.

b. What connections between function rules and their graphs allow you to match $f(x)$ and $g(x)$ to their graphs in this case?

c. Color the x-axis of your copy of the graphs to highlight the points corresponding to solutions of the following equation and inequalities. If possible, use the colors suggested.

i. In blue: $\frac{50}{x^2} = x^2 - 5x$

ii. In red: $\frac{50}{x^2} > x^2 - 5x$

iii. In green: $\frac{50}{x^2} < x^2 - 5x$

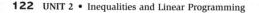

15 In solving quadratic equations by factoring, you used the fact that if $ab = 0$, then $a = 0$ or $b = 0$. Consider whether similar reasoning can be used to solve a quadratic inequality.

a. Complete a table like this.

If ...	and ... ,	then ... .
$a > 0$	$b > 0$	ab ? 0
$a > 0$	$b < 0$	ab ? 0
$a < 0$	$b > 0$	ab ? 0
$a < 0$	$b < 0$	ab ? 0

b. Based on your work in Part a, if $ab > 0$, then what can be said about a and b? What if $ab < 0$?

c. For what values of v is the inequality $(v + 3)(v - 4) > 0$ true?

d. How might you expand this kind of reasoning to determine the values of w for which the inequality $(w + 5)(w + 1)(w - 2) < 0$ is true?

14 **a.**

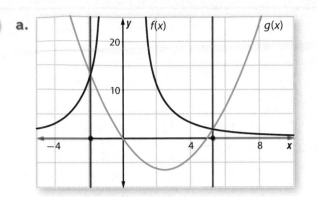

b. Possible responses include that $f(x)$ is undefined at zero and will always have positive values and that $g(x)$ is a quadratic function whose graph is therefore a parabola.

c. See the graph in Part a.

   i. $x = -1.9$ and $x = 5.3$

   ii. $-1.9 < x < 5.3 \ (x \neq 0)$

   iii. $x < -1.9$ and $x > 5.3$

15 **a.**

If ...	and ... ,	then ... .
$a > 0$	$b > 0$	$ab > 0$
$a > 0$	$b < 0$	$ab < 0$
$a < 0$	$b > 0$	$ab < 0$
$a < 0$	$b < 0$	$ab > 0$

b. If $ab > 0$, then either both a and b are positive (> 0) or both a and b are negative (< 0). If $ab < 0$, one is negative and one is positive ($a < 0$ and $b > 0$ or $a > 0$ and $b < 0$).

c. There are two possible cases.

   Case 1: If $v + 3 > 0$ and $v - 4 > 0$, then $v > -3$ and $v > 4$. So, $v > 4$.

   Case 2: If $v + 3 < 0$ and $v - 4 < 0$, then $v < -3$ and $v < 4$. So, $v < -3$.

   Therefore, $(v + 3)(v - 4) > 0$ when $v < -3$ or $v > 4$.

d. Either exactly one of the factors is less than zero (negative) or all three factors are less than zero.

   Case 1: If $w + 5 < 0$ and $w + 1 > 0$ and $w - 2 > 0$, then $w < -5$ and $w > -1$ and $w > 2$. Since no values of w can satisfy all three inequalities, there are no solutions.

   Case 2: If $w + 5 > 0$ and $w + 1 < 0$ and $w - 2 > 0$, then $w > -5$ and $w < -1$ and $w > 2$. Since no values of w can satisfy all three inequalities, there are no solutions.

   Case 3: If $w + 5 > 0$ and $w + 1 > 0$ and $w - 2 < 0$, then $w > -5$ and $w > -1$ and $w < 2$. So, $-1 < w < 2$.

   Case 4: If $w + 5 < 0$ and $w + 1 < 0$ and $w - 2 < 0$, then $w < -5$ and $w < -1$ and $w < 2$. So, $w < -5$.

   Therefore, $(w + 5)(w + 1)(w - 2) < 0$ when $w < -5$ or $-1 < w < 2$.

INSTRUCTIONAL NOTE
Students may color the graphs instead of the x-axis. You may wish to discuss the task instructions before assigning as homework.

Unit 2

16. In the *Reasoning and Proof* unit, you completed an argument to prove one case of the Law of Cosines.

    In $\triangle ABC$, $c^2 = a^2 + b^2 - 2ab \cos C$.

    Completing the tasks below will help you to see a connection between the Law of Cosines and the Triangle Inequality: $a + b > c$. Recall that $-1 < \cos C < 1$.

    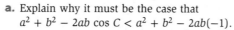

    a. Explain why it must be the case that
       $a^2 + b^2 - 2ab \cos C < a^2 + b^2 - 2ab(-1)$.

    b. Explain why $c^2 < (a + b)^2$.

    c. Explain why it follows that $a + b > c$.

    d. What form of the Law of Cosines would you use to prove this form of the Triangle Inequality: $a + c > b$?

17. You learned in Investigation 3 that the symbol ∪ indicates the *union* of two sets. The symbol ∩ indicates the *intersection* of two sets.

    a. Consider the Venn diagram to the right.

       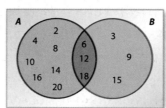

       i. How would you describe the numbers in circle A? In circle B?

       ii. How would you describe the numbers in $A \cup B$?

       iii. Why are the numbers 6, 12, and 18 in $A \cap B$?

    b. Consider the integers from -10 to 10. Create Venn diagrams that satisfy the conditions below for C and D. Then describe $C \cup D$ and $C \cap D$ using inequalities.

       i. C consists of integers greater than -5. D consists of integers less than 7.

       ii. C consists of integers less than -3. D consists of integers greater than 4.

       iii. C consists of integers less than 2. D consists of integers less than -1.

Reflections

18. Explain why the values of x indicated by $-3 < x < 7$ are *not* the same as the values indicated by $-3 < x$ or $x < 7$.

19. If $f(x) > c$ only when $a < x < b$, then what are the values of x for which $f(x) \leq c$?

LESSON 1 • Inequalities in One Variable **123**

16 **a.** Since $\cos C > -1$ and $2ab > 0$, $2ab \cos C > 2ab(-1)$.
So, $-2ab \cos C < 2ab$.
Hence, $(a^2 + b^2) - 2ab \cos C < (a^2 + b^2) - 2ab(-1)$.

b. From Part a, we have $a^2 + b^2 - 2ab \cos C < a^2 + b^2 + 2ab$.
Since $c^2 = a^2 + b^2 - 2ab \cos C$ and $a^2 + 2ab + b^2 = (a + b)^2$, by
substitution in the inequality in Part a, $c^2 < (a + b)^2$.

c. Since $(a + b)^2 > c^2$ and a, b, and c are positive, $\sqrt{(a + b)^2} > \sqrt{c^2}$.
So, $a + b > c$. This is the Triangle Inequality.

d. Use the form $b^2 = a^2 + c^2 - 2ac \cos B$.

17 **INSTRUCTIONAL NOTE** This task introduces the set operation of intersection.
Part a is intended to connect unions with "or" and intersections with "and."
Part b is intended to provide students with a way to visualize unions and
intersections of intervals and compound inequalities, which are introduced in
Extensions Task 23.

a. **i.** The numbers in circle A are the even numbers (multiples of 2)
from 1 to 20. The numbers in circle B are multiples of 3 from
1 to 20.

ii. The union consists of all integers from 1 to 20 that are multiples of
either 2 *or* 3.

iii. The intersection consists of all integers between 1 and 20 that are
multiples of both 2 *and* 3 (multiples of 6).

b. In parts i–iii, x is an integer.

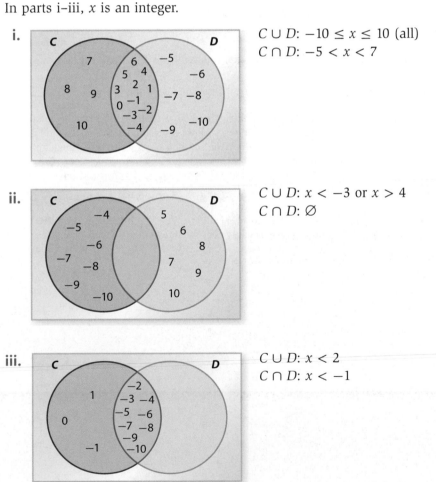

i.
$C \cup D$: $-10 \leq x \leq 10$ (all)
$C \cap D$: $-5 < x < 7$

ii.
$C \cup D$: $x < -3$ or $x > 4$
$C \cap D$: $\varnothing$

iii.
$C \cup D$: $x < 2$
$C \cap D$: $x < -1$

> **NOTE** Solutions to Task 18
> and Task 19 are on
> page T124.

20 In this lesson, the notation (a, b) has been used in two different ways.

- Graph the point $(-3, 2)$ on a coordinate plane.
- Graph the interval $(-3, 2)$ on a number line.

How can you tell, in any particular problem, whether (a, b) refers to a point in the plane or an interval on a number line?

Extensions

21 In your work on problems of this lesson, you focused on inequalities involving linear, quadratic, and inverse variation functions. But inequalities involving other powers and exponential functions are important as well. For each inequality given below:

- sketch a graph of the functions involved.
- use what you know about the functions involved to solve the inequality exactly or by accurate approximation.
- record the solution using symbols and a number line graph.

a. $\sqrt{x} > x$ $(x \geq 0)$ b. $x^3 < x^2$

c. $2^x < x^2$ d. $0.5^x < 0.5x$

22 In the *Trigonometric Methods* unit of Course 2, you studied the patterns of values for the sine, cosine, and tangent functions. In particular, for an angle θ in standard position with point $P(x, y)$ on the terminal side, if $r = \sqrt{x^2 + y^2}$, then $\sin \theta = \frac{y}{r}$, $\cos \theta = \frac{x}{r}$, and $\tan \theta = \frac{y}{x}$, if $x \neq 0$. For each inequality given below:

- use what you know about the functions involved to solve the inequality exactly or by accurate approximation for $0 \leq \theta \leq 180°$.
- record the solution using symbols and a number line graph.

a. $\cos \theta > 0$ b. $\cos \theta > \sin \theta$

c. $\tan \theta > 1$ d. $\sin \theta < 0.5$

23 For each *compound inequality* below, indicate whether the solution is the union or the intersection of the solutions to the individual inequalities. Then graph the solution of the compound inequality on a number line.

a. $v > -0.5$ and $v \leq 3$ b. $x < -2$ or $x \geq 7$

c. $3d + 2 \leq 5$ or $6 - d < 7$ d. $2p - 1 < 3$ and $p + 6 \geq 10$

24 Can the solution to an equation ever be an inequality? Can the solution to an inequality ever be an equation? Use sketches of graphs to illustrate your response.

Reflections

18 $-3 < x < 7$ means the values between -3 and 7. $-3 < x$ or $x < 7$ would refer to all real numbers. This can easily be seen by thinking about two number lines and then combining them:

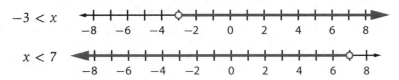

$-3 < x < 7$ if separated symbolically, should be $-3 < x$ *and* $x < 7$.

19 $f(x) \leq c$ when $x \leq a$ or $x \geq b$.

20 Student responses will vary but should suggest considering the context in which (a, b) occurs. (a, b) might indicate a point if the context indicates two variables. In this case, when one variable has the value a, the other variable has the value b.

The notation (a, b) might indicate an interval if the context indicates one variable. In this case, a is the lower bound for the values of the variable, and b is the upper bound. Some students might note that (a, b) can only indicate an interval if $a < b$.

> **DIFFERENTIATION** You may wish to reframe Reflections Task 19 with numbers for a and b or for a, b, and c. Alternatively, you could encourage students to choose their own values to investigate the relationship. This is a helpful problem solving technique to cultivate.

Extensions

21 a.

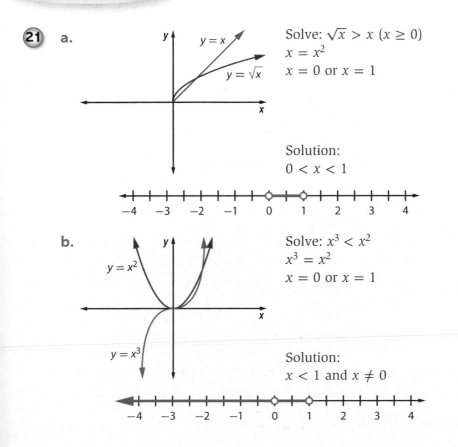

Solve: $\sqrt{x} > x$ $(x \geq 0)$
$x = x^2$
$x = 0$ or $x = 1$

Solution:
$0 < x < 1$

b.

Solve: $x^3 < x^2$
$x^3 = x^2$
$x = 0$ or $x = 1$

Solution:
$x < 1$ and $x \neq 0$

Unit 2

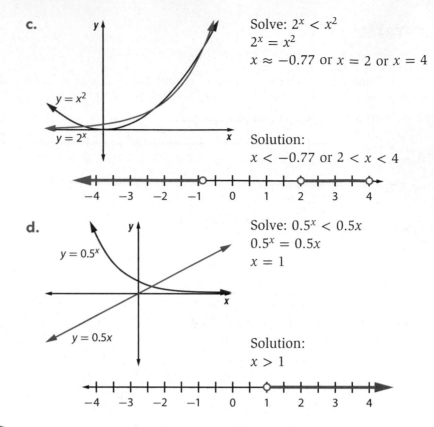

c.

Solve: $2^x < x^2$

$2^x = x^2$

$x \approx -0.77$ or $x = 2$ or $x = 4$

Solution:

$x < -0.77$ or $2 < x < 4$

d.

Solve: $0.5^x < 0.5x$

$0.5^x = 0.5x$

$x = 1$

Solution:

$x > 1$

22 Students may reason using the unit circle or graphs of the sine, cosine, and tangent functions to do this task.

a. $\cos \theta > 0$ when $0° < \theta < 90°$.

b. Solve: $\cos \theta > \sin \theta$

$\cos \theta = \sin \theta$

$\theta = 45°$

Solutions: $0° < \theta < 45°$

c. Solve: $\tan \theta > 1$

$\tan \theta = 1$ when $\theta = 45°$.

The tangent of an angle is negative in the second quadrant and undefined when $\theta = 90°$. In the first quadrant, θ must be between 45° and 90° for the tangent to be greater than 1.

Solutions: $45° < \theta < 90°$.

d. Solve: $\sin \theta < 0.5$

$\sin \theta = 0.5$ when $\theta = 30°$ or $\theta = 150°$.

Solutions: $0° \leq \theta < 30°$ or $150° < \theta \leq 180°$

23 **a.** Intersection

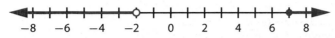

b. Union

c. Union (of $d \leq 1$, $d > -1$)

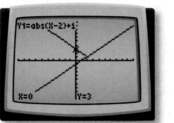

ASSIGNMENT NOTE
Assign Connections Task 17
before Extensions Task 23.

d. Intersection (of $p < 1$, $p \geq 4$)

No real solutions

24 The solution to an equation can be an inequality if the equation involves functions with overlapping graphs. (An example of such an equation is $|x - 2| + 1 = x - 1$, with solution $x \geq 2$.)

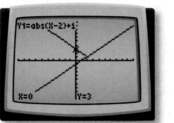

The solution to an inequality can be an equation if the inequality involves $\leq$ or $\geq$ and functions that intersect at a single point without crossing. (An example of such an inequality is $x^2 \leq 0$, with solution $x = 0$.)

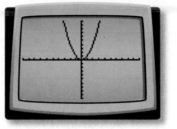

Unit 2

Review

25. For each of these quadratic functions, use the coefficients of the terms to help determine the shape and location of the graph: (1) whether the graph has a maximum or minimum point, (2) the location of the line of symmetry, and (3) where the graph will cross the y-axis.

   a. $f(x) = x^2 + 4x - 5$ **b.** $g(x) = -x^2 - 2x + 8$

   c. $h(x) = x^2 - 10x + 25$ **d.** $j(x) = -0.5x^2 + 2x + 4$

26. Solve each of these quadratic equations in two ways, by factoring and by use of the quadratic formula. Check the solutions you find by substitution in the original equation or by use of a CAS **solve** command.

   a. $x^2 - 6x + 5 = 0$ **b.** $x^2 + 4x = 0$

   c. $x^2 - 19 = -3$ **d.** $2x^2 - x - 6 = 0$

   e. $-x^2 - 5x - 4 = 0$ **f.** $-x^2 + 7x + 6 = 2x$

27. Solve each of the following for x.

   a. $3x - 12 < 24$ **b.** $-2x + 19 > 5x - 2$

   c. $10 - 6x < 2x + 90$ **d.** $x - 3 = \dfrac{18}{x}$

28. Without using your calculator, sketch a graph of each function below. Then check your sketches using a calculator or computer graphing tool.

   a. $f(x) = \dfrac{1}{x}$ **b.** $g(x) = x^2$

   c. $f(t) = 3(2^t)$ **d.** $f(p) = -p^2$

   e. $h(n) = -\dfrac{1}{n^2}$

29. Without using the graphing feature of your calculator or computer, find the coordinates of the intersection point for each pair of lines.

   a. $x = 5$ **b.** $3x + 2y = 24$

        $3x + 2y = 24$ $y = -0.5x + 6$

   c. $y = 8$ **d.** $x + y = 200$

        $x = 5$ $2x + y = 280$

30. You may recall that you can use the Law of Cosines and the Law of Sines to find side lengths and angle measures in any triangle. Below is one form of each of these useful laws for $\triangle ABC$.

   Law of Cosines

   $c^2 = a^2 + b^2 - 2ab \cos C$

   Law of Sines

   $\dfrac{a}{\sin A} = \dfrac{b}{\sin B} = \dfrac{c}{\sin C}$

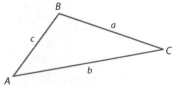

Review

ASSIGNMENT NOTE
Tasks 25 and 26 are "just-in-time review" for Problems 1–4 of Investigation 2. You should assign these problems as homework before exploring those problems in class.

Just in Time

25

a. (1) Lead coefficient is positive, so the graph has a minimum point.
(2) $\frac{-b}{2a} = -2$, so the line of symmetry is $x = -2$.
(3) The constant term is -5, so the y-intercept is $(0, -5)$.

b. (1) Lead coefficient is negative, so the graph has a maximum point.
(2) $\frac{-b}{2a} = -1$, so the line of symmetry is $x = -1$.
(3) The constant term is 8, so the y-intercept is $(0, 8)$.

c. (1) Lead coefficient is positive, so the graph has a minimum point.
(2) $\frac{-b}{2a} = 5$, so the line of symmetry is $x = 5$.
(3) The constant term is 25, so the y-intercept is $(0, 25)$.

d. (1) Lead coefficient is negative, so the graph has a maximum point.
(2) $\frac{-b}{2a} = 2$, so the line of symmetry is $x = 2$.
(3) The constant term is 4, so the y-intercept is $(0, 4)$.

Just in Time

26

a. $x = 1$ or $x = 5$

b. $x = 0$ or $x = -4$

c. $x = 4$ or $x = -4$

d. $x = -\frac{3}{2}$ or $x = 2$

e. $x = -4$ or $x = -1$

f. $x = -1$ or $x = 6$

Just in Time

27

a. $x < 12$

b. $x < 3$

c. $x > -10$

d. $x = 6$ or $x = -3$

28 **a.**   **b.**

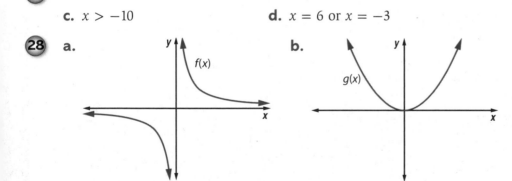

NOTE Solutions for the remainder of Task 28 and for Task 29 are on page T126.

Unit 2

For each triangle below, decide if you should use the Law of Cosines or the Law of Sines to find the indicated side length or angle measure. Then use your choice to find the indicated side length or angle measure.

a. Find *AB*.

b. Find m∠*B*.

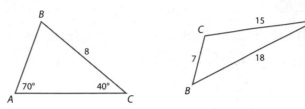

31 For the linear equations below:

- find coordinates of the *y*-intercept of the graph.
- find coordinates of the *x*-intercept of the graph.
- sketch the graph of all solutions.

a. $3x + 2y = 6$

b. $8y - 4x = 24$

32 It seems reasonable that the length of a person's stride is related to the length of his or her legs. Manish collected these two measurements for 20 different people.

a. Would you expect the correlation for the data to be positive or negative? Explain your reasoning.

b. Using his data, Manish created the scatterplot below. Describe the direction and strength of the relationship.

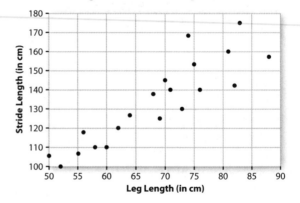

c. The linear regression line for these data is $y = 1.78x + 12$. Explain the meaning of the slope of this line in terms of the context.

c.

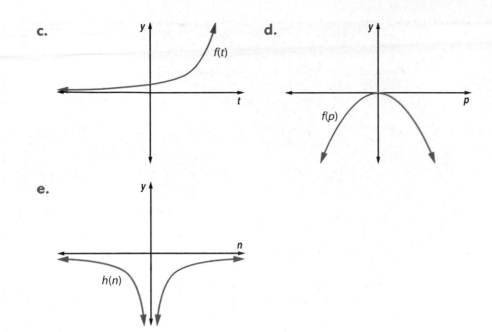

f(t)

d.

f(p)

e.

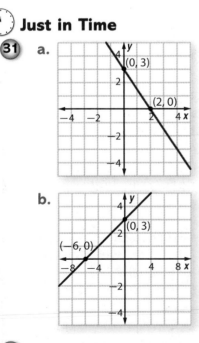

h(n)

Just in Time

29 **a.** (5, 4.5) **b.** (6, 3)

c. (5, 8) **d.** (80, 120)

30 **a.** Law of Sines **b.** Law of Cosines
$AB \approx 5.47$ $m\angle B \approx 54.0°$

Just in Time

31 **a.**

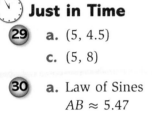

(0, 3)

(2, 0)

b.

(0, 3)

(−6, 0)

INSTRUCTIONAL NOTE
Discuss methods students used to do Task 32, particularly using x- and y-intercepts. Help students recognize that when finding pairs of values that satisfy an equation, choosing a value for one variable forces the choice of the second variable.

Teaching Resources

Assessment Masters 8–14.

UNIT ❷ *Inequalities and Linear Programming*

LESSON 1 QUIZ

Form A

32 **a.** Students should expect a positive correlation since it seems reasonable that as leg length increases, stride length will also increase.

b. The relationship between the leg length and stride length is strong and positive.

c. If one person's legs are 1 cm longer than another's, we would expect that person's stride length to be 1.78 cm longer.

Unit 2

LESSON
2

Inequalities with Two Variables

Important decisions in business often involve many variables and relations among those variables. The key to making good decisions is finding a way to organize and compare options.

For example, suppose that the manager of an electronics company must plan for and supervise production of two video game systems, the basic CP•I and the advanced CP•II. Assume that demand for both game systems is high, so the company will be able to sell whatever is produced. To plan the work schedule, the manager has to consider the following conditions.

- Assembly of each CP•I model takes 0.6 hours of technician time, and assembly of each CP•II model takes 0.3 hours of technician time. The plant can apply at most 240 hours of technician time to assembly work each day.

- Testing for each CP•I model takes 0.2 hours, and testing of each CP•II model takes 0.4 hours. The plant can apply at most 160 hours of technician time each day for testing.

- Packaging time is the same for each model. The packaging department of the plant can handle at most 500 game systems per day.

- The company makes a profit of $50 on each CP•I model and $75 on each CP•II model.

The production planning challenge is to maximize profit while operating under the constraints of limited technician time and packaging time.

Inequalities in Two Variables

In this lesson, students develop their understanding and skills working with graphs of linear inequalities and systems of linear inequalities with two variables. Then they are asked to apply that knowledge to the solution of linear programming problems.

The first investigation develops general ideas about linear inequalities with two variables, with a focus on visualization of solution sets. The second introduces the key concepts of linear programming with numeric and graphic explorations of prototypical problems. Then the third investigation develops (without proof) the fundamental result that solutions of linear programming problems occur at vertices of the feasible regions (with some attention to what can happen when the variables are not continuous).

> **INSTRUCTIONAL NOTE**
> In most problems in this lesson, students will be *crossing out* regions that they do not want so that the solution set is the *unshaded portion that remains*. This is not the conventional pattern. But it is helpful for students to be able to see the feasible region of a linear programming problem rather than to have it shaded over, particularly when labeling points within the feasible region with the value of the objective function at each point.

Lesson Objectives

- Graph the solution set of a linear inequality in two variables
- Graph the solution set of a system of inequalities in two variables
- Solve linear programming problems involving two independent variables

Lesson Launch

In this introductory situation, students are not expected to know the answers. The goal here is to stimulate their thinking and to help them understand that these are important questions to ask when you are in business and want to make a profit.

In order to help your students connect with this situation, you might want to have a preliminary discussion about the conditions listed. You could ask questions like the following:

- "Why might there be only 240 hours of technician time available for assembly work?" (There are only 30 trained technicians, each working an 8 hour day.)
- "Why might the packaging department be able to handle only 500 game systems per day?" (This might be a function of the number of employees in the department or of the equipment available.)
- "If they make more profit on the CP•II, why do they make the other model?"

The point of these questions is to make the situation easier to imagine: a busy factory with a specific number of employees, each engaged in his or her own task. Students should begin to realize that the variables (number of models, testing, assembling, packaging times) are interrelated. The formal term *constraint* is introduced in Investigation 2 and *objective function* in Investigation 3 *after* students use these ideas.

Unit 2

Suppose that you were the manager of the electronics plant and had to make production plans.

a How would you decide the time estimates for assembly, testing, and packaging?

b How would you decide the expected profit for each game system?

c How might you use all of the given data to decide on the number of CP•I and CP•II models that should be produced to maximize profit for the company?

Many problems like those facing the electronics plant manager are solved by a mathematical strategy called *linear programming*. In this lesson, you will learn how to use this important problem-solving technique and the mathematical ideas and skills on which it depends.

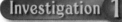

Investigation 1 Solving Inequalities

Many problems that arise in making plans for a business involve functions with two or more independent variables. For example, income for the Old Dominion Music Festival is given by the function $I = 8a + 12g$, where a is the number of admission tickets sold in advance and g is the number of tickets sold at the gate.

If expenses for operating the two-day festival total \$2,400, then solutions of $8a + 12g = 2,400$ give (a, g) combinations for which festival income will equal operating expenses. But festival organizers are probably interested in earning *more than* \$2,400 from ticket sales. They want solutions to the inequality $8a + 12g > 2,400$.

As you work on the problems of this investigation, look for answers to these questions:

How can one find and graph the solutions of a linear inequality in two variables?

How can one find the solutions of a system of inequalities in two variables?

Teaching Resources

Transparency Master 15.

UNIT ❷ Inequalities and Linear
Programming

Think About
This **Situation**

Suppose that you were the manager of the electronics plant
and had to make production plans.

ⓐ How would you decide the time estimates for assembly,
testing, and packaging?

ⓑ How would you decide the expected profit for each
game system?

ⓒ How might you use all of the given data to decide on the
number of CP-I and CP-II models that should be produced
to maximize profit for the company?

Electronics Company Production Conditions:

• Assembly of each CP-I model takes 0.6 hours of technician time, and
assembly of each CP-II model takes 0.3 hours of technician time. The
plant can apply at most 240 hours of technician time to assembly work
each day.

• Testing for each CP-I model takes 0.2 hours, and testing of each CP-II
model takes 0.4 hours. The plant can apply at most 160 hours of
technician time each day for testing.

• Packaging time is the same for each model. The packaging department of
the plant can handle at most 500 game systems per day.

• The company makes a profit of $50 on each CP-I model and $75 on each
CP-II model.

The production planning challenge is to maximize profit while operating
under the constraints of limited technician time and packaging time.

Transparency Master • use with page 128   UNIT 2 • Inequalities and Linear Programming   **15**

Think About
This Situation

ⓐ Students may suggest asking the technicians to give estimates. Other students may suggest keeping track of the production activities over a period of time to determine an average of how long each activity takes.

ⓑ The profit per model depends on how much each product costs to manufacture and market, including advertising, material, labor, and other costs. It also depends on the selling price that the market will bear. Profit will be the difference between costs and income based on sales.

ⓒ Students will probably suggest guess and check, which is fine. They should realize that the maximum profit is not easily found by guessing and checking.

Investigation 1 Solving Inequalities

The TATS introducing this lesson has all the elements of a typical linear programming problem with two independent variables, several constraints, and an objective. To make progress on such problems, it is important to get a picture of the constraints, and this requires graphing solution sets for two variable linear inequalities and combinations of such solution sets.

The problems of this investigation leave the context of a full-blown linear programming problem to tackle the issue of two-variable linear inequalities in a more gentle progression. For that reason, the investigation starts with a new problem context. We return to the video game production context in Investigations 2 and 3.

This investigation builds on prior work with linear equations of the form $ax + by = c$ in Course 2, Units 1 and 2, to examine related linear inequalities in Problems 1–3. Expanding on students' understanding of systems of linear equations, systems of inequalities are introduced informally in Problems 5 and 6 and more formally in Problem 7.

ASSIGNMENT NOTE
Students should have completed the Lesson 1 just-in-time Review Task 31 before starting this investigation.

COLLABORATION SKILL
Paraphrasing a group member's comments can help us all understand each other and math concepts more thoroughly. Practice paraphrasing.

Unit 2

1 The next diagram gives a first quadrant graph of the line representing solutions for the equation $8a + 12g = 2,400$, the combinations of tickets sold in advance and at the gate that will give festival income of exactly $2,400.

Use that graph as a starting point in solving the inequality $8a + 12g > 2,400$.

a. For each point on the diagram, give the (a, g) coordinates and the festival income from that combination of tickets sold in advance and tickets sold at the gate.

b. Based on your work in Part a, describe the graphical representation of solutions to these inequalities.

   i. $8a + 12g > 2,400$

  ii. $8a + 12g < 2,400$

c. Solve the equation $8a + 12g = 2,400$ for g in terms of a.

d. Use what you know about manipulation of inequality statements to express each inequality in Part b in an equivalent form $g < ...$ or $g > ...$. Then explain how those equivalent inequalities help to describe the solution graphs for the original inequalities.

2 A local bank is giving away souvenir Frisbees and sun visors at the Old Dominion Music Festival. The Frisbees will cost the bank $4 each, and the visors will cost the bank $2.50 each. The promotional cost for the bank depends on the number of Frisbees F and the number of visors V given away at the festival. The bank has budgeted $1,000 for the purchase of these items.

a. Write an inequality that represents the question, "How many souvenir Frisbees and visors can the bank give away for a total cost of no more than $1,000?"

b. Draw a graph that shows the region of the first quadrant in the coordinate plane containing all points (F, V) that satisfy the inequality in Part a.

1 **a. INSTRUCTIONAL NOTE** The aim of this task is to help students discover that the solution set of an inequality in two variables will in general be a half plane (or, when the variables can only be integers as in this situation, the lattice points in a half-plane). Evaluating the income function at many different points in the first quadrant lays a useful foundation for optimizing the objective function of a linear program. Students should share this work.

A: $I = 8(100) + 12(200) = 3{,}200$ B: $I = 4{,}600$ at $(200, 250)$

C: $I = 5{,}400$ at $(300, 250)$ D: $I = 3{,}800$ at $(250, 150)$

E: $I = 3{,}000$ at $(300, 50)$ F: $I = 2{,}000$ at $(250, 0)$

G: $I = 2{,}200$ at $(200, 50)$ H: $I = 1{,}400$ at $(100, 50)$

I: $I = 2{,}200$ at $(50, 150)$

b. INSTRUCTIONAL NOTE Student descriptions of the solution sets for the two inequalities will vary. In particular, they may or may not comment on the fact that the problem context (not the algebraic inequalities themselves) makes points outside the first quadrant meaningless in this problem. If not, when students have offered descriptions of the solutions to this particular problem, ask about points with coordinates like $(-100, 300)$ or $(-100, 100)$ or even $(-100, -100)$.

 i. The solutions to the inequality $8a + 12g > 2{,}400$ seem to lie in (and take up all of) the region above the line $8a + 12g = 2{,}400$.

 ii. The solutions to the inequality $8a + 12g < 2{,}400$ seem to lie in (and take up all of) the region below the line $8a + 12g = 2{,}400$.

c. One equivalent form of the equation would be $g = \dfrac{2{,}400 - 8a}{12}$, or $g = 200 - \dfrac{2}{3}a$.

d. **i.** The equivalent form would be $g > 200 - \dfrac{2}{3}a$, which indicates that points satisfying $8a + 12g > 2{,}400$ are those with g value greater than $200 - \dfrac{2}{3}a$ or points above the line with equation $g = 200 - \dfrac{2}{3}a$.

> **INSTRUCTIONAL NOTE**
> In Part d, students examine another way to see the solution set for an inequality in two variables.

 ii. The equivalent form would be $g < 200 - \dfrac{2}{3}a$, which indicates that points satisfying $8a + 12g < 2{,}400$ are those with g value less than $200 - \dfrac{2}{3}a$ or points below the line with equation $g = 200 - \dfrac{2}{3}a$.

2 **a.** $4F + 2.5V \leq 1{,}000$, or $V \leq -1.6F + 400$

b. Students' methods for showing the region containing all points that satisfy the inequalities may vary. One method is shown at the right.

> **INSTRUCTIONAL NOTE**
> Again, you might raise the question of the domain of the function $C = 4F + 2.5V$ and what this means for the solution of the inequality $4F + 2.5V \leq 1{,}000$.

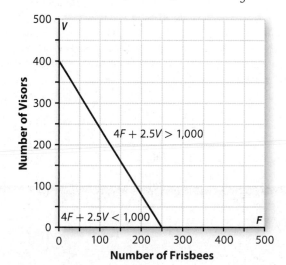

Graphing Conventions In Problems 1 and 2, the only meaningful solutions of inequalities were in the first quadrant. Negative values of a, g, F, and V make no sense in those situations. However, the ideas and graphing techniques you developed in work on those problems can be applied to situations without the constraint of only positive values.

For example, the following graph shows solutions with both positive and negative values for $x + 2y < -2$ and $x + 2y > -2$.

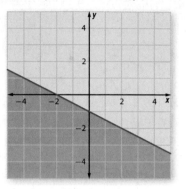

3 Compare the inequalities and the indicated graph regions.

  a. Which region corresponds to solutions of $x + 2y < -2$? How did you decide?

  b. How would you graph the solutions to a linear inequality like $x - y > 3$?

Just as with inequalities in one variable, the solution region of an inequality in two variables is generally bounded by the solution of a corresponding equation. Sometimes the boundary is *included* in the solution of the inequality, indicated on a graph by a *solid* boundary. A *dashed* boundary on a graph indicates that points on the boundary are *excluded* from the solution.

4 Draw graphs that show all points with x- and y-coordinates between -10 and 10 and satisfying these linear inequalities in two variables. Use either solid or dashed boundary lines as appropriate.

  a. $3x - 2y < 12$ **b.** $2x + y \geq 4$
  c. $8x - 5y > 20$ **d.** $4x + 3y \leq 15$

5 Suppose that the organizers of the Old Dominion Music Festival can sell no more than 1,000 admission tickets due to space constraints.

  a. Write an inequality whose solutions are the (a, g) pairs for which the number of tickets sold will be no more than 1,000.

  b. Draw a graph that uses appropriate boundary lines to show the region of the first quadrant in the coordinate plane that contains all points (a, g) satisfying both the inequality $8a + 12g > 2,400$ (from Problem 1) and the inequality from Part a of this problem.

3 **a.** The lower region corresponds to solutions of $x + 2y < -2$.

b. Determine the x- and y-intercepts for $x - y = 3$ and graph the line containing those points. Then select a test point on one side of the line to find the region where $x - y > 3$. Since there is no universal convention about shading, students should be alert to look for (or provide in their own graphs) the legend that tells how any particular graph has been constructed. Some students might feel that shading highlights a region of interest. Others might say (as will be the case in linear programming) that shading points that are of interest obscures them.

INSTRUCTIONAL NOTE
Before moving ahead to consideration of techniques for drawing boundaries to indicate > or ≥ inequalities, Problem 3 returns to the issue discussed at the outset of this lesson—conventions for highlighting regions in the plane that correspond to solutions of inequalities in two variables.

4 **a.** $3x - 2y < 12$ **b.** $2x + y \geq 4$

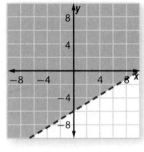   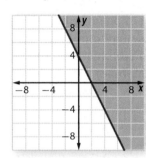

c. $8x - 5y > 20$ **d.** $4x + 3y \leq 15$

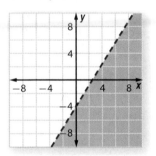   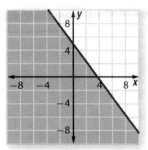

INSTRUCTIONAL NOTE
You may need to remind students that without context, there are no restrictions on the domain, so their graphs should not be confined to the first quadrant. In the solutions to Problems 4–7, all points in the shaded region are solutions of the corresponding inequality or systems of inequalities. You may wish to allow students to label their graphs to show inequalities in their own way or set a class convention.

5 **INSTRUCTIONAL NOTE** The graphs in solutions that follow include the equation for the boundary line or function as information. Notice that in Problem 6 Part a, only part of the line is solid indicating the solutions. In Investigation 3, students will be asked to write the linear boundary equations on their graphs for linear programming problems.

a. $a + g \leq 1,000$

b.

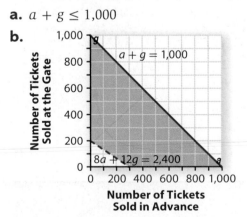

Unit 2

(6) Suppose that the bank wants to give away at least 300 promotional items at the Old Dominion Music Festival.

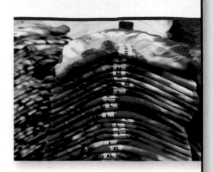

  a. Write an inequality whose solutions are the (F, V) combinations for which the total number of promotional items will be 300 or more.

  b. Draw a graph that shows the region of the first quadrant in the coordinate plane containing all points (F, V) that satisfy both the inequality $4F + 2.5V \leq 1,000$ (from Problem 2) and the inequality from Part a of this problem.

You have solved systems of equations in previous work. Recall that the goal in solving a system of equations is to find values of the variables that satisfy all equations in the system. Similarly, the goal in solving a *system of inequalities* is to find values of the variables that satisfy all inequalities in the system. As with systems of equations, systems of inequalities can be solved by graphing the solution of each inequality in the system and finding the points of intersection as you did in Problems 5 and 6.

(7) Draw graphs that show the solutions of these systems of inequalities.

  a. $\begin{cases} 2x - 3y > -12 \\ x + y \geq -2 \end{cases}$
  b. $\begin{cases} 3x - 4y > 18 \\ 5x + 2y \leq 15 \end{cases}$

  c. $\begin{cases} y > 4 - x^2 \\ 2x - y > -3 \end{cases}$
  d. $\begin{cases} y > x^2 - 4x - 5 \\ 2x - y \geq -2 \end{cases}$

Summarize
the Mathematics

In this investigation, you developed strategies for graphing the solution of a linear inequality in two variables and for graphing the solution of a system of inequalities in two variables.

a Describe a general strategy for graphing the solution of a linear inequality in two variables.

b How do you show whether the points on the graph of the corresponding linear equation are included as solutions?

c Describe the goal in solving a system of inequalities and a general strategy for finding the solutions.

Be prepared to share your ideas and reasoning with the class.

6 **a.** $F + V \geq 300$

b.
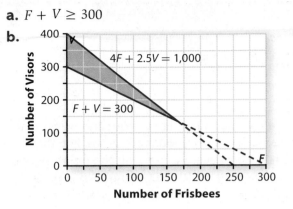

7 **DIFFERENTIATION** Some students may notice that inequalities such as $2x - 3y > -12$ in Problem 7 Part a have solutions below the line even though the inequality is "greater than." In Lesson 1, the inequalities were all in functional form, or "$y = \ldots$" form. Thus, the inequality direction aligned with the "above or below the graph" concept. Ask students to consider inequalities of the form $ax + by \geq k$ to think about why and for what values of a and b the inequality aligns with the "above or below the graph" concept and for what values the concept breaks down. Why does this occur? Considering this will help students recognize why testing a point to find solutions for inequalities is a good method.

a.
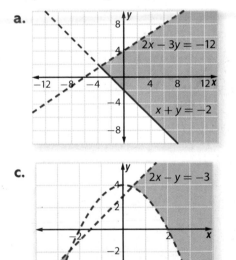

b.
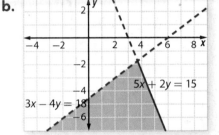

c.

d.
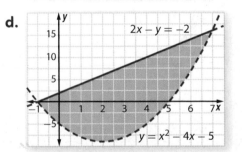

Unit 2

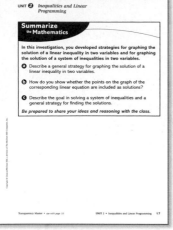

Unit 2

Summarize
the Mathematics

a Graph the solution of the corresponding linear equation using x- and y-intercepts. Then shade the half-plane bounded by the line that satisfies the inequality. It is only necessary to test one point on either side of the boundary to determine which half-plane to shade; (0, 0) is a convenient "test point" when it is not on the boundary line.

b A solid boundary line indicates that the points on the line are included in the solution; a dotted or dashed boundary line indicates that the points on the line are not included in the solution.

c The goal in solving a system of inequalities is to determine the region of the coordinate plane that contains all of the points that satisfy all inequalities in the system. Graph each corresponding equation. You might first consider each inequality individually to determine the "half-region" of the coordinate plane that satisfies each inequality, then shade the intersection of these regions.

Teacher Notes

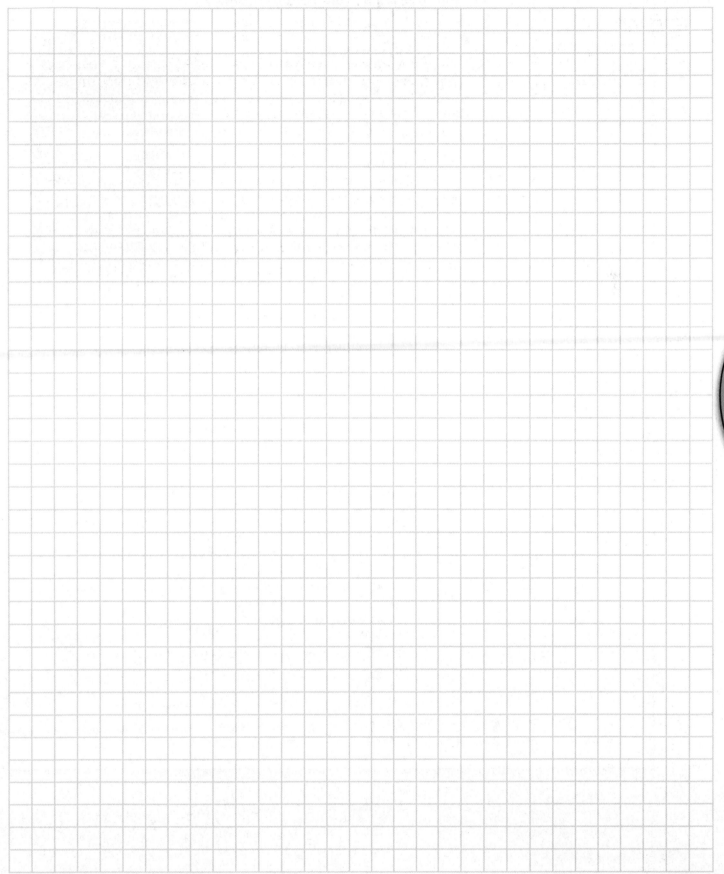

✔ Check Your Understanding

Jess has made a commitment to exercise in order to lose weight and improve overall fitness. Jess would like to burn *at least* 2,000 calories per week through exercise but wants to schedule *at most* five hours of exercise each week.

Jess will do both walking and bike riding for exercise. Brisk walking burns about 345 calories per hour, and biking at a moderate pace burns about 690 calories per hour.

a. Write a system of linear inequalities that describes Jess' exercise goals.

b. Identify at least three (*number of hours walking, number of hours biking*) combinations that satisfy both of Jess' conditions.

c. Graph the set of all points that satisfy the system from Part a.

Investigation 2   Linear Programming— A Graphic Approach

Linear programming problems, like that faced by managers of the video game factory described at the start of this lesson, involve finding an optimum choice among many options. As you work on the problems in this investigation, look for an answer to this question:

> *How can coordinate graphs be used to display and analyze the options in linear programming decision problems?*

Production Planning The production-scheduling problem at the electronics plant requires the plant manager to find a combination of CP•I and CP•II models that will give greatest profit. But there are **constraints** or limits on the choice. Each day, the plant has capacity for:

- *at most* 240 hours of assembly labor with each CP•I requiring 0.6 hours and each CP•II requiring 0.3 hours.

- *at most* 160 hours of testing labor with each CP•I requiring 0.2 hours and each CP•II requiring 0.4 hours.

- packing *at most* 500 video game systems with each model requiring the same time.

The company makes profit of $50 on each CP•I model and $75 on each CP•II model.

Check Your Understanding

a. $\begin{cases} w + b \leq 5 \\ 345w + 690b \geq 2{,}000 \end{cases}$

where w is the number of hours spent in brisk walking each week and b is the number of hours spent biking each week.

b. Three possible combinations are (1 hour walking, 3 hours biking), (2 hours walking, 2 hours biking), and (3 hours walking, 1.5 hours biking).

c.

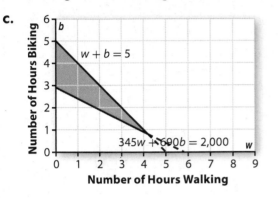

Investigation 2 — Linear Programming— A Graphic Approach

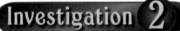

This investigation leads students to optimal solutions of linear programming problems using only graphs of the constraints and informal exploration of values for the objective function. Because students are not asked to define the constraints symbolically, their answers for the maximum profit or minimum weight may not agree at first attempt. This difficulty is resolved in the next investigation where the same two problem situations are revisited.

Unit 2

① One way to search for the production plan that will maximize profit is to make some guesses and test the profit prospects for those guesses. Here are three possible production plans for CP•I and CP•II video game models.

> **Plan 1:** Make 100 of model CP•I and 200 of model CP•II.
> **Plan 2:** Make 200 of model CP•I and 100 of model CP•II.
> **Plan 3:** Make 400 of model CP•I and 100 of model CP•II.

a. Check each production plan by answering the following questions.

  i. Will the required assembly time be within the limit of 240 hours per day?

  ii. Will the required testing time be within the limit of 160 hours per day?

  iii. Will the number of systems produced fall within the packing limit of 500 units per day?

  iv. If the constraints are satisfied, what profit will be earned?

b. Design and check a plan of your own that you think will produce greater profit than Plans 1, 2, and 3 while satisfying the assembly, testing, and packing constraints.

As you compared the possible production plans in Problem 1, you checked several different constraints and evaluated the profit prospects for each combination of CP•I and CP•II video game systems. However, you checked only a few of many possible production possibilities.

It would be nice to have a systematic way of organizing the search for a maximum profit plan. One strategy for solving **linear programming** problems begins with graphing the options. If x represents the number of CP•I game systems produced and y represents the number of CP•II game systems produced, then the scheduling goal or *objective* is to find a pair (x, y) that meets the constraints and gives maximum profit.

Using a grid like the one below, you can search for the combination of CP•I and CP•II video game system numbers that will give maximum profit. The point (100, 200) represents production of 100 CP•I and 200 CP•II game systems. These numbers satisfy the constraints and give a profit of

$$\$50(100) + \$75(200) = \$20,000.$$

Video Game System Profits (in dollars)

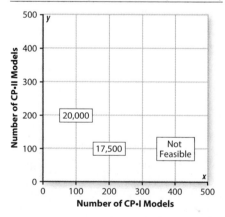

1 **a. Plan 1:**

- **i.** Yes, 120 hours $\leq$ 240 hours.
- **ii.** Yes, 100 hours $\leq$ 160 hours.
- **iii.** Yes, $300 \leq 500$.
- **iv.** $\$50(100) + \$75(200) = \$20{,}000$

Plan 2:

- **i.** Yes, 150 hours $\leq$ 240 hours.
- **ii.** Yes, 80 hours $\leq$ 160 hours.
- **iii.** Yes, $300 \leq 500$.
- **iv.** $\$50(200) + \$75(200) = \$17{,}500$

Plan 3:

- **i.** No, 270 hours $>$ 240 hours.
- **ii.** Yes, 120 hours $\leq$ 160 hours.
- **iii.** Yes, $500 \leq 500$.
- **iv.** This calculation is not needed since the assembly time condition is not met.

b. Student plans will vary but should produce a higher profit than $20,000 while satisfying the given conditions. One possible plan is to make 200 CP•I models and 200 CP•II models for a profit of $25,000.

INSTRUCTIONAL NOTE
For Part b, encourage students to verbalize their strategies for finding production plans that increase profit. Students should see that if the combination (100, 200) leads to a profit of $20,000 with "time to spare," then increasing the number of either or both models will increase profit.

2 Each **lattice point** on the grid (where horizontal and vertical grid lines intersect) represents a possible combination of CP•I and CP•II video game system numbers. Points with coordinates satisfying all the constraints are called **feasible points**.

a. What do the labels on the points with coordinates (200, 100) and (400, 100) tell about the production planning options?

b. Collaborate with others to check the remaining lattice points on the given graph to see which are feasible points and which are not. For each feasible point, find the profit for that production plan and record it on a copy of the graph. Label each nonfeasible point "NF."

c. Based on the completed graph:

   i. describe the region where coordinates of lattice points satisfy all three constraints.

   ii. pick the combination of CP•I and CP•II video game systems that you think the factory should produce in order to maximize daily profit. Be prepared to explain why you believe your answer is correct.

Balancing Astronaut Diets Problems like the challenge of planning video game system production to maximize profit occur in many quite different situations. For example, think about the variables, constraints, and objectives in choosing the foods you eat. Usually, you choose things that taste good. But it is also important to consider the cost of the food and the ways that it satisfies your body's dietary needs.

3 For some people, athletes and astronauts in particular, selection of a good diet is a carefully planned scientific process. Each person wants a high-performance diet at minimal cost. In the case of astronauts, the goal might be minimal total food weight onboard the spacecraft.

Consider the following simplified version of the problem facing NASA flight planners who must provide food for astronauts.

Teaching Resources

Student Master 18.

UNIT **2** *Inequalities and Linear Programming*   Name _____
                                                    Date _____

Video Game System Production Planning
Problem 2

Video Game System Profits (in dollars)

② **INSTRUCTIONAL NOTE** Divide the computational work among groups. An overhead transparency of the grid makes it possible for each group to show its conclusions to create a completed grid. You might ask students what strategies they used to check lattice points in their column. For example, if the point (100, 300) satisfies all of the constraints, then the points (100, 200), (100, 100), and (100, 0) will also. Likewise, if the point (100, 400) is not feasible, then the point (100, 500) is not feasible. Some students may observe that profit increases at a constant rate ($7,500 per 100 models) as the number of CP•II models increases.

a. The $17,500 at the point (200, 100) is the profit that would be made if 200 CP•I and 100 CP•II models were produced. The "not feasible" at the point (400, 100) indicates that it is not possible to produce that combination of models and stay within the constraints.

b. The labels for each lattice point are recorded below in the grid.

Video Game System Profits (in dollars)

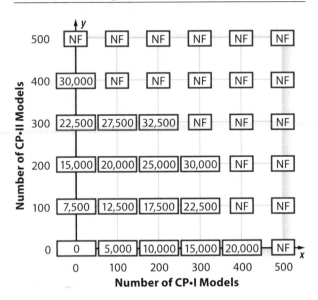

c. **i.** Descriptions may vary. The region is a pentagon, but that will be difficult for students to see at this time. It is not necessary that they draw this conclusion yet. Instead, students may describe this region as the lower-left corner of the graph. Some may think that all of the points lie below a line, and they may try to describe this line. Some may think that the shape is a stair-step or a quarter-circle.

ii. Producing 200 CP•I models and 300 CP•II models maximizes the profit because $32,500 is the largest profit in the region. (Some students may think that (200, 350) or (225, 300) may still be feasible while giving larger profits. They should check their thinking against the constraints and profit function.)

Suppose there are two kinds of food to be carried on a space shuttle trip, special food bars and cartons of a special drink.

- Each food bar provides 5 grams of fat, 40 grams of carbohydrate, and 8 grams of protein.

- Each drink carton provides 6 grams of fat, 25 grams of carbohydrate, and 15 grams of protein.

- Minimum daily requirements for each astronaut are *at least* 61 grams of fat, *at least* 350 grams of carbohydrate, and *at least* 103 grams of protein.

- Each food bar weighs 65 grams, and each drink weighs 118 grams.

The goal is to find a combination of food bars and drinks that will fulfill daily requirements of fat, carbohydrate, and protein with minimum total weight onboard the spacecraft.

This probably seems like a complicated problem. But you can get a good start toward a solution by doing some systematic testing of options.

a. For each of these numbers of food bars and drink cartons, check to see if they provide at least the daily minimums of fat, carbohydrate, and protein. Then find the total weight of each feasible combination.

    i. 4 food bars and 10 cartons of drink

    ii. 10 food bars and 4 cartons of drink

    iii. 4 food bars and 4 cartons of drink

    iv. 10 food bars and 10 cartons of drink

b. Record your findings on a copy of the following graph. The case of 4 food bars and 10 drink cartons has been plotted already.

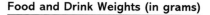

Food and Drink Weights (in grams)

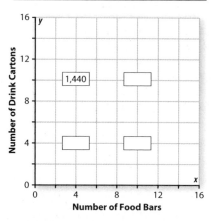

Number of Drink Cartons / Number of Food Bars

3　**a.** Fat, carbohydrate, protein, and weight values are reported in grams.

i. Fat:　　　　　$4(5) + 10(6) = 80 > 61$
Carbohydrate:　$4(40) + 10(25) = 410 > 350$
Protein:　　　　$4(8) + 10(15) = 182 > 103$
Weight:　　　　$4(65) + 10(118) = 1,440$

ii. Fat:　　　　　$10(5) + 4(6) = 74 > 61$
Carbohydrate:　$10(40) + 4(25) = 500 > 350$
Protein:　　　　$10(8) + 4(15) = 140 > 103$
Weight:　　　　$10(65) + 4(118) = 1,122$

iii. This option does not meet the constraints for fat, carbohydrate, and protein.
Fat:　　　　　$4(5) + 4(6) = 44 < 61$
Carbohydrate:　$4(40) + 4(25) = 260 < 350$
Protein:　　　　$4(8) + 4(15) = 92 < 103$

iv. Fat:　　　　　$10(5) + 10(6) = 110 > 61$
Carbohydrate:　$10(40) + 10(25) = 650 > 350$
Protein:　　　　$10(8) + 10(15) = 230 > 103$
Weight:　　　　$10(65) + 10(118) = 1,830$

b–c. The labels for each lattice point are recorded below in the grid.

Food and Drink Weights (in grams)

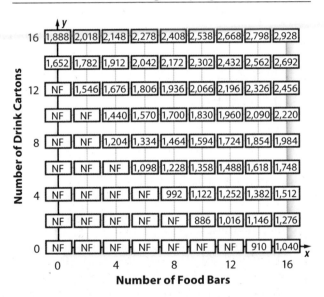

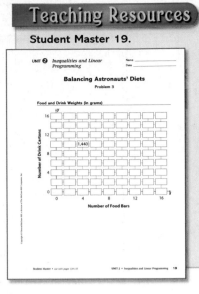

Unit 2

c. Collaborate with others to test the remaining lattice points on the grid to get a picture of the **feasible region**, the points with coordinates that meet all constraints. For each feasible point, find the total weight of the food and drink. Plot it on a copy of the grid.

4 Now analyze the pattern of *feasible points* and *objective values* (weights) for possible astronaut diets.

a. Describe the shape of the feasible region.

b. Study the pattern of weights for points in the feasible region. Decide on a combination of food bars and drink cartons that you think will meet the diet constraints with minimum weight. Be prepared to explain why you believe your answer is correct.

Summarize
the Mathematics

Problems that can be solved by linear programming have several common features: variables, constraints, and an objective.

a What are the variables, constraints, and objective in the video game system production problem?

b What are the variables, constraints, and objective in the astronaut diet problem?

c What are *feasible points* and the feasible region in a linear programming problem?

d What do coordinates of the feasible points and the "not feasible" points tell you in the video game system production problem? In the astronaut diet problem?

Be prepared to explain your ideas to the class.

✔Check Your Understanding

Suppose that a new store plans to lease selling space in a mall. The leased space would be divided into two sections, one for books and the other for music and videos.

- The store owners can lease up to 10,000 square feet of floor space.

- Furnishings for the two kinds of selling space cost $5 per square foot for books and $7 per square foot for music and videos. The store has a budget of at most $60,000 to spend for furnishings.

- Each square foot of book-selling space will generate an average of $75 per month in sales. Each square foot of music- and video-selling space will generate an average of $95 per month in sales.

(4) **INSTRUCTIONAL NOTE** Without boundary lines drawn, it is not clear exactly what shape the region is, but students should have realized that the optimal points seem to lie on or near the edge of the region they are describing. Ask them, "Why does it make sense that all the feasible points are contained downward and inward in the example about profit?" (We were trying to find combinations that would stay *under* certain limits.) "Why does it make sense that the feasible points extend upward and outward in the example about dietary needs?" (We were trying to find combinations that would stay *above* certain limits.)

a. Descriptions may vary. Some students may describe the region as the upper right-hand portion of the graph. Some students may believe that the feasible points all lie above some line in the first quadrant.

b. The minimum weight seems to be 886 grams with 10 bars and 2 drinks. That weight is the lowest of the lattice points shown in the region. (Some students may wonder about (9, 2) or (10, 1) as feasible while giving lower weights. They should check their thinking against the constraints and profit function. The actual minimum weight is 833 grams with 11 bars and 1 drink; however, students do not need to discover that at this time.)

Summarize
the Mathematics

Unit 2

 The variables are the number of CP•I models and the number of CP•II models. The constraints are the limitations on production. The total technician time for assembly work can be at most 240 hours each day, and testing time can be at most 160 hours per day. The company can pack at most 500 video game systems per day. The objective is to maximize the profit.

ⓑ The variables for the astronaut diet problem are the number of food bars and the number of drink cartons. The constraints of the problem are the amounts of fat, carbohydrate, and protein that are required. The objective is to minimize the weight of the food onboard the spacecraft.

ⓒ A feasible point is a point that satisfies all of the constraints (or conditions) of the problem. The feasible region contains all of the feasible points.

ⓓ The coordinates of feasible points tell a combination of CP•I and CP•II models that can be produced within the production constraints or a combination of food bars and drinks that will meet the nutrition requirements. A "not feasible" point does not satisfy at least one of the constraints. It tells you, for example, that the particular combination of video game systems (or food bars and drinks) should not be considered as a solution to the problem.

The store owners have to decide how to allocate space to the two kinds of items, books or music/video, to maximize monthly sales.

a. Identify the variables, constraints, and objective in this situation.

b. Find three feasible points and one point that is not feasible.

c. Evaluate the predicted total monthly sales at the three feasible points.

d. Plot the three feasible points and the nonfeasible point on an appropriate grid and label each feasible point with the corresponding value of predicted total monthly sales.

e. Which of the three sample feasible points comes closest to the problem objective?

Investigation 3 Linear Programming— Algebraic Methods

As you worked on the production-planning problem for the video game factory and the astronaut diet problem, you probably thought, "There's got to be an easier way than testing all those possible combinations." Computers have been programmed to help explore the options. But to use those tools, it is essential to express the problem in algebraic form. In this investigation, look for answers to these questions:

How can constraints and objectives of linear programming problems be expressed in symbolic form?

How can algebraic and graphical methods be combined to help solve the problems?

Video Game System Production Revisited Think again about the objective and the constraints in the production-planning problem. Each CP•I video game system earns $50 profit, and each CP•II system earns $75 profit. But daily production is constrained by the times required for assembly, testing, and packaging.

1 If x represents the number of CP•I models and y represents the number of CP•II models produced in a day, what algebraic rule shows how to calculate total profit P for the day? This rule is called the **objective function** for the linear programming problem because it shows how the goal of the problem is a function of, or depends on, the independent variables x and y.

✔Check Your Understanding

a. The variables are the amount of space allocated for books and for music and videos. The constraints are that the storeowners can lease up to 10,000 square feet of floor space and can spend at most $60,000 dollars for furniture. The objective is to maximize average monthly sales within these constraints.

b–d. Student grids should show three feasible points labeled with monthly sales and one not feasible point labeled NF. All feasible points will lie in the unshaded region shown in the graph below.

Average Monthly Sales (in dollars)

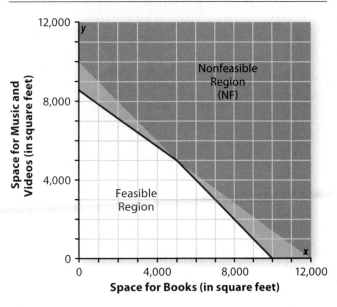

e. Student feasible points will vary. However, greater sales will occur at feasible points that are closer to utilizing all 10,000 square feet of space and all $60,000 of the furniture budget. The maximum sales income of $850,000 occurs when the owners allocate 5,000 square feet to music and videos and 5,000 square feet to books.

Investigation ③ Linear Programming— Algebraic Methods

In this investigation, students express the constraints for the linear programming problems from Investigation 2 with inequalities and use these symbolic expressions to create boundaries separating the feasible and not feasible regions. This removes the doubt about the shape of the feasible region and makes it possible to efficiently search for optimal points.

① $P = 50x + 75y$

INSTRUCTIONAL NOTE
For the problems in this investigation, the constraints $x \geq 0$ and $y \geq 0$ always border the feasible region. You may choose to make this explicit. This would then mean that $(0, 0)$ is a vertex of the feasible region.

② Recall that assembly time required for each CP•I model is 0.6 hours, and assembly time required for each CP•II model is 0.3 hours. Assembly capacity is limited by the constraint that the factory can use at most 240 hours of technician time per day.

a. Explain how the linear inequality $0.6x + 0.3y \leq 240$ represents the assembly time constraint.

b. The graph below shows points meeting the assembly time constraint. *Points that are* **not** *feasible have been shaded out of the picture.*

Video Game System Assembly Time (in hours)

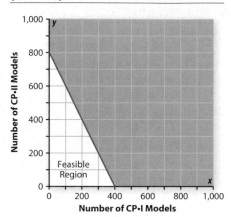

i. Why does the graph only show points in the first quadrant?

ii. Which feasible point(s) do you think will lead to greatest daily profit for the company? Test your ideas by evaluating the objective function at a variety of feasible points.

③ Next, recall that testing of each CP•I model requires 0.2 hours of technician time and testing of each CP•II model requires 0.4 hours. The factory can apply at most 160 hours of technician time to testing each day.

a. Write an inequality that expresses the testing time constraint. Be prepared to explain how you know that your algebraic representation of the constraint is correct.

b. Graph the solutions of that inequality, shading *out* the region of nonfeasible points.

c. Which feasible point(s) do you think will lead to greatest daily profit for the factory? Test your ideas by evaluating the objective function at a variety of feasible points.

INSTRUCTIONAL NOTE In Problem 2, students consider the assembly time constraint, temporarily ignoring the other constraints. In Problem 3, students consider the testing-time constraint, temporarily ignoring the other constraints. Students may be surprised that producing more CP•I models yields a greater profit under this constraint since the company earns more profit per CP•II model. Under this constraint, at most, 400 CP•II models can be produced. If the number of CP•II models is decreased by 1, then 2 more CP•I models can be produced. At the same time, profit decreases by $75 and increases by $100 for a net increase of $25.

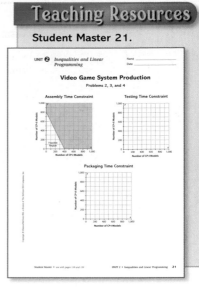

② **a.** 0.6x represents the number of hours to assemble the CP•I models. 0.3y represents the number of hours to assemble the CP•II models. 0.6x + 0.3y represents the total time spent assembling game systems, and it can be at most 240 hours.

    b. **i.** The graph only shows points in the first quadrant because negative numbers of video game systems do not make sense.

       ii. The greatest profit of $60,000 occurs under this constraint when no CP•I models are produced and 800 CP•II models are produced.

③ **a.** $0.2x + 0.4y \le 160$

    b. Testing Time (in hours)

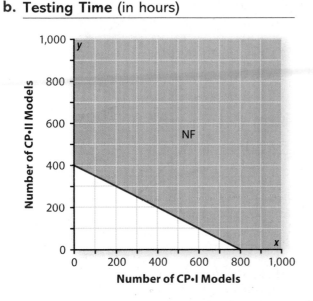

    c. Producing 800 CP•I models and no CP•II models will yield the maximum profit of $40,000 under only this constraint.

(4) Finally, recall that the factory can package and ship at most 500 video game systems each day.

  a. Write an inequality that expresses the packaging/shipping constraint. Be prepared to explain how you know that your algebraic expression of the constraint is correct.

  b. Graph the solutions of that inequality, shading *out* the region of nonfeasible points.

  c. Which feasible point(s) do you think will lead to greatest daily profit for the factory? Test your ideas.

(5) In work on Problems 2–4, you developed some ideas about how to maximize profit while satisfying each problem constraint separately. The actual production-planning problem requires maximizing profit while satisfying all three constraints. The feasible region for this problem is shown as the unshaded region in the diagram below.

Video Game System Production Feasibility

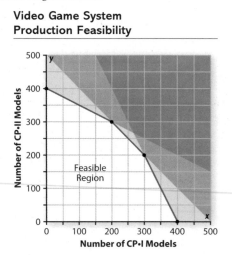

  a. On a copy of the graph, use results from Part a of Problems 2, 3, and 4 to label each segment of the feasible region boundary with its corresponding linear equation.

  b. Use the graph to estimate coordinates of points at the corners of the feasible region. Then explain how you could check the accuracy of your estimates and how you could calculate the coordinates by algebraic methods.

4 a. $x + y \leq 500$

b. Packaging and Shipping Constraint (in number)

c. Producing no CP•I models and 500 CP•II models will yield the maximum profit of $37,500 under only this constraint.

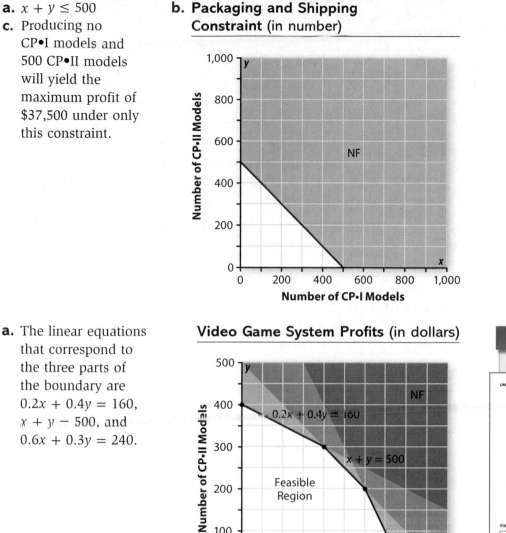

5 a. The linear equations that correspond to the three parts of the boundary are $0.2x + 0.4y = 160$, $x + y - 500$, and $0.6x + 0.3y = 240$.

Video Game System Profits (in dollars)

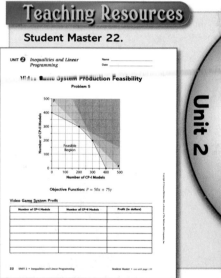

b. The corners of the feasible region lie at (0, 400), (200, 300), (300, 200), and (400, 0). These coordinates can be checked by substituting the coordinate values into the two boundary line equations that determine the corresponding parts of the boundary. Another way to find the coordinates is to determine them algebraically.

- Solve $0.2(0) + 0.4y = 160$ to find the y-intercept of the testing boundary line.
- Solve the system $0.2x + 0.4y = 160$ and $x + y = 500$ to find the point of intersection of the testing and packaging boundary lines.
- Solve the system $x + y = 500$ and $0.6x + 0.3y = 240$ to find the point of intersection of the packaging and assembly boundary lines.
- Solve $0.6x + 0.3(0) = 240$ to find the x-intercept of the assembly boundary line.

c. Now think about the objective function $P = 50x + 75y$.

   i. How does the value of P change as the numbers x and y increase within the feasible region?

   ii. Where in the feasible region would you expect a combination of production numbers (x, y) to give maximum profit?

   iii. List coordinates of some likely maximum profit points. Evaluate the profit corresponding to each point.

Video Game System Profit

Number of CP·I Models	Number of CP·II Models	Profit (in dollars)

   iv. Of these production options, which gives the maximum profit?

d. Compare your choice of maximum profit production plan to those of others in your class and resolve differences.

Astronaut Diet Planning Revisited Think again about the objective and constraints in the astronaut diet-planning problem. Each food bar weighs 65 grams, and each drink carton weighs 118 grams. But the diet plan is constrained by the minimum daily requirements of fat, carbohydrate, and protein.

⑥ If f represents the number of food bars and d represents the number of drink cartons in a daily diet, what algebraic rule shows how to calculate total weight W of that food? (This rule is the objective function for the diet linear programming problem.)

⑦ Recall that each food bar provides 5 grams of fat, 40 grams of carbohydrate, and 8 grams of protein. Each drink carton provides 6 grams of fat, 25 grams of carbohydrate, and 15 grams of protein. Write inequalities that express the constraints of providing the daily astronaut diet with:

a. at least 61 grams of fat.

b. at least 350 grams of carbohydrate.

c. at least 103 grams of protein.

c.   **i.** As x increases and/or y increases, the value of P increases.

  ii. Students should expect to find maximum values of the profit on the boundary of the feasible region.

  iii. Student responses will vary. The table at the right indicates the profit at the corner points listed in Part b, as well as selected boundary points.

Video Game System Profit

Number of CP·I Models	Number of CP·II Models	Profit (in dollars)
0	0	0
0	400	30,000
100	350	31,250
200	300	32,500
250	250	31,250
300	200	30,000
350	100	25,000
400	0	20,000

  iv. Students should come to a consensus that the maximum profit occurs at (200, 300).

d. Students should compare their choice of maximum profit prediction plan with others and resolve any differences.

INSTRUCTIONAL NOTE Encourage students to verbalize their strategies for choosing points to test. Students should be able to argue that the maximum profit will occur on the boundary, since for any point inside the feasible region, increasing the number of either model (moving right or up on the graph) will yield greater profit. Along any boundary segment, profit changes at a constant rate (since both the boundary segment and the profit are linear). Therefore, the maximum profit will occur at an endpoint of a boundary segment.

 6 $W = 65f + 118d$

7   **a.** $5f + 6d \geq 61$

  b. $40f + 25d \geq 350$

  c. $8f + 15d \geq 103$

(8) The next graph shows the feasible region for the astronaut diet problem. The feasible region for this problem is shown as the unshaded region in the graph.

Astronaut Food and Drink Feasibility

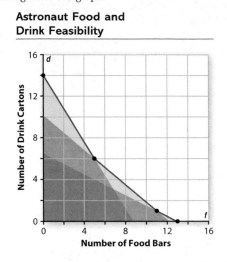

a. On a copy of the graph, label each segment of the feasible region boundary with its corresponding linear equation.

b. Use the graph to estimate coordinates of points at the corners of the feasible region. Then check the accuracy of your estimates by algebraic methods.

c. Now think about the objective function $W = 65f + 118d$.

   i. How does the value of W change as the numbers f and d decrease within the feasible region?

   ii. Where in the feasible region do you expect a pair of numbers (f, d) to give minimum weight?

   iii. List coordinates of some likely minimum weight points. Evaluate the weight corresponding to each point.

Astronaut Diet Options

Number of Food Bars	Number of Drink Cartons	Weight (in grams)

   iv. Of these diet options, which gives minimum weight?

d. Compare your choice of minimum weight diet plan to those of others in your class and resolve differences.

8 **a.** The equations of the lines that bound the region are shown below.

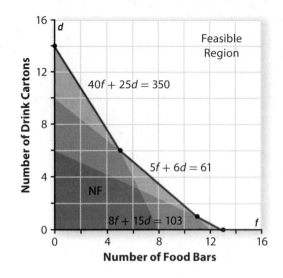

Astronaut Food and Drink Feasibility

b. The coordinates of corners of the feasible region are (0, 14), (5, 6), (11, 1), and (12.875, 0). The (12.875, 0) corner should be considered as (13, 0) since 13 is the first integer value for food bars associated with 0 drink cartons in the feasible region.

c. **i.** As f decreases and/or d decreases, the value of W decreases.

ii. Students should expect to find minimum values of the weight on the boundary of the feasible region.

iii. Student responses will vary. The following table indicates the weight at each of the boundary points listed in Part b. For the final point listed, the number of food bars has been rounded up to the nearest whole number (staying in the feasible region).

Astronaut Diet Options

Number of Food Bars	Number of Drink Cartons	Weight (in grams)
0	14	1,652
5	6	1,033
11	1	833
13	0	845

iv. The minimum weight occurs at the point (11, 1).

d. Students should compare their choice of minimum weight diet plan with others and resolve any differences.

POSSIBLE MISCONCEPTION
Students may come to think that the optimal point is always one of the "middle" vertices, never one of the intercepts with an axis. You might ask students to consider what combination would give the minimum weight if food bars weighed 118 grams and drink cartons weighed 65 grams. The minimum weight is then at (0, 14).

Unit 2

Summarize
the Mathematics

In this investigation, you explored ways that reasoning with symbolic expressions, inequalities, and graphs helps to solve linear programming problems.

a Why are the constraints in the video game system production and astronaut diet planning problems most accurately expressed as inequalities rather than equations?

b What shapes would you expect for the feasible regions in other linear programming problems where the goal is to maximize some objective function? In problems where the goal is to minimize some objective function?

c What seems to be the best way to locate feasible points that maximize (or minimize) the objective function in a linear programming problem?

Be prepared to explain your ideas to the class.

✔ Check Your Understanding

Paisan's Pizza makes gourmet frozen pizzas to sell to supermarket chains. The company makes two deluxe pizzas, one vegetarian and the other with meat.

- Each vegetarian pizza requires 12 minutes of labor, and each meat pizza requires 6 minutes of labor. The plant has at most 3,600 minutes of labor available each day.

- The plant freezer can handle at most 500 pizzas per day.

- Vegetarian pizza is not quite as popular as meat pizza, so the company can sell at most 200 vegetarian pizzas each day.

- Sale of each vegetarian pizza earns Paisan's $3 profit. Each meat pizza earns $2 profit.

Summarize
the Mathematics

a The constraints in the video game system production involve maximum times available for various tasks. These times cannot be exceeded, but it is possible that not all of the available time for one or more tasks will be used. In fact, it would not be possible to use the maximum time available for all tasks. The constraints in the astronaut diet planning involve minimum requirements that must be satisfied but may be exceeded. Here again, it is not possible to *exactly* meet all of the minimum requirements.

b In the linear programming problems, students have seen when the goal was to maximize an objective function (like in the video game system problem), the region was a convex polygon in the first quadrant with one corner at the origin. When the goal was to minimize an objective function (like in the astronaut diet problem), the region was infinite and bounded by the constraints, the *y*-axis, and the *x*-axis. (See the Possible Misconception below.)

c The best way to locate feasible points that maximize (or minimize) the objective function is to examine the corners of the feasible region, formed where the constraint equations intersect.

> **MATH TOOLKIT** What type of problem is best solved using linear programming? Explain how to use the linear programming method.

POSSIBLE MISCONCEPTION Students should not generalize the shape of the feasible region beyond the simple situations in the text. Feasible regions for maximizing problems do not always include the origin. Feasible regions for minimizing problems may be convex polygons. In general, feasible regions are either convex polygons or unbounded regions.

Unit 2

Paisan's Pizza would like to plan production to maximize daily profit.

a. Translate the objective and constraints in this situation into symbolic expressions and inequalities.

b. On a copy of a grid like the one below, graph the system of constraints to determine the feasible region for Paisan's linear programming problem. Label each segment of the feasible region boundary with the linear equation that determines it.

Pizza Production Feasibility Options

c. Evaluate the objective function at the point(s) that you believe will yield greatest daily profit for Paisan's Pizza. Compare that profit figure to the profit for several other feasible points that you think might be "next best."

Check Your Understanding

a. Objective Function: $P = 3x + 2y$ where x is the number of vegetarian pizzas made each day, y is the number of meat pizzas made each day, and P is the daily profit.

Constraints: $\begin{cases} 12x + 6y \leq 3{,}600 \\ x + y \leq 500 \\ x < 200 \end{cases}$

b. **Pizza Production Feasibility Options**

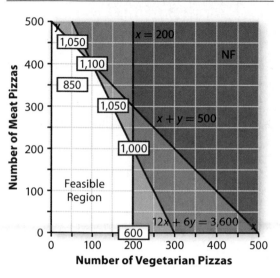

c. The maximum profit of $1,100 occurs when 100 vegetarian pizzas and 400 meat pizzas are made per day.

On Your Own

Applications

1 Match each inequality listed in Parts a–j with the region I–X that shows points (x, y) that satisfy the inequality. The scales on the coordinate axes are 1.

a. $y \geq x$

b. $y \leq x$

c. $2x + 3y \leq 3$

d. $2x + 3y \geq 3$

e. $y \geq 0.5x - 2$

f. $y \leq 0.5x - 2$

g. $x \leq 2$

h. $x \geq 2$

i. $3x + 2y \geq 4$

j. $3x + 2y \leq 4$

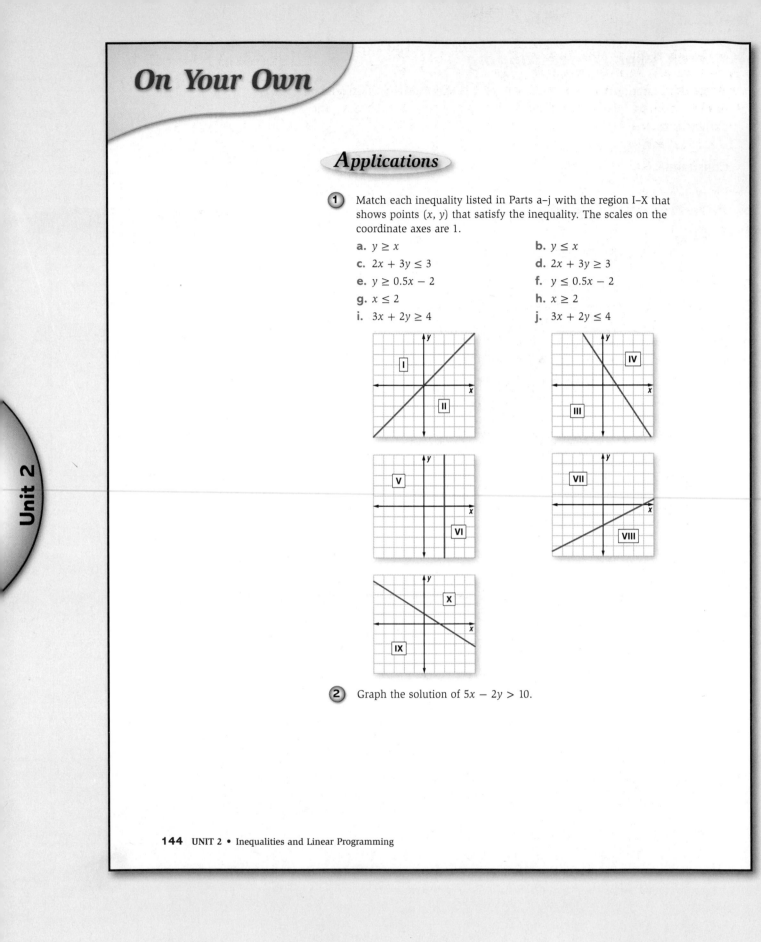

2 Graph the solution of $5x - 2y > 10$.

On Your Own

Applications

1 **a.** I   **b.** II

    c. IX   **d.** X

    e. VII   **f.** VIII

    g. V   **h.** VI

    i. IV   **j.** III

2 The solution half-plane is shaded in the following diagram.

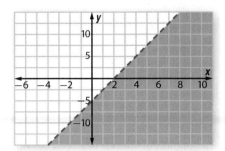

3 The symbol of Columbia, Maryland, is a people tree that stands by Lake Kittamaqundi. The tree is 14 feet tall with 66 gilded people as branches. As part of a renovation of downtown Columbia in 1992, residents purchased engraved brick pavers to pay for regilding of the people tree. The pavers were used to cover a new plaza around the tree.

Brick pavers engraved with one line of text sold for $25, and pavers engraved with two lines of text sold for $30. Each brick cost $18 to buy, engrave, and install. Regilding the people tree sculpture cost $11,000.

   a. Write an inequality whose solution gives the combinations of *one-line pavers* n_1 and *two-line pavers* n_2 that would cover the cost of regilding the people tree sculpture.

   b. Draw a graph that uses shading to show the region of the coordinate plane containing all points (n_1, n_2) that satisfy the inequality.

4 Refer back to Applications Task 3. Suppose that the Columbia people tree plaza has space for 1,200 engraved pavers.

   a. Write a system of inequalities whose solution will give the (n_1, n_2) combinations for which space is available and the cost of regilding the people tree sculpture will be covered.

   b. Draw a graph that shows the region of the first quadrant in the coordinate plane that contains all points (n_1, n_2) satisfying the system of inequalities from Part a.

5 Graph the solutions of the following systems of inequalities in a coordinate plane.

   a. $\begin{cases} x - y < 7 \\ 3x + 2y > 9 \end{cases}$

   b. $\begin{cases} y \geq x^2 + 5x \\ 3x + y \leq 15 \end{cases}$

3 **a.** $7n_1 + 12n_2 \geq 11{,}000$

Solution region is shaded below.

b.

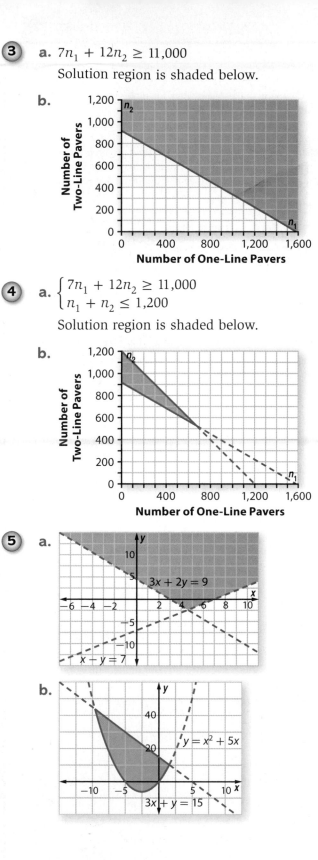

4 **a.** $\begin{cases} 7n_1 + 12n_2 \geq 11{,}000 \\ n_1 + n_2 \leq 1{,}200 \end{cases}$

Solution region is shaded below.

b.

5 **a.**

b.

6 The Bestform Ring Company makes class rings for high schools and colleges all over the country. The rings are made in production runs that each yield 100 rings. Each production run is a three-step process involving molding, engraving, and polishing.

The following chart gives information about the time required for the steps in each production run of high school or college rings and the time that machines and operators are available during one day.

Class Ring Production

Stage in Ring Making	Time to Make 100 High School Rings (in hours)	Time to Make 100 College Rings (in hours)	Machine and Operator Time Available Each Day (in hours)
Molding	1.2	2	14
Engraving	0.6	3	15
Polishing	2.0	2	20

a. Test the feasibility of these possible daily production plans.

Plan 1: 2 production runs of high school rings and 3 production runs of college rings

Plan 2: 3 production runs of high school rings and 5 production runs of college rings

Plan 3: 7 production runs of high school rings and 1 production run of college rings

Plan 4: 4 production runs of high school rings and 4 production runs of college rings

Plan 5: 5 production runs of high school rings and 3 production runs of college rings

b. The company makes $500 profit on each production run of high school rings and $525 profit on each production run of college rings.

i. Compute the daily profit from each feasible production plan in Part a.

ii. See if you can find a feasible production plan that results in higher profit than any of those in Part a.

7 The Junior Class of Oakland Mills High School sells drinks at the Columbia Fair to raise funds for the Junior Prom. The juniors mix and sell two drinks, Carnival Juice and Lemon Punch.

- Each batch of Carnival Juice uses two liters of orange juice and two liters of lemonade.

- Each batch of Lemon Punch uses one liter of orange juice and three liters of lemonade.

- The students have 120 liters of orange juice and 200 liters of lemonade to use.

- The profit is $9 per batch on the Carnival Juice and $12 per batch on the Lemon Punch.

6 **a.** **Plan 1:** Feasible

$$1.2(2) + 2(3) = 8.4 \leq 14$$
$$0.6(2) + 3(3) = 10.2 \leq 15$$
$$2(2) + 2(3) = 10 \leq 20$$

Plan 2: Not Feasible

$$1.2(3) + 2(5) = 13.6 \leq 14$$
$$0.6(3) + 3(5) = 16.8 > 15 \text{ NF}$$
$$2(3) + 2(5) = 16 \leq 20$$

Plan 3: Feasible

$$1.2(7) + 2(1) = 10.4 \leq 14$$
$$0.6(7) + 3(1) = 7.2 \leq 15$$
$$2(7) + 2(1) = 16 \leq 20$$

Plan 4: Feasible

$$1.2(4) + 2(4) = 12.8 \leq 14$$
$$0.6(4) + 3(4) = 14.4 \leq 15$$
$$2(4) + 2(4) = 16 \leq 20$$

Plan 5: Feasible

$$1.2(5) + 2(3) = 12 \leq 14$$
$$0.6(5) + 3(3) = 12 \leq 15$$
$$2(5) + 2(3) \quad 16 \leq 20$$

b. **i.** 200 high school rings and 300 college rings: $2,575
500 high school rings and 300 college rings: $4,075
700 high school rings and 100 college rings: $4,025
400 high school rings and 400 college rings: $4,100
300 high school rings and 500 college rings: Not Feasible

ii. Answers will vary. A higher profit could be made if 800 high school rings and 200 college rings are made (profit of $5,050).

Unit 2

a. Test the feasibility of these plans for mixing Carnival Juice and Lemon Punch.

Plan 1: 40 batches of Carnival Juice and 20 batches of Lemon Punch

Plan 2: 30 batches of Carnival Juice and 30 batches of Lemon Punch

Plan 3: 40 batches of Carnival Juice and 50 batches of Lemon Punch

Plan 4: 50 batches of Carnival Juice and 20 batches of Lemon Punch

b. Find the profit that the Junior Class will earn from each feasible combination of batches of Carnival Juice and Lemon Punch in Part a.

c. See if you can you find a feasible combination of drink batches that results in higher profit than any of those in Part a.

8 When candidates for political office plan their campaigns, they have choices to make about spending for advertising. Suppose that advisers told one candidate that radio and television ads might reach different audiences in the following ways.

- Every dollar spent on radio advertising will assure that the candidate's message will reach 5 Democratic voters, 2 Republican voters, and 4 Independent voters.

- Every dollar spent on television advertising will assure that the candidate's message will reach 4 Democratic voters, 4 Republican voters, and 1 Independent voter.

The candidate's goals are to reach at least 20,000 Democratic voters, 12,000 Republican voters, and 8,000 Independent voters with a minimum total advertising expense.

a. Test the feasibility of these campaign spending plans for reaching voters.

Plan 1: $2,000 on radio advertising and $3,000 on television advertising

Plan 2: $3,000 on radio advertising and $2,000 on television advertising

Plan 3: $2,000 on radio advertising and $2,000 on television advertising

Plan 4: $4,000 on radio advertising and $3,000 on television advertising

b. i. Find the total advertising cost for each feasible campaign plan in Part a.

ii. See if you can find a feasible combination of advertising dollars that results in a lower total expense for the candidate than any of those in Part a.

7 **a. Plan 1:** Feasible

$2(40) + 1(20) = 100 \le 120$ liters of orange juice

$2(40) + 3(20) = 140 \le 200$ liters of lemonade

Plan 2: Feasible

$2(30) + 1(30) = 90 \le 120$ liters of orange juice

$2(30) + 3(30) = 150 \le 200$ liters of lemonade

Plan 3: Not Feasible

$2(40) + 1(50) = 130 > 120$ liters of orange juice

$2(40) + 3(50) = 230 > 200$ liters of lemonade

Plan 4: Feasible

$2(50) + 1(20) = 120 \le 120$ liters of orange juice

$2(50) + 3(20) = 160 \le 200$ liters of lemonade

b. Plan 1: $9(40) + 12(20) = \$600$

Plan 2: $9(30) + 12(30) = \$630$

Plan 3: $(40, 50)$ was not feasible.

Plan 4: $9(50) + 12(20) = \$690$

c. From Part a, students know that $(40, 20)$, $(30, 30)$, and $(50, 20)$ are feasible combinations. They should reason that more profit will require moving horizontally out (increasing C values), moving vertically out (increasing L values), or both. Since $(50, 20)$ already uses all of the available orange juice, we cannot increase one without decreasing the other. Increasing C values may lead them to $(60, 0)$. Increasing L values could lead them to $(40, 40)$ (the maximum profit point). However, many other feasible points exist, for example, $(45, 30)$, $(31, 46)$, or $(34, 44)$.

8 **a. Plan 1:** Feasible

$5(2,000) + 4(3,000) = 22,000 > 20,000$ Democrats

$2(2,000) + 4(3,000) = 16,000 > 12,000$ Republicans

$4(2,000) + (3,000) = 11,000 > 8,000$ Independents

Plan 2: Feasible

$5(3,000) + 4(2,000) = 23,000 > 20,000$ Democrats

$2(3,000) + 4(2,000) = 14,000 > 12,000$ Republicans

$4(3,000) + (2,000) = 14,000 > 8,000$ Independents

Plan 3: Not Feasible

$5(2,000) + 4(2,000) = 18,000 < 20,000$ Democrats

$2(2,000) + 4(2,000) = 12,000 = 12,000$ Republicans

$4(2,000) + (2,000) = 10,000 > 8,000$ Independents

Plan 4: Feasible

$5(4,000) + 4(3,000) = 32,000 > 20,000$ Democrats

$2(4,000) + 4(3,000) = 20,000 > 12,000$ Republicans

$4(4,000) + (3,000) = 19,000 > 8,000$ Independents

b. i. Plan 1: $2,000 on radio and $3,000 on television: $5,000

Plan 2: $3,000 on radio and $2,000 on television: $5,000

Plan 4: $4,000 on radio and $3,000 on television: $7,000

ii. One example: If $1,100 is spent on radio advertising and $3,700 is spent on television advertising, the target audience will be reached for $4,800.

9 Refer back to Applications Task 6. Use h to represent the number of production runs of high school rings and c to represent the number of production runs of college rings.

 a. Write inequalities or rules that represent:

 i. the constraint on time available for molding rings.

 ii. the constraint on time available for engraving rings.

 iii. the constraint on time available for polishing rings.

 iv. the objective function.

 b. Use the constraint inequalities you wrote in Part a to create a graph showing the feasible region of the ring production planning problem. Label each segment of the feasible region boundary with the equation of that line.

 c. Find the production plan that will maximize profit for the Bestform Ring Company. Be prepared to explain how you know that your answer is correct.

10 Refer back to Applications Task 7. Use C to represent the number of batches of Carnival Juice and L to represent the number of batches of Lemon Punch to be mixed.

 a. Write inequalities or expressions that represent:

 i. the constraint on amount of orange juice available.

 ii. the constraint on amount of lemonade available.

 iii. the objective function.

 b. Use the constraint inequalities you wrote in Part a to create a graph showing the feasible region of the juice sale problem. Label each segment of the feasible region boundary with the equation of that line.

 c. Find the plan that will maximize profit for the Junior Class from drink sales. Be prepared to explain how you know that your answer is correct.

11 Refer back to Applications Task 8. Use r to represent the number of dollars spent on radio advertising and t to represent the number of dollars spent on television advertising.

 a. Write symbolic expressions that represent:

 i. the constraint on number of Democratic voters to be reached.

 ii. the constraint on number of Republican voters to be reached.

 iii. the constraint on number of Independent voters to be reached.

 iv. the objective function.

 b. Use the constraint inequalities you wrote in Part a to create a graph showing the feasible region of the campaign message problem. Label each segment of the boundary with the equation of that line.

 c. Use the results of your work on Parts a and b to find the plan that will minimize total advertising expense. Be prepared to explain how you know that your answer is correct.

9 **a.** **i.** $1.2h + 2c \leq 14$

    ii. $0.6h + 3c \leq 15$

    iii. $2h + 2c \leq 20$

    iv. $P = 500h + 525c$, where P is the profit.

b. The feasible region is unshaded.

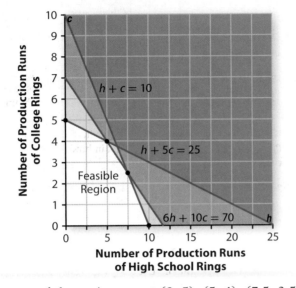

MATH NOTE Problems for which the variables must have integer values are called *integer programming* problems. It is not necessarily the case that the optimal integer solution will occur "nearby" the optimal vertex determined by the techniques described here. At this stage, be sure that students check the feasibility of any suggested solution and check that the profit is greater than that obtained at the other vertices.

c. The corners of the region are at (0, 5), (5, 4), (7.5, 2.5) and (10, 0). The profits for each pair are $2,625, $4,600, $5,062.50, and $5,000, respectively. The highest profit is at (7.5, 2.5). But since partial runs are not allowed, students might suggest checking nearby points such as (7, 3), (8, 2), and (8, 3). The only feasible pair is (8, 2) with a profit of $5,050. Therefore, the maximum profit seems likely to occur when 800 high school rings and 200 college rings are made.

10 **a.** **i.** $2C + L \leq 120$ liters of orange juice

    ii. $2C + 3L \leq 200$ liters of lemonade

    iii. $P = 9C + 12L$ dollars

b. The feasible region is unshaded.

c. The corners of the feasible region are (0, 66.67), (40, 40) and (60, 0). If 40 batches of each drink are made, then the profit will be maximized at $840, compared to $540 at (60, 0) and $792 at (0, 66).

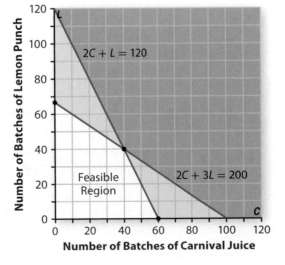

Unit 2

11

a. **i.** $5r + 4t \geq 20,000$

ii. $2r + 4t \geq 12,000$

iii. $4r + t \geq 8,000$

iv. $E = r + t$, where E represents the total advertising expense.

b. The feasible region is unshaded.

c. The corners of the unshaded region are at $(0, 8,000)$, $(1,090.91, 3,636.36)$, $(2,666.67, 1,666.67)$, and $(6,000, 0)$. To minimize advertising expenses, the candidate should spend \$2,667 on radio advertising and \$1,667 on television advertising for a total of \$4,334 in spending.

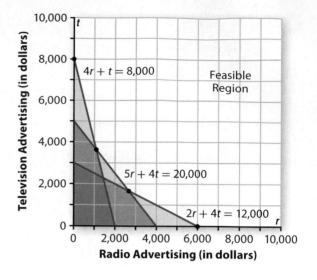

Teacher Notes

Sketch the feasible regions defined by the following inequalities. Use the given equations for profit P and cost C to find (x, y) combinations yielding maximum profit or minimum cost within the feasible regions.

a. $3y - 2x \geq 6$

$0 \leq x \leq 4$

$y \leq 5$

$P = 5x + 3y$

b. $x \leq 10$

$2x + y \geq 20$

$y \leq 14$

$C = 20x + 5y$

13 The director of the Backstage Dance Studio must plan for and operate many different classes, 7 days a week, at all hours of the day.

Each Saturday class fills up quickly. To plan the Saturday schedule, the director has to consider the following facts.

- It is difficult to find enough good teachers, so the studio can offer at most 8 tap classes and at most 5 jazz classes.

- Limited classroom space means the studio can offer at most 10 classes for the day.

- The studio makes profit of $150 from each tap class and $250 from each jazz class.

a. Write and graph the constraint inequalities.

b. The director wants to maximize profit. Write the objective function for this situation.

c. Find the schedule of classes that gives the maximum profit.

d. The director of Backstage Dance Studio really wants to promote interest in dance, so she also wants to maximize the number of children who can take classes. Each tap class can accommodate 10 students, and each jazz class can accommodate 15 students. Find the schedule that gives maximum student participation.

14 A city recreation department offers Saturday gymnastics classes for beginning and advanced students. Each beginner class enrolls 15 students, and each advanced class enrolls 10 students. Available teachers, space, and time lead to the following constraints.

- There can be at most 9 beginner classes and at most 6 advanced classes.

- The total number of classes can be at most 7.

- The number of beginner classes should be at most twice the number of advanced classes.

a. What are the variables in this situation?

b. Write algebraic inequalities giving the constraints on the variables.

c. The director wants as many children as possible to participate. Write the objective function for this situation.

12 **a.** The corners of the feasible region at the right are (0, 2), (0, 5), (4, 5), and $\left(4, 4\frac{2}{3}\right)$. The corresponding profits are 6, 15, 35, and 34. Therefore, maximum profit of $35 occurs at (4, 5).

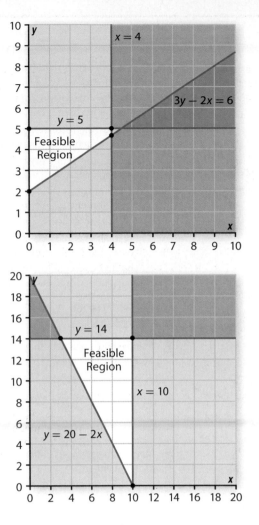

b. The corners of the feasible region at the right are (3, 14), (10, 14), and (10, 0). The corresponding costs are 130, 270, and 200. The minimum cost of $130 occurs at (3, 14).

13 **a.** The number of tap classes offered t and the number of jazz classes offered j are the two variables. $t \leq 8, j \leq 5, t + j \leq 10$

b. $P = 150t + 250j$, where P represents profit.

c. The maximum profit of $2,000 occurs when 5 tap classes and 5 jazz classes are offered.

d. $P = 10t + 15j$, where P represents participation number. Maximum participation (125 students) also occurs when 5 tap classes and 5 jazz classes are offered.

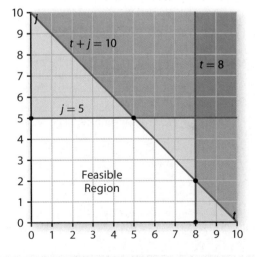

14 **a.** The number of beginner and advanced classes offered are the two variables. Let a stand for the number of advanced classes and let b stand for the number of beginner classes. Let P stand for the number of children participating.

b. $b \leq 9, a \leq 6, a + b \leq 7, b \leq 2a$

c. $P = 15b + 10a$

Unit 2

d. Graph the constraints and outline the feasible region for the situation.

e. Find the combination of beginner and advanced classes that will give the most children a chance to participate.

f. Suppose the recreation department director sets new constraints for the schedule of gymnastics classes.

- The same limits exist for teachers, so there can be at most 9 beginner and 6 advanced classes.

- The program should serve at least 150 students with 15 in each beginner class and 10 in each advanced class.

The new goal is to minimize the cost of the program. Each beginner class costs $500 to operate, and each advanced class costs $300. What combination of beginner and advanced classes should be offered to achieve the objective?

Connections

15 Identify the geometric shapes with interiors defined by these systems of inequalities.

a. $x \leq 1$, $y \leq 1$, $x \geq -1$, and $y \geq -1$

b. $-2x + y \leq 2$, $2x + y \geq -2$, $2x + y \leq 2$, and $-2x + y \geq -2$

c. $y \leq x$, $y \leq 1$, $y \geq x - 2$, and $y \geq 0$

d. $x + y \leq 1$, $x - y \leq 1$, $-x + y \geq 1$, and $x + y \geq 1$

16 Identify the geometric shapes with interiors defined by these systems of inequalities.

a. $x^2 + y^2 \leq 25$, $x \geq 0$, and $y \leq 0$

b. $x^2 + y^2 \leq 25$ and $y \geq x$

17 The linear programming problems in this lesson involve maximizing or minimizing a linear objective function in two variables. In previous work, you sought to find the maximum value of a quadratic function in one variable. For example, when Miguel Tejada hit a homerun in the 2005 major league baseball All-Star game, the function $h(t) = -16t^2 + 64t + 3$ might have been a reasonable model for the relationship between height of the ball (in feet) and time (in seconds) after it left his bat.

a. At what time was his hit at its maximum height and what was that height?

b. At what height did his bat hit the ball?

c. If the ball reached the outfield seats at a point 20 feet above the playing field, what was the approximate time it landed there?

d.

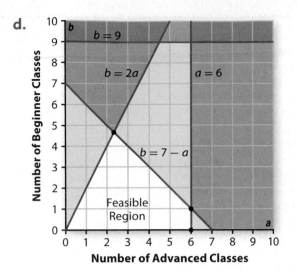

Number of Advanced Classes

e. The corners of the feasible region are $(6, 0)$, $(6, 1)$ and $\left(2\frac{1}{3}, 4\frac{2}{3}\right)$. The numbers of participants for each of these combinations are 60, 75, and $93\frac{2}{3}$. The maximum number of participants would occur at $\left(2\frac{1}{3}, 4\frac{2}{3}\right)$. But since fractions of a class do not make sense, students need to check the feasible lattice points near this vertex. Participation is maximized when there are 3 advanced classes and 4 beginner classes.

f. The corners of the feasible region are $(1.5, 9)$, $(6, 6)$, and $(6, 9)$. $C = 300a + 500b$. Since we cannot have 1.5 classes, we must choose 1 or 2 advanced classes with 9 beginning classes. Since $(1, 9)$ is not in the feasible region (does not satisfy $10a + 15b \geq 150$), we should check $(2, 9)$ for cost. The minimum cost of \$4,800 occurs when 6 classes are offered for each level.

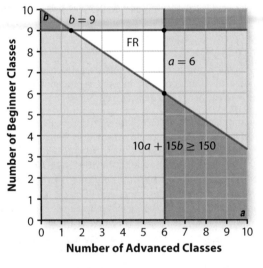

Number of Advanced Classes

Connections

15 **a.** Square

   b. Rhombus

   c. Parallelogram

   d. Ray

16 **a.** Quarter-circle (in Quadrant IV)

   b. Semicircle

> **NOTE** Solutions to Task 17 are on page T151.

Unit 2

18 Suppose that the following diagram shows the feasible region for a linear programming problem and that the objective function is $P = 2x + 3y$.

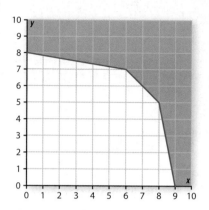

a. On a copy of the diagram, plot the line $2x + 3y = 6$. Explain why the objective function has the value 6 at each point on that line.

b. On the same diagram, plot the line $2x + 3y = 12$. What is the value of the objective function for each point on that line?

c. On the same diagram, plot the line $2x + 3y = 21$. What is the value of the objective function for each point on that line?

d. On the same diagram, plot the line $2x + 3y = 33$. What is the value of the objective function for each point on that line?

e. Explain how the pattern of results in Parts a–d suggests that the lines with equation $2x + 3y = k$ contain no feasible points if $k > 33$.

f. Explain how your work on Parts a–e illustrates the fact that the maximum objective function value in a linear programming problem like this will always occur at a "corner" of the feasible region.

19 The assembly and packaging of CP•I and CP•II video game systems is only one part of the business activity needed to develop a new product. The table below shows some other key tasks, their times to completion, and other tasks on which they depend. Use the information to find the *minimal time to completion* (earliest finish time) for the whole venture of designing and bringing to market products like the CP•I and CP•II video game systems.

Task	Time to Completion	Prerequisites
T1: Design of Game Concept	6 months	
T2: Market Research	3 months	T1
T3: Game Programming	3 months	T1
T4: Design of Production	2 months	T3
T5: Advance Advertising	4 months	T2
T6: Production and Testing of Initial Units	1 month	T4

LESSON 2 • Inequalities with Two Variables **151**

17 **a.** The ball reached a maximum height of 67 feet 2 seconds after it left the bat.

b. The bat hit the ball at a height of 3 feet as shown by the y-intercept.

c. $h(t) = 20$ for two values of t. $t = 0.3$ seconds or $t = 3.7$ seconds. Since the ball would reach the outfield on its way down, not up, it took 3.7 seconds for the ball to reach the outfield stands.

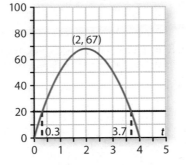

18 The graphs are shown at the right.

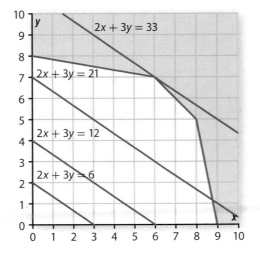

a. The objective function is $P = 2x + 3y$ and the coordinates of every point on the line will satisfy the equation $2x + 3y = 6$.

b. The objective function is $P = 2x + 3y$ and the coordinates of every point on the line will satisfy the equation $2x + 3y = 12$.

c. The objective function is $P = 2x + 3y$ and the coordinates of every point on the line will satisfy the equation $2x + 3y = 21$.

d. The objective function is $P = 2x + 3y$ and the coordinates of every point on the line will satisfy the equation $2x + 3y = 33$.

e. The lines representing feasible points with constant objective function value are all parallel. As the objective value increases, the y-intercepts of those lines rise higher and higher, with the line $2x + 3y = 33$ touching only one corner of the feasible set. When the value of k increases beyond 33, the line will be forced into the not-feasible region.

f. In any similar situation, one could imagine increasing the value of the objective function and thus the lines representing equal objective value points until one arrived at a line that was just at the edge (probably a corner) of the feasible region. In this case, the "escape" point is $(6, 7)$.

   If the objective function in this case had been $3x + 2y$, that "escape" from the feasible region would occur at the point $(8, 5)$ and the maximum value of the objective function there would be $3(8) + 2(5) = 34$.

19 The minimal time to completion for the video game system is 13 months since certain tasks can occur concurrently. The digraph below shows that the critical path is $S\text{-}T_1\text{-}T_2\text{-}T_5\text{-}F$.

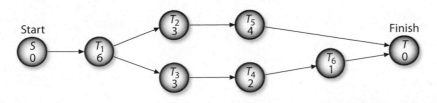

Unit 2

Reflections

20 How do the solutions of the following two inequalities differ?

$$2x + y \leq 6 \qquad\qquad 2x + y < 6$$

How could you show these differences in sketches of their graphs?

21 Solving linear programming problems includes finding the boundary of the feasible region. Describe at least three different ways to find the points where the boundary lines defining the region intersect.

22 How are the goals and constraints of linear programming problems similar to other optimization problems like finding a minimal spanning tree in a graph, analyzing a PERT chart, or finding selling prices that maximize profit from sale of a product?

23 Look back at your solutions of the linear programming problems in this lesson.

a. What kind of values made sense for the variables in these problems?

b. How would you proceed if you determine the optimal solution to a linear programming problem occurs at a point that has noninteger coordinates?

24 Why do you think linear programming has the word *linear* in its name? Do you think the process would work to find optimal solutions if any of the constraints or the objective function were not linear? Why or why not?

25 Realistic linear programming problems in business and engineering usually involve many variables and constraints. Why do you think that linear programming was not used in business and engineering until fairly recently?

Extensions

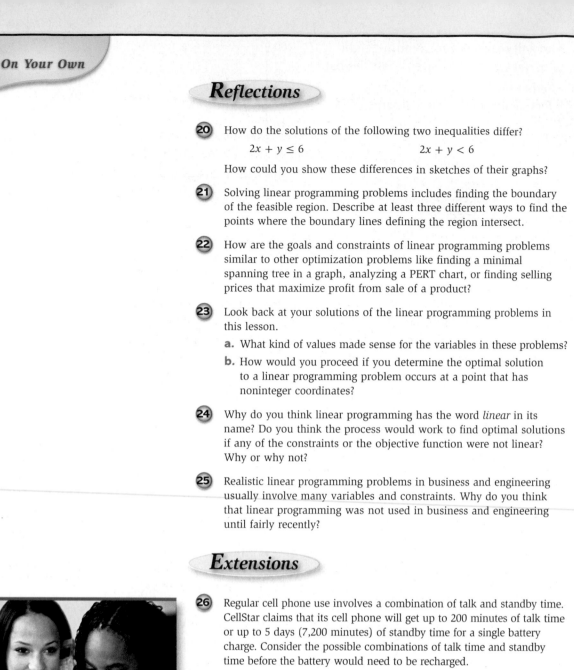

26 Regular cell phone use involves a combination of talk and standby time. CellStar claims that its cell phone will get up to 200 minutes of talk time or up to 5 days (7,200 minutes) of standby time for a single battery charge. Consider the possible combinations of talk time and standby time before the battery would need to be recharged.

a. Write an inequality whose solution will give the (t, s) combinations that will not completely drain a battery that begins use fully charged.

b. Draw a graph that uses appropriate boundary lines to show the region of the coordinate plane that contains all points with coordinates (t, s) that satisfy the inequality in Part a.

c. Solve the inequality from Part a for s to show how many minutes of standby time remain after t minutes of talk time before the battery will need to be recharged.

Reflections

20 Solutions to the first inequality include points on the boundary line with equation $2x + y = 6$, and solutions to the second inequality do not include those points. The difference is, by convention, shown by making the boundary line on the first graph a solid line and on the second graph a dashed line.

21 Students will likely suggest graphically finding points of intersection with or without technology or solving linear systems of equations using substitution or elimination. Other methods less likely to be suggested are using tables to find intersection points or using matrices.

22 When finding a minimal spanning tree in a graph, the goal is to minimize some variable (typically cost or distance) within the constraint of reaching every vertex of the graph. When analyzing a PERT chart, the goal is to minimize the time needed to complete the project within the constraint that certain tasks must be completed before others can begin. When finding selling prices that maximize profit from sale of a product, the goal is to maximize profit within the constraint of buyer demand.

23 **a.** Positive integer values make sense for most of the linear programming problems in this lesson.

b. Students might suggest that if the optimal solution occurs at a point with noninteger coordinates, consider the points immediately surrounding it with integer coordinates, checking for feasibility and comparing the value of the objective function for the feasible points.

> **MATH NOTE** Problems for which the variables must have integer values are called *integer programming* problems. It is not necessarily the case that the optimal integer solution will occur "nearby" the optimal vertex determined by the techniques described in this lesson.

24 The word *linear* is in the name of linear programming because it involves optimizing a linear objective function within a system of linear constraints. It is the fact (for maximization problems) that increases in the value of either variable generally lead to increases in the value of the objective function that force the optimal solution to occur on the boundary. It is the linearity of both the objective function and the segments of the boundary that force the optimal solution to an endpoint of one of the boundary segments. Therefore, there is no guarantee of an optimal solution at a corner point of a feasible region formed by nonlinear constraints nor for a nonlinear objective function. For example, consider maximizing the objective function $P = x + y$ over the feasible region formed by the constraints $y \geq x$ and $y \leq 4x - x^2$. The "corners" of the feasible region are $(0, 0)$ and $(3, 3)$. The objective function has a greater value at the feasible point $(2.5, 3.75)$.

> **ASSESSMENT NOTE** One of the projects in the Unit 2 *Unit Resource Masters* asks students to consider the founders of the Simplex Method and to look at how technology actually solves linear programming problems.

25 Except in the case of simple situations like those examined in this lesson, computers are necessary for most linear programming problems. Only in the past 40–50 years have computers been widely available.

> **NOTE** Solutions to Extensions Task 26 are on page T153.

Unit 2

27 Graph the solution of $\frac{x}{y} > 1$.

28 Look back at the mall space leasing problem in the Check Your Understanding on page 136. Suppose a new survey of consumer interests indicates that each square foot of book-selling space will generate an average of $65 per month in sales and each square foot of music- and video-selling space will generate an average of $95 per month in sales. What space allocations would you recommend to the store owners in this case? Explain your reasoning.

29 Refer back to Extensions Task 26. Suppose that Jovan has a CellStar phone and is planning to take a bus from Durham, North Carolina, to San Antonio, Texas, to visit his aunt. The trip is scheduled to take 1 day, 8 hours, and 10 minutes. Jovan will most likely not be able to recharge the phone during the long bus trip and would like to make sure that the phone maintains a charge during the entire trip.

   a. Jovan decides that the solution to the following system will give the number of minutes t of talk time and s of standby time for which the cell phone will maintain a charge for the whole trip.

   $$\begin{cases} \frac{t}{200} + \frac{s}{7,200} < 1 \\ t + s > 1,930 \end{cases}$$

   Do you agree with Jovan? Why or why not?

   b. Graph the solution to the system of inequalities from Part a.

   c. What number of talk-time minutes must Jovan stay below to ensure a charged cell phone for the entire trip?

30 Suppose the manufacturing company that supplies a chain of Packaging Plus stores receives a rush order for 290 boxes. It needs to fill the order in 8 hours or less.

   • The factory has a machine that can produce 30 boxes per hour and costs $15 per hour to operate.

   • The factory can also use two student workers from less urgent tasks. Together, those students can make 25 boxes per hour at a cost of $10 per hour.

   What combination of machine and student work times will meet the deadline with least total cost?

31 The Dutch Flower Bulb Company bags a variety of mixtures of bulbs. There are two customer favorites. The Moonbeam mixture contains 30 daffodils and 50 jonquils, and the Sunshine mixture contains 60 daffodils and 20 jonquils.

   The company imports 300,000 daffodils and 260,000 jonquils for sale each year. The profit for each bag of Moonbeam mixture is $2.30. The profit for each bag of Sunshine mixture is $2.50. The problem is deciding how many bags of each mixture the company should make in order to maximize profit without exceeding available supplies.

   Explore how to use the inequality graphing capability of a CAS like that in *CPMP-Tools* to help find the combination of Moonbeam and Sunshine bags that give maximum profit.

Extensions

26 a. $\frac{t}{200} + \frac{s}{7,200} < 1$ (Equivalently, $36t + s < 7,200$.)

b.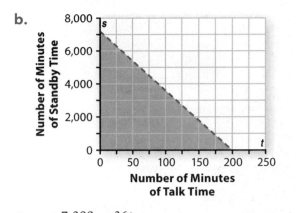

c. $s < 7,200 - 36t$

INSTRUCTIONAL NOTE
It may be helpful to suggest to students to first consider specific values of t and s when thinking about this task.

27 $\frac{x}{y} > 1$ is equivalent to $x > y$ when y is positive and $\frac{x}{y} > 1$ is equivalent to $x < y$ when y is negative.

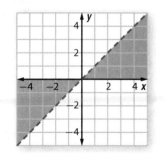

28 The maximum sales solution of just over $814,000 occurs when the owners allocate the maximum amount of space to music and videos, approximately 8,571 square feet, and none to books.

Students should locate feasible points near the y-axis or (0, 8,500) as optimal sales points. They should also discuss that this might not be a wise business decision, particularly if the owners want to draw customers who will buy both music/video items and books.

29 a. Jovan is correct. The first inequality in the system comes from Extensions Task 26 and represents the limitations on the life of the battery. The second inequality represents the new constraint that the battery retains a charge for more than 1,930 minutes.

NOTE Alternatively, the question could be viewed as finding the number of minutes of talk time t such that the number of standby minutes s remaining in the life of the battery exceeds the number of standby minutes needed for the remainder of the trip: $7,200 - 36t > 1,930 - t$.

b.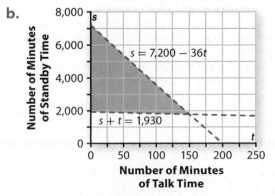

c. To keep the charge, Jovan must keep his talk time below 150 minutes.

NOTE Solutions to Task 30 and Task 31 are on page T154.

Unit 2

32 When architects design buildings, they have to consider many factors. Construction and operating costs, strength, ease of use, and style of design are only a few.

For example, when architects designing a large city office building began their design work, they had to deal with the following conditions.

- The front of the building had to use windows of traditional style to complement the surrounding historic buildings. There had to be at least 80 traditional windows on the front of the building. Those windows each had an area of 20 square feet and glass that was 0.25 inches thick.

- The back of the building was to use modern-style windows that had an area of 35 square feet and glass that was 0.5 inches thick. There had to be at least 60 of those windows.

- In order to provide as much natural lighting for the building as possible, the design had to use at least 150 windows.

a. One way to rate the possible designs is by how well they insulate the building from loss of heat in the winter. The heat loss R in BTU's (British Thermal Units) per hour through a glass window can be estimated by $R = \frac{5.8A}{t}$, where A stands for the area of the window in square feet and t stands for the thickness of the glass in inches.

  i. What are the heat flow rates of the traditional windows and the modern windows?

  ii. Without graphing the number of window constraints, find the combination of traditional and modern windows that will minimize heat flow from the building.

b. Minimizing construction cost is another consideration. The traditional windows cost $200 apiece, and the modern windows cost $250 each. Without graphing the number of window constraints, find the combination of traditional and modern windows that will minimize the total cost of the windows.

30 If m represents the machine work time (in hours) and s represents the students' work time (in hours), then the constraints are $m \leq 8$, $s \leq 8$, and $30m + 25s \geq 290$. The coordinates of vertices of the feasible region are $(3, 8)$, $(8, 8)$, and $(8, 2)$. The minimum cost $(15m + 10s)$ of \$125 occurs when the machine is operated for 3 hours and the students work for 8 hours.

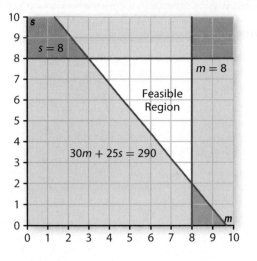

31 Let x be the number of Moonbeam mixtures and let y be the number of Sunshine mixtures. The constraint inequalities are $30x + 60y \leq 300{,}000$ for daffodils and $50x + 20y \leq 260{,}000$ for jonquils. Both are graphed at the right and the feasible region is shaded. The corners of the feasible region are $(0, 5{,}000)$, $(4{,}000, 3{,}000)$, and $(5{,}200, 0)$. $P = 2.3x + 2.5y$, where P represents profit. The maximum profit of \$16,700 occurs when 4,000 Moonbeam mixtures and 3,000 Sunshine mixtures are made.

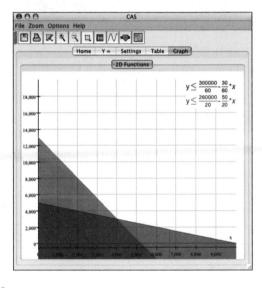

INSTRUCTIONAL NOTE
Students may find Task 31 difficult because they tend to assign variables to the bulbs rather than the mixtures. Suggest that they read all parts of the question before assigning variables.

32 a. i. Traditional windows: $R = \dfrac{5.8(20)}{(0.25)} = 464$ BTU

Modern windows: $R = \dfrac{5.8(35)}{0.5} = 406$ BTU

ii. To minimize heat flow, we want the minimum number of traditional windows. This is 80 traditional windows. Since we also want to minimize the total number of windows, we want 150 windows. This means that 70 modern windows and 80 traditional windows would minimize the heat flow.

b. To minimize the cost for windows, we want only 150 windows. The most costly windows are the modern windows, so use only 60 modern windows. This means that 60 modern windows and 90 traditional windows would minimize the cost for windows.

Unit 2

c. Now consider the constraints graphically.

    i. Write the constraint inequalities that match this situation and identify the feasible region.

    ii. Write the objective functions for minimizing heat flow and for minimizing construction costs. Find the combination of traditional and modern windows that will minimize heat flow and total cost of the windows.

    iii. Compare your responses to the minimization questions in Parts a and b to your region and objective functions. Adjust your solutions if necessary.

33 Graph the feasible regions for the following sets of inequalities in the first quadrant. A graphing calculator or CAS may be helpful in finding the "corner points" of the region.

a. $\begin{cases} y \le 10 - 3x \\ y \le x^2 - 4x + 5 \end{cases}$
          b. $\begin{cases} y \le \dfrac{1}{x^2} \\ x + y \le 4 \end{cases}$

c. $\begin{cases} y \ge 10(0.5^x) \\ y \ge 8 - 2x \end{cases}$

Review

34 In the diagram below, $\ell \parallel m$ and p bisects $\angle ABC$. Find the measure of each numbered angle.

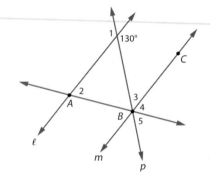

35 Rewrite each expression in equivalent factored form.

a. $x^2 - 16$
          b. $x^2 + 10x + 25$

c. $x^2 + 6x - 40$
          d. $2x^2 + 7x + 3$

c. i. Let t represent the number of traditional windows and let m represent the number of modern windows. Traditional windows are on the horizontal axis and modern windows are on the vertical axis.

$t \geq 80$, $m \geq 60$,
$t + m \geq 150$

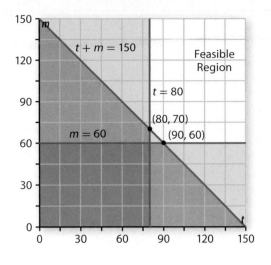

ii. $R = 464t + 406m$ is the objective function for heat flow and $C = 200t + 250m$ is the objective function for cost. Heat flow is minimized at 65,540 BTUs with 80 traditional and 70 modern windows. The minimum cost for windows is $33,000 with 90 traditional and 60 modern windows.

iii. Students should correct their answers if needed.

33 a.

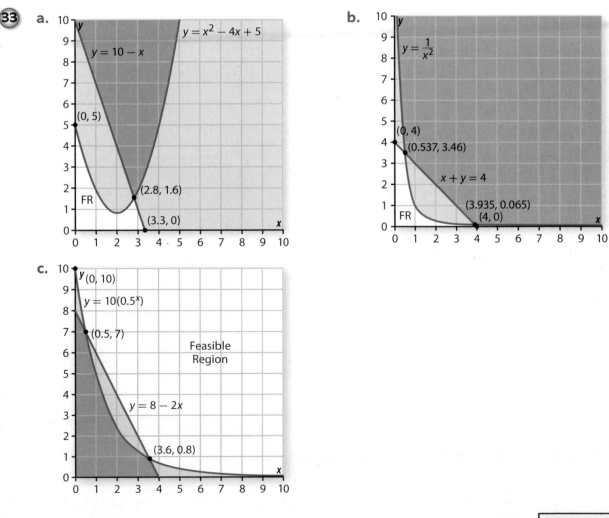

NOTE Solutions to Task 34 and Task 35 are on page T156.

36 Consider quadrilateral *ABCD* shown in the diagram below. The scale on both axes is 1.

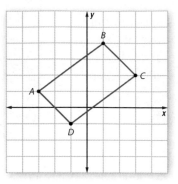

a. Explain why quadrilateral *ABCD* is *not* a rectangle.

b. Find the area of quadrilateral *ABCD*.

c. Quadrilateral *A'B'C'D'* is the image of quadrilateral *ABCD* under a size transformation of magnitude 2 centered at the origin. What is the coordinate matrix of quadrilateral *A'B'C'D'*?

d. How are the angle measures of quadrilateral *A'B'C'D'* related to the angle measures of quadrilateral *ABCD*?

e. Find the area of quadrilateral *A'B'C'D'*.

37 Cesar entered a summer reading challenge at his local library. A winner would be determined as the child who read the most pages during the summer. Each week, Cesar reported the minutes he had spent reading. The librarian told him his ranking and his percentile. After the fourth week, Cesar was ranked 52nd and was at the 94th percentile. How many people were entered in the summer reading contest?

38 Determine if each pair of algebraic expressions are equivalent. If they are equivalent, provide algebraic reasoning to prove your claim. If they are not equivalent, provide a counterexample.

a. $(x + b)^2$ and $x^2 + b^2$

b. $8x - 2(x - 4)^2$ and $32 - 2x^2$

c. $\dfrac{6x + 4}{4}$ and $1.5x + 1$

39 Rewrite each expression with the smallest possible integer under the radical sign.

a. $\sqrt{84}$ **b.** $\sqrt{160}$

c. $25\sqrt{18}$ **d.** $(3\sqrt{5})^2$

e. $\sqrt{\dfrac{125}{9}}$ **f.** $\sqrt{20a^2}, \ a \geq 0$

Review

Just in Time

34 $m\angle 1 = 130°$
$m\angle 2 = 80°$
$m\angle 3 = 50°$
$m\angle 4 = 80°$
$m\angle 5 = 50°$

35 **a.** $(x + 4)(x - 4)$ **b.** $(x + 5)^2$
     c. $(x + 10)(x - 4)$ **d.** $(2x + 1)(x + 3)$

Just in Time

36 **a.** The slope of $\overline{AD}$ is -1, and the slope of $\overline{AB}$ is $\frac{3}{4}$. Since $(-1)\left(\frac{3}{4}\right) \neq -1$, $\overline{AD}$ is not perpendicular to $\overline{AB}$. Therefore, $m\angle A \neq 90°$. Thus, quadrilateral *ABCD* is not a rectangle.

b. To facilitate finding the area of quadrilateral *ABCD*, students might consider a larger rectangle circumscribing *ABCD*.

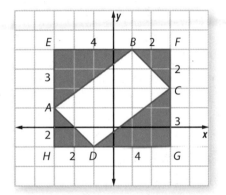

Then $Area(ABCD) = Area(EFGH) - (Area(AEB) + Area(BFC) + Area(CGD) + Area(AHD)) = 30 - (6 + 2 + 6 + 2) = 14$ square units.

c. The size transformation of magnitude 2 centered at the origin takes $(x, y) \rightarrow (2x, 2y)$. Therefore, the coordinates of $A'B'C'D'$ are $A'(-6, 2)$, $B'(2, 8)$, $C'(6, 4)$, and $D'(-2, -2)$.

d. The angle measures remain the same.

e. $Area(A'B'C'D') = 4 \cdot Area(ABCD) = 4(14) = 56$ square units

37 Cesar was at the 94th percentile. This means that 51 readers were ranked higher, in the top 6%. $\frac{51}{0.06} = 850$, so there were 850 readers in the contest.

38 **a.** Not equivalent; for example, $(2 + 3)^2 \neq 2^2 + 3^2$ since $25 \neq 13$.

b. Not equivalent; for example, $8(5) - 2(5 - 4)^2 \neq 32 - 2(5)^2$.

c. Equivalent; using the definition of fraction addition, $\frac{6x + 4}{4} = \frac{6x}{4} + \frac{4}{4} = 1.5x + 1$.

39 **a.** $2\sqrt{21}$ **b.** $4\sqrt{10}$
     c. $75\sqrt{2}$ **d.** 45
     e. $\frac{5}{3}\sqrt{5}$ **f.** $2a\sqrt{5}$

40 For each triangle below, find the measures of the remaining side(s) and angle(s).

a.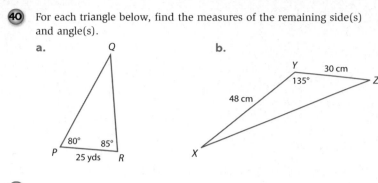

b.

41 Consider the following two sets of data.

- the daily low temperature in International Falls, Minnesota, each day during the month of February

- the temperature of your math classroom at noon each day during the same month

a. Which set of data would you expect to have the greater mean? Explain your reasoning.

b. Which set of data would you expect to have the greater standard deviation? Explain your reasoning.

Just in Time

40
  a. $m\angle Q = 15°$

  $PQ = \dfrac{25 \sin 85°}{\sin 15°} \approx 96$ yards

  $RQ = \dfrac{25 \sin 80°}{\sin 15°} \approx 95$ yards

  b. $XZ = \sqrt{48^2 + 30^2 - 2(48)(30) \cos 135°} \approx 72.4$ cm

  $m\angle X = \sin^{-1}\left(\dfrac{30 \sin 135°}{72.4}\right) = 17°$

  $m\angle Z = \sin^{-1}\left(\dfrac{48 \sin 135°}{72.4}\right) = 28°$

41
  a. Math class temperature should have the greater mean since the classroom temperature will be higher than the daily low temperature in International Falls for the month of February.

  b. The daily low temperature in International Falls for the month of February should have the greater standard deviation since it will most likely vary more than the daily classroom temperature.

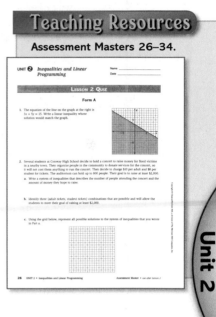

Teaching Resources

Assessment Masters 26–34.

Looking Back

The lessons in this unit involved situations in which important relationships among variables could be expressed by inequalities in one and two variables. In Lesson 1, you combined numeric, graphic, and algebraic methods for representing quadratic functions and solving quadratic equations in order to solve inequalities in one variable. You learned how to use inequality symbols, number line graphs, and interval notation to describe the solutions of those inequalities. In Lesson 2, you used graphs to identify the solutions for linear inequalities and systems of inequalities in two variables. You applied that knowledge to develop graphic and algebraic strategies for solving linear programming problems, optimizing a linear objective function given several linear constraints on the variables.

The tasks in this final lesson will help you review and organize your knowledge about solving inequalities and linear programming problems.

1. For each inequality below:

   - make a sketch to show how the functions and constants in the inequality are related.
   - use algebraic reasoning to locate the key intercepts and points of intersection.
   - combine what you learn from your sketch and algebraic reasoning to solve the inequality.
   - describe each solution set using symbols, a number line graph, and interval notation.

   a. $8 - x^2 \leq 6$ **b.** $x^2 + 4x + 4 < -3x - 8$

   c. $7 + x > 2 + 3x - x^2$ **d.** $3 - x^2 \geq x^2 + 5$

2. Write inequalities that express the same information as the interval notation in these situations.

   a. $[3, 6]$ **b.** $(-1, 4)$

   c. $(-7, 1.5]$ **d.** $(-\infty, -2) \cup [7, \infty)$

Looking Back

1 **a.**

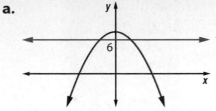

Solve: $8 - x^2 = 6$
$x^2 = 2$ when $x = \pm\sqrt{2}$.

Solution:
$x \leq -\sqrt{2}$ or $x \geq \sqrt{2}$
$(-\infty, -\sqrt{2}] \cup [\sqrt{2}, \infty)$

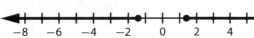

b.

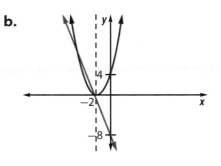

The graphs could intersect in 2, 1, or no points.

$x^2 + 7x + 12 = 0$ when
$x = -3$ or $x = -4$.

Solution: The graph of
$y = x^2 + 4x + 4$ is below the
graph of $y = -3x - 8$ for
$-4 < x < -3$; $(-4, -3)$

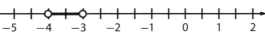

c.

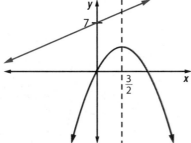

The graphs could intersect in 2, 1, or no points.

$-x^2 + 2x - 5 = 0$ when
$x = \dfrac{-2 \pm \sqrt{4 - 4(-1)(-5)}}{2(-1)} =$
$\dfrac{-2 \pm \sqrt{-16}}{2}$, which are not
real solutions.

Solution: The graph of the line is
above the graph of the parabola, so
$-\infty < x < \infty$; $(-\infty, \infty)$.

d.

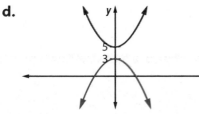

$3 - x^2 = x^2 + 5$ has no real solution
since $x^2 = -2$ has no solutions.

Since the graph of $y = 3 - x^2$ is
below the graph of $y = x^2 + 5$, the
inequality $3 - x^2 \geq x^2 + 5$ has no
solution ($\varnothing$).

INSTRUCTIONAL NOTE
The sketch at the left shows
the two intersection points.
Student sketches may show
1 or no points of intersection
until they solve the quadratic
equation.

Unit 2

NOTE Solutions to Task 2
are on page T159.

③ For each condition described below, write an inequality involving one linear function and one quadratic function that satisfies the condition. Then draw a graph that illustrates the relationship between the two functions.

   a. The inequality has no solutions.

   b. All real numbers are solutions of the inequality.

   c. Exactly one value satisfies the inequality.

④ Suppose that Lee wants to buy macadamia nuts and banana chips for an after-school snack. Both are available in the bulk foods section of a local grocery store. Macadamia nuts cost $8 per pound, and banana chips cost $5 per pound.

   a. If Lee has $4 to spend, write an inequality whose solution set gives the (*pounds of macadamia nuts m, pounds of banana chips b*) combinations that Lee can buy.

   b. Draw a graph that uses shading to show the region of the coordinate plane that contains all points (m, b) that satisfy the inequality.

⑤ The graphs representing the system of linear equations
$$\begin{cases} 3x + 5y = 12 \\ 2x - y = 10 \end{cases}$$
are shown to the right. How could you replace each of the "=" symbols in the two equations with a "<" or ">" symbol so that the solution of the resulting system of inequalities would be:

   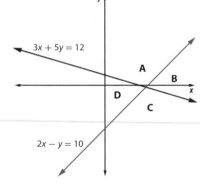

   • region A   • region B
   • region C   • region D

⑥ A small sporting goods manufacturer produces skateboards and in-line skates. Its dealers demand at least 30 skateboards per day and 20 pairs of in-line skates per day. The factory can make at most 60 skateboards and 40 pairs of in-line skates per day.

   a. Write inequalities expressing the given constraints on daily skateboard and in-line skate manufacturing.

   b. Graph the feasible region. Label each segment of the boundary of the region with the equation of that line.

   c. How many combinations of numbers of in-line skates and skateboards are possible?

   d. Suppose the total number of skateboards and pairs of in-line skates cannot exceed 90.

   i. What inequality expresses this constraint?

   ii. Show this new constraint on your graph.

2 Responses may vary. One example is provided for each part.

a. $3 \leq x \leq 6$ **b.** $-1 < x < 4$

c. $-7 < x \leq 1.5$ **d.** $x < -2$ or $x \geq 7$

3 Responses may vary. One example is provided for each part.

a. $x^2 - 3x + 2 \leq 2x - 7$

b. $x^2 - 3x + 2 \geq 2x - 7$

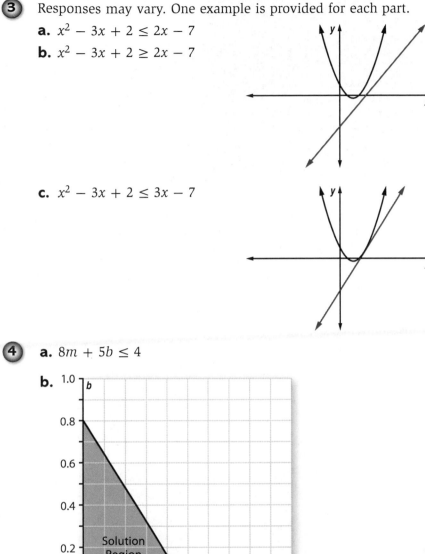

c. $x^2 - 3x + 2 \leq 3x - 7$

4 **a.** $8m + 5b \leq 4$

b.

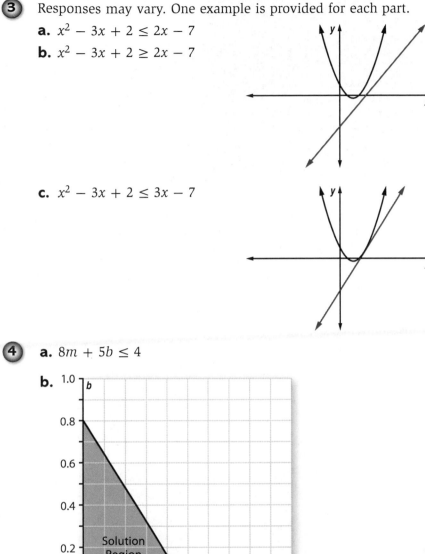

5 Region A $\begin{cases} 3x + 5y > 12 \\ 2x - y > 10 \end{cases}$ Region B $\begin{cases} 3x + 5y > 12 \\ 2x - y < 10 \end{cases}$

Region C $\begin{cases} 3x + 5y < 12 \\ 2x - y < 10 \end{cases}$ Region D $\begin{cases} 3x + 5y < 12 \\ 2x - y > 10 \end{cases}$

6 **a.** $s \geq 30, i \geq 20, s \leq 60, i \leq 40$

b.

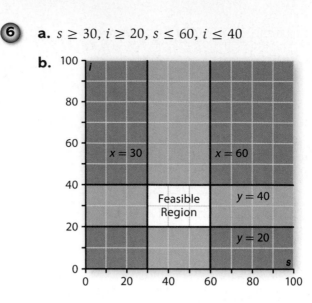

c. There are 651 possible combinations of production numbers for skateboards and in-line skates. There are 31 numbers of skateboards (from 30 to 60) possibly produced and 21 pairs of in-line skates possibly produced. $(31 \cdot 21) = 651$.

d. **i.** $s + i \leq 90$

   ii. The new constraint is graphed along with the old constraints on the graph below.

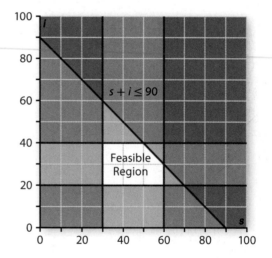

Teacher Notes

e. Find coordinates of the corners for the new feasible region.

f. Suppose the profit on each skateboard is $12 and on each pair of in-line skates is $18. Write the profit function.

g. How many of each product should the company manufacture to get maximum profit?

Summarize
the Mathematics

In this unit, you investigated problems that could be solved by writing and reasoning with inequalities in one or in two variables. In some cases, the problem could be represented with a single inequality. In other cases, as in linear programming problems, representation of the problem required a system of constraint inequalities and an objective function.

a Consider the two functions $f(x)$ and $g(x)$. Describe a general strategy for finding values of x for which each of the following is true.

   i. $f(x) = g(x)$ **ii.** $f(x) < g(x)$ **iii.** $f(x) > g(x)$

b The inequality $x^2 - 5x - 24 > 0$ is true for values of x that are less than -3 or greater than 8. Describe these values of x using:

   i. inequality symbols   **ii.** a graph on a   **iii.** interval notation
                          number line

c In what ways is solving an inequality like $x^2 - 5x - 24 > 0$ different from finding the solution set for one like $y > x^2 - 5x - 24$? How is it the same?

d What steps are involved in graphing the solutions of an inequality like $3x + 5y \leq 10$?

e Describe the roles played by the following elements of linear programming problems.

   i. constraints   **ii.** feasible region   **iii.** objective function

f In a linear programming problem, where in the feasible region will the objective function have its optimum (maximum or minimum) value? Why is that true?

Be prepared to explain your ideas and methods to the class.

✓Check Your Understanding

Write, in outline form, a summary of the important mathematical concepts and methods developed in this unit. Organize your summary so that it can be used as a quick reference in future units and courses.

e. The corners of this new feasible region are at (30, 20), (30, 40), (50, 40), (60, 30), and (60, 20).

f. $P = 12s + 18i$, where P is the profit.

g. The maximum profit is $1,320 when the company makes 50 skateboards and 40 in-line skates.

Summarize
the Mathematics

a **i.** General strategies are: (1) Solve algebraically by operating on both sides to try to isolate x, (2) graph and find the x-coordinate of any point(s) of intersection, and (3) locate values of x in a table of values for which both functions have the same value.

ii. Solve $f(x) = g(x)$ to find the x-coordinate of any point(s) of intersection, then reason about the graphs of the two functions to find the intervals where the graph of $f(x)$ is below that of $g(x)$.

iii. Solve $f(x) = g(x)$ to find the x-coordinate of any point(s) of intersection, then reason about the graphs of the two functions to find the intervals where the graph of $f(x)$ is above that of $g(x)$.

b **i.** $x < -3$ or $x > 8$

ii.

$$\begin{array}{ccccccccc} -4 & -2 & 0 & 2 & 4 & 6 & 8 & 10 & 12 \end{array}$$

iii. $(-\infty, -3) \cup (8, \infty)$

c The first inequality has one variable whose solution can be represented in interval notation or on a number line graph. The second inequality has two variables, and its solution is best shown as a shaded region on the coordinate plane. Both inequalities have an infinite number of solutions, which can be determined from a graph of the function $y = x^2 - 5x - 24$.

d First, the line $3x + 5y = 10$ is graphed with a solid line. Graph $3x + 5y = 10$ using x- and y-intercepts. Then, a test point not on the line (the origin works well) is tested to see if the inequality holds for that point. If the inequality holds, the half-plane on that side of the line displays the set of solutions to the inequality. If the inequality does not hold, then the other half-plane displays the set of solutions to the inequality.

e **i.** The constraints of a linear programming problem place limits on values for the variables that can be considered as potential optimum solutions of the problem.

ii. The feasible region is the set of all points that satisfies the constraints of the problem.

iii. The objective function states the relation between the variables and the goal quantity. Usually, the problem involves maximizing or minimizing this quantity.

Student Masters 37–38.

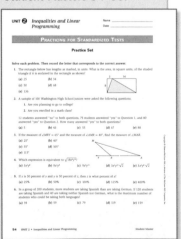

Assessment Masters 39–53.

Student Masters 54–55.

✓ Check Your Understanding

You may wish to have students use the Teaching Master, *Inequalities and Linear Programming* Unit Summary, to help them organize the information. Above all, this should be something that is useful to the individual student.

Practicing for Standardized Tests

Each Practicing for Standardized Tests master presents 10 questions in the multiple-choice format of test items similar to how they often appear in standardized tests. Answers are provided below.

Answers to Practice Set 2

1. (d)	**2.** (d)	**3.** (a)	**4.** (e)	**5.** (e)
6. (c)	**7.** (b)	**8.** (b)	**9.** (c)	**10.** (b)

Teacher Notes

UNIT 3

SIMILARITY AND CONGRUENCE

Similarity and congruence are key related ideas in design, manufacturing, and repair of products, from cell phones and MP3 players to automobiles and space shuttles. When individual components that comprise these products are manufactured to design plans and specifications, the components are similar in shape to the design images and congruent to each other, whether manufactured at the same or different plants. Because individual components are congruent, they can be easily interchanged in assembly line production or in repair work.

In this unit, you will develop understanding and skill in the use of similarity and congruence relations to solve problems involving shape and size. In each of the two lessons, you will have many opportunities to continue to develop skill and confidence in reasoning deductively using both synthetic and coordinate methods.

Lessons

① Reasoning about Similar Triangles

Derive sufficient conditions for similarity of triangles using the Law of Cosines and the Law of Sines. Use similarity conditions to prove properties of triangles and size transformations, and use those conditions and properties to solve applied problems.

② Reasoning about Congruent Triangles

Derive sufficient conditions for congruence of triangles. Use congruence conditions to prove properties of triangles and congruence-preserving transformations, to establish sufficient conditions for quadrilaterals to be (special) parallelograms and for special parallelograms to be congruent, and to solve applied problems.

Unit 3

SIMILARITY AND CONGRUENCE

Unit Overview

This unit focuses on two key related ideas in geometry—similarity (same shape) and congruence (same shape and size). The unit builds on prior experiences students have had with these ideas at van Hiele Levels 0–2, and somewhat at Level 3.

van Hiele Levels of Geometric Thinking

Level 0 Visualization (including recognizing, drawing, constructing, manipulating, and describing geometric figures)

Level 1 Analysis (including classifying geometric figures and recognizing how figures and parts of figures are related)

Level 2 Informal Deduction (including reasoning with definitions, analyzing and completing arguments, finding counterexamples, and applying properties of figures and relationships in problem situations)

Level 3 Deduction (including identifying given and to-prove information, understanding the distinction between a statement and its converse, understanding the role of postulates, theorems, and proof and constructing simple deductive arguments)

Level 4 Rigor (involving work in a variety of axiomatic systems, including non-Euclidean geometries)

In the Course 1 *Patterns in Shape* unit, the primary emphasis was on geometric thinking about triangles, quadrilaterals, and other polygons at Levels 0–2 with opportunities for beginning the transition to Level 3 in the context of triangle congruence conditions. The introduction of coordinates and trigonometry in Course 2 supported more formal deductive arguments by drawing on students' algebraic reasoning skills. Congruence was revisited in terms of rigid transformations. Similarity was introduced in terms of size transformations.

In Unit 1 of Course 3, *Reasoning and Proof*, students began to develop an understanding of formal mathematical reasoning strategies and principles of logic that support sound arguments. In that unit, students analyzed proofs presented in differing forms and prepared arguments to support conjectures. This unit builds on students' understanding of the characteristics of a sound argument and their understanding of relationships between pairs of angles formed by two intersecting lines or by two parallel lines cut by a transversal. It has been designed to support students' geometric thinking at Level 3 and the transition to Level 4.

The Law of Cosines, developed in Course 2 Unit 7, *Trigonometric Methods*, and proven in Course 3 Unit 1, *Reasoning and Proof*, is an especially powerful tool for use in reasoning about geometric situations involving triangles. This power is demonstrated in Lesson 1, where all the triangle similarity theorems are derived by examining expressions resulting from the Law of Cosines or the Law of Sines. In Lesson 2, the congruence theorems for triangles are easily and efficiently established by applying the corresponding similarity theorems when the scale factor is 1. Thus, congruent triangles are similar triangles with scale factor 1.

In Lesson 2, students use congruence conditions for triangles to investigate, justify, and apply properties of the incenter, circumcenter, and centroid of a triangle. They also use congruence conditions to support their reasoning about properties of special quadrilaterals and about necessary and sufficient conditions for a quadrilateral to be a parallelogram. Comparisons of synthetic and coordinate (analytic) proofs underscore the connectedness of mathematics and encourage flexibility in approach. Students also determine sufficient conditions for parallelograms to be congruent. Finally, they revisit congruence-preserving transformations (line reflections, translations, rotations, and glide-reflections) defined without the use of coordinates. Again, congruence conditions for triangles are used to establish important properties of these transformations.

Overall, this unit helps students extend their understanding of proof in geometric settings while also broadening their understanding and application of important geometric relationships. It recognizes that student construction of meaning and understanding is not linear. The progression of the treatment of congruence beginning in Course 1 and similarity beginning in Course 2 permits revisiting these ideas from different perspectives, contexts, and increasing levels of abstraction in Course 3. The unit illustrates development of important geometric ideas in an efficient manner, and it illustrates the connectedness of mathematics by drawing on algebraic and trigonometric concepts and methods of reasoning in geometric settings.

Additionally, there are numerous opportunities for students to develop a deep understanding of *why* a result is true using deductive reasoning. A few of these opportunities will be identified in the teacher's notes as examples of the *explanatory power of proof*.

Unit Objectives

- Build skill in using inductive and deductive reasoning to first discover and then prove geometric relationships and properties based on similarity and congruence of triangles
- Develop facility in producing deductive arguments in geometric situations using both synthetic and coordinate methods
- Know and be able to use triangle similarity and congruence theorems
- Know and be able to use properties of special centers of triangles
- Know and be able to use the necessary and sufficient conditions for quadrilaterals to be (special) parallelograms and for special quadrilaterals to be congruent
- Know and be able to use properties of size transformations and congruence-preserving transformations (line reflections, translations, rotations, and glide reflections)

Expectations for Student Proofs

The complete solutions in this unit for items that request proofs, careful reasoning, and plans for proofs have been polished. Acceptable student solutions will be less complete and well-organized. Complete, well-organized proofs, as with any writing (essays or stories), are usually the result of initial writing and then improving the work. After either individual feedback or a class discussion on a more complex proof, provide time for students to re-organize and improve their own work. Additionally, it would be beneficial to discuss in class student proofs that show reasoning at the level that you are expecting.

Student masters have been developed to provide scaffolding as students develop their proof-writing skills. (See page T1A for more information.) Notes and Teacher's Resource minis indicate the problems for which this support is provided.

CPMP-Tools

Multiple opportunities are offered in this unit for students to use interactive geometry software to look for relationships and provide evidence for conjectures. One custom tool, "Explore Similar Triangles," has been developed for use in Lesson 1. Items that could use interactive geometry software are:

Page 167, Problem 6
Page 183, Applications Task 10
Page 185, Connections Task 13
Page 188, Reflections Task 19
Page 189, Reflections Task 22
Page 191, Extensions Task 28
Page 197, Problem 3
Page 198, Problem 7
Page 200, Launch
Page 206, Problem 4
Page 220, Connections Task 19
Page 222, Extensions Task 28
Page 222, Extensions Task 29
Page 233, Task 7

A technology tip for Applications Task 10 in Lesson 1 is provided to help students construct size transformations with different centers.

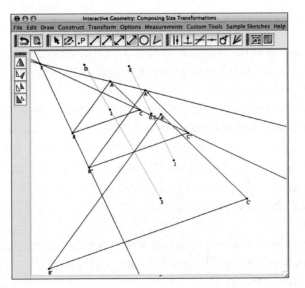

Lesson Objectives	On Your Own Assignments*	Suggested Pacing	Materials
Lesson 1 *Reasoning about Similar Triangles* • Identify similar polygons and determine the scale factor of similar polygons • Review and extend understanding of the Laws of Sines and Cosines • Know and be able to use the three theorems providing sufficient conditions to prove triangles are similar (SSS, SAS, AA) • Continue to develop the ability to write both synthetic and analytic arguments	**After Investigation 1:** A1, A2, C11, C12, R18, E23 or E24, Rv30–Rv33 **After Investigation 2:** A3–A5, C13, C14, R19, E25 or E26, Rv34–Rv36 **After Investigation 3:** Choose two of A6–A10, choose two of C15–C17, choose two of R20–R22, choose one of E27–E29, Rv37–Rv39	8 days (including assessment)	• Quarters (1 per pair of students) • Centimeter rulers • Linkage strips • *CPMP-Tools* interactive geometry software • *CPMP-Tools* "Explore Similar Triangles" custom tool • Unit Resources
Lesson 2 *Reasoning about Congruent Triangles* • Understand congruence of figures as a special case of similarity of figures • Know and be able to use the four theorems providing sufficient conditions to prove triangles are congruent (SSS, SAS, AAS, ASA) • Know and be able to use properties of the incenter, circumcenter, and centroid of a triangle • Continue to develop the ability to write both synthetic and analytic arguments • Know and be able to use both necessary and sufficient conditions for quadrilaterals to be (special) parallelograms • Know and be able to use the Midpoint Connector Theorems for Triangles and Quadrilaterals • Explore, prove, and apply properties of congruence-preserving transformations	**After Investigation 1:** Choose three of A1–A5, C14, R20, R21, E26 or E27, Rv35–Rv37 **After Investigation 2:** A6, A7, choose two of C15–C17, R22, choose one of E28–E30, Rv38, Rv39 **After Investigation 3:** A8, A9, C18 or C19, R24, E31 or E32, Rv40, Rv41 **After Investigation 4:** A10 or A12, A11 or A13, R24, E33 or E34, Rv42–Rv45	13 days (including assessment)	• Compasses • Rulers • *CPMP-Tools* interactive geometry software • Unit Resources
Lesson 3 *Looking Back* • Review and synthesize the major objectives of the unit		3 days (including assessment)	• *CPMP-Tools* interactive geometry software • Unit Resources

* When choice is indicated, it is important to leave the choice to the student.

Note: It is best if Connections tasks are discussed as a whole class after they have been assigned as homework.

Teacher Notes

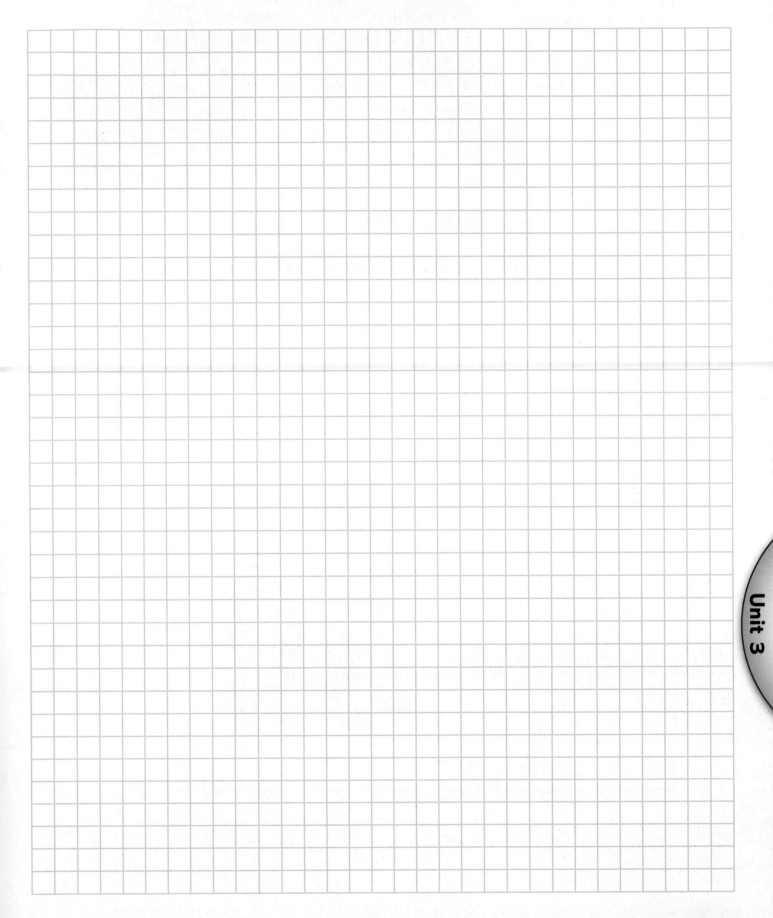

Reasoning about Similar Triangles

In Course 1 of *Core-Plus Mathematics*, you discovered combinations of side or angle measures that were sufficient to determine if two triangles were congruent, that is, whether they had the same shape and size. You also explored conditions under which congruent copies of triangles or other polygons could tile a plane.

The mathematically inspired print shown below was created by the Dutch artist M. C. Escher for a book about tilings of a plane. The print provides an interesting twist on use of a basic shape to cover a portion of a plane. It also represents an early attempt by the artist to depict infinity.

Source: *M. C. Escher, His Life and Complete Graphic Works* © 1981

Reasoning about Similar Triangles

Lesson 1 is designed to help students develop mathematical power simultaneously in two areas: reasoning skills and geometric content. Therefore, formal reasoning or proof continues to be developed and emphasized using the same process employed in Courses 1 and 2 and the Course 3 *Reasoning and Proof* unit: explore, conjecture, and then verify.

The definition of similar polygons is introduced in Investigation 1. Emphasis is placed on the conditions for triangles that are sufficient to ensure that they are similar. In Investigation 1, students are guided through the development of the theorems used to prove two triangles are similar. In Investigation 3, students are asked to prove increasingly sophisticated conjectures that require a working knowledge of the full set of theorems they have proven thus far.

Two characteristics of this lesson should be noted here. The Laws of Cosines and Sines are used to deduce the triangle similarity theorems. The tactic is to demonstrate that a set of conditions on a triangle, such as knowing the lengths of two sides and the measure of the included angle, uniquely determines the triangle. Once this has been demonstrated, then two sets of conditions uniquely determine two triangles; and thus, their similarity can be tested. The key concept is the use of the Law of Cosines or Law of Sines to solve for an angle measure or a side length.

A second characteristic of this development is that similarity is covered first and congruence is considered a special case of similarity: congruence is similarity with a scale factor of 1. This approach allows the congruence theorems to be deduced easily in Lesson 2.

Lesson Objectives

- Identify similar polygons and determine the scale factor of similar polygons
- Review and extend understanding of the Laws of Sines and Cosines
- Know and be able to use the three theorems providing sufficient conditions to prove triangles are similar (SSS, SAS, AA)
- Continue to develop the ability to write both synthetic and analytic arguments

Lesson Launch

Many students may be familiar with M. C. Escher's work. Even students not typically interested in art find his work fascinating. In addition to the motivational aspect, this TATS allows students an opportunity to develop algorithms and for you to assess what students recall about similar and congruent triangles. Students will consider the similar triangles in the framework (Part b) more formally in Investigation 1, Problem 4. So, details in this solution may be delayed to that point.

Escher's framework for the design of his print is shown below. Isosceles right triangle *ABC* is the starting point.

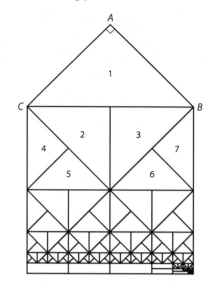

Think About This Situation

Study the Escher print and the framework used to create it.

a How are the lizards in the Escher print alike? How are they different? How could you test your ideas?

b Starting with △*ABC*, the framework was created by next drawing right isosceles triangles 2 and 3. How do you think these two triangles were determined? How are triangles 2 and 3 related to each other? To triangle 1? Why?

c How do you think triangles 4 and 5 and triangles 6 and 7 were created? How are these pairs of triangles related? How are they related to triangle 1? Explain your reasoning.

d Describe a way to generate the remaining portion of the framework.

In the first lesson of this unit, you will explore similarity of polygons and use deductive reasoning to determine sufficient conditions for similarity of triangles. You will use those relationships to solve applied problems and prove important geometric theorems.

Think About This Situation

a If one considers parts of these lizards, such as their feet size or body width, one notices the lizards in the print are *not* all the same shape. For example, the upper-most lizards (which fall into isosceles right triangles 1, 2, 3, 4, and 7 in the framework) are all different in both shape and size. However, common to each lizard is the exaggerated size of one of the front or back feet. The lizards are alike in that they all have curving bodies. In addition, there are smaller and smaller copies of the five top-most lizards as you travel down the print. To test these ideas, one might trace copies of the distinct lizards, scale these tracings down using a copy machine, and overlay transformed images of the scaled copies onto the picture.

b Students might offer a variety of ways to determine $\triangle 2$ and $\triangle 3$.

(1) Reflect $\triangle ABC$ across $\overleftrightarrow{BC}$, locate the midpoint of $\overline{BC}$, and draw $\overline{ZD}$. Since $CZ = BZ$, $DZ = DZ$, and $DC = BD$, $\triangle CZD \cong \triangle BZD$ (SSS congruence condition).

(2) Construct $\triangle DBC$ congruent to $\triangle ABC$ on the hypotenuse $\overline{BC}$, then construct the altitude of the new triangle. Triangles 2 and 3 are right triangles and are congruent by HL since they have a common leg and the length of the hypotenuse of each triangle is the same as the congruent lengths of the legs of $\triangle 1$.

(3) Locate the midpoint Z of $\overline{BC}$ and construct two congruent squares, $CZDE$ and $BZDF$, on the hypotenuse, $\overline{BC}$. Then draw the diagonals $\overline{CD}$ and $\overline{BD}$. Since $CZDE$ and $BZDF$ are squares, $\overline{CZ}$, $\overline{DZ}$, and $\overline{BZ}$ are all the same length and $\triangle CZD$ is congruent to $\triangle BZD$ by the SAS congruence condition.

INSTRUCTIONAL NOTE
During this discussion, the language of "similar" should not be expected from students, even though it might be used.

Unit 3

(4) Locate the midpoint Z of $\overline{BC}$ and construct a ray at Z perpendicular to $\overline{BC}$. Then mark off $\overline{DZ}$ to be half the length of $\overline{BC}$. Draw $\overline{CD}$ and $\overline{BD}$. From this, you can justify the two smaller isosceles triangles congruent using the SAS congruence condition as in (2) above. (One advantage to this approach is that you can continue extending $\overrightarrow{DZ}$ to form more of the framework.)

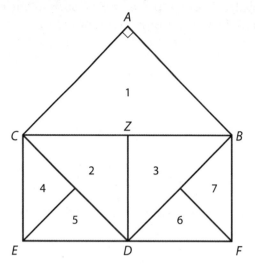

Students will likely conjecture that △2 and △3 are similar to △1 and may explain by referring to the angle sizes of 45°, 45°, and 90° or proportional sides. A second approach offered might involve constructing squares rather than triangles as explained in Part b (3). A third method suggested might be using reflections. If this method is suggested, students must recognize that the leg common to both triangles must be constructed the same length as the other leg (i.e., half the length of the hypotenuse).

c The construction algorithm of choice can be continued to form each new pair of triangles on the hypotenuse of the last constructed triangle. The pairs of triangles will always be right isosceles triangles as outlined in Part b. The new pairs of triangles again seem to be similar to △1 because they have the same size angles, 45°, 45°, and 90°. (More detailed analysis about the relationship of side lengths occurs in Problem 4.)

d Students may suggest repeating the algorithm they have suggested in Parts b and c. Alternatively, they may switch methods.

Teacher Notes

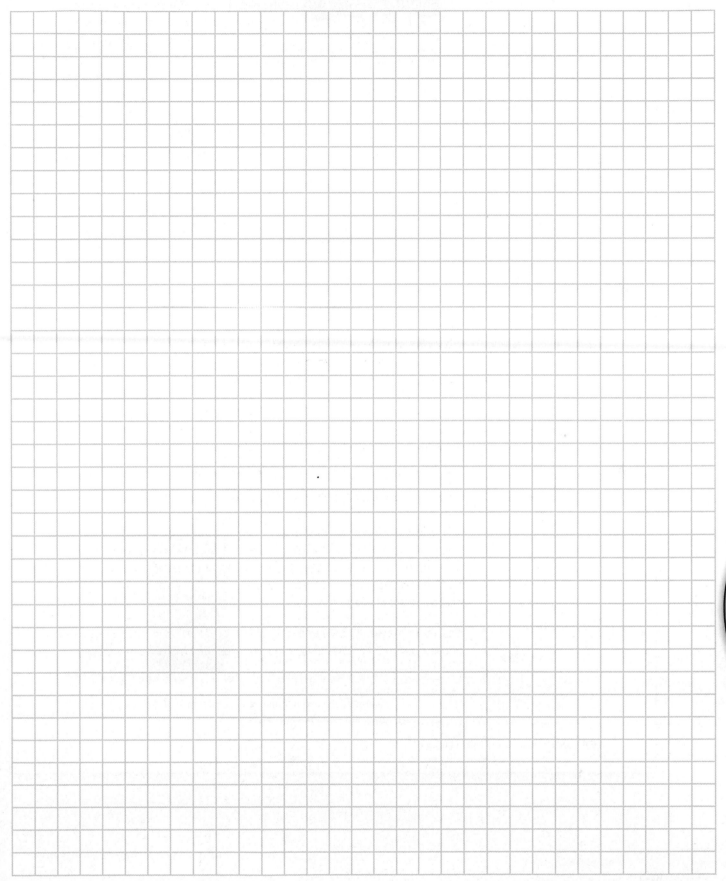

Investigation 1 **When Are Two Polygons Similar?**

Whenever the light source of a projector is positioned perpendicular to a screen, it enlarges images on the film into *similar* images on the screen. The enlargement factor from the original object to the projected object depends on the distance from the projector to the screen (and special lens features of the projector).

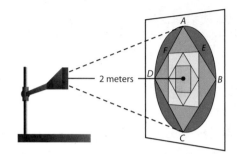

2 meters

As you work on the problems of this investigation, look for answers to the following questions:

How can you test whether two polygons are similar?

How can you create a polygon similar to a given polygon?

1. Examine the test pattern shown on the screen.

   a. How would you test if quadrilateral *ABCD* on the screen is similar to the original quadrilateral that is being projected?

   b. How would you test if △*AEF* on the screen is similar to the original triangle that is being projected?

   c. How would you move the projector if you wanted to make the test pattern larger? Smaller?

   d. How could you determine how much larger projected △*AEF* is than the original triangle? Explain what measurements you would make and how you would use them.

   e. Compare your answers with other students. Resolve any differences.

2. Cameras record images digitally and on film. When a camera lens is positioned perpendicular to the plane containing an object, the object and its recorded image are similar. This photograph was taken by a digital camera.

   a. Describe how you could use information in the photograph to help determine the actual dimensions of the face of the cell phone.

   b. What are those dimensions?

This investigation develops the concept of similar polygons. The focus is on testing for similarity of triangles.

Launch

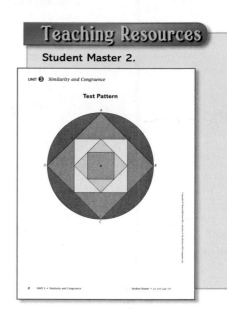
The master for this launch can be used with a document camera or made into a transparency to facilitate a whole-class discussion of Problem 1. Students do not need to write responses to this problem.

1 a. Students will likely suggest measuring the side lengths of the shape and its image, since in Course 2 Unit 3, they learned that for similarity transformations, the lengths of the sides of an image shape are a scale factor times the lengths of the preimage shape. By measuring, they can see if the lengths of the corresponding sides of quadrilateral *ABCD* on the screen are approximately the same factor times the lengths of the image quadrilateral. Side lengths alone is not enough; angles must be preserved in order to have the same shape. Some students may suggest measuring the corresponding angles of *ABCD*. (The formal definition of similar polygons is introduced in Problem 3.)

   b. Some students may give an identical response to Part a. Others may suggest measuring the corresponding angles of $\triangle AEF$ and its preimage to see if the angles are congruent.

   c. While keeping the light source of the projector perpendicular to the screen, move the projector farther away from the screen to make the test pattern larger and closer to the screen to make the test pattern smaller.

   d. Students might consider "larger" as an area comparison but will most likely discuss lengths as follows. Calculate the ratio of the length of one side of the image triangle to the length of the corresponding preimage side. For example, the projected image side length of $\overline{AE}$ divided by the preimage side length of $\overline{AE}$ gives the enlargement factor from the original to the projected image.

   e. Students will compare their answers with other students and resolve any differences.

2 a. Since the picture depicts similar but smaller copies of the actual objects, the enlargement factor can be calculated by the ratio $\frac{actual\ dimension}{photo\ dimension} = enlargement\ factor$. Assuming that the cell phone is not available for measurement, measure the diameter of an actual quarter and the diameter of the quarter in the picture to calculate the enlargement factor. Then for the cell phone, $(actual\ dimension) = (enlargement\ factor) \cdot (photo\ dimension)$.

> **NOTE** The solution to Problem 2 Part b is on page T165.

Unit 3

The following problem formalizes some of the ideas you used in Problems 1 and 2.

 Two polygons with the same number of sides are **similar** provided their corresponding angles have the same measure and the ratios of lengths of corresponding sides is a constant.

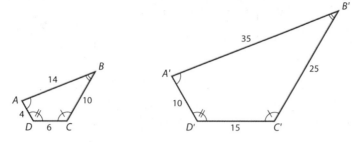

In the above diagram, *quadrilateral A′B′C′D′* ~ *quadrilateral ABCD*. The symbol ~ means "is similar to."

$$m\angle A' = m\angle A, \ m\angle B' = m\angle B, \ m\angle C' = m\angle C, \text{ and } m\angle D' = m\angle D.$$

$\dfrac{A'B'}{AB} = \dfrac{35}{14} = \dfrac{5}{2}$ or equivalently $A'B' = \dfrac{5}{2}AB$.

$\dfrac{B'C'}{BC} = \dfrac{25}{10} = \dfrac{5}{2}$ or equivalently $B'C' = \dfrac{5}{2}BC$.

$\dfrac{C'D'}{CD} = \dfrac{15}{6} = \dfrac{5}{2}$ or equivalently $C'D' = \dfrac{5}{2}CD$.

$\dfrac{D'A'}{DA} = \dfrac{10}{4} = \dfrac{5}{2}$ or equivalently $D'A' = \dfrac{5}{2}DA$.

The constant $\dfrac{5}{2}$ is called the **scale factor** *from quadrilateral ABCD to quadrilateral A′B′C′D′*. It scales (multiplies) the length of each side of quadrilateral *ABCD* to produce the length of the corresponding side of quadrilateral *A′B′C′D′*.

a. What is the scale factor from quadrilateral *A′B′C′D′* to quadrilateral *ABCD*?

b. How, if at all, would you modify your similarity test in Problem 1 Part b using the above definition of similarity?

c. If two pentagons are similar, describe how to find the scale factor from the smaller pentagon to the larger pentagon. Then describe how to find the scale factor from the larger pentagon to the smaller pentagon.

d. Suppose $\triangle PQR \sim \triangle XYZ$ and the scale factor from $\triangle PQR$ to $\triangle XYZ$ is $\dfrac{3}{4}$. Write as many mathematical statements as you can about pairs of corresponding angles and about pairs of corresponding sides. Compare your statements with other students. Resolve any differences.

b. The actual diameter of a U.S. quarter is 2.426 cm. Students' measurement of the quarter's diameter in the photo should be about 1 cm. A sample solution follows.

- *enlargement factor* $= \dfrac{2.426 \text{ cm}}{1 \text{ cm}} = 2.426$
- *length of cell phone* $= (2.426)(4.7) = 11.4022 \text{ cm} \approx 4.5$ inches
- *width of cell phone* $= (2.426)(2.5) = 6.065 \text{ cm} \approx 2.4$ inches

(The actual dimensions of the cell phone are 4.5 × 2.4 inches, according to the product manufacturer.)

③ a. $\dfrac{2}{5}$

b. Responses will vary. Students might revise their test using either ratios of side lengths or scale factors. The test should include checking that corresponding angles are congruent and ratios of corresponding side lengths are the same.

c. Compute the ratio $\dfrac{length \ of \ side \ of \ larger \ pentagon}{length \ of \ corresponding \ side \ of \ smaller \ pentagon}$.

The scale factor from the larger pentagon to the smaller similar pentagon is the reciprocal of the previous scale factor.

d. $m\angle P = m\angle X$; $m\angle Q = m\angle Y$; $m\angle R = m\angle Z$;

$XY = \frac{3}{4}PQ$; $YZ = \frac{3}{4}QR$; $XZ = \frac{3}{4}PR$

Knowing that two triangles are similar allows you to conclude that the three pairs of corresponding angles are congruent and that the three pairs of corresponding sides are related by the same scale factor. Conversely, if you know that the three pairs of corresponding angles are congruent and the three pairs of corresponding sides are related by the same scale factor, you can conclude that the triangles are similar.

4 The diagram below is a portion of the framework for Escher's print that you examined in the Think About This Situation (page 163). Recall that $\triangle ABC$ is an isosceles right triangle. Assume $BC = 2$ units.

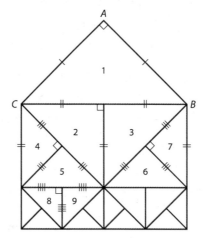

a. Compare the markings on the sides and angles of the triangles with your analysis of the framework. Explain why the markings are correct.

b. Determine if each statement below is correct. If so, explain why and give the scale factor from the first triangle to the second triangle. If the statement is not correct, explain why.

   i. $\triangle 1 \sim \triangle 3$ **ii.** $\triangle 2 \sim \triangle 6$

  iii. $\triangle 4 \sim \triangle 6$ **iv.** $\triangle 8 \sim \triangle 3$

   v. $\triangle 9 \sim \triangle 1$

5 Based on their work in Problem 4, several students at Black River High School made conjectures about families of polygons. Each student tried to outdo the previous student. For each claim, explain as precisely as you can why it is true or give a counterexample.

a. Monisha conjectured that *all isosceles right triangles are similar.*

b. Ahmed conjectured that *all equilateral triangles are similar.*

c. Loreen claimed that *all squares are similar.*

d. Jeff conjectured that *all rhombuses are similar.*

e. Amy claimed that *all regular hexagons are similar.*

4 **a.** Since it is given that $\triangle ABC$ is an isosceles right triangle, $\angle A$ is correctly marked with a right angle and sides $\overline{AC}$ and $\overline{AB}$ are correctly marked to be congruent. (See diagram at the right.)

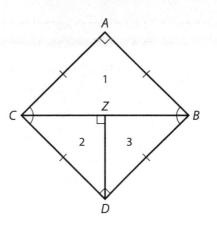

INSTRUCTIONAL NOTE
Student explanations will depend on the construction algorithm they prefer. (See TATS Part b.) One option using $BC = 2$ is given in Part a.

   Using an algorithm that constructs $\triangle 2$ and $\triangle 3$, these triangles are shown to be congruent (see the various constructions listed with the TATS Part b on page T163). In one construction, $\overline{ZD}$ is constructed perpendicular to $\overline{BC}$; in others, $\overline{ZD} \perp \overline{BC}$ is derived. For example, if students described Z as the midpoint of $\overline{BC}$, they will likely use the SSS congruence condition to justify $\triangle 2$ congruent to $\triangle 3$ and then CPCTC to determine that the right angles of the two triangles are correctly marked. If they describe $\overline{DZ}$ as the altitude or perpendicular to $\overline{BC}$, they will likely identify the two triangles as right triangles and use the SAS or HL congruence conditions.

   Since $\triangle 2 \cong \triangle 3$, the angle and side markings are correct; repeating the algorithm on subsequent triangles ensures that all markings are correct; all triangles in the framework are isosceles right triangles.

b. **INSTRUCTIONAL NOTE** In parts i–v, students should reason that all conditions of the definition of similar triangles are satisfied. They should also recognize that all triangles in this diagram are isosceles right triangles, so all corresponding angles are congruent.

SCOPE AND SEQUENCE
Students have not spent time rewriting radical expressions that contain a radical in the denominator. You may wish to use this problem to introduce the procedure since its value is evident here.

   i. $\triangle 1 \sim \triangle 3$
   (Consider the labeling scheme at the right.)

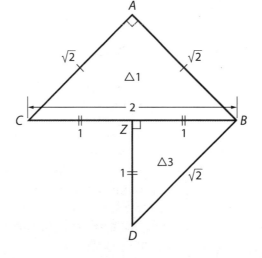

   $\triangle 1 = \triangle ABC$
   $\triangle 3 = \triangle ZBD$
   Since $BC = 2$, using the Pythagorean Theorem, $AC = AB = \sqrt{2}$.
   $CZ = BZ = \frac{1}{2}BC = DZ = 1$
   $DB = \sqrt{1^2 + 1^2} = \sqrt{2}$

   With this setup, you can establish $ZB = k \cdot AB$, $ZD = k \cdot AC$, and $DB = k \cdot CB$.
   Solve any one of these equations for k;
   $$k = \frac{1}{\sqrt{2}} = \frac{\sqrt{2}}{2}.$$
   For example,

   $$ZB = k \cdot AB$$
   $$1 = \sqrt{2}k$$
   $$k = \frac{1}{\sqrt{2}} = \frac{\sqrt{2}}{2}.$$

   The scale factor from $\triangle 1$ to $\triangle 3$ is $k = \frac{\sqrt{2}}{2}$.

Unit 3

ii. Similar reasoning can be applied each time a new pair of triangles, such as △6 and △7, are formed on the hypotenuse of a triangle, such as △3. So, the scale factor from △3 to △6 is $\frac{\sqrt{2}}{2}$. Since △2 ≅ △3 (SAS or HL), the scale factor from △2 to △6 is also $\frac{\sqrt{2}}{2}$. Thus, △2 ~ △6.

iii. △4 ≅ △6 by the SAS congruence condition. So, △4 ~ △6 with scale factor 1.

iv. The scale factor from △3 to △6 and also from △3 to △5 is $\frac{\sqrt{2}}{2}$. The scale factor from △5 to △8 is $\frac{\sqrt{2}}{2}$. Thus, the scale factor from △3 to △8 is $\frac{\sqrt{2}}{2} \cdot \frac{\sqrt{2}}{2} = \frac{1}{2}$. The scale factor from △8 to △3 is the reciprocal of this, so △8 ~ △3 with scale factor 2.

v. Rather than reasoning from the larger triangle to a smaller triangle and using the reciprocal of this scale factor, as in part iv, students may reason as follows. The scale factor going from a smaller triangle to the next larger triangle is $\sqrt{2}$. △9 must go through 3 scale factor changes to become congruent to △1. So, the scale factor from △9 to △1 is $(\sqrt{2})^3 = 2\sqrt{2}$ and △9 ~ △1.

5 **a.** *True:* All isosceles right triangles are similar.

Since the base angles of an isosceles triangle are congruent, the two base angles for any isosceles right triangle measure $\frac{180° - 90°}{2} = 45°$.

For any two general isosceles right triangles as shown at the right, the scale factor from △ABC to △DEF is $\frac{b}{a}$. This can be determined by comparing the three ratios formed for corresponding sides. $\frac{b}{a}, \frac{b}{a}$, and $\frac{\sqrt{2}b}{\sqrt{2}a} = \frac{b}{a}$.

Knowing that the three pairs of corresponding angles have the same measures and the three pairs of corresponding sides are related by the same scale factor means that all isosceles right triangles are similar.

b. *True:* All equilateral triangles are similar.

Since the angles of any equilateral triangle each measure 60°, corresponding angles are congruent.

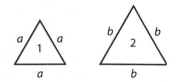

For any two general equilateral triangles as shown at the right, the ratios of corresponding side lengths from △1 to △2 are the same, $\frac{b}{a}$. Thus, all equilateral triangles are similar.

c. *True*: All squares are similar.

Since all angles are right angles, corresponding angles have the same measure. The scale factor relating the two squares with side lengths a and b is the ratio of the lengths of the sides, either $\frac{a}{b}$ or $\frac{b}{a}$.

d. *False*: All rhombuses are not similar.

As a counterexample, consider a rhombus with side lengths 4 and four right angles, and a rhombus with side lengths 8 and pairs of congruent opposite angles with measures other than 90°, say 120° and 60°. Although the corresponding sides are constant multiples of each other, the corresponding angles are not congruent.

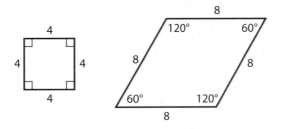

e. *True*: All regular hexagons are similar.

By definition, a regular hexagon is a six-sided polygon in which all sides are congruent and all angles are congruent (their measure is 120°). Reasoning similar to that for the equilateral triangle can be used to show that any two general hexagons with side lengths a and b are related by a scale factor of either $\frac{b}{a}$ or $\frac{a}{b}$. Therefore, all regular hexagons are similar.

6) The "Explore Similar Triangles" custom tool is designed to help you construct similar triangles based on a chosen scale factor. As a class or in pairs, experiment with the software. Conduct at least three trials. Observe what happens to the angle and side measures of the triangle as you drag the red vertices.

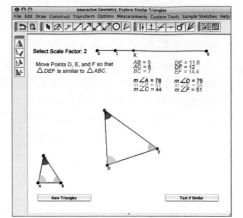

a. For each trial:

• choose a target scale factor and construct △DEF so that it is similar to △ABC.

• use the definition of similarity to justify that your triangles are similar.

b. Think about the process you used to create a triangle similar to △ABC.

i. When dragging △DEF to form a triangle similar to △ABC, how did you decide how to initially drag the vertices?

• Did you use the angle measurements?

• Did you use the length measurements?

ii. Once you knew that two pairs of corresponding sides were related by the same scale factor, did that guarantee that the third pair was automatically related by the same scale factor?

c. How do you think the software determines if your constructed triangle is similar to the original triangle?

d. How does the software visually demonstrate the similarity of two triangles?

Summarize
the Mathematics

In this investigation, you explored similarity of polygons with a focus on testing for similarity of triangles.

a Explain why not all rectangles are similar.

b What is the fewest number of measurements needed to test if two rectangles are similar? Explain.

c Explain why any two regular *n*-gons are similar. How would you determine a scale factor relating the two *n*-gons?

d What needs to be verified before you can conclude that two triangles, △PQR and △UVW, are similar?

Be prepared to share your ideas and reasoning with the class.

6 **a.** Students should drag the vertices of △DEF so that △DEF is similar to △ABC. In other words, each pair of corresponding angles are equal in measure (m∠A = m∠D, m∠B = m∠E, and m∠C = m∠F) and each pair of corresponding sides are proportional with the chosen scale factor k (DE = k · AB, DF = k · AC, EF = k · BC).

b. **i.** Students may have used different strategies when dragging vertices D, E, and F. Since each vertex must be dragged individually, this may have prompted students to initially focus on either the length or angle measures. Sample reasoning strategy: "I dragged vertex D until DE = k · AB, then I dragged vertex F until DF = k · AC and m∠D = m∠A. Then I noticed that the other side and angles were related by the correct correspondence, so I tested my construction."

ii. No, not unless the included angle between the two sides was congruent to its corresponding angle. (This may prompt students to investigate further with the tool, exploring with a different strategy of dragging.)

c. Student might conjecture that the software uses the definition of similarity to test all corresponding angles and sides. Based on the work in Part bii, some students may conjecture that not all conditions need to be tested.

d. If the triangles are similar, a shaded copy of △ABC is translated to a vertex of △DEF, then scaled, rotated, and flipped as needed to coincide with △DEF.

Summarize
the Mathematics

Teaching Resources

Transparency Master 3.

ⓐ Although all angles are 90°, ratios of corresponding sides of two rectangles can be different. A counterexample can be given, for example, a 1 × 2 rectangle and a 1 × 3 rectangle.

ⓑ Only side measures of two consecutive sides are needed to test for similarity of rectangles since by definition opposite sides are congruent and all angles are congruent (90°).

ⓒ A regular n-gon is defined to be a polygon in which all sides are congruent and all angles are congruent. The angle measure for any regular n-gon is $\frac{180°(n-2)}{n}$, or $360° - \frac{360°}{n}$. (See pages 404–406 of Course 1.) So, any two regular n-gons with the same number of sides have congruent corresponding angles. Corresponding side lengths are related by a scale factor of k. To determine the scale factor k from n-gon$_1$ to n-gon$_2$, compute $\frac{length\ of\ side\ of\ n\text{-}gon_2}{length\ of\ corresponding\ side\ of\ n\text{-}gon_1}$.

ⓓ To verify △PQR ~ △UVW, demonstrate that corresponding angles have the same measure and corresponding sides are related by the same scale factor. In this case, m∠P = m∠U, m∠Q = m∠V, m∠R = m∠W, UV = k · PQ, VW = k · QR, and UW = k · PR for some k > 0.

MATH TOOLKIT Record the definition of similar polygons with an example.

Unit 3

Check Your Understanding

Each triangle described in the table below is similar to $\triangle ABC$. For each triangle, use this fact and the additional information given to:

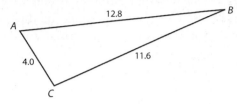

a. identify the correspondence between its vertices and those of $\triangle ABC$.

b. determine the remaining table entries.

Triangle Angle Measures			Shortest Side Length	Longest Side Length	Third Side Length	Scale Factor from $\triangle ABC$
m∠A = 64°	m∠B = 18°	m∠C = 98°	AC = 4.0	AB = 12.8	BC = 11.6	1
m∠D = ?	m∠E = 64°	m∠F = 18°				2
m∠G = ?	m∠H = ?	m∠I = ?		IG = 6.4	GH = 5.8	
m∠J = ?	m∠K = 18°	m∠L = 98°	JL = 14.0			

Investigation 2 — Sufficient Conditions for Similarity of Triangles

In Investigation 1, you proposed a method by which computer software could test if two triangles were similar. As you tested pairs of triangles, you compared corresponding angle measures and corresponding side lengths. You may have observed that if certain conditions on measures of some corresponding sides or angles are met, similar relationships must then hold for the remaining corresponding parts. In this investigation, you will explore minimal conditions that will ensure that two triangles are similar. You will find the previously proven Law of Sines and Law of Cosines helpful in your work. These two laws are reproduced here for easy reference.

Law of Sines

In any triangle ABC with sides of lengths a, b, and c opposite $\angle A$, $\angle B$, and $\angle C$, respectively, $\frac{\sin A}{a} = \frac{\sin B}{b} = \frac{\sin C}{c}$ or equivalently, $\frac{a}{\sin A} = \frac{b}{\sin B} = \frac{c}{\sin C}$.

Law of Cosines

In any triangle ABC with sides of lengths a, b, and c opposite $\angle A$, $\angle B$, and $\angle C$, respectively, $c^2 = a^2 + b^2 - 2ab \cos C$.

✓ Check Your Understanding

a. $\triangle ABC \sim \triangle EFD$
$\triangle ABC \sim \triangle IGH$
$\triangle ABC \sim \triangle JKL$

b.

Triangle Angle Measures			Shortest Side Length	Longest Side Length	Third Side Length	Scale Factor from $\triangle ABC$
$m\angle A = 64°$	$m\angle B = 18°$	$m\angle C = 98°$	$AC = 4.0$	$AB = 12.8$	$BC = 11.6$	1
$m\angle D = 98°$	$m\angle E = 64°$	$m\angle F = 18°$	$ED = 8.0$	$EF = 25.6$	$FD = 23.2$	2
$m\angle G = 18°$	$m\angle H = 98°$	$m\angle I = 64°$	$IH = 2.0$	$IG = 6.4$	$GH = 5.8$	$\frac{1}{2} = 0.5$
$m\angle J = 64°$	$m\angle K = 18°$	$m\angle L = 98°$	$JL = 14.0$	$JK = 44.8$	$KL = 40.6$	$\frac{7}{2} = 3.5$

Investigation 2 — Sufficient Conditions for Similarity of Triangles

In this investigation, students use the previously proved Law of Sines and Law of Cosines to prove the Side-Angle-Side, Side-Side-Side, and Angle-Angle Similarity Theorems for triangles.

Proof Support Masters See page T1A for information on these masters. In this investigation, proof support masters are available for Problems 4 and 5.

As you work on the problems of this investigation, look for answers to the following question:

> *What combinations of side or angle measures are sufficient to determine that two triangles are similar?*

1 To begin, consider $\triangle ABC$ with b, c, and $m\angle A$ given as shown below.

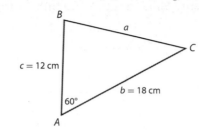

a. Calculate a, $m\angle B$, and $m\angle C$.

b. Are a, $m\angle B$, and $m\angle C$ *uniquely determined*? That is, is there exactly one value possible for each? Explain your reasoning.

c. In general, if you know values of b, c, and $m\angle A$, can values for a, $m\angle B$, and $m\angle C$ always be found? Could any of a, $m\angle B$, or $m\angle C$ have two or more values when b, c, and $m\angle A$ are given? Explain.

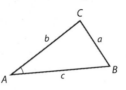

d. Summarize your work in Parts a–c in an if-then statement that begins as follows:

> *In a triangle, if the lengths of two sides and the measure of the angle included between those sides are known, then ... .*

2 Next, examine $\triangle ABC$ and $\triangle XYZ$ shown below. In both cases, you have information given about two sides and an included angle. In $\triangle XYZ$, k is a constant. Test if this information is sufficient to conclude that $\triangle ABC \sim \triangle XYZ$ using Parts a–d as a guide.

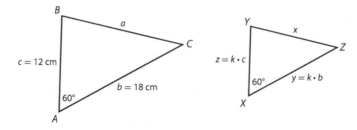

a. In $\triangle XYZ$, $m\angle X = m\angle A = 60°$, $z = k \cdot c = 12k$ cm, and $y = k \cdot b = 18k$ cm, where k is a constant. Explain why x, $m\angle Y$, and $m\angle Z$ are uniquely determined.

b. Use the information given for $\triangle XYZ$ to write and then solve an equation to find length x. Based on your work in Problem 1, how is x related to a?

1 **a.** Using the Law of Cosines and solving for a:

$$a = \sqrt{18^2 + 12^2 - 2(18)(12)\cos 60°} = \sqrt{252}$$

$$\frac{\sin B}{18} = \frac{\sin 60°}{\sqrt{252}}; \text{ m}\angle B \approx 79°$$

$$\text{m}\angle C \approx 180° - 60° - 79° = 41°$$

b. Students should recognize that the calculation using the Law of Cosines in Part a yielded only one positive value for the third side of the triangle. Similarly, the proportional calculations with the Law of Sines determined only one value for the second (and thus the third) angle.

c. When values for b, c, and m$\angle A$ are known, it is always possible to find the unique value for a using the Law of Cosines. Using the Law of Sines when all three side lengths and one angle measure are known results in unique measures for the remaining two angles.

d. In a triangle, if the lengths of two sides and the measure of the angle included between those sides are known, then the measures of the remaining angles and the length of the third side are uniquely determined.

2 **a.** x is uniquely determined because two side lengths and an included angle measure (y, z, and m$\angle X$) are known. Similarly, m$\angle Y$ and m$\angle Z$ are determined when x, y, and z are known.

b. $x^2 = y^2 + z^2 - 2yz \cos X$
$$= (18k)^2 + (12k)^2 - 2(18k)(12k)(\cos 60°)$$
$$= 252k^2$$

$a = \sqrt{252}$ (Problem 1 Part a). $x = \sqrt{252}k$, x and a are related by the equation $x = ka$.

EXPLANATORY POWER OF PROOF This investigation offers many opportunities for using deductive reasoning to understand why a result is true.

INSTRUCTIONAL NOTE Some students may need help recognizing that the values for y and z are known values since k is a constant. Be sure that students are not *assuming* that the triangles are similar for Parts b–d.

c. Find $m\angle Y$. How are $m\angle B$ and $m\angle Y$ related?

d. Find $m\angle Z$. How are $m\angle C$ and $m\angle Z$ related?

e. Considering all the information in Parts a–d, what can you conclude about $\triangle ABC$ and $\triangle XYZ$?

③ Suppose you know that in $\triangle ABC$ and $\triangle DEF$, $m\angle C = m\angle F$, $d = k \cdot a$, and $e = k \cdot b$.

a. Could you prove that $\triangle ABC \sim \triangle DEF$? If so, explain how. If not, explain why not.

b. Complete the following statement.

> *If an angle of one triangle has the same measure as an angle of a second triangle, and if the lengths of the corresponding sides including these angles are multiplied by the same scale factor k, then … .*

c. Compare your statement in Part b with those of your classmates. Resolve any differences.

The conclusion you reached in Part c of Problem 3 is called the **Side-Angle-Side (SAS) Similarity Theorem**. This theorem gives at least a partial answer to the question of finding minimal conditions that will guarantee two triangles are similar. In the next several problems, you will explore other sets of sufficient conditions.

④ Suppose you know that in $\triangle ABC$ and $\triangle XYZ$, the lengths of corresponding sides are related by a scale factor k as in the diagram below.

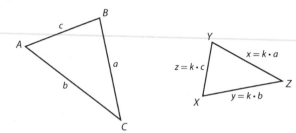

a. What additional relationship would you need to know in order to conclude that $\triangle ABC \sim \triangle XYZ$? What is a possible strategy you could use to establish the relationship?

b. Write a deductive argument proving the relationship you stated in Part a. What can you conclude?

c. The results of your work in Parts a and b establish a **Side-Side-Side (SSS) Similarity Theorem**. Write this SSS Similarity Theorem in if-then form.

c. The Law of Sines can be used as in Problem 1 Part a:

$$\frac{\sin Y}{18k} = \frac{\sin 60°}{\sqrt{252}k}$$

$$\frac{\sin Y}{18} = \frac{\sin 60°}{\sqrt{252}}; \text{ so, } m\angle Y \approx 79°, \text{ as before, and } m\angle B = m\angle Y.$$

Also, the Law of Cosines may be used:

$$\cos Y = \frac{x^2 + z^2 - y^2}{2xz} = \frac{(\sqrt{252}k)^2 + (12k)^2 - (18k)^2}{2(\sqrt{252}k)(12k)} = \frac{72k^2}{24\sqrt{252}k^2} \approx 0.189$$

$$m\angle Y \approx 79°$$

d. Both $m\angle C$ and $m\angle Z$ could be found using the Law of Cosines or the fact that the sum of the angle measures in a triangle is 180°.

$$m\angle Z = 180° - m\angle X - m\angle Y = 180° - 60° - 79° = 41°; \ m\angle C = m\angle Z$$

e. $\triangle ABC \sim \triangle XYZ$

3 a. Yes, you could prove that the two triangles are similar. It would be done by repeating Parts a–e of Problem 2. Students should understand that the steps given in those parts could be completed for any values of $m\angle A$ and lengths of sides b and c. The arguments also hold if the angles are relabeled and their opposite sides are relabeled consistently. (Some students may note that this might be considered an inductive argument rather than a general proof. Many students could follow the example to create a more complete deductive argument, but it is time-consuming and not particularly instructive. However, it could be an extra credit task for interested students to complete outside of class.)

b. *If an angle of one triangle has the same measure as an angle of a second triangle, and if the lengths of the corresponding sides including these angles are multiplied by the same scale factor k, then the two triangles are similar.*

c. Students should compare their work with others.

4 a. Knowing corresponding angles have the same measure for just one pair is sufficient to apply the SAS Similarity Theorem (Problem 3). The Law of Cosines could be used to find these values.

b. PROOF SUPPORT Your students may have trouble with the logic needed for this problem, or they may get lost in the algebraic manipulations. If so, you may find it helpful to direct them to write formulas for cos A and for cos X. You may have to help them simplify the fraction they get for cos X. Then you can ask, "If cos X and cos A have the same value, will the angles be the same size?" Alternatively, you might provide statement-reason strips to assist some or all students complete this proof. (See the *Unit 3 Resource Masters* pages 5–6.)

Consider $\angle A$ and $\angle X$:

$$\cos A = \frac{b^2 + c^2 - a^2}{2bc}$$

$$\cos X = \frac{y^2 + z^2 - x^2}{2yz} = \frac{(bk)^2 + (ck)^2 - (ak)^2}{2(bk)(ck)} = \frac{k^2(b^2 + c^2 - a^2)}{k^2(2bc)} = \frac{b^2 + c^2 - a^2}{2bc}$$

Since cos A and cos X are equal and $m\angle A$ and $m\angle X$ are both less than 180°, it follows that $m\angle A = m\angle X$. So, $\triangle ABC \sim \triangle XYZ$ by the SAS Similarity Theorem.

c. *If the lengths of the three sides of one triangle are multiplied by the same scale factor k to obtain the lengths of the three sides of another triangle, then the two triangles are similar.*

(5) In Problems 2 and 4, given two triangles, you needed to know three of their corresponding measures in order to determine that the triangles were similar. In this problem, you will examine a situation in which only two corresponding measures of two triangles are known.

Suppose you are given $\triangle ABC$ and $\triangle XYZ$ in which $m\angle X = m\angle A$ and $m\angle Y = m\angle B$.

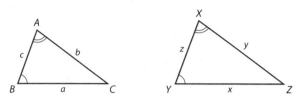

a. Do you think $\triangle ABC \sim \triangle XYZ$? Why or why not?

b. What additional relationship(s) would you need to know to conclude for sure that the triangles are similar?

c. Students at Madison East High School believed the answer to Part a was "yes." Study their proof. Provide reasons that support each of their statements.

Proof:

We first looked at the ratio of the lengths a and x of a pair of corresponding sides.

If we let k represent the ratio $\frac{x}{a}$, then $x = ka$.   (1)

For $\triangle ABC$, we know that $\frac{a}{\sin A} = \frac{b}{\sin B}$. So, $b = \frac{a \sin B}{\sin A}$.   (2)

Similarly for $\triangle XYZ$, we know that $\frac{x}{\sin X} = \frac{y}{\sin Y}$. So, $y = \frac{x \sin Y}{\sin X}$.   (3)

It follows that $y = \frac{ka \sin Y}{\sin X}$.   (4)

Since $m\angle Y = m\angle B$ and $m\angle X = m\angle A$, it follows that $y = \frac{ka \sin B}{\sin A}$.   (5)

Since $b = \frac{a \sin B}{\sin A}$, it follows that $y = kb$.   (6)

Since $m\angle X = m\angle A$ and $m\angle Y = m\angle B$, then $m\angle Z = m\angle C$.   (7)

We've shown $x = ka$, $y = kb$, and $m\angle Z = m\angle C$.

So, $\triangle ABC \sim \triangle XYZ$.   (8)

d. Could the students have reasoned differently at the end of their argument? How?

e. Write an if-then statement of the theorem proved in this problem. What name would you give the theorem?

5 **a.** Students will likely conjecture that with two pairs of corresponding angles having the same measure, the third pair also has the same measure, so the triangles are similar.

b. Some students may go back to first principles (the definition); others may use the SSS or SAS Similarity Theorems. To use the definition, in addition to the third pair of angles having the same measure, you need to show that corresponding side lengths are related by the same scale factor, or the ratios of corresponding sides are equal.

c. (1) $k = \frac{x}{a} \Rightarrow x = ka$ by multiplication.

(2) Law of Sines; multiply both sides of the equation by sin B

(3) Law of Sines; multiply both sides of the equation by sin Y

(4) Substitute from Step 1 into Step 3.

(5) Substitute given congruent angles in Step 4.

(6) Substitute Step 2 into Step 5.

(7) If the measures of two angles of one triangle are equal to the measures of two angles of another triangle, then the measures of the third angles are the same. (See Unit 1 Lesson 2, Connections Task 15 Part a.)

(8) SAS Similarity Theorem

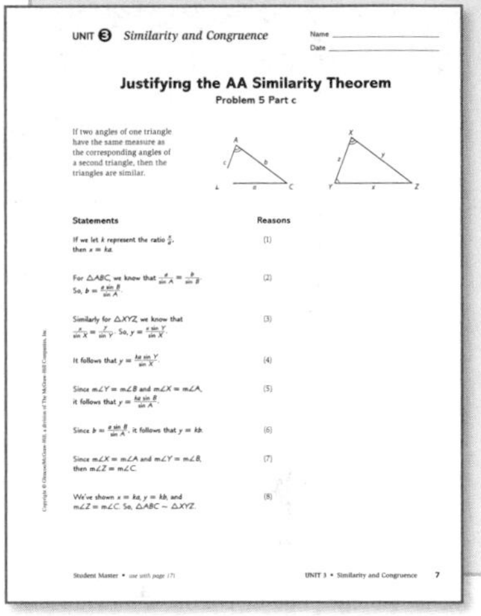

d. Students may notice the group could have repeated the first four steps of the proof using $\frac{b}{\sin B} = \frac{c}{\sin C}$ and $\frac{y}{\sin Y} = \frac{z}{\sin Z}$, concluding $z = kc$. Therefore, the triangles are similar by definition of similarity or by using the SSS Similarity Theorem (Problem 4).

e. *If the measures of two angles of one triangle are the same as the measures of two angles of another triangle, then the two triangles are similar.*
This is called the AA (Angle-Angle) Similarity Theorem.

Unit 3

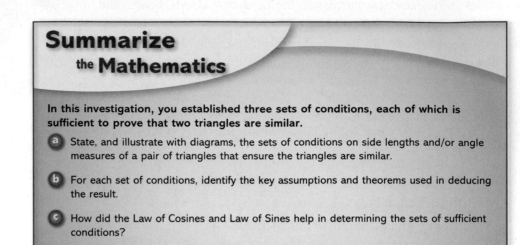

Summarize the Mathematics

In this investigation, you established three sets of conditions, each of which is sufficient to prove that two triangles are similar.

a State, and illustrate with diagrams, the sets of conditions on side lengths and/or angle measures of a pair of triangles that ensure the triangles are similar.

b For each set of conditions, identify the key assumptions and theorems used in deducing the result.

c How did the Law of Cosines and Law of Sines help in determining the sets of sufficient conditions?

Be prepared to share your descriptions and reasoning with the class.

✔ Check Your Understanding

The design of homes and office buildings often requires roof trusses that are of different sizes but have the same pitch. The trusses shown below are designed for roofs with solar hot-water collectors. For each Part a through e, suppose a pair of roof trusses have the given characteristics. Determine if △ABC ~ △PQR. If so, explain how you know that the triangles are similar and give the scale factor from △ABC to △PQR. If not, give a reason for your conclusion.

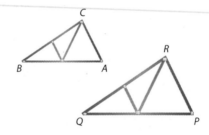

a. m∠A = 57°, m∠B = 38°, m∠P = 57°, m∠R = 95°

b. AB = 12, BC = 15, m∠B = 35°, PQ = 16, QR = 20, m∠Q = 35°

c. AB = BC, m∠B = m∠Q, PQ = QR

d. AC = 4, BC = 16, BA = 18, PR = 10, QR = 40, QP = 48

e. AB = 12, m∠A = 63°, m∠C = 83°, m∠P = 63°, m∠Q = 34°, PQ = 12

Part b provides an opportunity for students to think about when to use the Law of Sines or Law of Cosines. In particular, they should again recognize that when no angle measures are known, or when no angle measure and its opposite side length are known, the Law of Sines cannot be used to find other measures. But in the case of the AA Similarity proof, it could be used to show sides of two triangles are proportional.

Students can sometimes give the impression that they are fluent with the use of these theorems, while really they are skimming over the meaning. As part of this Summarize the Mathematics, you may want to provide some examples that challenge students to think about what they are saying. Such challenges might be drawings showing pairs of triangles that are not conveniently oriented, including reflections, and deliberately not drawn accurately, so that simple visual clues will not suffice. (See the example at the right.) Providing insufficient or disorganized information, such as two sides and a nonincluded angle, only two sides, two angles in one triangle (say 36° and 49°) and a different pair in another triangle (36° and 95°), or a special case with a right triangle and only two sides given, will give students an opportunity to explain what they are looking for and will give you a chance to assess their true understanding.

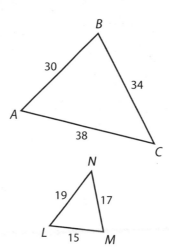

Summarize
the Mathematics

(a) SAS: If an angle of one triangle has the same measure as an angle of a second triangle, and if the lengths of the corresponding sides including these angles are multiplied by the same scale factor k, then the two triangles are similar.

If $DE = f$ and $D'E' = kf$, $DF = e$ and $D'F' = ke$, and $m\angle D = m\angle D'$, then the SAS Similarity Theorem guarantees $\triangle DEF \sim \triangle D'E'F'$.

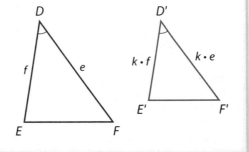

Unit 3

INSTRUCTIONAL NOTE
After the discussion in Part a, ask students why there is no need to have an ASA Similarity condition. They should recognize that the AA Similarity Theorem covers this condition.

SSS: If the lengths of the three sides of one triangle are multiplied by the same scale factor k to obtain the lengths of the three sides of a second triangle, then the triangles are similar.

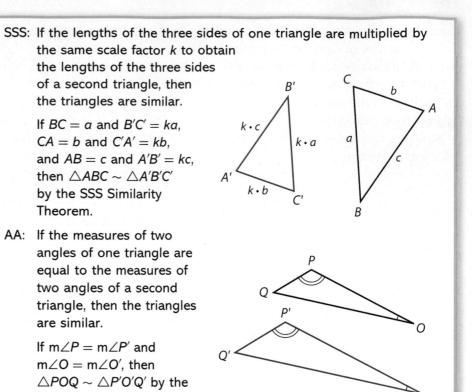

If $BC = a$ and $B'C' = ka$, $CA = b$ and $C'A' = kb$, and $AB = c$ and $A'B' = kc$, then $\triangle ABC \sim \triangle A'B'C'$ by the SSS Similarity Theorem.

AA: If the measures of two angles of one triangle are equal to the measures of two angles of a second triangle, then the triangles are similar.

If $m\angle P = m\angle P'$ and $m\angle O = m\angle O'$, then $\triangle POQ \sim \triangle P'O'Q'$ by the AA Similarity Theorem.

b To prove the SAS Similarity Theorem, we assumed two pairs of corresponding sides were related by a scale factor and the included corresponding angles were the same measure. The Law of Cosines was used to determine that the third pair of sides was related by the same scale factor. Then the Law of Sines was used to show corresponding angles had the same measure.

To prove the SSS Similarity Theorem, the Law of Cosines was used to determine that one pair of corresponding angles had the same measure; then the SAS theorem was used to prove similarity.

To prove the AA Similarity Theorem, the Law of Sines was used with the fact that two pairs of corresponding angles had the same measure to show that two pairs of corresponding side lengths were proportional. The remaining angles in the triangles have the same measure. Since this final pair of corresponding angles were included angles for the proportional sides, the triangles were proved similar by the SAS theorem.

c The Law of Cosines and Law of Sines helped in determining the sets of sufficient conditions for similar triangles because when certain side or angle measures are known, the remaining side or angle measures are uniquely determined by these laws.

MATH TOOLKIT State and illustrate with examples the three theorems that ensure two triangles are similar.

✔ Check Your Understanding

a. Not similar: From m∠A and m∠B, you can conclude m∠C = 85°. From m∠P and m∠R, you know m∠Q = 28°. There are not two pairs of equal angles.

b. Similar: The ratios $\frac{PQ}{AB}$ and $\frac{QR}{BC}$ are both equal to $\frac{4}{3}$ and the included angles (B and Q) have the same measure. By SAS, the triangles are similar. The scale factor from △ABC to △PQR is $\frac{4}{3}$.

c. Similar: The ratios of sides $\overline{PQ}$ to $\overline{AB}$ and $\overline{QR}$ to $\overline{BC}$ will be equal, and the included angles (B and Q) have the same measure. By SAS, the triangles are similar. The scale factor from △ABC to △PQR cannot be determined numerically; but symbolically, it is $\frac{PQ}{AB}$.

d. Not similar: $\frac{PQ}{AC} = \frac{5}{2} = \frac{QR}{BC}$, but $\frac{QP}{AB} = \frac{8}{3}$.

e. Similar: From m∠A and m∠C, you can conclude m∠B = 34°; then use the AA Similarity Theorem since m∠A = m∠P and m∠B = m∠Q. The scale factor from △ABC to △PQR is 1 since $\frac{PQ}{AB} = 1$.

Investigation 3 — Reasoning with Similarity Conditions

Similarity and proportionality are important ideas in mathematics. They provide tools for designing mechanisms, calculating heights and distances, and proving mathematical relationships. For example, a *pantograph* is a parallelogram linkage used for copying drawings and maps to a different scale. The pantograph is fastened down with a pivot at *F*. A stylus is inserted at *D*. A pencil is inserted at *P*. As the stylus at *D* traces out a path on the map, the pencil at *P* draws a scaled copy of that path.

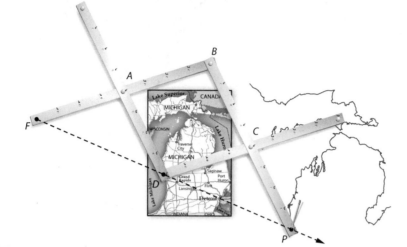

As you work on the problems of this investigation, look for answers to why a pantograph works as it does and the more general question:

What strategies are useful in solving problems using similar triangles?

1. **Designing Pantographs** Working with a partner, construct a model of a pantograph like the one shown below. Connect four linkage strips at points *A*, *B*, *C*, and *D* with paper fasteners.

   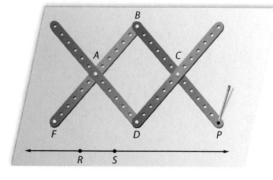

   a. Mark points *R* and *S* on a sheet of paper about two inches apart. Draw $\overleftrightarrow{RS}$. Place the pantograph so that point *F* is on the line near the left end. Label your placement of point *F* for future reference. Hold point *F* fixed. Place point *D* somewhere else on the line. Where is point *P* in relation to the line?

Investigation 3 — Reasoning with Similarity Conditions

In this investigation, students consider how similarity and proportionality are used in a variety of applied situations and in proving mathematical relationships such as the Midpoint Connector Theorem.

INSTRUCTIONAL NOTE When using the pantograph, students should work in pairs so one student can hold point F fixed by pressing a pencil point there. Alternatively, a paper fastener could be used to secure the pantograph on the line at point F. Also, distances should be measured by using the distances between holes as the unit of measure. For example, strip FB has length 12 units.

1   **a.** If F and D are both on $\overleftrightarrow{RS}$, then point P is also on line $\overleftrightarrow{RS}$.

As you move point *D* along the line:

   i. describe the path a pencil at point *P* follows.

   ii. what kind of quadrilateral is *ABCD*? Why?

   iii. how is the triangle determined by points *F*, *B*, and *P* related to the triangle determined by points *F*, *A*, and *D*? Explain your reasoning.

   iv. what can you conclude about the lengths *FP* and *FD*?

b. Now, holding point *F* fixed in the same place as before, find the image of point *S* by placing point *D* over point *S* and marking the location of point *P*. Label your mark as the image point *S′*. What is true about points *F*, *S*, and *S′*?

c. Keeping *F* fixed in the same position, find the image of point *R* in the same manner. Label it *R′*.

   i. What is true about the points *F*, *R*, and *R′*?

   ii. Compare the lengths *RS* and *R′S′*. How does the relationship compare with what you established in Part aiii?

d. Mark a point *T* on your paper so that △*RST* is a right triangle with right angle at *R*. Find the image of point *T* as you did for points *R* and *S*.

e. How is △*R′S′T′* related to △*RST*? Explain your reasoning.

2 Examine the pantograph illustrated in the diagram below.

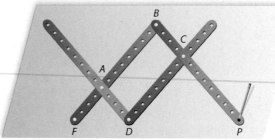

a. Draw a segment, $\overline{XY}$, that is 5 cm long. Imagine drawing the image of $\overline{XY}$ with this pantograph. Predict the length of the image $\overline{X'Y'}$. Explain the basis for your prediction and then check it using your pantograph.

b. How would you assemble your pantograph so that it multiplies distances by 4?

c. How will the pantograph affect distances if it is assembled so that $FB = k \cdot FA$? Why?

i. Point *P* will follow a path of a straight line (along $\overleftrightarrow{RS}$).

ii. Quadrilateral *ABCD* is a rhombus (a parallelogram with four sides the same length).

iii. △*FBP* ~ △*FAD* (AA Similarity Theorem). Since m∠*F* = m∠*F*, $\overline{AD} \parallel \overline{BP}$ implies corresponding angles ∠*FAD* and ∠*FBP* have equal measure. Alternatively, notice that $\frac{FB}{FA} = \frac{BP}{AD} = \frac{2}{1}$ and m∠*FAD* = m∠*FBP* (since ∠*FAD* is supplementary to ∠*BAD*, and ∠*FBP* is consecutive to ∠*BAD* in a parallelogram). So by the SAS Similarity Theorem, the triangles are similar.

iv. Since △*FBP* ~ △*FAD*, *FP* = 2*FD*.

b. A possible sketch is shown at the right. *F*, *S*, and *S'* are collinear.

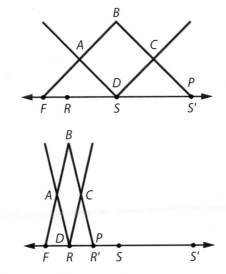

c. **i.** *F*, *R*, and *R'* are collinear.

ii. *R'S'* = 2*RS*. This is the same relationship established in Part aiv for $\overline{FD}$ and $\overline{FP}$.

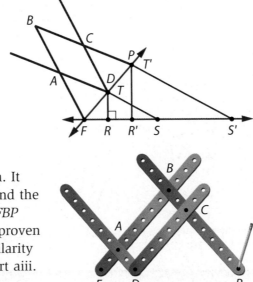

d. Students will have a drawing on their paper. They can place a corner of a sheet of paper at *R*. The corner will be a vertex of a right angle. Alternatively, they could use a protractor or make a compass and straightedge construction.

e. 2*FT* = *FT'*
2*FR* = *FR'*
Therefore, △*FRT* ~ △*F'R'T'* (SAS) with a scale factor of 2.
2*TR* = *T'R'*
2*RS* = *R'S'*
So, △*TRS* ~ △*T'R'S'* (SAS), again with a scale factor of 2.

2 **a.** Since *FB* = 3*FA*, a reasonable prediction is that *X'Y'* = 15 cm. It appears that △*FAD* ~ △*FBP* and the scale factor from △*FAD* to △*FBP* is 3. This relationship can be proven true using the AA or SAS Similarity Theorems, as in Problem 1 Part aiii.

b. Assemble it so that *FB* = 4*FA*, *BP* = 4*BC*, *AD* = *BC*, and *AB* = *DC*.

c. The pantograph will scale image lengths to *k* times the corresponding preimage lengths. As in Problem 1 Part aiii, △*FAD* ~ △*FBP* by the AA or SAS Similarity Theorems. The scale factor from △*FAD* to △*FBP* is *k*.

③ Calculating Heights and Distances In Course 2, you
calculated the height of Chicago's *Bat Column* and other structures
using trigonometry. Triangle similarity provides another method.

Suppose a mirror is placed on the ground as shown. You position
yourself to see the top of the sculpture reflected in the mirror. An
important property of physics states that in such a case, the *angle of
incidence* is congruent to the *angle of reflection*.

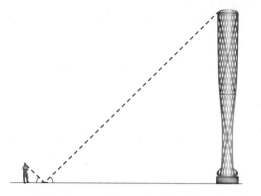

a. On a copy of the diagram above, sketch and label a pair of
triangles which, if proven similar, could be used to calculate the
height of the *Bat Column*. Write a similarity statement relating
the triangles you identified.

b. Prove that the two identified triangles are similar.

c. Add to your diagram the following measurements.

- The ground distance between you and the mirror image of the
top of the column is 6 feet 5 inches.

- The ground distance between the mirror image and the base
of the column is 116 feet 8 inches.

- Assume that the distance from the ground up to your eyes
is 66 inches.

About how tall is the column?

d. How could you use a trigonometric ratio and the ground distance
from the mirror image to the column to calculate the height of the
Bat Column? What measurement would you need? How could you
obtain it?

④ As part of their annual October outing to study the changing colors
of trees in northern Maine, several science club members from
Poland Regional High School decided to test what they were
learning in their math class by finding the width of the Penobscot
River at a particular point *A* as shown on the next page.

3 **a.** Similarity statement to be proved: $\triangle ABC \sim \triangle EDC$
(The measurements in the diagram are for Part c below.)

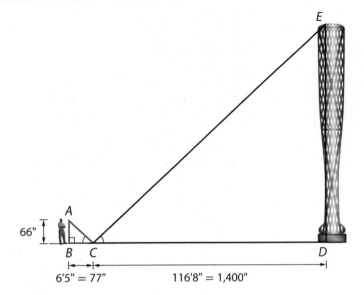

b. Since you and *Bat Column* can be assumed to be perpendicular to the ground, $m\angle B = m\angle D$. In the diagram, we are given that $m\angle ACB = m\angle ECD$. (The angle of incidence is the same measure as the angle of reflection.) So by the AA Similarity Theorem, $\triangle ABC \sim \triangle EDC$.

c. Using the labeling scheme from Part a:

$$\frac{ED}{AB} = \frac{DC}{BC}$$

$$ED = AB\left(\frac{DC}{BC}\right)$$

$$= 66\left(\frac{1,400}{77}\right)$$

$$= 1,200 \text{ inches, or } 100 \text{ feet}$$

An alternative solution method is:

Since $\triangle ABC \sim \triangle EDC$, $DC = k \cdot BC$.
To find k, solve $DC = k \cdot BC$.
$$1,400 = 77k$$
$$k = \frac{1,400}{77}$$
To find ED, solve: $ED = \frac{1,400}{77} \cdot 66 = 1,200$ inches, or 100 feet

d. You can calculate the height of *Bat Column* if you know the measure of the angle of reflection. $ED = (\tan \angle ECD)(CD) = (\tan \angle ACB)(CD)$. The measure of the angle of reflection, $\angle ECD$, could be found by calculating $90° - m\angle BAC$ since $m\angle BAC + m\angle ACB = 90°$ and $m\angle ACB = m\angle ECD$. Thus, $m\angle BAC$ could be found as the angle of sighting to the mirror.

INSTRUCTIONAL NOTE
Some students may suggest measuring the angle of elevation $\angle ECD$. The solution to Part d at the left assumes that angle cannot be measured by the person using the mirror.

Unit 3

Pacing from point *A*, they located points *D*, *E*, and *C* as shown in the diagram below.

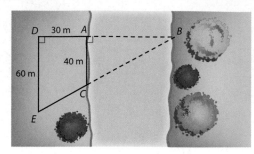

a. How do you think they used similarity to calculate the distance *AB*? Be as precise as possible in your answer.

b. What is your estimate of the width of the river at point *A*?

c. Another group of students repeated the measurement, again pacing from point *A* to locate points *D*, *E*, and *C*. In this case, *AD* = 18 m, *DE* = 26 m, and *AC* = 20 m. Would you expect that this second group got the same estimate for the width of the river as you did in Part b? Explain.

d. What trigonometric ratio could be used to calculate the width of the river? What measurements would you need and how could you obtain them?

⑤ **Discovering and Proving New Relationships** Study the diagram below of △*ABC*. $\overline{MN}$ connects the midpoints *M* and *N* of sides $\overline{AB}$ and $\overline{BC}$, respectively.

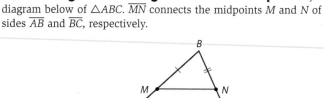

a. How does $\overline{MN}$ appear to be related to $\overline{AC}$?

b. How does the length of $\overline{MN}$ appear to be related to the length of $\overline{AC}$?

c. Use interactive geometry software or careful paper-and-pencil drawings to investigate if your observations in Parts a and b hold for triangles of different shapes. Compare your findings with those of your classmates.

d. Complete the following statement.

If a line segment joins the midpoints of two sides of a triangle, then it … .

e. Collaborating with others as needed, write a proof of the statement in Part d. That statement is often called the **Midpoint Connector Theorem for Triangles**.

4. **a.** Responses may vary. One response might be to note that $\triangle DBE \sim \triangle ABC$ by the AA Similarity Theorem. Then the scale factor from $\triangle DBE$ to $\triangle ABC$ $\left(\frac{40}{60}\right)$ can be used to find AB.

b. To find the scale factor from $\triangle DBE$ to $\triangle ABC$ (as identified in Part a), use the known measures of corresponding sides, AC and DE, to get $k = \frac{40}{60} = \frac{2}{3}$. To solve for AB, let $x = AB$ and $DB = x + 30$.

$$x = \frac{2}{3}(x + 30)$$
$$3x = 2x + 60$$
$$x = 60 \text{ meters (Encourage students to check their work.)}$$

c. Yes. This time, the scale factor from $\triangle DBE$ to $\triangle ABC$ is $\frac{20}{26} = \frac{10}{13}$. If, as before, $x = AB$, then $DB = x + 18$ and $x = \frac{10}{13}(x + 18)$. So, $x = 60$ meters.

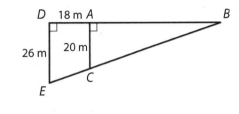

d. The tangent function could be used since we know the length of one leg of right $\triangle ABC$ and want to find the length of the other leg. You need to measure $\angle E$ (or its congruent angle $\angle C$). You can find the measure using a sighting tool or by marking $\angle DEB$ on the ground. Then $\tan \angle C = \frac{AB}{AC}$, so $AB = AC(\tan \angle C)$ meters.

5. **a.** $\overline{MN}$ appears to be parallel to $\overline{AC}$.

b. MN appears to be one-half of AC.

c. Student drawings should support the hypotheses in Parts a and b.

d. The Midpoint Connector Theorem for Triangles
If a line segment joins the midpoints of two sides of a triangle, then it is parallel to the third side of the triangle and half the length of the third side.

e. See the diagram at the right. If point M is the midpoint of $\overline{AB}$, then $AB = 2MB$. If point N is the midpoint of $\overline{BC}$, then $BC = 2BN$. Since $AB = 2MB$, $BC = 2BN$, and $m\angle B = m\angle B$, $\triangle ABC \sim \triangle MBN$ (SAS Similarity Theorem). The scale factor from $\triangle ABC$ to $\triangle MBN$ is $\frac{1}{2}$. So, $MN = \frac{1}{2}AC$. Since $\triangle ABC \sim \triangle MBN$, $m\angle BMN = m\angle BAC$ because corresponding angles of similar triangles have equal measure. $\angle BMN$ and $\angle BAC$ are congruent corresponding angles formed by $\overline{MN}$, $\overline{AC}$, and transversal $\overline{AB}$, so $\overleftrightarrow{MN} \parallel \overleftrightarrow{AC}$.

MATH TOOLKIT NOTE
Students should add the Midpoint Connector Theorem for Triangles to the list of theorems.

Unit 3

6 Possible new theorems are often discovered by studying several cases and looking for patterns as you did in Problem 5. Another way of generating possible theorems is to modify the statement of a theorem you have already proven. For example, consider the following statement.

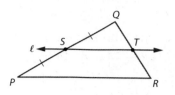

> *If a line intersects the midpoint of one side of a triangle and is parallel to a second side, then it intersects the third side at its midpoint.*

Do you think this statement is always true? If so, prove it. If not, provide a counterexample.

Proving Properties of Size Transformations In Course 2, you studied size transformations with center at the origin, defined by coordinate rules of the form $(x, y) \rightarrow (kx, ky)$, where $k > 0$. Your work with pantographs suggests a way of defining size transformations without using coordinates and with *any* point in the plane as the center.

For any point C and real number $k > 0$, a **size transformation** with **center** C and **magnitude** k is a function that maps each point of the plane onto an image point as follows:

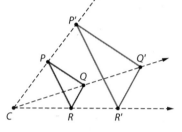

- Point C is its own image.
- For any point P other than C, the image of point P is the point P' on $\overrightarrow{CP}$ for which $CP' = k \cdot CP$.

7 Use the definition of a size transformation and the diagram below to prove each statement.

> *If a size transformation with center C and magnitude k maps A onto A' and B onto B', then:*

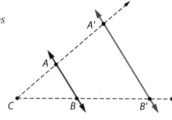

- $A'B' = k \cdot AB$
- $\overleftrightarrow{A'B'} \parallel \overline{AB}$

8 In the diagram below, $\triangle E'F'G'$ is the image of $\triangle EFG$ under a size transformation with center C and magnitude k.

a. What is true of magnitude k?

b. How do $\angle FEG$ and $\angle F'E'G'$ appear to be related?

c. How do $\triangle EFG$ and $\triangle E'F'G'$ appear to be related?

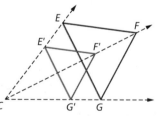

6 Yes. We know that $\overleftrightarrow{ST} \parallel \overline{PR}$. Thus, m$\angle QST =$ m$\angle QPR$ (corresponding angles formed by a transversal and parallel lines). Also, $\angle Q$ is an angle of $\triangle SQT$ and $\triangle PQR$. So, $\triangle PQR \sim \triangle SQT$ (AA Similarity Theorem). Notice that $SQ = \frac{1}{2}PQ$, so the scale factor from $\triangle PQR$ to $\triangle SQT$ is $\frac{1}{2}$. Thus, $QT = \frac{1}{2}QR$ and T is the midpoint of $\overline{QR}$.

7 • $CA' = k \cdot CA$ and $CB' = k \cdot CB$
          (definition of a size transformation and the given diagram)
   m$\angle C =$ m$\angle C$ (common to both $\triangle ABC$ and $\triangle A'B'C$)
   $\triangle ABC \sim \triangle A'B'C$
          (SAS Similarity Theorem)

The scale factor from $\triangle ABC$ to $\triangle A'B'C$ is k. Thus, $A'B' = k \cdot AB$.
          (definition of similar triangles)

• Since $\triangle ABC \sim \triangle A'B'C$, m$\angle ABC =$ m$\angle A'B'C$. If you consider $\overrightarrow{CB'}$ to be a transversal of $\overleftrightarrow{AB}$ and $\overleftrightarrow{A'B'}$, notice that $\angle ABC$ and $\angle A'B'C$ are corresponding angles with equal measures. So, $\overleftrightarrow{AB} \parallel \overleftrightarrow{A'B'}$.

8 **a.** $k = \dfrac{E'C}{EC} = \dfrac{F'C}{FC} = \dfrac{G'C}{GC}$ and $0 < k < 1$.
   b. The angles appear to be congruent.
   c. The triangles appear to be similar.

> **INSTRUCTIONAL NOTE**
> The Midpoint Connector Theorem is a special case when $k = 2$ of the statements proved in Problem 7.

d. Use the diagram (bottom of page 177) and the results of Problem 7 to help you prove these generalizations of your observations.

- *Under a size transformation, a triangle and its image are similar.*

- *Under a size transformation, an angle and its image are congruent.*

Summarize
the Mathematics

In this investigation, you explored how conditions for similarity of triangles could be used to solve applied problems and to prove important mathematical relationships.

a How would you assemble a pantograph to make an enlargement of a shape using a scale factor of 8? Of *r*?

b How could you calculate the height of a structure like the *Bat Column* using shadows cast on a sunny day?

c Suppose in a diagram, △*M'N'O'* is the image of △*MNO* under a size transformation of magnitude $k \neq 1$.

   i. How could you locate the center of the size transformation?

   ii. How could you determine the magnitude *k*?

   iii. How are the side lengths and angle measures of the two triangles related?

d What strategies are helpful in using similarity to solve problems in applied contexts? To prove mathematical statements?

Be prepared to explain your ideas and strategies to the class.

✓Check Your Understanding

Examine the diagram of a pantograph enlargement of △*PQR*.

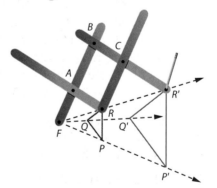

a. Prove each statement.

   i. △*FAR* ~ △*FBR'*

   ii. △*FRQ* ~ △*FR'Q'*

   iii. △*PQR* ~ △*P'Q'R'*

b. How could you represent the scale factor of this enlargement?

c. Describe the center and magnitude of a size transformation that will map △*P'Q'R'* onto △*PQR*.

d. • From Problem 7, we know that the length of each image segment will be k times the length of the original segment. Thus, $E'F' = k \cdot EF$, $F'G' = k \cdot FG$, and $E'G' = k \cdot EG$. So, $\triangle EFG \sim \triangle E'F'G'$ (SSS Similarity Theorem).

• For any angle, you can form a triangle. The image angle will be congruent to the original angle because the triangle and its size-transformed image are similar.

Summarize
the Mathematics

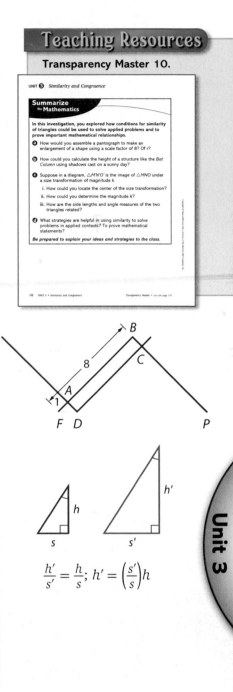

a Using the labels used in Problems 1 and 2, the pantograph should be assembled so that F, D, and P are collinear, $\overline{FB} \parallel \overline{DC}$ and $\overline{AD} \parallel \overline{BP}$. The scale factor from the smaller triangle ($\triangle FAD$) to the larger triangle ($\triangle FBP$) must be 8. Thus, $FB = 8FA$. For a scale factor of r, $FB = r \cdot FA$.

b Use the height of a known object (such as yourself, or a measurable object) perpendicular to the ground. Note that the angle that the sun shines to cast a shadow will be equal for both objects. The triangles formed by the objects and their shadows are similar triangles (90° angles and congruent shadow angles). The scale factor from the measurable object to the nonmeasurable object is the ratio of the length of the nonmeasurable object's shadow to the measurable object's shadow. Once the scale factor k is found, the height of the nonmeasurable object is the height of the measurable object times k.

c **i.** Draw two of the lines $\overleftrightarrow{OO'}$, $\overleftrightarrow{MM'}$, or $\overleftrightarrow{NN'}$. Their point of intersection is the center of the size transformation.

ii. The magnitude of the size transformation is the ratio of the distance of an image point from the center to the distance of the preimage point from the center. More formally, call the center of the size transformation point C. Then the magnitude of the size transformation from $\triangle MNO$ to $\triangle M'N'O'$ is the common ratio $\dfrac{CM'}{CM}$, $\dfrac{CN'}{CN}$, or $\dfrac{CO'}{CO}$.

iii. Corresponding side lengths are proportional with common ratio the magnitude in part ii. Corresponding angle measures are equal.

d For applied problems, it is helpful to identify similar triangles where the length x of one side of a triangle is to be found. Then determine the scale factor from one triangle to the other and use this to find the unknown length x. To use this strategy, you need to know in the second triangle, the length of its side corresponding to x. (Sometimes in applied problems, you need to measure some lengths.)

To prove mathematical statements, it is helpful to make diagrams and label the diagrams. Then look for conditions that ensure similar triangles or use given similar triangles to deduce congruent angles and side lengths related by a scale factor. Conditions to ensure similarity are the AA, SAS, and SSS Similarity Theorems.

✔ Check Your Understanding

INSTRUCTIONAL NOTE Since it is given that the enlargement was performed using a pantograph, it can be assumed that $\overline{FB}$ and $\overline{RC}$ are parallel, that $\overline{AR}$ and $\overline{BC}$ are parallel, and that F, R, R' are collinear. (It will be important that students have summarized this known information in the STM.)

a.
  i. $\triangle FAR \sim \triangle FBR'$ by the AA Similarity Theorem since $\overline{AR} \parallel \overline{BR'}$ implies corresponding angles $\angle FAR$ and $\angle FBR'$ have equal measure and $m\angle F = m\angle F$.

  ii. By construction with the pantograph, $FR' = k \cdot FR$, $FQ' = k \cdot FQ$, and $m\angle RFQ = m\angle R'FQ'$. By the SAS Similarity Theorem, $\triangle FRQ \sim \triangle FR'Q'$ and the scale factor from $\triangle FRQ$ to $\triangle FR'Q'$ is k.

  iii. From part ii, the scale factor from $\triangle FRQ$ to $\triangle FR'Q'$ is k, so $Q'R' = k \cdot QR$. By construction with the pantograph, $FP' = k \cdot FP$ and $FQ' = k \cdot FQ$, and $m\angle Q'FP' = m\angle QFP$. Thus, $\triangle FPQ \sim \triangle FP'Q'$ (SAS Similarity Theorem), and so $Q'P' = k \cdot QP$. Similarly, $\triangle FPR \sim \triangle FP'R'$ with scale factor k, so $P'R' = k \cdot PR$. By the SSS Similarity Theorem, $\triangle PQR \sim \triangle P'Q'R'$.

b. The scale factor is $\frac{FB}{FA}$.

c. The center of the size transformation is F. The scale factor from $\triangle P'Q'R'$ to $\triangle PQR$ can be represented as $\frac{FR}{FR'}$, $\frac{FQ}{FQ'}$, $\frac{FP}{FP'}$, or $\frac{FB}{FA}$.

Teacher Notes

Applications

1 A flashlight is directed perpendicularly at a vertical wall 24 cm away. A cardboard triangle with sides of lengths 3, 4, and 5 cm is positioned directly between the light and the wall, parallel to the wall so that its projected shadow image is similar to it.

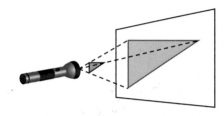

   a. Suppose the shadow of the 4-cm side is 10 cm. Find the lengths of the shadows of the other two sides.

   b. Suppose the shadow of the 5-cm side is 7.5 cm. Find the lengths of the other two sides of the shadow.

   c. How far from the light source should you place the cardboard triangle so that the 4-cm side has a 12-cm shadow?

2 While pumping gas on his way to work, Josh witnessed a robber run out of the station, get into his car, and drive off. An off-duty police detective, Josh knew that he needed to document the scene before the evidence was destroyed. Using his cell phone camera and whatever he could find in his pockets, Josh took the following four pictures.

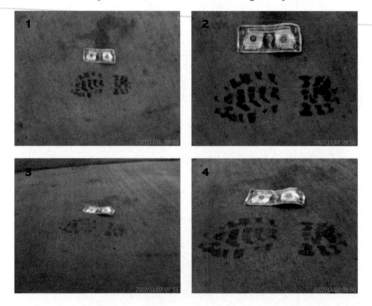

Applications

1 **a.** The scale factor from the preimage triangle to the image triangle is $\frac{10}{4} = \frac{5}{2}$, so the lengths of the images of the 3-cm and 5-cm sides are 7.5 cm and 12.5 cm, respectively.

b. In this case, the scale factor from the preimage triangle to the image triangle is $\frac{3}{2}$, so the lengths of the images of the 3-cm and 4-cm sides are 4.5 cm and 6 cm, respectively.

c. Since you want the 4-cm side to increase to 12 cm, the needed scale factor from the preimage triangle to the image triangle is 3. Since the flashlight is 24 cm from the wall, placing the cardboard triangle 8 cm from the flashlight will produce the scale factor of 3 $\left(\frac{1}{3} \text{ of 24 is 8} \right)$.

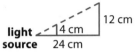

a. Consider the dimensions of the standard dollar bill in each of the photos. In each case below, which photo provides more useful or reliable information? Explain your reasoning.

   i. Photo 1 or Photo 2

   ii. Photo 3 or Photo 4

b. How could a technician use your selected photos to calculate the actual dimensions of the impression? What are those dimensions?

c. Would you need to consider two photos to determine the actual dimensions of the impression, or could you use just one? How might having two different photos strengthen the case?

3 Amber and Christina had different ideas about how to use grid paper to reduce triangles to half their original size. Each was given $\triangle ABC$ drawn on half-inch grid paper. Amber drew $\triangle A'B'C'$ as shown on quarter-inch grid paper. Christina drew $\triangle A''B''C''$ as shown on half-inch grid paper.

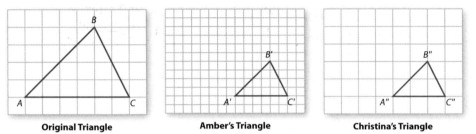

| Original Triangle | Amber's Triangle | Christina's Triangle |

a. Explain why Amber's triangle is similar to the original. What is the scale factor?

b. Explain why Christina's triangle is similar to the original and has a scale factor of $\frac{1}{2}$.

c. Are Christina's triangle and Amber's triangle similar to one another? If so, what is the scale factor?

4 Examine each pair of triangles. Using the information given, determine whether the triangles are similar or the information is inconclusive. Explain your reasoning.

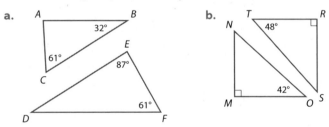

a.

b.

2 a. i. Photo 2: Both photos were taken parallel to the plane of the footwear impression, yet Photo 2 provides more useful information regarding the actual size of the impression because a known measurable object (standard dollar bill) is positioned next to the impression. It is impossible to determine anything about the actual size of the print in Photo 1 because there are no known measurable objects in the photo.

ii. Photo 3: Both photos include the dollar bill in order to determine the actual size of the print, yet the scaled image shown in Photo 4 provides less reliable information because the camera was not aligned parallel to the plane of the object (the image is skewed).

b. Since the actual size of a dollar bill is known (6.14 in. × 2.61 in. ≈ 156 mm × 66 mm), a technician could use the dimensions of the dollar bill in Photo 2 or Photo 3 to determine a scale factor from the dimensions of the dollar in the photo to its actual dimensions. With this scale factor, the actual dimensions of the footprint can be determined.

Approximate dimensions of dollar bill from Photo 2: 22 mm × 9 mm

$(actual\ dimensions) = k(photo\ dimensions)$, or $k = \dfrac{actual\ dimensions}{photo\ dimensions}$

$\dfrac{156\ mm}{22\ mm} \approx 7.09$ and $\dfrac{66\ mm}{9\ mm} \approx 7.33$

A reasonable estimate for a scale factor is 7.2.

Approximate dimensions of impression at longest and widest parts from Photo 2: 44 mm × 17 mm

$actual\ length \approx (7.2)(44\ mm) = 317\ mm$

$actual\ width \approx (7.2)(17\ mm) = 122\ mm$

c. One photo would be sufficient, but having multiple photos would certainly strengthen the case. There are actually very strict guidelines for investigators regarding the types of photos that need to be taken for a particular case to fully document a crime scene. Having close up, midrange, and wide range photos is helpful for setting the scene, for determining more information about the crime, and for making accurate estimates of size.

3 a. If you measure the lengths of the sides of Amber's triangle by units on the quarter-inch grid, the sides are the same number of units as the original triangle. Thus, the corresponding side lengths for all sides of $\triangle A'B'C'$ are $\frac{1}{2}$ the lengths of the sides of $\triangle ABC$, so the scale factor from $\triangle ABC$ to $\triangle A'B'C'$ is $\frac{1}{2}$.

b. $AC = 3"$ $\qquad\qquad A''C'' = 1.5"$ $\qquad\qquad AB = \sqrt{8} = 2\sqrt{2}\,"$

$A''B'' = \sqrt{2}\,"$ $\qquad\quad BC = \sqrt{5}\,"$ $\qquad\qquad B''C'' = \sqrt{\dfrac{5}{4}} = \dfrac{1}{2}\sqrt{5}\,"$

Christina's triangle ($\triangle A''B''C''$) is similar to the original triangle ($\triangle ABC$) (SSS Similarity Theorem). The scale factor from $\triangle ABC$ to $\triangle A''B''C''$ is $\frac{1}{2}$.

c. Yes, the scale factor from Amber's to Christina's triangles is 1 (they are congruent).

4 a. $\triangle ABC \sim \triangle EDF$:

$m\angle D = 180° - 87° - 61° = 32° = m\angle B$ and $m\angle F = 61° = m\angle C$.

So by the AA Similarity Theorem, the triangles are similar.

b. $\triangle MNO \sim \triangle RTS$:

$m\angle N = 180° - 90° - 42° = 48° = m\angle T$ and $m\angle M = 90° = m\angle R$.

So by the AA Similarity Theorem, the triangles are similar.

Unit 3

c.

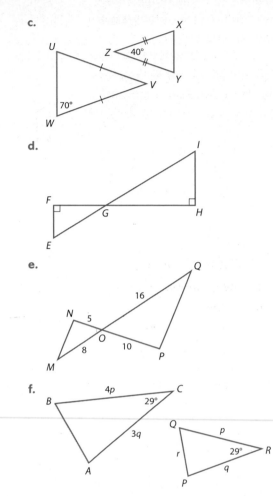

d.

e.

f.

⑤ In the diagram below, △*ABC* is a right triangle. $\overline{BD}$ is the altitude drawn to the hypotenuse $\overline{AC}$.

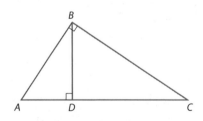

a. Identify three pairs of similar triangles. Be sure that corresponding vertices are labeled in the same order.

b. Describe the strategies you would use to prove each pair of triangles similar.

LESSON 1 • Reasoning about Similar Triangles **181**

c. $\triangle UVW \sim \triangle YZX$ and $\triangle UVW \sim \triangle XZY$:

$\triangle UVW$ and $\triangle YZX$ are isosceles triangles, so m$\angle U =$ m$\angle W = 70°$ and m$\angle X =$ m$\angle Y = \dfrac{180° - 40°}{2} = 70°$. So by the AA Similarity Theorem or the SAS Similarity Theorem, the triangles are similar.

d. $\triangle FGE \sim \triangle HGI$:

Since $\angle FGE$ and $\angle HGI$ are vertical angles, they have the same measure. Since $\angle F$ and $\angle H$ are right angles, they have the same measure. So by the AA Similarity Theorem, the triangles are similar.

e. $\triangle MNO \sim \triangle QPO$:

$PO = 2NO$, $QO = 2MO$, and m$\angle NOM =$ m$\angle POQ$ (vertical angles). So by the SAS Similarity Theorem, the triangles are similar.

f. $\triangle ABC$ is not similar to $\triangle PQR$ or $\triangle PRQ$ because the corresponding sides are not related by the same scale factor.

5 **a.** $\triangle ABC \sim \triangle ADB$, $\triangle ABC \sim \triangle BDC$, $\triangle BDC \sim \triangle ADB$

b. Student strategies will likely utilize the AA Similarity Theorem.

(1) $\triangle ABC \sim \triangle ADB$; use the right angles and the common angle at A.

(2) $\triangle ABC \sim \triangle BDC$; use the right angles and the common angle at C.

(3) $\triangle BCD \sim \triangle ABD$; use the right angles and identify another pair of angles having the same measure based on corresponding pairs of angles from (1) or (2) above. For example, m$\angle ABD =$ m$\angle ACB$ from (1), so m$\angle ABD =$ m$\angle BCD$ (C is the common angle).

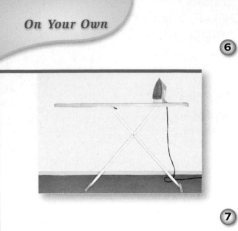

6 Most ironing boards can be adjusted to different heights. One ironing board, with a design similar to the one shown here, has legs that are each 110 cm long and are hinged at a point that is 40 cm from the top end of each. Possible working heights are 90 cm, 85 cm, 80 cm, 75 cm, and 70 cm.

a. Make a sketch of the ironing board, labeling vertices of important triangles. Carefully explain why, for any of the working heights, the surface of the ironing board is parallel to the floor.

b. For a working height of 90 cm, determine the distance between the two points at which the legs connect to the ironing board. Find the measures of the angles of the top triangle.

7 In Investigation 2, you established three sets of conditions that are sufficient to prove that two triangles are similar: SAS, SSS, and AA. Here, you are asked to replace the word "triangle" in these statements with the word "parallelogram." Then decide if the new statement is true or not.

a. Rewrite the SAS Similarity Theorem for triangles as a statement about two parallelograms. Prove or disprove your statement.

b. Rewrite the SSS Similarity Theorem for triangles as a statement about two parallelograms. Prove or disprove your statement.

c. Rewrite the AA Similarity Theorem for triangles as a statement about two parallelograms. Prove or disprove your statement.

8 Wildlife photographers use sophisticated film cameras in their field work. Negatives from the film are then resized for publication in books and magazines. In this task, you will examine how a photographic enlarger uses the principles of size transformations. The light source is the center of the size transformation, a photographic negative or slide is the preimage, and the projection onto the photographic paper is the image. On one enlarger, the distance between the light source and film negative is fixed at 5 cm. The distance between the paper and the negative adjusts to distances between 5 cm and 30 cm.

a. If the distance from the light source to the paper is 20 cm, what ratio gives the magnitude of the size transformation represented?

b. If the distance between the negative and the paper is 8 cm, what is the magnitude of the size transformation?

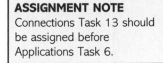

6 a. To justify $\overleftrightarrow{AD} \parallel \overleftrightarrow{BC}$, we could determine that $\angle 1 \cong \angle 4$ or $\angle 2 \cong \angle 3$. These pairs are alternate interior angles for $\overleftrightarrow{AD}$ and $\overleftrightarrow{BC}$. Students might use the congruent vertical angles to explain why $\angle 1 \cong \angle 2 \cong \angle 3 \cong \angle 4$. (Note that $m\angle 1 = m\angle 2 = \frac{1}{2}(180° - m\angle DEA) = \frac{1}{2}(180° - m\angle CEB) = m\angle 3 = m\angle 4$.)

Alternatively, students could use the scale factor of $\frac{4}{7}$ relating $\triangle CEB$ to $\triangle AED$ for $\overline{AE}$ and $\overline{CE}$, and $\overline{DE}$ and $\overline{BE}$, along with the vertical angles to deduce that $\triangle AED \sim \triangle CEB$ (SAS Similarity Theorem). Then the alternate interior angles are congruent because they are corresponding angles of similar triangles. Thus, $\overleftrightarrow{AD} \parallel \overleftrightarrow{BC}$.

ASSIGNMENT NOTE
Connections Task 13 should be assigned before Applications Task 6.

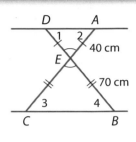

b. 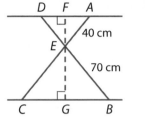 The altitudes of the similar triangles are in the same proportion as the sides. Use $4x$ for EF and $7x$ for EG.

$$4x + 7x = 90$$
$$11x = 90$$
$$x = \frac{90}{11} \approx 8.18$$
$$EF = 4x = 32.72 \text{ cm}$$

Find AD:
$$AF = \sqrt{40^2 - 32.72^2} \approx 23 \text{ cm}$$
$$AD = 2AF \approx 46 \text{ cm}$$
$$m\angle DAE = \sin^{-1}\left(\frac{32.72}{40}\right) \approx 55°$$

7 Known about parallelograms: opposite sides are parallel, opposite sides are congruent, opposite angles are congruent, consecutive angles are supplementary.

a. SAS similarity conjecture for parallelograms:
If the lengths of two consecutive sides of one parallelogram are related by a scale factor k to the lengths of two consecutive sides of a second parallelogram and the included angles are the same measure, then the parallelograms are similar.

PROOF SUPPORT
Since this is an individual task, you may wish to provide students with a two-column format of this proof and possible reasons to provide for each step. See Student Masters 11 and 12.

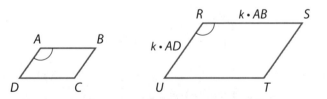

Proof: Given two arbitrary parallelograms $ABCD$ and $RSTU$, suppose you know $\angle A \cong \angle R$, $RS = k \cdot AB$, and $RU = k \cdot AD$. By definition of a parallelogram, $\overline{AB} \cong \overline{CD}$ and $\overline{RS} \cong \overline{TU}$, so $TU = k \cdot CD$. Similarly, $\overline{AD} \cong \overline{BC}$ and $\overline{RU} \cong \overline{ST}$, so $ST = k \cdot BC$. Furthermore, since opposite angles are congruent, $\angle A \cong \angle C$ and $\angle R \cong \angle T$, and since $\angle A \cong \angle R$, $\angle C \cong \angle T$. Additionally, $\angle B \cong \angle D$ and $\angle S \cong \angle U$. Since consecutive angles in a parallelogram are supplementary, $m\angle A + m\angle D = 180° = m\angle R + m\angle U$. Since $m\angle A = m\angle R$, $m\angle D = m\angle U$. Finally, $m\angle B = m\angle S$ because $m\angle D = m\angle B$ and $m\angle U = m\angle S$. Since pairs of corresponding side lengths are related by the same scale factor and corresponding angles are the same measure, $\square ABCD \sim \square RSTU$.

Thus, we have proved the SAS Similarity Theorem for parallelograms.

Teaching Resources

Student Masters 11–12.

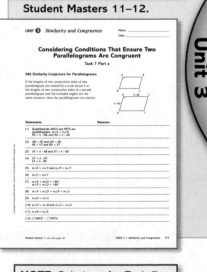

NOTE Solutions for Task 7 Parts b and c and Task 8 Parts a and b are on page T183.

c. Deonna uses 35 mm film in her camera, so her negatives measure 35 mm by 23 mm.

   i. When the paper is 5 cm from the negative, her prints are 70 mm by 46 mm (7.0 cm by 4.6 cm). Use a diagram and your understanding of size transformations to explain why this is the case.

   ii. When she adjusts the distance between the paper and the negative to 10 cm, her prints are 105 mm by 69 mm (10.5 cm by 6.9 cm). Explain why this is the case.

   iii. What is the magnitude of the enlargement in each of the two settings above? How does this affect the distances involving the light source, negative, and photographic paper?

d. Recall that the distance between the paper and the negative can be adjusted to distances from 5 cm to 30 cm. What are the dimensions of the *smallest* print that Deonna can make from a negative using this brand of enlarger? What are the dimensions of the *largest* print?

e. Suppose the paper is 20 cm from Deonna's negative. What size print is produced?

f. How far should the paper be from Deonna's negative to produce a print whose longest side is 12 cm?

9 In the diagram below, quadrilateral *PQRS* is a parallelogram, $\overline{SQ}$ is a diagonal, and $\overleftrightarrow{SQ} \parallel \overleftrightarrow{XY}$.

a. Prove that $\triangle XYR \sim \triangle SQR$.

b. Prove that $\triangle XYR \sim \triangle QSP$.

c. Identify the center and magnitude of a size transformation that maps $\triangle RXY$ onto $\triangle RSQ$.

10 Using interactive geometry software (without coordinates) or paper and pencil, conduct the following experiment.

- Draw $\triangle ABC$.
- Mark a point D and then find the image of $\triangle ABC$ under a size transformation with center at D and scale factor 3. Label the image $\triangle A'B'C'$.
- Mark a second point E and then find the image of $\triangle A'B'C'$ under a size transformation with center E and scale factor $\frac{1}{2}$. Label the image $\triangle A''B''C''$.

a. How are $\triangle ABC$ and $\triangle A''B''C''$ related? Explain your reasoning.

b. Can you find a single size transformation that maps $\triangle ABC$ onto $\triangle A''B''C''$? If so, what is the center of the size transformation? What is the scale factor?

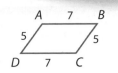

b. SSS similarity conjecture for parallelograms:

If the lengths of three sides of one parallelogram are related by a scale factor k to the lengths of three sides of a second parallelogram, then the parallelograms are similar.

This is *false*; a counterexample is shown at the right.

c. AA similarity conjecture for parallelograms:

If two consecutive angles of a parallelogram are congruent to the corresponding angles of a second parallelogram, then the parallelograms are similar.

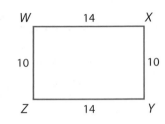

False. Counterexample: Consider any rectangle and square. All corresponding angles are congruent yet the corresponding sides are not necessarily related by a scale factor k.

8 **a.** $\dfrac{light\ source\ to\ paper}{light\ source\ to\ negative} = \dfrac{20}{5} = \dfrac{4}{1}$

b. The ratio we are looking for is $\dfrac{light\ source\ to\ paper}{light\ source\ to\ negative}$. In this case, we are told the distance from negative to paper. The distance from light source to negative is fixed at 5 cm. Thus, the ratio is $\dfrac{8+5}{5}$, or 2.6. So, the magnitude of the size transformation is 2.6.

c. **i.** The paper is 5 cm below the negative, or 10 cm from the light source, and so the magnitude of the size transformation is $\dfrac{10}{5}$, or 2. Thus, the size of the original picture is doubled from 35 mm by 23 mm to 70 mm by 46 mm.

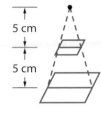

ii. When the paper is 10 cm from the negative, it is 15 cm from the light source. So, the magnitude of the size transformation will be $\dfrac{15}{5}$, or 3. Therefore, the image or print will have dimensions 3 times the dimensions of the original.

iii. The magnitudes are 2 and 3, respectively. These are the ratios of distances, $\dfrac{light\ source\ to\ paper}{light\ source\ to\ negative}$. The magnitude of the enlargement affects only the distance between the negative and photographic paper, since the distance between the light source and the negative is fixed at 5 cm. If x is the distance from the negative to the photographic paper, then $magnitude = \dfrac{5+x}{5}$.

d. The closest the paper tray can be to the light source is 10 cm. This gives a size transformation of magnitude $\dfrac{10}{5}$, or 2. The dimensions of the smallest print are therefore 7.0 cm by 4.6 cm, twice the original dimensions. At the maximum setting of 30 cm from the negative, the paper is 35 cm from the light source. So, the magnitude of the size transformation is $\dfrac{35}{5}$, or 7. Thus, the dimensions of the largest print are 24.5 cm by 16.1 cm, 7 times the dimensions of the original print.

Unit 3

e. At 20 cm from the negative, the paper is 25 cm from the light source, so the magnitude of the size transformation is $\frac{25}{5}$, or 5. The dimensions of the print will be 17.5 cm by 11.5 cm, 5 times the original dimensions.

f. To produce a print whose longest side is 12 cm, we need a size transformation of magnitude $\frac{12}{3.5}$, or approximately 3.429. So,
$$3.429 = \frac{distance\ from\ light\ source\ to\ paper}{5}.$$
Thus, the distance from the light source to the paper should be approximately $5 \cdot 3.429 \approx 17.14$ cm. The paper should be about $17.14 - 5 = 12.14$ cm from the negative.

9 **a.** Since $\overleftrightarrow{SQ} \parallel \overleftrightarrow{XY}$ and $\overline{SR}$ is a transversal of these lines, the pair of corresponding angles ($\angle 1$ and $\angle 2$) are congruent. Also, $\angle R$ is common to both triangles. So, by the AA Similarity Theorem, $\triangle XYR \sim \triangle SQR$.

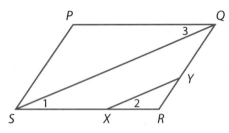

b. $\angle 1 \cong \angle 3$ because they are alternate interior angles for parallel lines $\overleftrightarrow{PQ}$ and $\overleftrightarrow{SR}$. In Part a, we showed that $\angle 1 \cong \angle 2$, thus $\angle 3 \cong \angle 2$. $\angle P$ and $\angle R$ are opposite angles of $\square PQRS$ and are thus congruent. So, $\triangle XYR \sim \triangle QSP$ (AA Similarity Theorem).

c. The center of the size transformation is R and the magnitude is $\frac{SR}{XR} = \frac{QR}{YR} = \frac{SQ}{XY}$.

10 The easiest way to do this in *CPMP-Tools* is to choose the Draw Figure or Polygon button 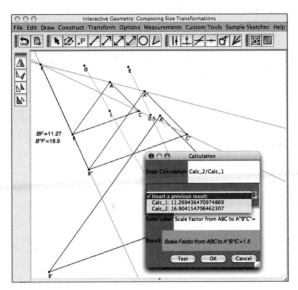, draw the triangle, choose the Scale Objects button , click on the triangle, and drag away from where you clicked. The center and magnitude of the size transformation can then be dragged on the screen to consider multiple cases. This can be repeated for all transformations.

a. Since $\triangle ABC$ and $\triangle A'B'C'$ are related by a size transformation, $\triangle ABC \sim \triangle A'B'C'$. The scale factor from $\triangle ABC$ to $\triangle A'B'C'$ is 3. Similarly, since $\triangle A'B'C'$ and $\triangle A''B''C''$ are related by a size transformation, $\triangle A'B'C' \sim \triangle A''B''C''$. The scale factor from $\triangle A'B'C'$ to $\triangle A''B''C''$ is $\frac{1}{2}$. $\triangle ABC$ is therefore related to $\triangle A''B''C''$ by a size transformation with scale factor from $\triangle ABC$ to $\triangle A''B''C''$ of $3\left(\frac{1}{2}\right) = \frac{3}{2}$. So, $\triangle ABC \sim \triangle A''B''C''$.

INSTRUCTIONAL NOTE
Alert students to the fact that in Parts c and d, they do not need to reconstruct the transformations they can adjust their original construction.

Teaching Resources

Student Masters 13–15.

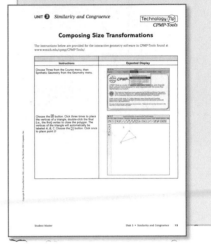

b. Yes, the center of the size transformation is the point F of intersection for $\overleftrightarrow{AA''}$, $\overleftrightarrow{BB''}$, and $\overleftrightarrow{CC''}$. The scale factor from $\triangle ABC$ to $\triangle A''B''C''$ is $\frac{3}{2} = 1.5$.

Unit 3

c. Repeat the experiment for a different △*ABC*, different points *D* and *E*, and different scale factors. Include a case where the two centers are the same point. Answer Parts a and b for these new cases.

d. Repeat Part c. But this time, use scale factors 2 and $\frac{1}{2}$.

e. Conduct additional experiments as necessary in search of general patterns to complete this statement.

> *The composition of two size transformations with scale factors m and n is ... .*

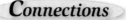

Connections

The French architect Le Corbusier incorporated the golden rectangle in the design of this villa.

11 **Golden rectangles** have the special property that if you cut off a square from one side, the remaining rectangle is similar to the original rectangle. The ratio $\frac{\text{length of long side}}{\text{length of short side}}$ leads to the special proportion,

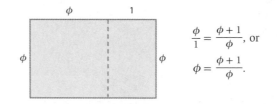

$$\frac{\phi}{1} = \frac{\phi + 1}{\phi}, \text{ or}$$

$$\phi = \frac{\phi + 1}{\phi}.$$

The number ϕ (the Greek letter "phi") is called the **golden ratio**. Golden rectangles are often judged to be the most attractive rectangles from an artistic and architectural point of view.

a. Use algebraic reasoning to determine exact and approximate values of ϕ.

b. Determine which of the rectangles below are golden rectangles. Describe your test.

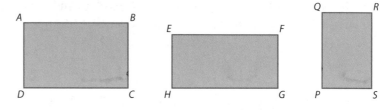

c. Is rectangle *ABCD* similar to rectangle *PQRS*? Explain your reasoning.

d. Prove or disprove that all golden rectangles are similar.

c. Repeat Parts a and b for new scale factors that the student chooses. $\triangle A''B''C''$ will always be similar to $\triangle ABC$. The scale factor from $\triangle ABC$ to $\triangle A''B''C''$ will be the product of the two scale factors used, and the center will be the intersection of lines $\overleftrightarrow{AA''}$, $\overleftrightarrow{BB''}$, and $\overleftrightarrow{CC''}$. For the case when the two centers are the same, the center for the composition is also the same.

d. Repeat Parts a and b for scale factors 2 and $\frac{1}{2}$. For Part a, the same conclusion holds with these new scale factors. For Part b, $\overleftrightarrow{AA''}$, $\overleftrightarrow{BB''}$, and $\overleftrightarrow{CC''}$ are parallel, so the resulting composite transformation is a translation, with "scale factor" 1.

e. The composite of two size transformations with different centers and scale factors m and n (where $mn \neq 1$) is a size transformation with scale factor mn and center at the intersection of the lines defined by corresponding points of the preimage and final image. When $mn = 1$, the composite transformation is a translation in the direction from the first center to the second center through half the distance between the two centers.

Connections

(11) **NOTE** A *golden rectangle* is comprised of a square and a smaller golden rectangle. If you remove the largest possible square inside the smaller golden rectangle, you are left with an even smaller golden rectangle. This process can be continued to create a sequence of increasingly smaller golden rectangles.

a. To find ϕ, use the quadratic formula to solve $\phi^2 = 1 + \phi$ for ϕ.
$\phi = \frac{1 + \sqrt{5}}{2} \approx 1.618$ or $\phi = \frac{1 - \sqrt{5}}{2} \approx -0.618$. Since ϕ is a length of a side of a rectangle, only the first solution makes sense.

b. Check the ratio of the length of the larger side to the length of the smaller side. If that ratio is about 1.6, then the rectangle is a golden rectangle. Out of these examples, only rectangle *ABCD* is a golden rectangle. Or, use a compass or ruler to cut off a square and see if the remaining rectangle is similar to the original.

c. Answers will vary based on measurements. Rectangle *ABCD* is not similar to rectangle *PQRS*.
$\frac{AB}{PQ} \approx \frac{3.5 \text{ cm}}{2.5 \text{ cm}} = 1.4 \text{ cm}$; $\frac{AD}{QR} \approx \frac{2.1 \text{ cm}}{1.6 \text{ cm}} \approx 1.31 \text{ cm}$

d. All golden rectangles are similar. Since all rectangles have four equal angles, the corresponding angles are congruent. To determine whether or not corresponding sides are proportional, consider the ratios of $\frac{length\ of\ long\ side}{length\ of\ short\ side}$ for two golden rectangles, ☐1 and ☐2.
$\frac{length\ of\ long\ side\ \square 1}{length\ of\ short\ side\ \square 1} = \frac{length\ of\ long\ side\ \square 2}{length\ of\ short\ side\ \square 2}$ because each ratio is ϕ.
This means that $\frac{length\ of\ long\ side\ \square 1}{length\ of\ short\ side\ \square 2} = \frac{length\ of\ long\ side\ \square 1}{length\ of\ short\ side\ \square 2}$. So, the ratio of the corresponding side lengths is the same. Thus, all golden rectangles are similar.

NOTE Le Corbusier was one of the architects that designed the United Nations Building in New York City. The influence of the golden rectangle can also be seen in the design of that building.

Teaching Resources

Student Master 16.

EXPLANATORY POWER OF PROOF Task 11 offers a good opportunity for using deductive reasoning to understand why a result is true.

Unit 3

12 Suppose $\triangle ABC \sim \triangle XYZ$ with k as the scale factor from $\triangle ABC$ to $\triangle XYZ$.

a. Explain why $\frac{XY}{AB} = \frac{YZ}{BC} = \frac{XZ}{AC}$.

b. Explain why $\frac{AB}{XY} = \frac{BC}{YZ} = \frac{AC}{XZ}$.

c. Recall that a *proportion* is a statement of equality between ratios. Restate the definition of similar polygons (page 165) using the idea of proportion.

13 In similar triangles, the ratios of lengths of the corresponding sides are equal.

a. Use interactive geometry software to test each of the following claims by a group of students at Clayton High School. Which claims appear to be true statements?

Claim 1: In similar triangles, the ratio of the lengths of the bisectors of corresponding angles is the same as the ratio of the lengths of corresponding sides. For example, if $\triangle ABC \sim \triangle A'B'C'$, $\overline{BD}$ bisects $\angle ABC$, and $\overline{B'D'}$ bisects $\angle A'B'C'$, then $\frac{BD}{B'D'} = \frac{AC}{A'C'}$.

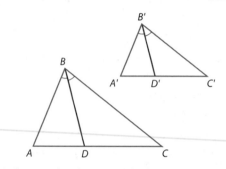

Claim 2: In similar triangles, the ratio of the lengths of the altitudes from corresponding vertices is the same as the ratio of the lengths of corresponding sides.

Claim 3: In similar triangles, the ratio of the lengths of the medians from corresponding vertices is the same as the ratio of the lengths of corresponding sides.

b. Write an argument proving one of the claims that you think is true.

c. Restate the claim you proved in Part b using the language of proportions.

12 **a.** $\frac{XY}{AB} = \frac{YZ}{BC} = \frac{XZ}{AC}$ since each ratio is equal to k, the scale factor.

b. Each ratio in this proportion is the reciprocal of one in Part a; thus, all equal $\frac{1}{k}$.

c. Two polygons are similar provided their corresponding angles have the same measure and corresponding sides are proportional.

13 **a.** Students will investigate these claims using interactive geometry software and should conjecture that all claims are true.

b. **Proof of Claim 1:** Since $\triangle ABC \sim \triangle A'B'C'$, $m\angle A = m\angle A'$ and $m\angle B = m\angle B'$. Since $\overline{BD}$ and $\overline{B'D'}$ bisect $\angle B$ and $\angle B'$, respectively, it follows that $m\angle ABD = m\angle A'B'D'$. So, $\triangle ABD \sim \triangle A'B'D'$ (AA Similarity Theorem). By the definition of similar triangles $\frac{BD}{B'D'} = \frac{AB}{A'B'}$. But $\frac{AB}{A'B'}$ is the common ratio of corresponding sides of the original triangle. So, the ratio of the lengths of the bisectors of corresponding angles is the same as the ratio of the corresponding sides.

Proof of Claim 2:

Acute $\angle A$ and altitude from B to $\overline{AC}$:

$\triangle ABC$ and $\triangle A'B'C'$ are similar. (given)

$m\angle A = m\angle A'$ (corresponding parts of similar triangles)

$\overline{AH}$ and $\overline{A'H'}$ are altitudes, so $m\angle AHB = m\angle A'H'B' = 90°$ (definition of altitude)

$\triangle AHB \sim \triangle A'H'B'$ (AA Similarity Theorem)

$\frac{B'H'}{BH} = \frac{A'B'}{AB}$ (definition of similar triangles)

Therefore, the ratio of the lengths of corresponding altitudes is the same as the ratio of the lengths of corresponding sides of the similar triangles.

INSTRUCTIONAL NOTE
Task 13 Part a foreshadows explorations in Lesson 2 on incenter, orthocenter, and circumcenter.

DIFFERENTIATION You may wish to ask students to also consider Claim 2 for obtuse and right triangles.

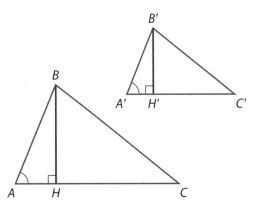

Obtuse $\angle A$:

The proof when $\angle A$ is obtuse will need to show that $\triangle AHB \sim \triangle A'H'B'$, using exterior angles $\angle HAB$ and $\angle H'A'B'$.

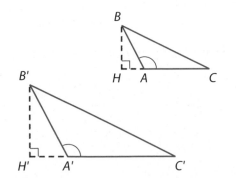

Unit 3

Right $\angle A$:

When $\angle A$ is a right angle, the claim is obviously true since $\overline{BA}$ is both a side and an altitude of $\triangle ABC$.

Proof of Claim 3: Since $\triangle ABC \sim \triangle A'B'C'$, $m\angle C = m\angle C'$ and $\frac{A'C'}{AC} = \frac{B'C'}{BC} = k$ where k is the common ratio of corresponding sides. Since J and J' are midpoints of $\overline{AC}$ and $\overline{A'C'}$, respectively, $CJ = \frac{1}{2}AC$ and $C'J' = \frac{1}{2}A'C'$ (definition of median). $\frac{C'J'}{CJ} = \frac{\frac{1}{2}A'C'}{\frac{1}{2}AC} = k$. So, $\triangle BCJ \sim \triangle B'C'J'$ (SAS Similarity Theorem) and $\frac{B'J'}{BJ} = \frac{B'C'}{BC} = k$. Thus, the ratio of lengths of the medians from corresponding vertices is the same as the ratio of lengths of corresponding sides.

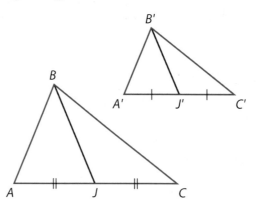

c. **Claim 1:** In similar triangles, the lengths of the bisectors of corresponding angles are proportional to the lengths of corresponding sides.

Claim 2: In similar triangles, the lengths of the altitudes from corresponding vertices are proportional to the lengths of corresponding sides.

Claim 3: In similar triangles, the lengths of the medians from corresponding vertices are proportional to the lengths of corresponding sides.

TECHNOLOGY TIP Use the *CPMP-Tools* Interactive Geometry software for Task 13.

A general outline of construction:

(1) Select the Draw a Figure or Polygon button ![icon], and draw a triangle.

(2) To create a similar image, choose the Scale Objects button ![icon], click on the triangle and drag away from where you clicked.

(3) Draw an angle (![icon]) or segment (![icon]) on each figure in order to construct angle bisectors (![icon]), midpoints (![icon]), or perpendiculars (![icon]).

(4) Select (![icon]) the desired objects to measure.

(5) With objects selected, choose Calculation from the Measurements menu to compute a ratio of measured lengths, as shown in the screen below.

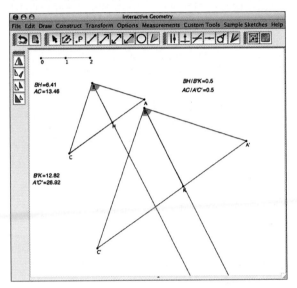

Unit 3

14 Look back at your work for Applications Task 5. Since $\triangle ABD \sim \triangle BCD$, it follows that $\frac{AD}{BD} = \frac{BD}{CD}$. Note that BD appears twice in the proportion. The length of $\overline{BD}$ is the *geometric mean* of the lengths of $\overline{AD}$ and $\overline{CD}$.

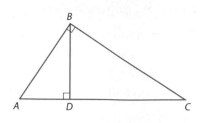

a. Using the language of geometric mean, state a theorem about the altitude to the hypotenuse of any right triangle.

b. The **geometric mean** of two positive numbers a and b is the positive number x such that $\frac{a}{x} = \frac{x}{b}$, or $x = \sqrt{ab}$. What is the geometric mean of 4 and 9? Of 7 and 12?

c. For any two positive numbers, describe the relation between the arithmetic mean and the geometric mean using $<, \leq, =, >,$ or $\geq$.

d. At the right is a circle with center T.

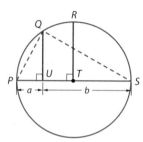

   i. Explain why one of the segments, $\overline{QU}$ and $\overline{RT}$, has length the geometric mean of a and b and the other has length the arithmetic mean of a and b.

   ii. How could you use the diagram to justify your answer to Part c?

e. Under what circumstances are the arithmetic mean and geometric mean of a and b equal?

15 In the Course 2 *Coordinate Methods* unit, you discovered that two nonvertical lines in a coordinate plane are perpendicular if and only if their slopes are opposite reciprocals. In this task, you will prove that *if the lines are perpendicular, then the slopes are opposite reciprocals. In Extensions Task 27, you will prove the converse. You now have the necessary tools to prove these claims. In the diagram at the right, $\ell_1 \perp \ell_2$.

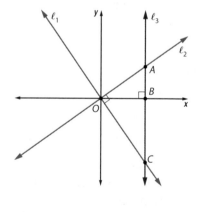

a. Why can line ℓ_3 be drawn through point A on ℓ_2 perpendicular to the x-axis?

b. What is the slope of ℓ_1? Of ℓ_2?

c. Prove that $\triangle AOB \sim \triangle OCB$.

d. Using Parts b and c, justify that the slopes of ℓ_1 and ℓ_2 are opposite reciprocals.

14 **a.** The length of the altitude to the hypotenuse of a right triangle is the geometric mean of the lengths of the segments into which the altitude divides the hypotenuse.

b. $\frac{4}{x} = \frac{x}{9}$, so $x = 6$.

$\frac{7}{x} = \frac{x}{12}$, so $x = \sqrt{84}$.

c. $\frac{a+b}{2} \geq \sqrt{ab}$

d. **i.** *RT*

Since *T* is the center, $\overline{RT}$ is a radius. So, $RT = \frac{a+b}{2}$, the arithmetic mean of *a* and *b*.

QU

Assuming from the diagram that point *Q* is on the circle, $\angle PQS$ is a right angle (inscribed in a semicircle). $\angle PUQ$ is a right angle, so $\overline{QU}$ is an altitude of $\triangle PQS$. By Part a, *QU* is the geometric mean $\sqrt{ab}$.

Alternatively, some students may use the Pythagorean Theorem and algebraic reasoning to deduce that $QU = \sqrt{ab}$ as follows.

$\overline{QU}$ is a leg of $\triangle PUQ$ and $\triangle QUS$.
So, $QU^2 = QS^2 - b^2$ and $QU^2 = PQ^2 - a^2$.

$2QU^2 = QS^2 + PQ^2 - (a^2 + b^2)$ and $QS^2 + PQ^2 = (a+b)^2$
So, $2QU^2 = (a+b)^2 - (a^2 + b^2) = 2ab$.

$QU^2 = ab$

Thus, $QU = \sqrt{ab}$, the geometric mean.

ii. *RT* (the arithmetic mean) is the length of a radius of the circle. *QU* (the geometric mean) is either equal to *RT* or less than *RT* since the perpendicular distance from the diameter $\overline{PS}$ to any point *Q* on the circle is less than or equal to *RT*, the radius of the circle.

e. The geometric mean and the arithmetic mean are equal if and only if $a = b$.

15 **a.** We proved in the *Reasoning and Proof* unit that there is one line through a point not on a given line that is perpendicular to the given line.

b. The slope of ℓ_1 is $-\frac{BC}{OB}$.

The slope of ℓ_2 is $\frac{AB}{OB}$.

c. Students might directly apply Applications Task 5 (page 181) to justify $\triangle AOB \sim \triangle OCB$ or show two pairs of corresponding angles are the same measure.

d. We want to show that $-\frac{BC}{OB} \cdot \frac{AB}{OB} = -1$. By Part c, $\triangle AOB \sim \triangle OCB$,

so $\frac{BC}{OB} = \frac{OB}{AB}$. So by substitution, $-\frac{BC}{OB} \cdot \frac{AB}{OB} = -\frac{OB}{AB} \cdot \frac{AB}{OB} = -1$.

SCOPE AND SEQUENCE
In Course 2 pages 178–179, it was shown that an angle inscribed in a semicircle is a right angle.

Unit 3

16 In Problem 5 of Investigation 3, you used similar triangles to prove this statement.

If a line segment joins the midpoints of two sides of a triangle, then it is parallel to the third side and one half its length.

Your proof involved reasoning from a combination of assumed or established statements that were independent of a coordinate system. Such proofs are sometimes called *synthetic proofs.*

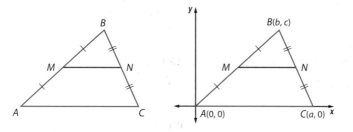

a. Use the labeled diagram on the right above to help you write a proof, using coordinates, that $\overleftrightarrow{MN} \parallel \overleftrightarrow{AC}$.

b. Use coordinate methods to prove $MN = \frac{1}{2}AC$.

c. Compare the proofs you constructed in Parts a and b with those you constructed in Problem 5 (page 176).

  • Which proof was easier for you to construct? Why?

  • Which proof would be easier for you to explain to someone else? Why?

d. Suppose M is $\frac{1}{3}$ the distance from point B to point A and N is $\frac{1}{3}$ the distance from point B to point C. How is $\overline{MN}$ related to $\overline{AC}$?

e. Write a proof of your conjecture in Part d. Did you use synthetic or coordinate methods? Why?

17 There are important connections between the perimeters of similar figures and between the areas of similar figures.

a. Suppose $\triangle P'Q'R'$ is the image of $\triangle PQR$ under a size transformation with center C and magnitude k.

  i. Write an argument to prove that *perimeter* $\triangle P'Q'R' = k(perimeter \triangle PQR)$.

  ii. Use a result from Connections Task 13 to help prove that *area* $\triangle P'Q'R' = k^2(area \triangle PQR)$.

b. Suppose one polygon is the image of another polygon under a size transformation with center C and magnitude k.

  i. How are their perimeters related? Explain your reasoning.

  ii. How are their areas related? Explain your reasoning.

16 **a.** Since M is the midpoint of $\overline{AB}$, its coordinates are $\left(\frac{b}{2}, \frac{c}{2}\right)$. Since N

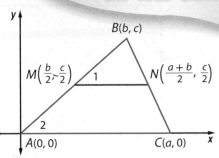

is the midpoint of $\overline{BC}$, its coordinates are $\left(\frac{a+b}{2}, \frac{c}{2}\right)$. The points M and N have the same y-coordinate; also the points A and C have the same y-coordinate. So, $\overline{MN}$ and $\overline{AC}$ are both horizontal, and thus are parallel.

Alternatively, the slope of $\overline{AC}$ is $\frac{0-0}{a-0} = 0$ and the slope of $\overline{MN}$

is $\dfrac{\frac{c}{2} - \frac{c}{2}}{\frac{a+b}{2} - \frac{b}{2}} = \dfrac{0}{\frac{a}{2}} = 0$. Since the slope of $\overline{MN}$ is the same as the

slope of $\overline{AC}$, $\overleftrightarrow{MN} \parallel \overleftrightarrow{AC}$.

b. The length of $\overline{MN}$ is the difference of the x-coordinates since $\overline{MN}$ is horizontal (same y-coordinate). $MN = \frac{a+b}{2} - \frac{b}{2} = \frac{a}{2}$. The length of $\overline{AC}$ is a. So, $MN = \frac{1}{2}AB$.

c. • Student responses will vary, depending on their preferences.

• It might be easier to explain the coordinate proof to someone else because it does not use the definition of similarity or any of the similarity theorems.

d. Conjecture: $\overline{MN}$ is $\frac{1}{3}$ the length of $\overline{AC}$ and $\overline{MN} \parallel \overline{AC}$.

e. Students should explain why they chose to use synthetic or coordinate methods to prove their claim. One synthetic proof is provided here; an analytic proof is similar to that in Parts a and b.

Proof: Since M is $\frac{1}{3}$ the distance from point B to point A, $BM = \frac{1}{3}BA$. Since N is $\frac{1}{3}$ the distance from B to C, $BN = \frac{1}{3}BC$. Since $\angle B$ is common to both $\triangle ABC$ and $\triangle MBN$, $\triangle ABC \sim \triangle MBN$ (SAS Similarity Theorem). The scale factor relating $\triangle ABC$ to $\triangle MBN$ is $\frac{1}{3}$. From this information, one can infer that $MN = \frac{1}{3}AC$.

To show $\overline{MN} \parallel \overline{AC}$, notice that $\angle 1 \cong \angle 2$ (definition of similar triangles). Considering $\overleftrightarrow{BA}$ to be a transversal of $\overleftrightarrow{MN}$ and $\overleftrightarrow{AC}$, these angles are congruent corresponding angles. Thus, $\overline{MN}$ is parallel to $\overline{AC}$.

17 **a.** **i.** Where p, q, and r are the side lengths of $\triangle PQR$ and $p' = kp$, $q' = kq$, and $r' = kr$ are the side lengths of $\triangle P'Q'R'$, so *perimeter* $\triangle P'Q'R' = kp + kq + kr = k(p + q + r) = k(perimeter\ \triangle PQR)$.

ii. From Connections Task 13, in similar triangles, the ratio of lengths of the altitudes from corresponding vertices is the same as the ratio of the lengths of corresponding sides. This ratio is the scale factor, or magnitude k, of the size transformation. Where h is an altitude of $\triangle PQR$ to side p and $h' = kh$ is the altitude of $\triangle P'Q'R'$ to side p', *area* $\triangle P'Q'R' = \frac{1}{2}p'h' = \frac{1}{2}pkhk = \frac{1}{2}k^2ph = k^2(area\ \triangle PQR)$.

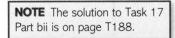

NOTE The solution to Task 17 Part bii is on page T188.

b. **i.** The perimeter of the image is equal to k times the perimeter of the preimage. To justify this claim, the same reasoning that is used in Part ai for triangles can be extended to be true for any polygon.

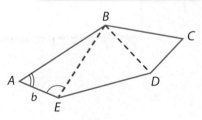

Unit 3

Reflections

18 A quick test that engravers and photographers use to determine whether two rectangular shapes are similar is illustrated in the diagram below.

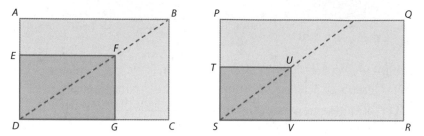

a. Explain why *rectangle ABCD ~ rectangle EFGD* but rectangle *PQRS* is not similar to rectangle *TUVS*.

b. Can this *diagonal test* be used to determine if two nonrectangular parallelograms are similar? Explain your reasoning.

19 A *Sierpinski triangle* is constructed through a sequence of steps illustrated by the figures below. At Stage $n = 0$, you construct an equilateral triangle whose sides are all of length 1 unit. In succeeding stages, you remove the "middle triangles," from each of the remaining colored triangles as shown in Stages $n = 1, 2$, and 3. This process continues indefinitely.

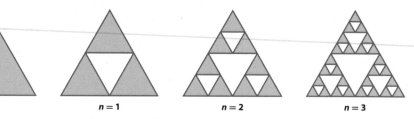

$n = 0$ $n = 1$ $n = 2$ $n = 3$

The Sierpinski triangle is an example of a *fractal* in that small portions of the design are similar to the design as a whole.

a. How is the idea of "self-similarity" seen at Stage 3?

b. Using the Stage 3 triangle, attach, or imagine attaching, a congruent copy of that triangle to each side of the Stage 3 triangle. How is the larger triangle formed related to the stages of construction?

c. In what sense can the triangle at Stage 0 be considered similar to itself?

d. How many colored similar triangles are formed at Stage 1? At Stage 2?

e. Use a computer program like the interactive geometry "Sierpinski Triangle" sketch to explore cases where the initial triangle is not an equilateral triangle. How, if at all, would you change your answers for Parts a–d?

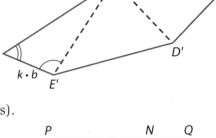

ii. The area of the image is equal to k^2 times the area of the preimage. To justify this claim, the same reasoning that is used in Part aii for triangles can be extended to be true for any polygon.

Reflections

18 **a.** m∠A = m∠E (right angles) and m∠ADB = m∠EDF (common angles). So, △ABD ~ △EFD (AA Similarity Theorem). Thus, corresponding sides $\overline{AD}$ and $\overline{ED}$, and $\overline{AB}$ and $\overline{EF}$, are related by the same scale factor (corresponding sides of similar triangles). Since opposite sides of a rectangle are congruent, $\overline{CD}$ and $\overline{GD}$, and $\overline{BC}$ and $\overline{FG}$ are also related by the same scale factor as the other corresponding sides. Thus, the two rectangles are similar (definition of similar polygons).

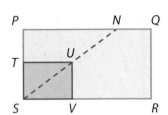

Using similar reasoning, △PSN ~ △TSU. So, $\frac{PN}{TU} = \frac{PS}{TS} = k$. Since $PQ > PN$, $\frac{PQ}{TU} \neq k$.

b. Yes, since opposite sides are parallel, the corresponding angles (∠A and ∠E) are the same measure, although not right angles. The remainder of the reasoning in Part a does not rely on the polygons being rectangles.

19 **TECHNOLOGY TIP** To access the "Sierpinski Triangle" sample sketch, first open the Course 3 Interactive Geometry tool in the Synthetic environment. Choose Sierpinski Triangle in the Sample Sketches menu. Use the buttons to go forward (or backward) one stage at a time. Notice that all three vertices of the triangle can be dragged.

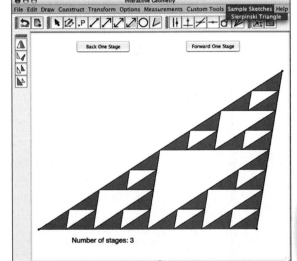

a. In Stage 3, you see three smaller congruent copies of the Stage 2 triangle placed on each side of the interior cut-out triangle. If you zoom in on part of the Stage 3 triangle, it looks like the whole.

b. Attaching a congruent copy of the Stage 3 triangle to each side of a Stage 3 triangle and then removing the Stage 3 triangle (from the middle) will give a larger Stage 4 triangle. (*Note:* It is much simpler to visualize this happening when you consider the Stage 0 and Stage 1 iterations.)

c. It is congruent to itself, or similar with a scale factor of 1.

d. At Stage 1, there are three congruent colored triangles, all similar to the colored triangle at Stage 0. At Stage 2, there are nine colored triangles, all similar to the colored triangles at Stage 1.

e. The solutions provided above are the same for the cases when the triangle is not equilateral.

Unit 3

20 Look back at the pantograph setup in Investigation 3, Problem 1 (page 173). Suppose the tracing stylus at point *D* and the pencil at point *P* were interchanged. Suppose *S'* is the image produced when tracing a shape *S* with the stylus so positioned.

   a. How are shapes *S* and *S'* related?

   b. How would you modify your answer in the case of the pantograph shown in Problem 2 (page 174)?

21 In Problem 5 of Investigation 3, you wrote a synthetic proof of the Midpoint Connector Theorem for Triangles. In Connections Task 16, you prepared a coordinate proof of the theorem.

   a. Using the diagram in Problem 5 (page 176), describe how the theorem could be proved using a size transformation with center at vertex *B* of $\triangle ABC$.

   b. If you were asked to demonstrate a proof of this theorem later in the year, which proof method would you use? Why?

22 How could you use a size transformation to explain why a circle of radius 5 is similar to a circle of radius 12? Why any two circles are similar?

Extensions

23 Pietro's Pizza makes rectangular pizzas. The shop posted an inviting message on its sign, "Now! Our large is 20% bigger!" The original large pizza had dimensions 20 inches by 15 inches.

   a. Assume 20% bigger means that the dimensions of the new pizza are 120% of the original size.

   i. Why is the new pizza similar (in shape) to the original pizza?

   ii. What is the scale factor relating the original pizza to the new pizza?

   iii. What are the dimensions of the new pizza?

   iv. Calculate the ratio of the perimeter of the new pizza to that of the original. How is this ratio related to the scale factor?

   v. Calculate the ratio of the areas of the new pizza to the original pizza. How is this ratio related to the scale factor?

   b. Assume 20% bigger means that the area of the new pizza is 120% of the original size.

   i. What is the area of the new pizza?

   ii. If the new pizza is similar to the original, what are its dimensions?

   iii. What is the scale factor relating the original pizza to the new pizza?

   c. Which interpretation favors the consumer?

20 a. If the tracing stylus and pencil are interchanged, S' is similar to S under a size transformation with scale factor of $\frac{1}{2}$.

b. In the modified pantograph in Problem 2, the scale factor relating the preimage to its image will be $\frac{1}{3}$ instead of 3.

21 a. Since $MB = \frac{1}{2}AB$ and $BN = \frac{1}{2}BC$, B is the center of a size transformation of $\triangle ABC$ with scale factor $\frac{1}{2}$ and image $\triangle MBN$. Then by Problem 7 of Investigation 3 (page 177), $MN = \frac{1}{2}AC$ and $\overline{MN}$ is parallel to $\overline{AC}$.

b. Student answers will vary.

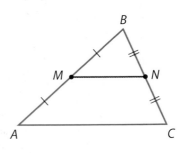

22 Make the circles concentric by translating the center C_1 of the small circle to the center C_2 of the large circle. Then the circle of radius 12 is the result of a size transformation centered at C_2 with factor $\frac{12}{5}$ of the circle with radius 5. In general, any two circles with radii r_1 and r_2 (with $r_1 \neq r_2$) are similar because they too are related by the composition of a translation and a size transformation of factor either $\frac{r_1}{r_2}$ or $\frac{r_2}{r_1}$. When $r_1 = r_2$, the circles are congruent and related by a translation.

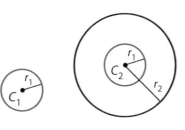

EXTENSION If the circles are concentric, the center of the size transformation is the center of the circles. If the circles are not concentric, then the center of the size transformation is the intersection of the line containing two corresponding points on the circles. One strategy to find these corresponding points is to construct the diameter of one circle, then construct a parallel line to that diameter through the center of the other circle. The corresponding points of intersection of the diameter and the parallel line with their respective circles can be connected by lines to obtain a common intersection point that is also shared by a line through the centers of the circles. Students might find it interesting and helpful to investigate this task using *CPMP-Tools*.

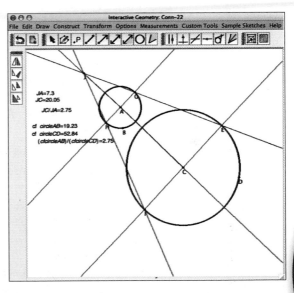

Extensions

23 a. i. The pizzas are similar because the scale factor from the smaller pizza to the larger pizza is 1.2. The lengths of the sides of the rectangle are proportional. (SSS Similarity Theorem)

ii. 1.2

iii. The dimensions of the new pizza are $(1.2)(20) = 24$ inches and $(1.2)(15) = 18$ inches.

iv. *perimeter of original pizza* $= 20(2) + 15(2) = 70$ inches
perimeter of new pizza $= 24(2) + 18(2) = 84$ inches
$\dfrac{\textit{perimeter of new pizza}}{\textit{perimeter of original pizza}} = \dfrac{84}{70} = 1.2$, which is equal to the scale factor.

NOTE The solution for the remainder of Task 23 is on page T190.

Unit 3

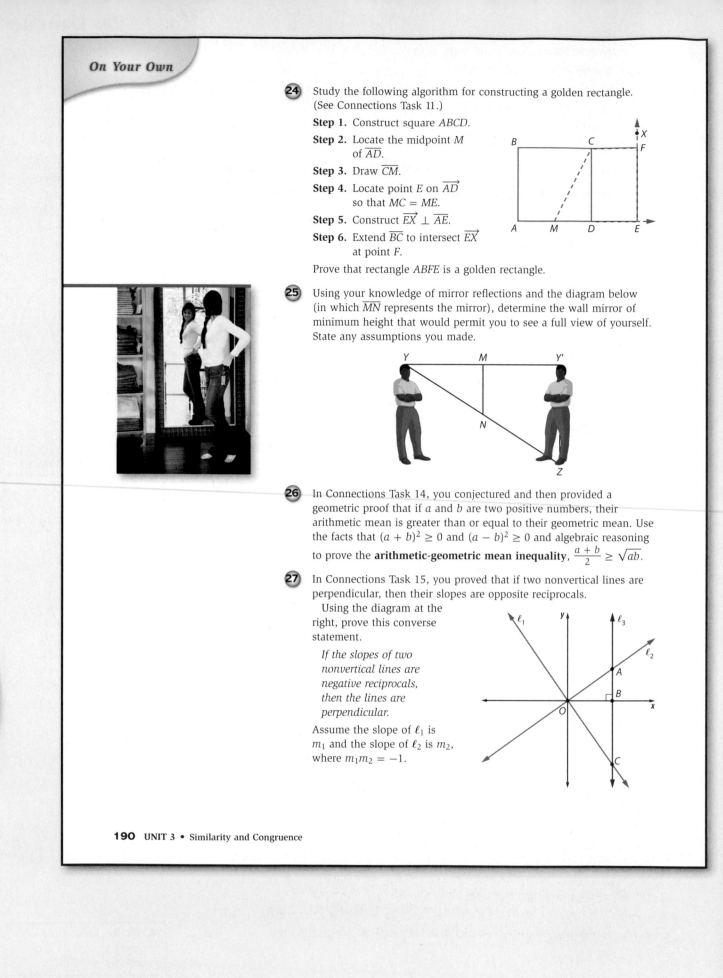

24. Study the following algorithm for constructing a golden rectangle. (See Connections Task 11.)

     Step 1. Construct square $ABCD$.

     Step 2. Locate the midpoint M of $\overline{AD}$.

     Step 3. Draw $\overline{CM}$.

     Step 4. Locate point E on $\overrightarrow{AD}$ so that $MC = ME$.

     Step 5. Construct $\overrightarrow{EX} \perp \overline{AE}$.

     Step 6. Extend $\overrightarrow{BC}$ to intersect $\overrightarrow{EX}$ at point F.

     Prove that rectangle $ABFE$ is a golden rectangle.

25. Using your knowledge of mirror reflections and the diagram below (in which $\overline{MN}$ represents the mirror), determine the wall mirror of minimum height that would permit you to see a full view of yourself. State any assumptions you made.

26. In Connections Task 14, you conjectured and then provided a geometric proof that if a and b are two positive numbers, their arithmetic mean is greater than or equal to their geometric mean. Use the facts that $(a + b)^2 \geq 0$ and $(a - b)^2 \geq 0$ and algebraic reasoning to prove the **arithmetic-geometric mean inequality**, $\dfrac{a + b}{2} \geq \sqrt{ab}$.

27. In Connections Task 15, you proved that if two nonvertical lines are perpendicular, then their slopes are opposite reciprocals.

     Using the diagram at the right, prove this converse statement.

     If the slopes of two nonvertical lines are negative reciprocals, then the lines are perpendicular.

     Assume the slope of ℓ_1 is m_1 and the slope of ℓ_2 is m_2, where $m_1 m_2 = -1$.

v. $\dfrac{\text{area of new pizza}}{\text{area of original pizza}} = \dfrac{24(18)}{15(20)} = 1.44 = (1.2)^2$, which is equal to the scale factor.

b. i. (original area)1.2 = new area, so $(20)(15)(1.2) = 360$. An alternative solution method is to calculate 20% of the original area, and add it to the original area: $(20)(15)(0.2) = 60$, so the new area is $300 + 60 = 360$ square inches.

> **INSTRUCTIONAL NOTE**
> In Part b, students are first asked to find the area rather than the dimensions of the new pizza to allow the solution shown in part i.

ii. Since *original pizza ~ enlarged pizza*, notice that $\dfrac{\text{area of new pizza}}{\text{area of original pizza}} = k^2$, so $k = \sqrt{\dfrac{360}{300}} = \sqrt{1.2}$. The new dimensions are $\sqrt{1.2} \cdot 20 \approx 21.9$ inches and $\sqrt{1.2} \cdot 15 \approx 16.4$ inches.

iii. The scale factor relating the original pizza to the new pizza is $\sqrt{1.2} \approx 1.0954$.

c. The interpretation in Part a of a 20% increase in the lengths of the edges of the pizza favors the consumer because the total area in that case is $(18)(24) = 432$ square inches and in Part b is 360 square inches.

24 **Prove:** *ABFE* is a golden rectangle.

Given: *ABCD* is a square with side length x.

Using the Pythagorean Theorem, $MC = ME = \sqrt{\left(\dfrac{x}{2}\right)^2 + x^2}$. For *ABFE*, the ratio of the longer side to the shorter

side is $\dfrac{AE}{AB} = \dfrac{AM + ME}{AB} = \dfrac{\dfrac{x}{2} + \sqrt{\left(\dfrac{x}{2}\right)^2 + x^2}}{x}$

$= \dfrac{1}{2} + \sqrt{\dfrac{1}{4} + 1} = \dfrac{1 + \sqrt{5}}{2} = \phi.$

> **DIFFERENTIATION** You may wish to allow some students to assume $x = 1$ to prove that this construction produces a golden rectangle for that case only. Since any length *AB* can be chosen as 1 unit, this proof without the variable x actually proves the statement for any golden rectangle.

25 An image in a mirror is as far "behind" the mirror as the person is in front of the mirror. So in the diagram, $YM = MY'$. Assuming that the mirror and the person are vertical, $\overleftrightarrow{MN} \parallel \overleftrightarrow{Y'Z}$ and $\triangle YMN \sim \triangle YY'Z$ (AA). The scale factor relating $\triangle YMN$ to $\triangle YY'Z$ is 2 since $YY' = 2YM$. So, the height of the mirror should be half the person's height.

26 Since $(a + b)^2$ and $(a - b)^2$ have terms of $2ab$ and $-2ab$, we could start by either adding or subtracting these binomials. But adding them, once the trinomials are found, will lose the *ab* term. So instead, subtract them:

$(a + b)^2 - (a - b)^2 = 4ab$

$(a - b)^2 \geq 0$, so $(a + b)^2 \geq 4ab$.

$\dfrac{(a + b)^2}{4} \geq ab$ and thus, since $a > 0$ and $b > 0$, $\dfrac{a + b}{4} \geq \sqrt{ab}$.

> **INSTRUCTIONAL NOTE**
> Task 26 allows for a discussion about *proof strategies*. In this case, one might work backwards to notice the form $(a + b)^2 \geq 4ab$ before beginning the proof.

27 **Assume:** The slope of ℓ_1 and ℓ_2 are negative reciprocals. $m_1 m_2 = -1$

Prove: $\ell_1 \perp \ell_2$

The slope of ℓ_1 is $-\dfrac{BC}{OB}$. The slope of ℓ_2 is $\dfrac{AB}{OB}$. Since the slopes are negative reciprocals, $\dfrac{AB}{OB}\left(-\dfrac{BC}{OB}\right) = -1$, or $\dfrac{AB}{OB} = \dfrac{OB}{BC}$. This means that for $\triangle ABO$ and $\triangle OBC$, two pairs of corresponding sides are proportional. Since the angles at B are right angles, $\triangle ABO \sim \triangle OBC$ (SAS Similarity Theorem). $m\angle AOB + m\angle BOC = 90°$ since those two angles are the two different acute angles of the similar triangles. Thus, $\ell_1 \perp \ell_2$.

Unit 3

28 Using interactive geometry software, draw $\triangle ABC$ with altitudes $\overline{AD}$, $\overline{BE}$, and $\overline{CF}$.

a. Calculate the product $\left(\frac{AF}{FB}\right)\left(\frac{BD}{DC}\right)\left(\frac{CE}{EA}\right)$.

b. Use the dragging capability of your software to explore if the relationship you found in Part a holds for other triangles.

c. Make a conjecture based on your work in Parts a and b.

d. Check your conjecture with that made by other students. Resolve any differences. Then prove the statement upon which you agreed.

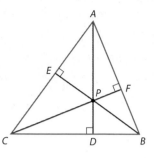

29 The linkage shown below is made up of three rhombuses. The longer bars such as $\overline{PQ}$ are three times the lengths of the shorter bars such as $\overline{XP}$.

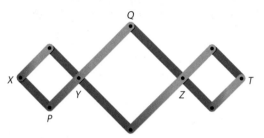

a. Suppose you hold the linkage fixed at X and copy a shape at Y with pencils inserted at both Z and T. What is the scale factor relating the shape copied at Y to the shape copied at Z? To the shape copied at T?

b. Suppose you fix X and copy a shape at Z with pencils at both Y and T. What is the scale factor relating the shape copied at Z to the shape copied at Y? To the shape copied at T?

c. How can the linkage be used to produce similar shapes with each scale factor below?

    i. $\frac{1}{4}$ **ii.** $\frac{3}{4}$

    iii. $\frac{3}{2}$ **iv.** $\frac{2}{3}$

d. Make a model of the linkage to check your conclusions in Parts a–c.

e. Design three different linkages that are capable of making a copy similar to the original with scale factor 4.

28 **a–b.** Students should explore this relationship.

c. Students should conjecture that $\left(\frac{AF}{FB}\right)\left(\frac{BD}{DC}\right)\left(\frac{CE}{EA}\right) = 1$.

d. Given: $\triangle ABC$ with altitudes as shown.

Prove: $\left(\frac{AF}{FB}\right)\left(\frac{BD}{DC}\right)\left(\frac{CE}{EA}\right) = 1$

The following pairs of right triangles are similar because of the vertical angles and the AA Similarity Theorem.

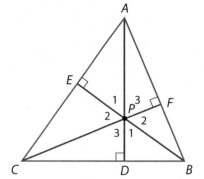

$\triangle BPD \sim \triangle APE$ (Let k_1 be the scale factor from $\triangle BPD$ to $\triangle APE$.)

$\triangle BPF \sim \triangle CPE$ (Let k_2 be the scale factor from $\triangle BPF$ to $\triangle CPE$.)

$\triangle CPD \sim \triangle APF$ (Let k_3 be the scale factor from $\triangle CPD$ to $\triangle APF$.)

This means that the ratios of corresponding side lengths of $\triangle APE$ and $\triangle BPD$ all equal k_1; and similar equations hold for the other two pairs of similar triangles.

(1) $\frac{AP}{BP} = \frac{AE}{BD} = \frac{PE}{PD} = k_1$

(2) $\frac{CP}{BP} = \frac{CE}{BF} = \frac{PE}{PF} = k_2$

(3) $\frac{AP}{CP} = \frac{AF}{CD} = \frac{PF}{PD} = k_3$

Since we want to show that $\left(\frac{AF}{FB}\right)\left(\frac{BD}{DC}\right)\left(\frac{CE}{EA}\right) = 1$, that would be the same as showing $\left(\frac{AF}{CD}\right)\left(\frac{BD}{AE}\right)\left(\frac{CE}{FB}\right) = 1$ (reorder terms in denominator product and interchange order of letters in segment labels). $\frac{AF}{CD} = k_3$, $\frac{BD}{AE} = \frac{1}{k_1}$, and $\frac{CE}{FB} = k_2$. So, we want to show $\frac{k_2 k_3}{k_1} = 1$. Notice that the last terms in the three proportions above are $\frac{PE}{PD} = k_1$, $\frac{PE}{PF} = k_2$, and $\frac{PF}{PD} = k_3$. So, $\frac{k_2 k_3}{k_1} = \left(\frac{PE}{PF}\right)\left(\frac{PF}{PD}\right)\left(\frac{PD}{PE}\right) = \left(\frac{PE}{PE}\right)\left(\frac{PF}{PF}\right)\left(\frac{PD}{PD}\right) = 1$.

Thus, $\left(\frac{AF}{FB}\right)\left(\frac{BD}{DC}\right)\left(\frac{CE}{EA}\right) = 1$.

Alternatively, using scale factors:

$PE = k_1 \cdot PD$ and $PE = k_2 \cdot PF$

So, $k_1 \cdot PD = k_2 \cdot PF$ (by substitution)

and $\frac{k_2 \cdot PF}{k_1 \cdot PD} = 1$ (by division).

Since $\frac{PF}{PD} = k_3$, $\frac{k_2 k_3}{k_1} = 1$ (by substitution).

So again, $\left(\frac{AF}{FB}\right)\left(\frac{BD}{DC}\right)\left(\frac{CE}{EA}\right) = 1$.

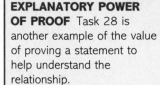

Unit 3

29

a. The size of the shape copied at Z will be 3 times the size of the shape at Y. The size of the shape copied at T will be 4 times the size of the shape at Y.

b. This "double" linkage is equivalent to two separate linkages: The size of the shape copied at Y will be $\frac{1}{3}$ the size of the shape at Z, since $\frac{XY}{XZ} = \frac{1}{3}$. The size of the shape copied at T will be $\frac{4}{3}$ the size of the shape at Z, since $\frac{XT}{XZ} = \frac{4}{3}$.

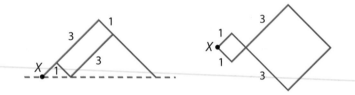

c. i. Shape at T, copy at Y with X fixed

   ii. Shape at T, copy at Z with X fixed

   iii. Shape at Z, copy at T with Y fixed

   iv. Shape at T, copy at Z with Y fixed

d. See student models and drawings.

e. Linkages will vary. Possibilities include the following, each with fixed point X.

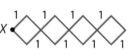

Review

30 Answer these questions using only mental computation. Then check your work using pencil and paper or a calculator.

a. What number is $\frac{2}{3}$ of 18?

b. What number is $\frac{5}{4}$ of 12.8?

c. 25 is $\frac{5}{4}$ of what number?

d. 10 is $\frac{2}{5}$ of what number?

e. If $x \neq 0$, which of the following ratios are equivalent to $\frac{1}{3}$?

$$\frac{1.2}{3.6} \qquad \frac{12}{4} \qquad \frac{2}{6} \qquad \frac{1}{3x} \qquad \frac{5x}{15x} \qquad \frac{x+6}{x+18} \qquad \frac{x+2}{3x+6}$$

31 For each statement, write the converse of the statement. Then decide if the converse is true or false. If the converse is false, provide a counterexample. If the converse is true, provide reasoning to support your conclusion.

a. If $a > 0$, then $a^2 > 0$.

b. If a is an even number and b is an even number, then ab is a multiple of 4.

c. All quadrilaterals that are rectangles have four right angles.

d. If the linear regression line for two variables has positive slope, then the correlation is positive.

32 Use algebraic reasoning to show that the expressions in each pair are equivalent.

a. $(\sqrt{8k})^2$ and $8k$, for $k > 0$

b. $(12k)^2 + (k\sqrt{5})^2$ and $149k^2$

c. $\dfrac{(5a)^2 - (4a)^2}{2a^2}$ and $\dfrac{9}{2}$

d. $\dfrac{(ab)^2 + 3b^2 - (4ab)^2}{2ab^2}$ and $\dfrac{-15a^2 + 3}{2a}$

e. $\dfrac{5x^3 - 3x^2y + 10x^2}{x^2}$ and $5x - 3y + 10$

33 Solve each equation for the indicated variable.

a. $k = \dfrac{a}{b}$ for a

b. $\dfrac{a}{b} = \dfrac{c}{d}$ for d

c. $x^2 = 36k^2$ for x (assume $k > 0$)

d. $x^2 = y^2 + z^2 - 2yz \cos X$ for $\cos X$

34 Solve each proportion.

a. $\dfrac{t}{12} = \dfrac{6}{9}$

b. $\dfrac{m+4}{m} = \dfrac{12}{5}$

c. $\dfrac{y-3}{10} = \dfrac{2y+5}{3}$

Review

30 **a.** 12

b. 16

c. 20

d. 25

e. $\dfrac{1.2}{3.6}$, $\dfrac{2}{6}$, $\dfrac{5x}{15x}$, $\dfrac{x+2}{3x+6}$

31 **a.** If $a^2 > 0$, then $a > 0$. This converse is *false*; $(-2)^2 = 4 > 0$, but $-2 < 0$.

b. If ab is a multiple of 4, then a is an even number and b is an even number.
This converse is *false*. If $a = 3$ and $b = 8$, then $3(8) = 24$ is a multiple of 4, but $a = 3$ is not an even number.

c. All quadrilaterals that have four right angles are rectangles.
True: A quadrilateral with four right angles is defined to be a rectangle.

d. If the correlation for two variables is positive, then the linear regression line has positive slope.
True: The correlation and slope of the linear regression line always have the same sign.

Just in Time

32 **a.** $(\sqrt{8k})^2 = (\sqrt{8k})(\sqrt{8k}) = \sqrt{64k^2} = \sqrt{64}\sqrt{k^2} = 8k$

b. $(12k)^2 + (k\sqrt{5})^2 = 144k^2 + 5k^2 = 149k^2$

c. $\dfrac{(5a)^2 - (4a)^2}{2a^2} = \dfrac{25a^2 - 16a^2}{2a^2} = \dfrac{9a^2}{2a^2} = \dfrac{9}{2}$

d. $\dfrac{(ab)^2 + 3b^2 - (4ab)^2}{2ab^2} = \dfrac{a^2b^2 + 3b^2 - 16a^2b^2}{2ab^2} = \dfrac{-15a^2b^2 + 3b^2}{2ab^2} =$
$\dfrac{b^2(-15a^2 + 3)}{2ab^2} = \dfrac{-15a^2 + 3}{2a}$

e. $\dfrac{5x^3 - 3x^2y + 10x^2}{x^2} = \dfrac{x^2(5x - 3y + 10)}{x^2} = 5x - 3y + 10$

Just in Time

33 **a.** $a = kb$

b. $d = \dfrac{bc}{a}$

c. $x = \pm 6k$

d. $\cos X = \dfrac{x^2 - y^2 - z^2}{-2yz}$

Just in Time

34 **a.** $9t = 72$
$t = 8$

b. $5(m + 4) = 12m$
$5m + 20 = 12m$
$20 = 7m$
$\dfrac{20}{7} = m$

c. $3(y - 3) = 10(2y + 5)$
$3y - 9 = 20y + 50$
$-17y = 59$
$y = -\dfrac{59}{17}$

Unit 3

35 Use the provided information to find the measure of each indicated angle.

a. If $m\angle A = 25°$ and $m\angle C = 120°$, find $m\angle B$.

b. If $\ell \parallel m$, $a \parallel b$, and $m\angle ABD = 70°$, find $m\angle CEF$.

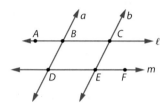

c. If $m\angle JLK = 123°$, $m\angle LMN = 37°$, and $\overline{JK} \parallel \overline{MN}$, find $m\angle JKL$ and $m\angle MNL$.

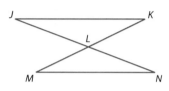

36 Rewrite each expression in $ax^2 + bx + c$ form.

a. $(x - 5)(x + 5)$

b. $3(2x + 1)(6 - x)$

c. $x(8 - 3x) + (5x + 3)$

d. $(10x - 6)^2$

37 Find the solution to each inequality. Display your solution two ways, using symbols and using a number line graph.

a. $x^2 + 3x < x + 8$

b. $\dfrac{20}{x} \geq 10$

c. $2x + 3 > x^2 + 5$

Just in Time

35

a. m∠B = 35°

b. m∠CEF = 70°

c. m∠JKL = 37°
m∠MNL = 20°

36

a. $x^2 - 25$

b. $-6x^2 + 33x + 18$

c. $-3x^2 + 13x + 3$

d. $100x^2 - 120x + 36$

37

a. $-4 < x < 2$

b. $0 < x \leq 2$

c. No solution

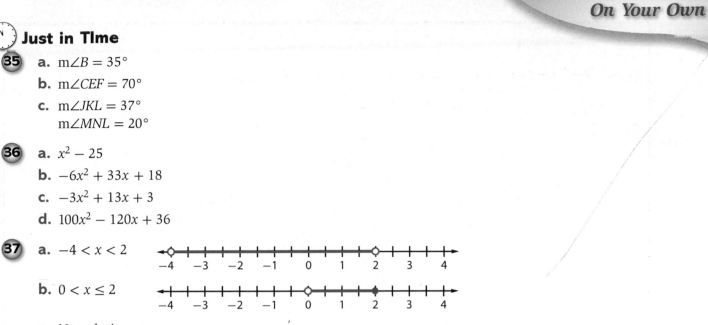

Unit 3

38 Skyler has the responsibility of planning what the free gift will be for people who test drive a car during the month of January. He has been given a budget of $5,000 for the month.

a. If he wants to have at least 400 gifts available, what is the maximum amount he can spend on each gift?

b. If he spends $18.50 on each gift, what is the maximum number of gifts he can purchase?

c. Write an equation that indicates the relationship between the cost c of the gift and the maximum number g of gifts he can make available.

d. Is this relationship a direct variation relationship, an inverse variation relationship, or neither?

e. Suppose he decides to have two prizes available, a watch that costs $31.25 and a $25 gift card to a book store. Draw a graph that indicates all possible combinations of watches and gift cards that he could use.

39 $\triangle ABC \cong \triangle LMP$. Complete each statement about the relationships between the corresponding side lengths and angle measures of the two triangles.

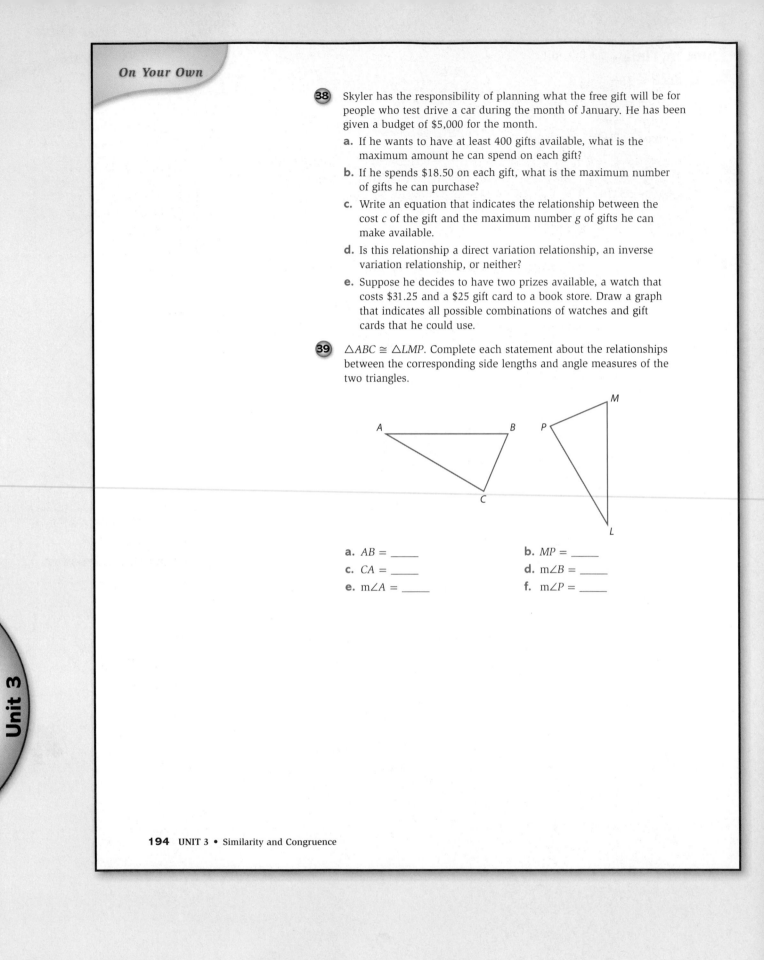

a. $AB =$ _____   **b.** $MP =$ _____

c. $CA =$ _____   **d.** $m\angle B =$ _____

e. $m\angle A =$ _____   **f.** $m\angle P =$ _____

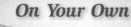

38 **a.** $\dfrac{5{,}000}{400} = \$12.50$ per gift

b. $\dfrac{5{,}000}{18.50} \approx 270$ gifts

c. $c = \dfrac{5{,}000}{g}$ or $g = \dfrac{5{,}000}{c}$

d. Inverse variation

e. If x is the number of watches and y is the number of gift cards, then $31.25x + 25y \le 5{,}000$. The solution is all points (with integer coordinates) in the shaded portion of the graph below.

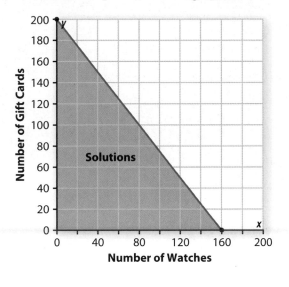

INSTRUCTIONAL NOTE

If in Course 3 Unit 1, your class reported solutions restricted to integer ordered pairs, you should also expect that here.

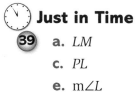 **Just in Time**

39 **a.** LM **b.** BC

c. PL **d.** $m\angle M$

e. $m\angle L$ **f.** $m\angle C$

Teaching Resources

Assessment Masters 17–26.

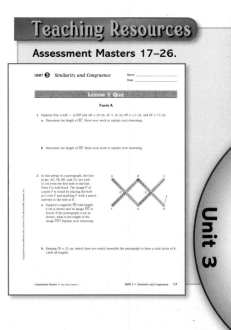

Unit 3

2

Reasoning about Concept Congruent Triangles

The Rock and Roll Hall of Fame is located in Cleveland, Ohio. The building complex was designed by I.M. Pei to "echo the energy of rock and roll." A glass pyramidal structure covers the interior exhibits. The front surface design of the "glass tent" is an isosceles triangle with a lattice framework like that shown below. The labeling of points helps to reveal some of the many similar and congruent triangles embedded in the framework.

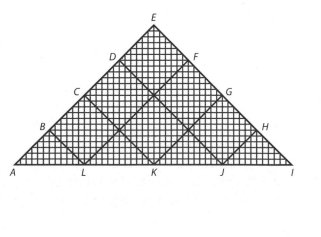

Reasoning about Congruent Triangles

ASSESSMENT NOTE
Since this is a longer lesson, there are two forms of a quiz for Investigations 1 and 2 and another two quizzes for Investigations 3 and 4.

In this lesson, students will explore the relationship between sufficient conditions for congruence of triangles and sufficient conditions for similarity of triangles. They will then use congruence conditions for triangles to solve problems in applied and in mathematical contexts.

In addition to discussing the Summarize the Mathematics questions, it may be helpful to ask students to share their work with one another. As they work, groups could record their proofs on the board, large sheets of paper, or acetate sheets for the overhead projector to be reviewed and discussed by the entire class. Students should note that there is more than one correct way to construct a valid argument. Having at least two groups work on the same proof will provide more fruitful comparisons.

Students should also generally consider how to go about constructing a sound argument. Possible questions to use to prompt them include the following.

How could the given information help you?

How might you begin the proof?

Where do you search for other information that might be helpful for your proof?

How would you decide what congruence or similarity theorems might be appropriate to use in your proof?

In this lesson, students will have lots of practice constructing valid proofs using all of the theorems they have proven in this unit. The important thing is to be sure students understand how a proof should flow from the given information to a final conclusion that includes the original hypotheses, with all supporting information between these beginning and end points supplied. Encourage students to write initial notes (plans for proofs) that show intended reasoning strategies. Polishing can be done as needed once the reasoning to be used is evident.

Lesson Objectives

- Understand congruence of figures as a special case of similarity of figures
- Know and be able to use the four theorems providing sufficient conditions to prove triangles are congruent (SSS, SAS, AAS, ASA)
- Know and be able to use properties of the incenter, circumcenter, and centroid of a triangle
- Continue to develop the ability to write both synthetic and analytic arguments

Think About This Situation

Carefully examine the design of the framework for the front portion of the glass pyramid.

a) Identify pairs of triangles that are similar on the basis of the SAS Similarity Theorem.

b) Identify pairs of triangles that are similar on the basis of the SSS Similarity Theorem.

c) Explain why $\triangle ACK \sim \triangle AEI$ and $\triangle AEI \sim \triangle KGI$.

d) Based on the similarity relationships in Part c, why would it make sense to say that $\triangle ACK \sim \triangle KGI$? What is the scale factor relating these two triangles?

e) How are $\triangle ACK$ and $\triangle KGI$ related?

f) Why are any two congruent triangles also similar? What is the scale factor?

In this lesson, you will explore the relationship between sufficient conditions for congruence of triangles and sufficient conditions for similarity of triangles. You will then use congruence conditions for triangles to solve problems in applied and mathematical contexts.

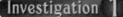 **Investigation 1** **Congruence of Triangles Revisited**

Congruent triangles have the same shape and size. Your analysis of the Think About This Situation suggests the following equivalent definition of **congruent triangles**.

> *Two triangles are congruent if and only if they are similar with a scale factor of 1.*

In Course 1, you discovered sufficient conditions on side and angle measures to conclude that two triangles are congruent. You assumed those conditions were correct. As you work on the problems of this investigation, look for answers to the following questions:

> *How are sufficient conditions for congruence of triangles related to sufficient conditions for similarity of triangles?*

> *How is reasoning with congruence conditions for triangles similar to, and different from, reasoning with similarity conditions for triangles?*

1 Look back at the similarity theorems that you proved in Lesson 1.

    a. How would you modify the hypothesis of the SSS Similarity Theorem so that it can be used to show that two triangles are not only similar but also congruent? Write a statement of the corresponding **SSS Congruence Theorem**.

- Know and be able to use both necessary and sufficient conditions for quadrilaterals to be (special) parallelograms
- Know and be able to use the Midpoint Connector Theorems for Triangles and Quadrilaterals
- Explore, prove, and apply properties of congruence-preserving transformations

Think About This Situation

Teaching Resources

Transparency Master 27.

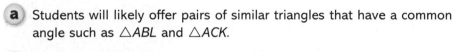

a Students will likely offer pairs of similar triangles that have a common angle such as △ABL and △ACK.

b In addition to the triangles identified in Part a, students could use the grid provided and identify overlapping triangles that do not have a common angle, such as and △ACK and △LFI.

c Students could explain the similarity relationships using the SAS Similarity Theorem, the SSS Similarity Theorem, or the AA Similarity Theorem. To justify using the AA Similarity Theorem, use the corresponding angles formed by the parallel lines.

d Students' explanations might include recognizing that if one triangle is similar to another, the corresponding angles are the same measure. So, with correct correspondences, the angles in △ACK and △KGI will be the same measure since they are the same measures as the corresponding angles of △AEI. Other correct explanations involving scale factors may be given.

 The scale factor relating △ACK to △AEI is 2. The scale factor relating △AEI to △KGI is $\frac{1}{2}$. So, the scale factor relating △ACK to △KGI is 1.

e △ACK ≅ △KGI

f Any two congruent triangles satisfy the SSS, the SAS, and the AA Similarity Theorems since corresponding sides and corresponding angles have the same measures. They are related by a scale factor of 1.

Investigation 1 — Congruence of Triangles Revisited

In this investigation, students will use the definition of congruent triangles as a special case of similar triangles with scale factor 1 to develop the triangle congruence theorems. They will then explore congruence theorems for the special case of right triangles. Then, in the context of locating a telecommunications tower that it is equidistant from three communities, congruent triangles are used to prove that the point of intersection of the perpendicular bisectors of the sides of a triangle are equidistant from the vertices of the triangle and, more generally, that a point is on the perpendicular bisector of a segment if and only if it is equidistant from the endpoints of the segment.

NOTE The solution for Problem 1 Part a is on page T197.

Unit 3

b. Write a theorem for congruence of triangles corresponding to the SAS Similarity Theorem.

c. What needs to be added to the AA Similarity Theorem to make it into a correct statement about conditions that ensure congruence of the triangles? There are two possible different additions. Find them both. Give names to those congruence conditions.

2 The architectural design used in the roof structure of this rest area building along Interstate 94 may remind you of portions of the design of the glass tent of the Rock and Roll Hall of Fame. Similarity, as well as congruence, is suggested visually in both structures.

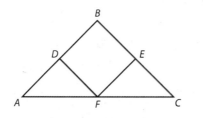

In the diagram above, △ABC is an isosceles triangle with $\overline{AB} \cong \overline{BC}$. Points D, E, and F are midpoints of $\overline{AB}$, $\overline{BC}$, and $\overline{AC}$, respectively.

a. Identify as many pairs of similar triangles as you can. Then carefully explain how you know they are similar.

b. Identify as many pairs of congruent triangles as you can. Carefully explain how you know they are congruent.

3 For each set of information given below, draw and mark a copy of the diagram. Using only the given conditions, decide if △ABC ≅ △DEF or △ABC ~ △DEF. Explain your reasoning.

a. $\angle B \cong \angle E$, $\angle A \cong \angle EDF$, and $\overline{AC} \cong \overline{FD}$

b. $\overleftrightarrow{AB} \parallel \overleftrightarrow{DE}$ and $\overleftrightarrow{BC} \parallel \overleftrightarrow{EF}$

c. $\overline{AD} \cong \overline{FC}$, $\overline{BC} \parallel \overline{EF}$, and $\angle B \cong \angle E$

d. $\overline{BC} \cong \overline{ED}$, $\overline{AB} \cong \overline{FE}$, and $\angle A \cong \angle F$

e. $\overline{AD} \cong \overline{FC}$, $\overline{BC} \parallel \overline{EF}$, and $\overline{AB} \cong \overline{DE}$

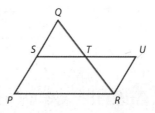

4 In the diagram at the right, S and T are the midpoints of $\overline{PQ}$ and $\overline{QR}$, respectively, and $ST = TU$.

a. Describe a strategy that you would use to prove that $SQ = UR$.

b. Describe a strategy that you would use to prove $ST = \frac{1}{2}PR$.

c. What type of quadrilateral does PSUR appear to be? Describe a strategy that you would use to prove your conjecture.

1 **a.** Modifications to the SSS Similarity Theorem should indicate that the scale factor must be 1 or that corresponding sides must be congruent.

    SSS Congruence Theorem: If three sides of one triangle are congruent to three sides of a second triangle, then the triangles are congruent.

b. SAS Congruence Theorem: If two sides and the included angle of one triangle are congruent to the corresponding sides and included angle of a second triangle, then the triangles are congruent.

c. You must know that a pair of sides are congruent in order to have similarity with a scale factor of 1. The pair of congruent sides could be included between the congruent angles or not.

- ASA Congruence Theorem: If two angles and the included side of one triangle are congruent to the corresponding angles and included side of a second triangle, then the triangles are congruent.

- AAS Congruence Theorem: If two angles and a nonincluded side of one triangle are congruent to the corresponding two angles and nonincluded side of a second triangle, then the triangles are congruent.

2 **a.** There are three distinct triangles, and any pair of these are similar. $\triangle ABC \sim \triangle ADF$, $\triangle ABC \sim \triangle FEC$, and $\triangle ADF \sim \triangle FEC$. Since the triangles are isosceles, we can also write $\triangle ABC \sim \triangle FDA$, $\triangle ABC \sim \triangle CEF$, and $\triangle ADF \sim \triangle CEF$.

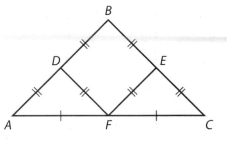

    Since D and E are midpoints of congruent segments, $\overline{AB}$ and $\overline{BC}$, $AD = DB = BE = EC = \frac{1}{2}AB = \frac{1}{2}BC$. By the Midpoint Connector Theorem, the lengths of $\overline{EF}$ and $\overline{FD}$ are half the lengths of $\overline{AB}$ and $\overline{BC}$ and thus also the same length as the four segments above. (See the diagram.) $AF = FC$ because F is the midpoint of $\overline{AC}$. This side length information allows us to conclude that $\triangle ADF \sim \triangle ABC$ and $\triangle FEC \sim \triangle ABC$. The scale factor from the two smaller triangles to $\triangle ABC$ is 2.

b. $\triangle ADF \cong \triangle FEC$, because all three pairs of corresponding sides are congruent (SSS Congruence Theorem).

3 **a.** $\triangle ABC \cong \triangle DEF$ by the AAS Congruence Theorem.

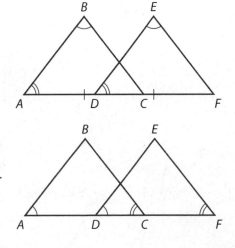

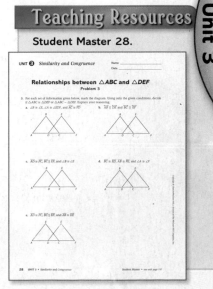

b. $\angle BAC \cong \angle EDF$ since they are corresponding angles when $\overleftrightarrow{AB}$ and $\overleftrightarrow{DE}$ are cut by transversal $\overleftrightarrow{AF}$. Similarly, $\angle ACB \cong \angle DFE$. $\triangle ABC \sim \triangle DEF$ by the AA Similarity Theorem. We have no information about side lengths to conclude congruence.

Unit 3

c. Since $\overline{AD} \cong \overline{FC}$ and $\overline{DC} \cong \overline{CD}$, $\overline{AC} \cong \overline{DF}$. Corresponding angles, $\angle BCA$ and $\angle EFD$, are congruent and $\angle B \cong \angle E$. So, $\triangle ABC \cong \triangle DEF$ by the AAS Congruence Theorem.

d. The triangles are not necessarily congruent or similar. The conditions given are SSA.

e. The triangles are not necessarily congruent or similar. The conditions given are SSA.

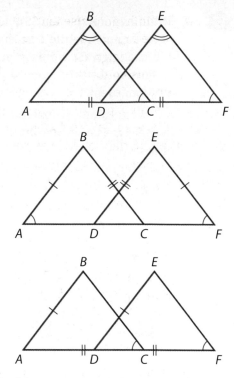

4 **a.** Show that $\triangle QTS \cong \triangle RTU$ by using the SAS Congruence Theorem. Then the corresponding parts $\overline{SQ}$ and $\overline{UR}$ must also be congruent.

b. $ST = \frac{1}{2}PR$ by the Midpoint Connector Theorem. Alternatively, students might suggest using the SAS Similarity Theorem to show that $\triangle QST \sim \triangle QPR$ with corresponding side lengths of $\triangle QPR$ twice those of $\triangle QST$. Thus, $\frac{PR}{ST} = 2$ and $ST = \frac{1}{2}PR$.

c. Quadrilateral $PSUR$ appears to be a parallelogram. Strategies suggested might include showing that both pairs of opposite sides are parallel or congruent. Parts a and b show opposite sides are congruent; the Midpoint Connector Theorem shows $\overline{SU} \parallel \overline{PR}$, and the Alternate Interior Angle Theorem shows $\overline{QP} \parallel \overline{UR}$.

5 **a.** If the hypotenuse and the leg of one right triangle are related by a scale factor k to the corresponding parts of another right triangle, then the triangles are similar.

   This could be proved by using the Pythagorean Theorem to find the third sides of each triangle and determine that they are also related by a scale factor of k. So, the triangles are similar by the SSS Similarity Theorem. Alternatively, some students might suggest finding trigonometric ratios to conclude that a pair of corresponding acute angles are congruent then using the AA Similarity Theorem.

b. If the hypotenuse and the leg of one right triangle are congruent to the corresponding parts of another right triangle, then the triangles are congruent.

   This could be proved by using the Pythagorean Theorem to determine that the other legs of each triangle are congruent and then using the SSS Congruence Theorem.

c. If one pair of acute angles are congruent, then the triangles are similar. Since each triangle has a right angle and a pair of congruent corresponding angles, the triangles are similar by the AA Similarity Theorem.

d. If the hypotenuse and an acute angle are congruent to the corresponding parts of another right triangle, then the triangles are congruent, by the AAS Triangle Congruence Theorem.

5 For each part below, draw and label two right triangles.

a. What conditions on the hypotenuse and leg of one triangle would guarantee that it is similar to the other triangle? How would you prove your claim?

b. What conditions on the hypotenuse and leg of one triangle would guarantee that it is congruent to the other triangle? How would you prove your claim?

c. What conditions on the hypotenuse and an acute angle of one triangle would guarantee that it is similar to the other triangle? How would you prove your claim?

d. What conditions on the hypotenuse and an acute angle of one triangle would guarantee that it is congruent to the other triangle? How would you prove your claim?

6 Plans for the location of a telecommunications tower that is to serve three northern suburbs of Milwaukee are shown at the right. Design specifications indicate the tower should be located so that it is equidistant

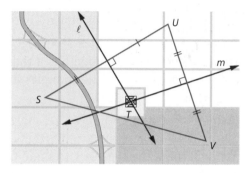

from the center S, U, and V of each of the suburbs. In the diagram, line ℓ is the *perpendicular bisector* of $\overline{SU}$. Line m is the perpendicular bisector of $\overline{UV}$. Lines ℓ and m intersect at point T.

a. On a copy of the diagram, draw $\overline{TS}$ and $\overline{TU}$. Prove that $TS = TU$.

b. Draw $\overline{TV}$ on your diagram. Prove that $TU = TV$.

c. Explain why the tower should be located at point T.

7 Now try to generalize your finding in Problem 6.

a. Is it the case that *any* point on the perpendicular bisector of a line segment is equidistant from the endpoints of the segment? Justify your answer in terms of the diagram at the right.

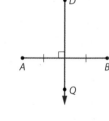

b. Is it the case that if a point is equidistant from the endpoints of a line segment, then it is on the perpendicular bisector of the segment? Justify your answer in terms of a modified diagram.

c. Summarize your work in Parts a and b by completing this statement.

> *A point is on the perpendicular bisector
> of a segment if and only if … .*

6 a. Given: $\ell \perp \overline{SU}$, $PS = PU$

Prove: $TS = TU$

Since $\overline{PT}$ is a side common to $\triangle SPT$ and $\triangle UPT$, the triangles are congruent (SAS). So, $TS = TU$ (CPCTC).

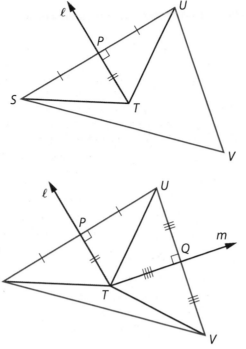

NOTE Solutions for Problem 5 are on page T197B.

b. Given: $m \perp \overline{UV}$, $QV = QU$

Prove: $TU = TV$

Since $\overline{QT}$ is a side common to $\triangle UQT$ and $\triangle VQT$, the triangles are congruent (SAS). So, $TU = TV$ (CPCTC).

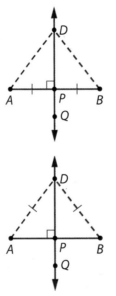

c. Since $TS = TU = TV$, point T is the same distance from all three suburbs and so T should be the location for the tower.

7 a. Let D represent any point on the perpendicular bisector. Call the intersection of $\overleftrightarrow{DQ}$ and $\overline{AB}$ point P. $\overline{AP} \cong \overline{BP}$ and $\angle DPA \cong \angle DPB$ (by definition of perpendicular bisector and right angles). $\overline{DP} \cong \overline{DP}$ (common side to both triangles). So, $\triangle ADP \cong \triangle BDP$ (SAS) and $\overline{AD} \cong \overline{BD}$ (CPCTC). So, any point on the perpendicular bisector of a segment will be equidistant from the endpoints of the segment.

b. Given: D, any point that is equidistant from A and B, or $AD = BD$

Prove: D is on the perpendicular bisector of $\overline{AB}$.

Construct the perpendicular from D to $\overline{AB}$. Call the intersection point P. (There exists one line perpendicular to a line through a point not on the line.) We need to show that $\overline{DP}$ is the perpendicular bisector of $\overline{AB}$. $\overline{PD}$ is a leg of right triangles $\triangle APD$ and $\triangle BPD$. $\triangle APD \cong \triangle BPD$ (HL Triangle Congruence Theorem). So, $\overline{AP} \cong \overline{BP}$ (CPCTC) and $\overline{DP}$ bisects $\overline{AB}$. Thus, D lies on the perpendicular bisector of $\overline{AB}$.

c. A point is on the perpendicular bisector of a segment if and only if the point is equidistant from the endpoints of the segment.

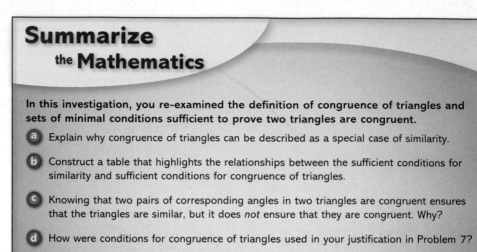

Summarize
the Mathematics

In this investigation, you re-examined the definition of congruence of triangles and sets of minimal conditions sufficient to prove two triangles are congruent.

a Explain why congruence of triangles can be described as a special case of similarity.

b Construct a table that highlights the relationships between the sufficient conditions for similarity and sufficient conditions for congruence of triangles.

c Knowing that two pairs of corresponding angles in two triangles are congruent ensures that the triangles are similar, but it does *not* ensure that they are congruent. Why?

d How were conditions for congruence of triangles used in your justification in Problem 7?

Be prepared to explain your ideas to the class.

✓ Check Your Understanding

Examine each of the following pairs of triangles and their markings showing congruence of corresponding angles and sides. In each case, decide whether the information given by the markings ensures that the triangles are congruent. If the triangles are congruent, write a congruence relation showing the correspondence between vertices. Cite an appropriate congruence theorem to support your conclusion.

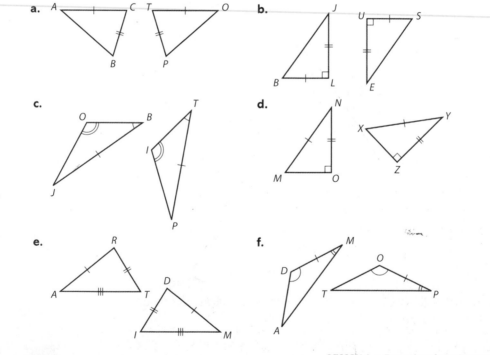

Summarize the Mathematics

a Congruence of triangles can be described as a special case of similarity of triangles because all congruent triangles are also similar (with a scale factor of 1). Students may also note that the conditions that define congruence are a special case of those that define similarity.

b **Sufficient Conditions for Similarity and Congruence of Triangles**

Similar Triangles		Congruent Triangles	
SSS	3 pairs of corresponding sides related by a scale factor k	SSS	3 pairs of congruent corresponding sides
SAS	2 pairs of corresponding sides related by a scale factor k and included angles with equal measure (congruent)	SAS	2 pairs of corresponding sides congruent and included angles congruent
AA	2 pairs of corresponding angles with equal measures (congruent)	AA	Not sufficient conditions for congruence
		ASA	2 pairs of congruent corresponding angles and included sides congruent
		AAS	2 pairs of congruent corresponding angles and nonincluded sides congruent

c Knowing that two triangles are similar ensures that the triangles are related by a scale factor k, but it does not ensure that the scale factor is 1, i.e., that the corresponding sides are congruent.

d In Problem 7, triangles were formed by the given segment and a point on its perpendicular bisector in Part a, and a point equidistant from the endpoints of the segment in Part b. This information was used to determine congruent triangles. Then corresponding parts provided the conclusion being proved. These conclusions can be summarized in the statement: *A point is equidistant from the endpoints of a segment iff it is on the perpendicular bisector of the segment.*

MATH TOOLKIT Include the theorems you have proved in this investigation along with diagrams.

Unit 3

✓ Check Your Understanding

a. The markings are not sufficient to ensure that the triangles are congruent. (You would need a third pair of congruent corresponding sides or $\angle C \cong \angle T$.)

b. $\triangle JLB \cong \triangle EUS$ by the SAS Congruence Theorem.

c. $\triangle OBJ \cong \triangle ITP$ by the AAS Congruence Theorem.

d. $\triangle NOM \cong \triangle YZX$ by the HL Congruence Theorem for right triangles. Students might also indicate that $\overline{MO} \cong \overline{XZ}$ by the Pythagorean Theorem and thus the triangles are congruent by the SAS or SSS Congruence Theorems.

e. $\triangle ART \cong \triangle MDI$ by the SSS Congruence Theorem.

f. $\triangle DMA \cong \triangle OPT$ by the ASA Congruence Theorem.

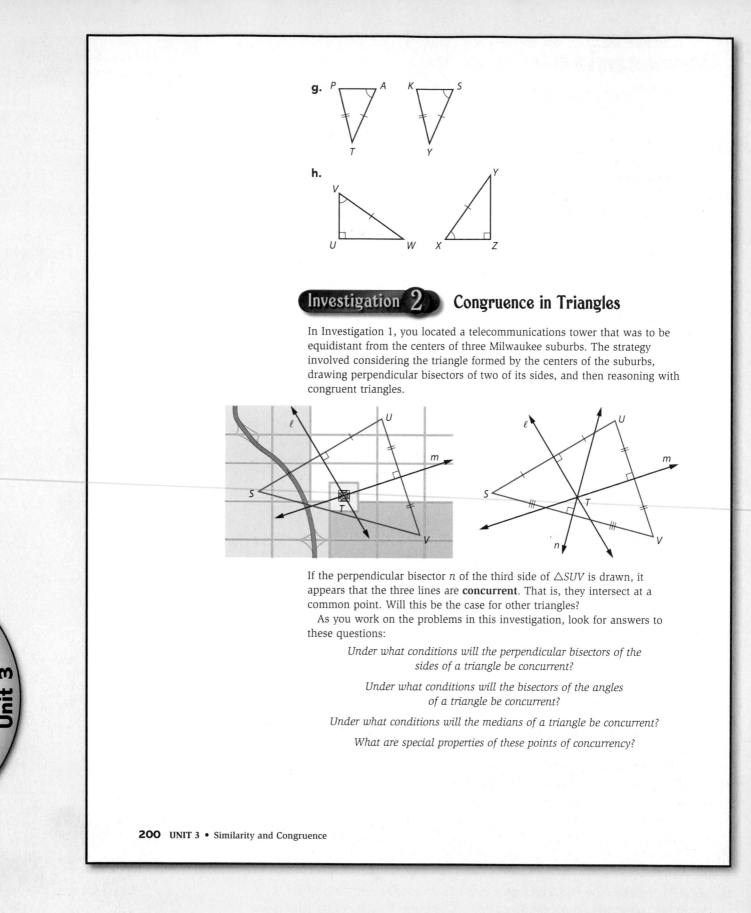

g.

h.

Investigation 2 · Congruence in Triangles

In Investigation 1, you located a telecommunications tower that was to be equidistant from the centers of three Milwaukee suburbs. The strategy involved considering the triangle formed by the centers of the suburbs, drawing perpendicular bisectors of two of its sides, and then reasoning with congruent triangles.

If the perpendicular bisector *n* of the third side of △*SUV* is drawn, it appears that the three lines are **concurrent**. That is, they intersect at a common point. Will this be the case for other triangles?

As you work on the problems in this investigation, look for answers to these questions:

> *Under what conditions will the perpendicular bisectors of the sides of a triangle be concurrent?*

> *Under what conditions will the bisectors of the angles of a triangle be concurrent?*

> *Under what conditions will the medians of a triangle be concurrent?*

> *What are special properties of these points of concurrency?*

g. The markings (SSA) do not ensure congruence or similarity.

h. $\triangle UVW \cong \triangle ZXY$ by the AAS Congruence Theorem.

Investigation 2 Congruence in Triangles

In this investigation, students will explore three centers of triangles and their properties:

- the circumcenter (the center of a circle circumscribed about the triangle), which is the intersection point of the perpendicular bisectors of the sides of the triangle;
- the incenter (the center of a circle inscribed in the triangle), which is the intersection point of the angle bisectors of the angles of the triangle; and
- the centroid (the center of gravity), which is the intersection point of the three medians of the triangle.

Launch

Launch this investigation using interactive geometry software to consider the first focus question about the perpendicular bisectors of the sides of a triangle. Then a class discussion around Problem 1 can consider acute, obtuse, and right triangles by dragging one of the vertices of a triangle once the perpendicular bisectors of the sides are constructed. Students need not write solutions to Problem 1 but should discuss all parts.

Problem 1 and Problem 5 in this investigation ask students to reason about why three lines must intersect in a point. *Indirect reasoning* is typically used to verify concurrence of points. This type of reasoning is difficult for many students. You may wish to lead a class discussion around Problem 1 or wait to discuss Problem 1 Part a and Problem 5 Part a at the STM. See the Promoting Mathematical Discourse scenario on pages T203A and T203B. One option is to use a *think-pair-share* strategy around the question: "Why is it not possible for lines ℓ and m to be parallel?" After students have time to think individually and discuss their thoughts with a partner or group, a class discussion can help make the reasoning by contradiction evident to all. Some ideas for orchestrating a discussion follow.

Students may suggest that the lines are not parallel because they intersect inside the triangle. If so, follow up by indicating that the picture itself cannot be used to make this statement. Ask, "What would be true about the figure if lines ℓ and m *were* parallel?" Encourage them to think about *all* the theorems in their toolkits that involve parallel lines. If they do not suggest that this would imply that ℓ would be perpendicular to $\overline{UV}$ in addition to being perpendicular to $\overline{SU}$ (or that m is perpendicular to both $\overline{SU}$ and $\overline{UV}$) and thus that $\overline{SU} \parallel \overline{UV}$, encourage this by focusing their thinking on relationships of parallel and perpendicular lines. Then, indirect reasoning can be applied by recognizing that $\overline{SU}$ and $\overline{UV}$ are two sides of a triangle and thus cannot be parallel. Thus, it is not possible that ℓ and m are parallel. Providing opportunities such as this for students to use indirect reasoning (if p is true, then q is true, but q is not true, so p is not true) as a group will help develop their appreciation of such reasoning.

① **Focusing on Perpendicular Bisectors of Sides** Look more closely at your solution of the telecommunications tower location problem. Refer to the diagram on the lower right of the previous page.

a. If $\ell \perp \overline{SU}$ and $m \perp \overline{UV}$, then ℓ and m must intersect at a point T as shown. Why is it not possible that $\ell \parallel m$?

b. On a copy of the diagram, draw in a second color $\overline{TS}$, $\overline{TU}$, and $\overline{TV}$. Discuss with classmates how you used congruent triangles to show that $TU = TV$. That $TU = TS$.

c. From Part b, you were able to conclude that $TS = TU = TV$ and therefore a telecommunications tower located at point T would be equidistant from points S, U, and V. Why must point T be on line n, the perpendicular bisector of $\overline{SV}$?

d. Your work in Parts a–c proves that the perpendicular bisectors of the sides of $\triangle SUV$ are concurrent. $\triangle SUV$ is an acute triangle. Draw a diagram for the case where $\triangle SUV$ is a right triangle. Where $\triangle SUV$ is an obtuse triangle. Explain why the reasoning in Parts a–c applies to any triangle.

② The point of concurrency of the perpendicular bisectors of the sides of a triangle is called the **circumcenter** of the triangle.

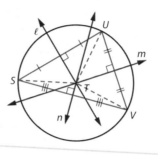

a. Why can a circle with center T and radius $\overline{TS}$ be *circumscribed* about $\triangle SUV$ as shown?

b. Explain with an illustration why a circle can be circumscribed about *any* triangle.

③ **Focusing on Angle Bisectors** In each of the four triangles below, the angle bisectors at each vertex have been constructed.

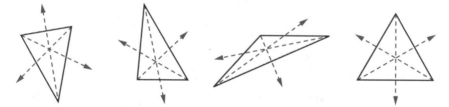

a. What appears to be true about the three angle bisectors in each case?

b. Use interactive geometry software or a compass and straightedge to test your ideas in the case of other triangles. Compare your findings with those of your classmates.

c. If you pick *any* point on the bisector of one of the angles, how does that point seem to be related to the sides of the angle? Compare your ideas with other students. Resolve any differences.

1 a. To be parallel, lines ℓ and m would need to be perpendicular to the same line or to two parallel lines. Since $\overline{SU}$ is not parallel to $\overline{UV}$, ℓ and m are not parallel.

b. Students should recall or look back at their work on Problem 6 on page 198 to identify the congruent triangles they used in that task. For the diagram at the right, the congruent triangles are shaded with the same color.

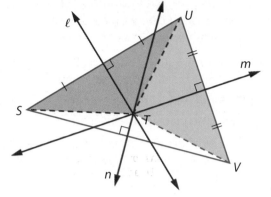

c. T is on n because a point equidistant from two endpoints of a segment is on the perpendicular bisector of that segment. (This was proved in Problem 7 Part b on page 198.)

d. There were no assumptions or theorems used in the reasoning in Parts a–c that restricted us to acute triangles. The triangles formed by the intersection of lines ℓ and m and vertices of the original triangle are more difficult to identify but can still be shown to be congruent.

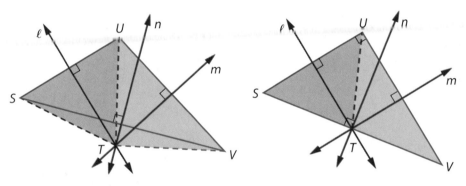

2 a. Since $TS = TU = TV$, a circle with center T and radius $\overline{TS}$ also has radii $\overline{TU}$ and $\overline{TV}$.

b. See the diagrams. Since for any triangle, the perpendicular bisectors of the sides can be constructed, and this point of intersection T is equidistant from the three vertices, a circle with center T can be constructed that circumscribes the triangle. Students may recall from Course 2 that a right triangle can be inscribed in a circle where the hypotenuse is the diameter of the circumscribed circle.

EXPLANATORY POWER OF PROOF Problem 2 Part b offers many opportunities for using deductive reasoning to understand why a result is true.

3 a. They appear to intersect in one point, or to be concurrent.

b. Students should provide some test cases.

c. It seems to be the same perpendicular distance from each side of the angle that it bisects.

INSTRUCTIONAL NOTE
You may wish to have students investigate their ideas outside of class using *CPMP-Tools*. See page T201A for a Technology Tip.

Unit 3

(1) Choose the 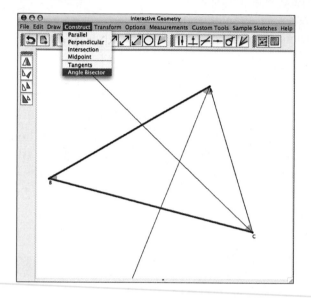 button, then draw a triangle.

(2) Select the button and click on the three vertices of the triangle in a clockwise direction to form an angle with the middle vertex as the angle vertex.

(3) With the angle selected (it will remain highlighted once it is drawn), choose Angle Bisector in the Construct menu or the button.

(4) Repeat Steps 2 and 3 for the remaining triangle vertices; first draw an angle, then construct its bisector.

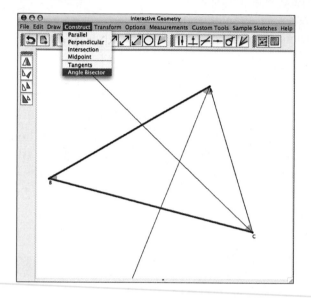

Unit 3

Teacher Notes

To find logical explanations for your observations in Problem 3, it is helpful to consider the angle bisectors of a triangle, one angle bisector at a time.

4 In the diagram at the right, $\overrightarrow{KX}$ is the bisector of $\angle JKL$ and P is a point on $\overrightarrow{KX}$. $\overline{PQ} \perp \overleftrightarrow{JK}$ and $\overline{PR} \perp \overleftrightarrow{KL}$. The **distance from a point to a line** is the length of the perpendicular segment from the point to the line.

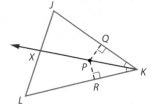

a. Prove that point P is equidistant from the sides of $\angle JKL$ by showing $PQ = PR$.

b. Is it also the case that if a point is equidistant from the sides of an angle, then it is on the bisector of the angle? Justify your answer in terms of a modified diagram.

c. Summarize your work in Parts a and b by completing this statement.

A point is on the bisector of an angle if and only if … .

5 The diagram in Problem 4 is reproduced at the right with $\overrightarrow{LY}$ the bisector of $\angle JLK$ added to the diagram.

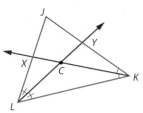

a. Why must angle bisectors $\overrightarrow{KX}$ and $\overrightarrow{LY}$ intersect at some point C?

b. How is point C related to the sides of $\angle JKL$? The sides of $\angle JLK$?

c. Why must point C be on the bisector of $\angle LJK$?

d. Your work in Parts a–c proves that the bisector of the angles of $\triangle JKL$ are concurrent. $\triangle JKL$ is an acute triangle. Draw a diagram for the case where $\triangle JKL$ is a right triangle. Where $\triangle JKL$ is an obtuse triangle. Explain why the reasoning in Parts a–c applies to *any* triangle.

6 The point of concurrency of the bisectors of the angles of a triangle is called the **incenter** of the triangle.

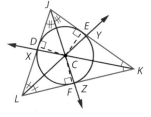

a. Why can a circle with center C and radius $\overline{CD}$ be *inscribed* in $\triangle JKL$ as shown?

b. Explain with an illustration why a circle can be inscribed in *any* triangle.

7 **Focusing on Medians** You have now been able to prove that the three perpendicular bisectors of the sides of a triangle are concurrent and so are the three angle bisectors. Now investigate to see if the three medians of a triangle are concurrent.

a. Use interactive geometry software or a compass and straightedge to draw a triangle. Then construct the three medians. What appears to be true?

4. a. Given: $\overrightarrow{KX}$ is the angle bisector of $\angle JKL$; P is a point on $\overline{KX}$; $\overline{PQ} \perp \overline{JK}$ and $\overline{PR} \perp \overline{KL}$

Prove: $PQ = PR$

$\triangle PQK \cong \triangle PRK$ because the hypotenuse $\overline{PK}$ is common to both triangles, acute angles at K are congruent because $\overrightarrow{KX}$ is an angle bisector, and right angles at Q and R are congruent (AAS). So, $PQ = PR$ (CPCTC).

b. Given: Point P is equidistant from $\overline{JK}$ and $\overline{LK}$, which means that $\overline{PQ} \perp \overline{JK}$, $\overline{PR} \perp \overline{LK}$, and $PR = PQ$.

Prove: $\angle QKP \cong \angle RKP$ (P is on the angle bisector.)

$\triangle QKP \cong \triangle RKP$ because they are right triangles that have congruent hypotenuses and one pair of legs congruent (HL). So, $\angle QKP \cong \angle RKP$ (CPCTC). Thus, P is on the angle bisector of $\angle QKR$.

c. *A point is on the bisector of an angle if and only if it is equidistant from the sides of the angle.*

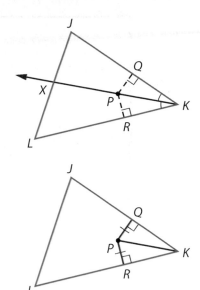

INSTRUCTIONAL NOTE
See the Launch on page T201 for discussion ideas. Students might respond to Problem 5 Part a assuming that $\triangle JKL$ is an acute triangle. If so, in Part d, they should come back to this question and conclude that $\overrightarrow{KX}$ and $\overrightarrow{LY}$ would intersect if one of the angles was obtuse also.

5. a. $\overrightarrow{KX}$ and $\overrightarrow{LY}$ are on the same side of $\overleftrightarrow{LK}$ and they must either intersect or be parallel. Using indirect reasoning, assume $\overrightarrow{KX} \parallel \overrightarrow{LY}$, then $m\angle YLK + m\angle XKL = 180°$ (interior angles on the same side of transversal $\overleftrightarrow{LK}$). But $m\angle YLK + m\angle XKL$ must be less than $180°$ since their sum is half the measure of two angles of a triangle. This is a contradiction, so $\overrightarrow{KX}$ and $\overrightarrow{LY}$ intersect at some point C.

b. Point C is equidistant from the sides of $\angle JKL$ and also equidistant from the sides of $\angle JLK$.

c. The sides of $\angle LJK$ are $\overline{LJ}$ and $\overline{JK}$. C is the same distance from $\overline{JK}$, $\overline{KL}$, and $\overline{LJ}$ because C is on the angle bisector of $\angle JKL$ and $\angle JLK$. So, C is on the bisector of $\angle LJK$ also.

d. There were no assumptions or theorems used in the reasoning in Parts a–c that restricted us to acute triangles. See the triangles at the right.

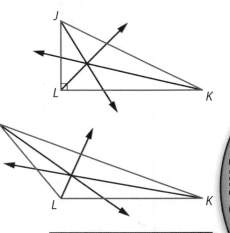

6. a. The point C is the same distance from each of the sides of the triangle. Since $CD = CE = CF$, the circle with center C and radius $\overline{CD}$ is inscribed in the triangle.

b. The angle bisectors can be constructed for any triangle, and at their point of intersection, lines can be constructed perpendicular to the sides of the triangle. This allows the incircle to be constructed.

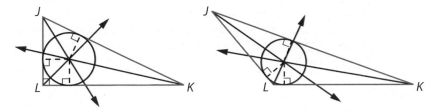

EXPLANATORY POWER OF PROOF Problem 6 offers another good opportunity to realize that deductive reasoning helps you understand why a result is true.

7. a. The medians (segments that connect the midpoint of a side to the vertex of the triangle opposite that side) are concurrent.

INSTRUCTIONAL NOTE
In Problem 7, some students may consider the distance from a vertex to the centroid and the length of the median. If not, they will as they complete Connections Task 16.

Unit 3

b. Test your observations in the case of other triangles. Compare your findings with those of your classmates. Then write a statement summarizing your findings. In Extensions Task 30, you are asked to prove your claim.

8 The point of concurrency of the medians of a triangle is called the **centroid** of the triangle.

- Cut a triangle from poster board or cardboard.
- Find and mark the centroid of your triangle.
- Verify that the centroid is the *center of gravity* of the triangle by balancing the triangle on the tip of a pencil or pen.

Summarize
the Mathematics

In this investigation, you explored centers of triangles and their properties.

a Under what conditions will the three perpendicular bisectors of the sides of a triangle be concurrent? The three angle bisectors? The three medians?

b How can you locate the center of a circle inscribed in a triangle?

c How can you locate the center of a circle circumscribed about a triangle?

d How can you locate the center of gravity of a triangular shape of uniform density?

Be prepared to share your ideas and reasoning with the class.

✔Check Your Understanding

In the diagram, △*ABC* is an equilateral triangle. Point *P* is the circumcenter of △*ABC*.

a. Use congruent triangles to prove that point *P* is also the incenter of △*ABC*.

b. Prove that point *P* is also the centroid of △*ABC*.

c. Suppose *AB* = 12 cm.

   i. Find the length of the radius of the circumscribed circle.

   ii. Find the length of the radius of the inscribed circle.

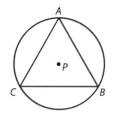

b. Students should test the conjecture with other cases.

8 Students should try to balance at other points to notice that the centroid is the only point that is the center of gravity.

Summary

Although not necessary, if you choose to introduce the terms *incircle* (circle tangent to the sides of a polygon) and *circumcircle* (circle through the vertices of a polygon), be sure students connect these terms to the incenter and circumcenter.

Summarize
the Mathematics

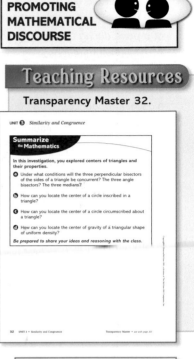

ⓐ For all three cases, there are no special conditions that need to be fulfilled in order that the three specified lines be concurrent. In other words, the points of concurrency occur for *any* triangle.

ⓑ The center of a circle inscribed in a triangle is the intersection point of the three angle bisectors of the triangle. This point is called the *incenter*.

ⓒ The center of a circle circumscribed about a triangle is the intersection point of the perpendicular bisectors to the sides of the triangle. This point is called the *circumcenter*.

ⓓ The center of gravity of a triangular shape of uniform density is the intersection point of the medians. This point is called the *centroid*.

MATH TOOLKIT Summarize what you have learned about the three centers for triangles.

✔Check Your Understanding

a. Point *P* is the intersection of the perpendicular bisectors. Since point *A* is equidistant from the endpoints of $\overline{BC}$, *A* is also on the perpendicular bisector $\overline{AP}$. Call *D* the intersection point. $\triangle ADC \cong \triangle ADB$ (SSS or SAS). By CPCTC, $\angle CAD \cong \angle BAD$, so $\overline{AD}$ is also the angle bisector of $\angle CAB$. Similar reasoning would show $\overline{CP}$ and $\overline{BP}$ are angle bisectors of $\angle C$ and $\angle B$, respectively. So, *P* is also the incenter of $\triangle ABC$.

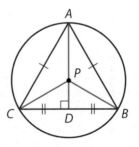

b. Since $\overline{AD}$ is the perpendicular bisector of $\overline{BC}$, $\overline{AD}$ is also a median of $\triangle ABC$ (definition of median). Similarly, the perpendicular bisectors of $\overline{AC}$ and $\overline{AB}$ are also medians. So, *P* is the centroid of $\triangle ABC$.

c. Given: $AB = 12$ cm

i. $m\angle ABC = 60°$, so $m\angle 1 = 30°$ (angle bisector Part a). $\triangle PBD$ is a $30°$-$60°$ right triangle, so the radius of the circumscribed circle is $PB = \frac{12}{\sqrt{3}} = 4\sqrt{3}$.

ii. $\triangle PBD$ is a $30°$-$60°$ right triangle, so the radius of the inscribed circle is $PD = \frac{6}{\sqrt{3}} = 2\sqrt{3}$.

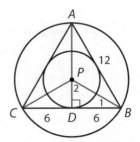

Unit 3

Summarize the Mathematics, *page 203*

The teacher did not take class time to discuss students' ideas on why the perpendicular bisectors and the angle bisectors intersect at a point during the investigation. He noticed that students struggled with the reasoning involved but decided to let the investigation work continue since having correct reasoning would not affect the following work. Thus, he is choosing to discuss reasoning about concurrent points at this time.

Teacher: In this investigation, you explored three different centers of triangles. Individually, think about this question: "Under what conditions will the perpendicular bisectors of the sides of a triangle be concurrent?" *(Teacher waits a few seconds.)* Now see if the conditions you arrived at agree with those of someone near you. *(Teacher listens, then asks Seb for his thoughts.)*

Seb: Well, they always intersect in a point.

Teacher: Others, do you all agree? *(Students indicate agreement.)* Look back at the reasoning you used for Problem 1 Part a. How did you decide that it is not possible for the perpendicular bisectors ℓ and m to be parallel?

Germaine: We said that ℓ and m intersect so they can't be parallel.

Teacher: Well, it is true that either lines ℓ and m intersect or they are parallel. But the point of the question is to justify that the lines must intersect by ruling out the possibility that they are parallel. So, think about this again. If ℓ and m are perpendicular to the two sides of the triangle shown on page 200, why can't they be parallel to each other? Talk with your group about this question. *(The teacher listens. Most groups are floundering, but he notices one group that seems to be heading in the right direction.)* Asha, what is your group thinking?

Asha: We said that they could not be parallel because they would have to be perpendicular to the same line for that to happen. We thought about moving the sides of the triangle $\overline{SU}$ and $\overline{UV}$ up, until ℓ and m are parallel. Here, let me draw our sketch on the board. See if ℓ and m are parallel but stay perpendicular to the sides, the angle at U becomes a straight angle, $180°$. But that is not possible because we have a triangle, $\triangle SUV$.

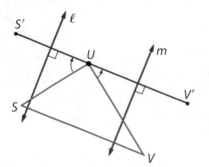

Teacher: Oh, so if the perpendicular bisectors are not parallel, then what, Jon?

Jon: Then they must intersect.

Teacher: Did you notice Asha's and Jon's reasoning? They were thinking that either lines are parallel or they are not—if not parallel, then they must intersect. Then she explained why they could not be parallel. With that option eliminated, Jon stated that the ℓ and m must intersect. This type of reasoning by considering cases and eliminating until you are left with one option is reasoning that you sometimes do naturally in areas other than mathematics. Watch for this type of reasoning. If you use reasoning by eliminating cases in your daily life, please tell us about it. Now let's think about the conditions that ensure that the three angle bisectors are concurrent. Regina, what do you think?

Regina: They always intersect.

Teacher: In Problem 5 Part a, you were to explain why the angle bisectors intersect in a point. James, what did your group say about this?

James: We said the angle bisectors intersect inside the triangle.

Teacher: How did you know that?

James: We saw it in the picture.

Teacher: Let's think about that some more. We cannot just use the drawing and say that we see that the angle bisectors are inside of the triangle. We need to explain either why they intersect or why the other option is not possible. What is the other option again class? *(Students indicate that the other option is for the lines to be parallel.)* How do you know that the angle bisectors are not parallel?

Celine: The angles are too small.

Teacher: What do you mean?

Celine: Well, look, the angle bisectors make these angles half the size of the angles of the triangle. The sides of the triangle already intersect, so the sides of the angle bisectors which are smaller must also intersect.

Teacher: Interesting thinking. Can we extend Celine's thinking to explain why the two bisector rays are not parallel so we can eliminate that option? What would happen if the bisector rays were parallel?

Kristen: They would be outside of the triangle.

Theo: Hey, look. If I draw the bisectors $\overrightarrow{LY}$ and $\overrightarrow{KX}$ parallel, then the interior angles formed by $\overline{LK}$ and the two rays would sum to $180°$. No way can that happen. All three of the angles of the triangle are 180°. So, the angles made by the bisectors must sum to less than 180°. They are half the size of the original ones. *(Theo uses a sketch to help explain his thinking as shown below.)*

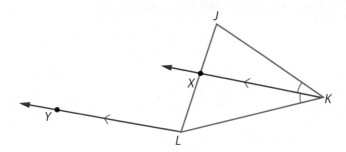

Teacher: *(He notices that some students are following Theo's reasoning and others are not. At this time, he judges that his goal of exposing more students to indirect reasoning has been achieved and that it is not necessary for all students to understand this at this time.)* Notice that the main point to determining whether lines intersected was to decide that it was not possible for them to be parallel. Some known fact was violated if the lines were assumed to be parallel. Again watch for this type of thinking—eliminating options—in your daily activities. You might find this type of reasoning is used in a crime show or movie. Let us know if it is. Now, on to the remainder of the STM. Under what conditions were the medians of a triangle concurrent? Dailia?

Dailia: There are no conditions for medians either. They are always concurrent.

Teacher: How do you locate the center of a circle inscribed in a triangle? Juan?

Juan: Ah … *(He turns to page 202 in the textbook.)* You use the angle bisectors.

Nan: They intersect in a point called the "incenter." I remember by saying, we call the center of the circle inside (inscribed in) the incenter. Notice all the "ins."

Teacher: How can you locate the center of a circle circumscribed about a triangle?

Chiang: It is the intersection of the perpendicular bisectors—called the circumcenter. I remember circumcenter by thinking about the circle going around the outside of the triangle— kinda like a "circumference" around the triangle. You can see the picture on page 201.

Teacher: Now, it seemed to me that to determine the location of the center of a circle inscribed in a triangle or circumscribed about a triangle, some of you were looking at the textbook and your notes. What if you did not have access to these resources? How could you recall which center is formed by the angle bisectors and the perpendicular bisectors?

Nan: I do it by the "in" idea. The point made by the angle bisectors is always inside the triangle. So, the angle bisectors go with the inscribed circle.

Steven: I make a picture in my head.

Teacher: Show us what you mean.

Steven: I use a triangle like this. *(He draws an obtuse triangle.)* Then I think about the circle inscribed in the triangle and the one around the outside, like this. *(He draws a sketch.)* Then I can see in my mind that the angle bisectors intersect inside the triangle and they go with the inscribed circle. See, the perpendicular bisectors give the center for the circumscribed circle.

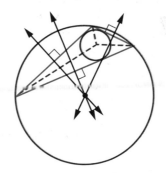

Teacher: Interesting, Steven. You were using visual thinking to support remembering about these triangle centers. Did others think about this visually also? *(Some students indicate they did.)* Now how can you locate the center of gravity of a triangular shape of uniform density?

Sophia: That one is the centroid. That is the point where the medians meet. If you think about Steven's obtuse triangle, you can think about balancing and realize that the angle bisectors will not help find this center. The center would be more to the right on his drawing. This center can be found by drawing the segments from each vertex to the midpoint of the side across from it.

Teacher: Good thinking class. Now use what you know to complete the Check Your Understanding tasks on page 203.

Investigation **3** Congruence in Quadrilaterals

In Investigations 1 and 2, you saw that strategies for solving problems and proving claims using congruent triangles were similar to strategies you used in Lesson 1 when reasoning with similar triangles. You identified triangles that could be proven congruent and then used the congruence of some corresponding sides or angles to draw desired conclusions.

In this investigation, you will extend those reasoning strategies to solve more complex problems by drawing on your knowledge of relations among parallel lines. For example, when the midpoints of the sides of a quadrilateral are connected in order, a new quadrilateral is formed.

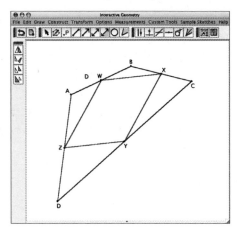

What kind of special quadrilateral is formed?
Will that always be the case?

As you work on the problems of this investigation, look for answers to those questions and the more general questions:

> *How can you use congruent triangles to establish properties of special quadrilaterals, and what are those properties?*

1 Quadrilaterals come in a variety of specialized shapes. There are trapezoids, kites, parallelograms, rhombuses, rectangles, and squares, as well as quadrilaterals with no special additional characteristics.

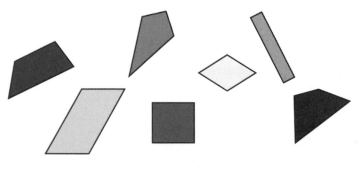

Investigation 3   Congruence in Quadrilaterals

In this investigation, students will use congruent triangles and properties of
parallel lines to prove properties of special quadrilaterals. Sufficient conditions
for a quadrilateral to be a parallelogram or a special parallelogram are
developed including conditions on diagonals that ensure special quadrilaterals.
The Midpoint Connector Theorem for Quadrilaterals is proved using the
corresponding theorem for triangles.

Launch

You may wish to have *CPMP-Tools* geometry software available for a dynamic
investigation of the question: "If the midpoints of a quadrilateral are connected
in order, what kind of special quadrilateral is formed?" Students will be asked
in Problem 6 to prove that a parallelogram is formed.

Assessment Since this is a longer lesson, there are two forms of a quiz for
Investigations 1 and 2 and another two quizzes for Investigations 3 and 4.

a. Complete a copy of the *quadrilateral tree* shown below by filling in each oval with the name of one of the six special quadrilaterals listed. If the oval for a quadrilateral is connected to one or more ovals *above* it, then that quadrilateral must also have the properties of the quadrilateral(s) in the ovals above it to which it is connected.

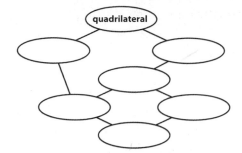

b. Suppose you know that a characteristic X (such as opposite sides congruent) is true for parallelograms. For which other quadrilaterals must characteristic X also be true? Explain your reasoning.

c. Suppose a characteristic Y is true for all kites. Which other quadrilaterals must also have characteristic Y?

② In your work in Course 1 and Course 2, you showed that the following two statements are equivalent. That is, if you accepted one statement as the definition of a parallelogram, you could prove the other statement as a theorem.

I. *A parallelogram is a quadrilateral that has two pair of opposite sides congruent.*

II. *A parallelogram is a quadrilateral that has two pair of opposite sides parallel.*

Using the diagram at the right and your knowledge of congruent triangles and properties of parallel lines:

a. explain how you could prove Statement II using Statement I.

b. explain how you could prove Statement I using Statement II.

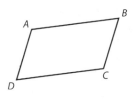

③ **Properties of Parallelograms** A class at Rockbridge High School was asked to make a list of properties of *every* parallelogram, and students prepared the following list. Working in groups, examine each statement to see if you think it is correct. If you think it is correct, construct a proof. If you think it is incorrect, give a counterexample. Share the work. Be prepared to explain your conclusions and reasoning to the entire class.

If a quadrilateral is a parallelogram, then:

a. each diagonal divides the parallelogram into two congruent triangles.

b. opposite angles are congruent.

1 a.

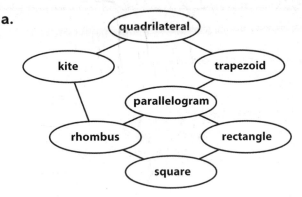

b. The characteristic would also be true for rectangles, rhombuses, and squares since they are all special parallelograms.

c. The characteristics would be true for any rhombuses and squares since they are quadrilaterals that have the properties of kites.

2 a. Given: *ABCD* is a parallelogram and thus has two pair of opposite sides congruent. (Assuming I)

We need to prove that *ABCD* has two pair of opposite sides parallel, or $\overline{AB} \parallel \overline{DC}$ and $\overline{BC} \parallel \overline{AD}$.

Plan for proof: Draw diagonal $\overline{BD}$. Show $\triangle ADB \cong \triangle CBD$ by the SSS Triangle Congruence Theorem. Then use the corresponding congruent angles (∠1 and ∠2 in the diagram) and transversal $\overline{BD}$ to deduce that $\overline{AD}$ and $\overline{BC}$ are parallel. Similarly, $\overline{AB} \parallel \overline{DC}$ because ∠3 ≅ ∠4.

b. Given: *ABCD* is a parallelogram and thus has two pair of opposite sides parallel. (Assuming II)

We need to show that *ABCD* has two pair of opposite sides congruent.

Plan for proof: Draw diagonal $\overline{BD}$. The diagonal is common to $\triangle ADB$ and $\triangle CBD$. ∠1 and ∠2 are alternate interior angles formed by the parallel sides $\overline{BC}$ and $\overline{AD}$ and are thus congruent. Similarly, show that ∠3 and ∠4 are congruent. So, $\triangle ADB \cong \triangle CBD$ (ASA) and the opposite sides of the parallelogram are congruent (CPCTC).

3 If a quadrilateral is a parallelogram, then:

a. each diagonal divides the parallelogram into two congruent triangles.—*True*

Students will likely use the SSS Congruence Theorem but may choose other methods that involve parallel lines and congruent corresponding angles of the two triangles. It should be noted that the proof for one diagonal can be duplicated for the other diagonal.

b. opposite angles are congruent.—*True*

The two congruent triangles formed by the diagonals can be used to show that the opposite angles are congruent (CPCTC).

Teaching Resources

Student Master 33.

UNIT ❸ *Similarity and Congruence* Name
Date

Quadrilateral Tree
Problem 1

1. Quadrilaterals come in a variety of specialized shapes. There are trapezoids, kites, parallelograms, rhombuses, rectangles, and squares, as well as quadrilaterals with no special additional characteristics.

a. Complete the quadrilateral tree shown below by filling in each oval with the name of one of the six special quadrilaterals listed. If the oval for a quadrilateral is connected to one or more ovals above it, then that quadrilateral must also have the properties of the quadrilateral(s) in the ovals above it to which it is connected.

quadrilateral

b. Suppose you know that a characteristic X (such as opposite sides congruent) is true for parallelograms. For which other quadrilaterals must characteristic X also be true? Explain your reasoning.

c. Suppose a characteristic Y is true for all kites. Which other quadrilaterals must also have characteristic Y?

Student Master • use with pages 204 and 205   UNIT 3 • Similarity and Congruence   33

INSTRUCTIONAL NOTE

Following work on Problem 1, or at the STM, remind students of the logical form:
(1) all parallelograms have characteristic X,
(2) all rectangles are parallelograms, thus
(3) all rectangles have characteristic X.

INSTRUCTIONAL NOTE

For some problems, such as Problem 2, you may wish to have students write brief notes or mark a diagram rather than write extensive responses as shown here.

Teaching Resources

Student Master 34.

UNIT ❸ *Similarity and Congruence* Name
Date

Properties of Parallelograms
Problem 3

3. **Properties of Parallelograms** When a class at Rockbridge High School was asked to make a list of properties of every parallelogram, students prepared the following list. Working in groups, examine each statement to see if you think it is correct. If you think it is correct, construct a proof. If you think it is incorrect, give a counterexample. Share the work. Be prepared to explain your conclusions and reasoning to the entire class.

If a quadrilateral is a parallelogram, then:	Correct?	Plan for Proof or Countersample
each diagonal divides the parallelogram into two congruent triangles	T F	
opposite angles are congruent	T F	
consecutive angles are supplementary	T F	
the diagonals are congruent	T F	
the diagonals bisect each other	T F	
the diagonals are perpendicular	T F	

34   UNIT 3 • Similarity and Congruence   Student Master • use with pages 205 and 208

Unit 3

c. consecutive angles are supplementary.

d. the diagonals are congruent.

e. the diagonals bisect each other.

f. the diagonals are perpendicular.

④ How would your answers to Problem 3 change if "parallelogram" was replaced by:

a. "rectangle"?

b. "rhombus"?

c. "kite"?

⑤ How are your responses to Problem 4 reflected in the quadrilateral tree you completed for Problem 1 Part a?

⑥ **Sufficient Conditions for Parallelograms** Here are additional conditions that may or may not ensure that a quadrilateral is a parallelogram. Investigate each conjecture by drawing shapes satisfying the conditions and checking to see if the quadrilateral is a parallelogram. Share the workload among members of your group. Compile a group list of conditions that seem to guarantee that a quadrilateral is a parallelogram. Be prepared to explain your conclusions and reasoning to the entire class.

a. If a diagonal of a quadrilateral divides it into two congruent triangles, then the quadrilateral is a parallelogram.

b. If a quadrilateral has two pairs of opposite angles congruent, then it is a parallelogram.

c. If a quadrilateral has one pair of opposite sides parallel and the other pair of opposite sides congruent, then it is a parallelogram.

d. If a quadrilateral has two distinct pairs of consecutive sides congruent, then it is a parallelogram.

e. If a quadrilateral has one pair of opposite sides congruent and parallel, then it is a parallelogram.

⑦ Now refer back to the interactive geometry software screen and questions posed at the beginning of this investigation. Compare the conjecture that you and your classmates made with the statement below.

> *If the midpoints of consecutive sides of any quadrilateral are connected in order, the resulting quadrilateral is a parallelogram.*

a. Draw and label a diagram representing this statement. Then add a diagonal of the original quadrilateral to your diagram.

b. Write an argument to prove this **Midpoint Connector Theorem for Quadrilaterals**.

c. What was the key previously proven result on which your proof depended?

c. consecutive angles are supplementary.—*True*

Proofs might use the previously proven fact (Unit 1) that interior angles on the same side of a transversal formed by parallel lines are supplementary. Alternatively, the congruent triangles formed by a diagonal and the angle sum of triangles can be used to show the sum of consecutive angles in a parallelogram is 180°.

d. diagonals are congruent.—*False*

Any parallelogram that does not have right angles will provide a counterexample. The lengths of the sides can be chosen so that the length of the diagonals are obviously not congruent.

e. the diagonals bisect each other.—*True*

Using the diagram at the right, congruent alternate interior angles, vertical angles, and congruent opposite sides can be used to show △1 ≅ △2 (AAS). Then by CPCTC, the diagonals can be determined to bisect each other.

f. the diagonals are perpendicular.—*False*

Any parallelogram that is not a rhombus or a kite is a counterexample

4 **a.** Since a rectangle is a parallelogram, all of the statements true for parallelograms are also true for rectangles. In addition, the diagonals are congruent.

b. Since a rhombus is a parallelogram, all of the statements true for parallelograms are also true for rhombuses. In addition, the diagonals are perpendicular.

c. A kite is not a special parallelogram, so each statement needs to be individually considered for a kite. The only statement that is true is that the diagonals are perpendicular. (Students may also observe that one pair of opposite angles are congruent.)

5 The quadrilateral tree shows you which quadrilaterals are special quadrilaterals of the ones above them in the diagram. This means that properties of a quadrilateral transfer to any quadrilateral below it to which it is connected directly or indirectly.

6 **a.** Not sufficient condition
One of the diagonals of a kite divides it into two congruent triangles.

b. **Proof plan:** Use the fact that the sum of the angles of a quadrilateral is 360° and the congruent opposite angles to show m∠A + m∠D = 180° and m∠C + m∠D = 180°. Since interior angles on the same side of a transversal are supplementary, $\overline{AB} \parallel \overline{DC}$ and $\overline{AD} \parallel \overline{BC}$.

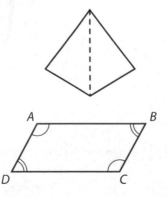

> **INSTRUCTIONAL NOTE**
> Students should be prepared to explain their thinking in Problems 6 and 8. Their notes might take the form of a diagram, explanation, proof plan, or counterexample rather than a formal proof.

c. Not sufficient conditions
A counterexample is an isosceles trapezoid.

d. Not sufficient conditions
A kite is a counterexample.

e. Proof: Draw a diagonal $\overline{AC}$. Assume $\overline{AB}$ and $\overline{DC}$ are parallel and congruent. Since $\overline{AB} \parallel \overline{DC}$, alternate interior angles, $\angle 1$ and $\angle 2$ are the same measure. $\overline{AC}$ is common to both $\triangle ACD$ and $\triangle CAB$. $\triangle ACD \cong \triangle CAB$ (SAS). $\overline{AD} \cong \overline{CB}$ (CPCTC), so $ABCD$ is a parallelogram (two pairs of congruent opposite sides).

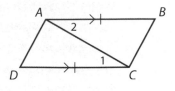

MATH TOOLKIT NOTE
Students should record the Midpoint Connector Theorem for Quadrilaterals in their list of theorems. Ask students why it is important to include the word "consecutive" in the theorem for quadrilaterals and why it is not necessary for triangles.

7 a.

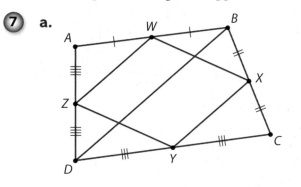

b. By the Midpoint Connector Theorem for Triangles, $\overline{ZW} \parallel \overline{BD}$ and $ZW = \frac{1}{2}BD$. Also, $\overline{XY} \parallel \overline{BD}$ and $XY = \frac{1}{2}BD$. Thus, $\overline{ZW} \parallel \overline{XY}$ and $ZW = XY$. Since one pair of sides of a quadrilateral are congruent and parallel, $WXYZ$ is a parallelogram (Problem 6 Part e).

c. The Midpoint Connector Theorem for Triangles was the key result used.

Unit 3

(8) Sample proof plans for each part are given below.

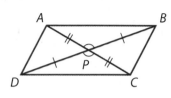
	If the diagonals of a quadrilateral ... ,	**then the quadrilateral is a ... .**
a.	bisect each other	parallelogram
b.	bisect each other and are equal in length	rectangle
c.	are perpendicular bisectors of each other	rhombus
d.	are the same length and are perpendicular bisectors of each other	square
e.	are such that one diagonal is the perpendicular bisector of the other	kite

a. Proof plan: Use $\triangle ABP \cong \triangle CDP$ (SAS) to show that opposite sides $\overline{AB}$ and $\overline{DC}$ are parallel and congruent.

b. Proof plan: Quadrilateral $ABCD$ is a parallelogram by Part a, so opposite sides are congruent. $\overline{BD} \cong \overline{AC}$, so $\triangle ACD \cong \triangle BDC$ (SSS). $\angle ADC \cong \angle BCD$ (CPCTC). These two angles are supplementary because they are consecutive angles of a parallelogram. Since they are equal, they are right angles and $ABCD$ is a rectangle.

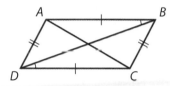

c. Proof plan: Since $\overline{AC}$ and $\overline{BD}$ are perpendicular bisectors of each other, four congruent right triangles are formed by the diagonals. So, all sides (hypotenuses) of quadrilateral $ABCD$ are congruent. Thus, quadrilateral $ABCD$ is a rhombus.

d. Proof plan: Since the diagonals are the same length and perpendicular bisectors of each other, quadrilateral $ABCD$ is both a rectangle and a rhombus. So, it is a square.

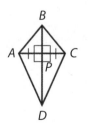

e. Proof plan: $\triangle ABP \cong \triangle CBP$ and $\triangle DPA \cong \triangle DPC$ (SAS). By CPCTC, $\overline{AB} \cong \overline{BC}$ and $\overline{DA} \cong \overline{DC}$, so quadrilateral $ABCD$ is a kite.

Unit 3

⑧ **Diagonal Connections** In your earlier work, you represented the diagonals of a quadrilateral with two linkage strips attached at a point. Complete the following table that relates conditions on diagonals to special quadrilaterals. Be prepared to explain how you can use congruent triangles to help justify your conclusion.

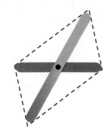

If the diagonals of a quadrilateral ... ,   then the quadrilateral is a ... .

a. bisect each other   _____

b. bisect each other and are equal in length   _____

c. are perpendicular bisectors of each other   _____

d. are the same length and are perpendicular bisectors of each other   _____

e. are such that one diagonal is the perpendicular bisector of the other   _____

Summarize
the Mathematics

In this investigation, you explored how conditions for congruence of triangles could be used to prove properties of special quadrilaterals and sufficient conditions for a quadrilateral to be a parallelogram or a special parallelogram.

a Rectangles are a special type of parallelogram. List all the properties they have in common. Identify at least two properties of rectangles that are *not* properties of all parallelograms.

b A square is a special type of rhombus. What properties do they have in common? Identify at least two properties of squares that are *not* properties of all rhombuses.

c Summarize your work in Problems 3, 4, and 8 by writing if-and-only-if statements characterizing special quadrilaterals in terms of relationships involving their diagonals.

d What strategies are helpful in using congruence to establish properties of special quadrilaterals?

Be prepared to share your lists and reasoning with the class.

Summarize
the Mathematics

NOTE Solutions to Problem 8 are on page T206B.

Teaching Resources

Transparency Master 36.

a Properties of parallelograms and rectangles:

Opposite sides are congruent.
Opposite angles are congruent.
Opposite sides are parallel.
Each diagonal divides the parallelogram into two congruent triangles.
Diagonals bisect each other.

Consecutive angles are supplementary.

Properties of rectangles that are not properties of parallelograms:

Diagonals are congruent.
All four angles are congruent (right angles).

b Properties of rhombuses:

All of the properties in Part a listed for parallelograms hold.
All four sides are congruent.
Diagonals are perpendicular.

Properties of squares that are not properties of rhombuses:

Diagonals are congruent.
All four angles are congruent (right angles).

c A quadrilateral is a parallelogram iff each diagonal divides the quadrilateral into two congruent triangles.
A quadrilateral is a parallelogram iff the diagonals bisect each other.
A quadrilateral is a rectangle iff the diagonals are congruent and bisect each other.
A quadrilateral is a rhombus iff the diagonals are perpendicular bisectors of each other.
A quadrilateral is a square iff the diagonals are congruent and perpendicular bisectors of each other.
A quadrilateral is a kite iff one diagonal is the perpendicular bisector of the other.

d Helpful strategies include making a diagram and labeling it with given information, showing triangles are congruent, showing corresponding parts are congruent, using parallel lines cut by a transversal and the angles formed, using previously proved theorems such as the Midpoint Connector Theorem for Triangles.

MATH TOOLKIT Record the properties of special quadrilaterals. You may wish to also record properties that characterize special quadrilaterals in terms of relationships involving diagonals, but you should be able to visualize these rather than memorize or look them up.

Unit 3

✓Check Your Understanding

For each set of conditions, explain why they do or do not ensure that quadrilateral *PQRS* is a parallelogram.

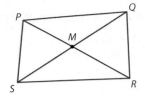

a. $\angle SPQ \cong \angle QRS$ and $\angle PQR \cong \angle PSR$
b. $\overline{PQ} \parallel \overline{RS}$ and $\overline{QR} \cong \overline{PS}$
c. $\overline{PQ} \cong \overline{RS}$ and $\overline{QR} \cong \overline{PS}$
d. $\overline{PQ} \cong \overline{QR}$ and $\overline{RS} \cong \overline{PS}$
e. *M* is the midpoint of $\overline{PR}$ and of $\overline{QS}$.

Investigation 4 Congruence-Preserving Transformations

In Course 2, you studied transformations of a plane defined by coordinate rules. You explored translations, rotations about the origin, and the line reflections across the *x*- and *y*-axes, lines parallel to the axes, and lines with equations $y = x$ and $y = -x$. Using the distance formula, you were able to prove that these transformations preserve distances and therefore images of transformed figures are congruent to the original figures. You used these *congruence-preserving transformations* to reposition figures on a computer screen and create interesting animations.

In this investigation, you will explore properties and applications of these transformations without the use of coordinates and without restrictions on the positions of the lines of reflection or the centers of rotation. Once again, congruence of triangles will be a key tool in your work.

As you work on the problems in this investigation, look for answers to these questions:

What are the connections between line reflections and translations and rotations?

How can you prove properties of these congruence-preserving transformations without the use of coordinates and how can you use those properties to solve problems?

✔ Check Your Understanding

a. *PQRS* is a parallelogram because both pairs of opposite angles are congruent.

b. *PQRS* is not a parallelogram. A counterexample is an isosceles trapezoid.

c. *PQRS* is a parallelogram because both pairs of opposite sides are congruent.

d. *PQRS* is not a parallelogram. A kite is a counterexample.

e. *PQRS* is a parallelogram because the diagonals bisect each other.

Investigation 4 — Congruence-Preserving Transformations

In Course 2 Unit 3, *Coordinate Methods*, students studied transformations (translations, specific line reflections, and rotations about the origin) of a plane defined by coordinate rules. In that unit, they also used coordinate geometry to establish properties of such transformations.

In this investigation, students will re-examine line reflections, translations, and rotations from a synthetic perspective and use congruent triangles to establish properties of these transformations. Students prove that line reflections preserve length and angle measure; that the composition of two line reflections across parallel lines is a translation; and that the composition of two line reflections across intersecting lines is a rotation about the center of the intersecting lines.

DIFFERENTIATION Depending on time and background of class, teachers may want to focus on discovery and application of the answers to the STM prompts and to briefly discuss how triangle congruence provides a means to justify those discoveries.

Launch

Problem 1 is a good opportunity to allow students to tackle a more difficult proof by alternating small-group discussions and whole-class discussions. One approach is to discuss the introduction and definition of a reflection across line ℓ in the student text as a class. Then provide pairs of students a few minutes to draw the diagram indicated in Part a and begin to think about how to prove $PQ = P'Q'$ in Part b. After students have thought about it, you will likely need to assist them.

Ask students, "What have you been discussing as a plan for your proof?" Having some students report what they were thinking even when they rejected their ideas because they did not have enough information provides a window for other students into effective reasoning strategies. Students will likely indicate that they do not have enough information to prove $\triangle QPM \cong \triangle Q'MP'$.

So, to focus students on a plan to use two pairs of congruent triangles, ask questions such as, "What information do we know?", "Are there other triangles that could be shown congruent?", and "Would it be helpful to label any angles with numbers?" After this discussion, you can give students several minutes to develop a proof plan before discussing the proof as a whole class. It is not necessary for students to write out the entire proofs for Parts b and d.

Reasoning with Line Reflections In Escher's *Magic Mirror* shown below, figures and their reflected images reside in the same plane. The relationship between a figure and its reflected image agrees with the following definition of a line reflection.

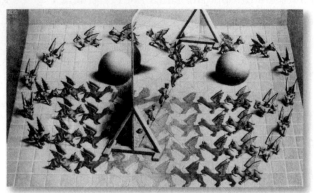

A **reflection across line ℓ** is a transformation that maps each point P of the plane onto an image point P' as follows:

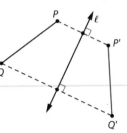

- If point P is not on ℓ, then ℓ is the perpendicular bisector of $\overline{PP'}$.
- If point P is on ℓ, then $P' = P$. That is, P is its own image.

1 The diagram above illustrating the definition of a line reflection suggests that a *line segment and its reflected image are the same length*. That is, $PQ = P'Q'$. Parts a–d will help you justify that conclusion for any choice of points P and Q.

   a. On a copy of the diagram, draw $\overline{PP'}$ and $\overline{QQ'}$. Label the points of intersection with line ℓ, M and N, respectively. Draw $\overline{QM}$ and $\overline{Q'M}$.

   b. Use reasoning with congruent triangles to prove that $PQ = P'Q'$.

   c. In the case above, points P and Q are on the same side of the line of reflection. Draw three diagrams illustrating other possible positions of points P and Q relative to line ℓ.

   d. Discuss with classmates how you could prove that $PQ = P'Q'$ in each of the cases in Part c.

1 **a.**

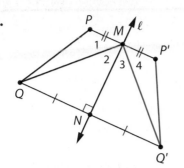

b. Given: P' and Q' are reflected images of P and Q across line ℓ.

Prove: $PQ = P'Q'$

ℓ is the perpendicular bisector of $\overline{QQ'}$ and $\overline{PP'}$ by the definition of a line reflection, so $QN = Q'N$, $PM = P'M$, and $m\angle QNM = m\angle Q'NM = 90°$. $\triangle QNM \cong \triangle Q'NM$ (SAS). $\overline{QM} \cong \overline{Q'M}$ and $\angle 2 \cong \angle 3$ (CPCTC).

$\angle PMN \cong \angle P'MN$ because ℓ is the perpendicular bisector of $\overline{PP'}$ and both angles are right angles. So, $m\angle 1 + m\angle 2 = m\angle 3 + m\angle 4$ (Angle Addition Postulate). Since $m\angle 2 = m\angle 3$, $m\angle 1 = m\angle 4$ (subtract same value from both sides of equation). Since $\angle 1 \cong \angle 4$, $\overline{QM} \cong \overline{Q'M}$, and $\overline{PM} \cong \overline{P'M}$, $\triangle QPM \cong \triangle Q'P'M$ (SAS). Therefore, $PQ = P'Q'$ (CPCTC).

c.

Diagram I   **Diagram II**   **Diagram III**

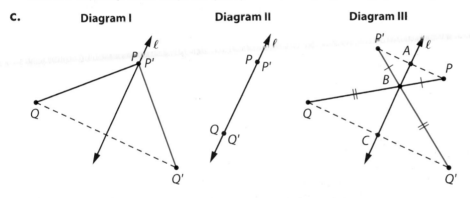

d. The proof for Diagram I could use the previously proved theorem that a point P on the perpendicular bisector of a segment $\overline{QQ'}$ is equidistant from the endpoints Q and Q'. So, $PQ = P'Q'$.

For Diagram II, $\overline{PQ} \cong \overline{P'Q'}$ because they are the same segment.

For Diagram III, you could show $\triangle P'AB \cong \triangle PAB$ (SAS) and $\triangle QBC \cong \triangle Q'BC$ (SAS). Thus, $BP' = BP$ and $QB = Q'B$ (CPCTC). So, $PQ = P'Q'$ because $PQ = QB + BP$ and $P'Q' = P'B + BQ'$.

Unit 3

(2) Draw a line ℓ and a triangle ABC.

a. Find the reflected image of $\triangle ABC$ across line ℓ. Label the image $\triangle A'B'C'$.

b. Use the result of Problem 1 to prove that $\triangle A'B'C' \cong \triangle ABC$.

c. How could you justify the claim that an *angle and its reflected image across a line are congruent*?

Playing Smarter When a ball with no spin and medium speed is banked off a flat surface, the angles at which it strikes and leaves the surface are congruent. You can use this fact and knowledge of line reflections to your advantage in games of miniature golf and billiards.

(3) To make a hole-in-one on the miniature golf green on the left below, visualize point H', the reflected image of the hole H across line ℓ. Aim for the point P where $\overline{BH'}$ intersects ℓ.

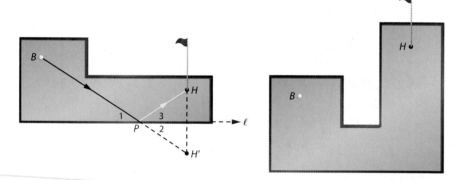

a. If you aim for point P, give reasons to justify that the ball will follow the indicated path to the hole. That is, show $\angle 1 \cong \angle 3$.

b. The diagram at the right shows another par 2 green. On a copy of that diagram, test if you can make a hole-in-one using a single line reflection as in Part a.

c. Is there a way that by finding the reflection image of the hole H across one side and then the reflection of that image across another side, that you can find a point to aim and still make a hole-in-one? Illustrate your answer. Explain why a hit golf ball will follow the path you have drawn.

The Reflection-Translation Connection Recall that a **translation** is a transformation that "slides" all points in the plane the same distance and same direction. That is, if points P' and Q' are the images of points P and Q under a translation, then $PP' = QQ'$ and $\overline{PP'} \parallel \overline{QQ'}$.

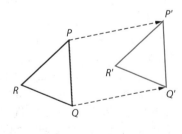

2 a.

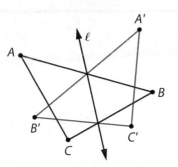

b. Since a line segment and its reflected image are the same length, $AB = A'B'$, $BC = B'C'$, and $AC = A'C'$. So, $\triangle A'B'C' \cong \triangle ABC$ (SSS).

c. An angle and its image across a line are congruent because the angle vertex and a point on each ray defining the angle could be used to form a triangle. Then the reflected image of that triangle, across a line is congruent to the triangle. By CPCTC, the angle and its image are congruent.

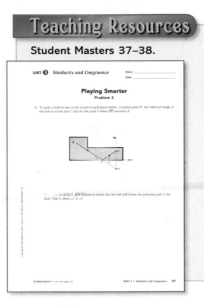
3 a. Show: $\angle 1 \cong \angle 3$

$\angle 1 \cong \angle 2$ (vertical angles)
$\angle 2 \cong \angle 3$ (angle reflected across line ℓ and angle measure is preserved)
Therefore, $\angle 1 \cong \angle 3$.

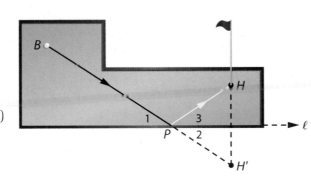

b. INSTRUCTIONAL NOTE Students should test using a copy from the *Unit 3 Resource Masters*. Encourage them to test strategically using their knowledge of line reflections.

It is not possible to make a hole-in-one with only one bounce. If you reflect H across line m and draw $\overline{BH'}$, the path (which is not possible) is shown at the right in red.

c. You could reflect H across ℓ and m in the diagram at the right. Since H'' is the reflected image of H', $\angle 1 \cong \angle 2$; and since H' is the reflected image of H, $\angle 3 \cong \angle 4$. The ball will follow the path from B to P to Q to H because $\angle 1 \cong \angle 2$ and $\angle 3 \cong \angle 4$. That is, the path satisfies the law of physics—the angle of incidence equals the angle of reflection.

INSTRUCTIONAL NOTE Some students might reflect point B across line m and point H across line ℓ in order to find point P on m for which to aim. This procedure works for this problem but is not generalizable.

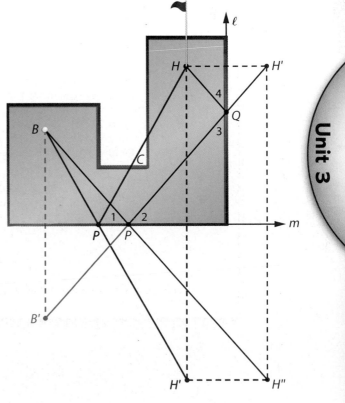

Unit 3

Reasoning about Congruent Triangles **T210**

In Problems 4 and 5, you will investigate connections between translations and line reflections.

4 The diagram below shows the image of $\triangle ABC$ under a composition of two line reflections, first across line ℓ (image $\triangle A_1B_1C_1$) and then across line m, where $\ell \parallel m$ (image $\triangle A'B'C'$).

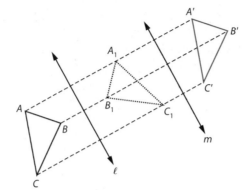

a. Explain why $\triangle A'B'C' \cong \triangle ABC$.

b. How does $\triangle A'B'C'$ appear to be related to $\triangle ABC$ by position?

c. What kind of special quadrilateral is $AA'C'C$? Justify your claim.

d. Explain why $AA' = CC'$ and $\overline{AA'} \cong \overline{CC'}$.

e. Is it also the case that $BB' = CC'$ and $\overline{BB'} \parallel \overline{CC'}$? Justify your answer.

f. Suppose P is a point on ℓ and P' is the image of P under the composition of the two reflections. Draw a diagram. Explain why it is also the case that $PP' = AA'$ and $\overline{PP'} \parallel \overline{AA'}$.

5 Look back at your work in Parts d–f of Problem 4.

a. Explain why the composition of two reflections across parallel lines is a translation.

b. How would you describe the *magnitude* (distance points are translated) of the translation? The direction?

c. In the diagram at the right, point T' is the translated image of point T. On a copy of the diagram, find two lines so that the composition of reflections across those lines maps T to T'. Compare the two lines you found with those found by other students. Resolve any differences.

4

a. A triangle and its image under a line reflection are congruent. $\triangle ABC$ is congruent to $\triangle A_1B_1C_1$, which in turn is congruent to $\triangle A'B'C'$. So, $\triangle ABC \cong \triangle A'B'C'$.

b. $\triangle A'B'C'$ seems to be a translated image of $\triangle ABC$.

c. Claim: $AA'C'C$ is a parallelogram.

Show: One pair of sides are parallel and congruent

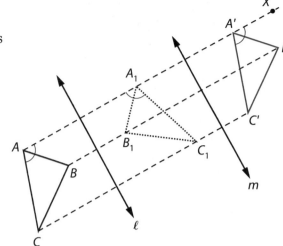

$AC = A'C'$ (CPCTC). Extend $\overrightarrow{AA'}$ to $\overrightarrow{AX}$. $\angle CAA_1 \cong \angle C_1A_1A \cong \angle C'A'X$ since the angles are related by line reflections. Since congruent angles $\angle CAA_1$ and $\angle C'A'X$ are corresponding angles on the same side of transversal $\overleftrightarrow{AA'}$, $\overline{AC} \parallel \overline{A'C'}$. So, $AA'C'C$ is a parallelogram. (One pair of opposite sides are parallel and congruent.)

d. $\overline{AA'}$ and $\overline{CC'}$ are the other pair of opposite sides of parallelogram $AA'C'C$, so $AA' = CC'$ and $\overline{AA'} \parallel \overline{CC'}$.

e. Reasoning similar to that used in Part c can be used here to justify $BB' = CC'$ and $\overline{BB'} \parallel \overline{CC'}$.

f. Since P is on ℓ, $P = P_1$, and the composition of the two reflections sends P to its reflected image across m. $\angle 1 \cong \angle 3$ and $AP = A'P'$ (line reflection preserves distance and angle measure). So, $APP'A'$ is a parallelogram (one pair of opposite sides are parallel and congruent). Since $APP'A'$ is a parallelogram, the other pair of opposite sides are parallel and congruent. $\overline{PP'} \parallel \overline{AA'}$ and $PP' = AA'$.

Teaching Resources

Student Master 39.

UNIT ❸ *Similarity and Congruence*   Name

Date

The Reflection-Translation Connection
Problem 4

4. The diagram below shows the image of △ABC under a composition of two line reflections, first across line ℓ and then across line m, where ℓ ∥ m.

a. Explain why △A'B'C' ≅ △ABC.

b. How does △A'B'C' appear to be related to △ABC by position?

c. What kind of special quadrilateral is AA'C'C? Justify your claim.

d. Explain why AA' ≅ CC' and AA' ∥ CC'.

e. Is it also the case that BB' ≅ CC' and BB' ∥ CC'? Justify your answer.

f. Suppose P is a point on ℓ and P' is the image of P under the composition of the two reflections. Draw a diagram. Explain why it is also the case that PP' ≅ AA' and PP' ∥ AA'.

Student Master • *use with page 261*   UNIT 3 • Similarity and Congruence   **39**

INSTRUCTIONAL NOTE
You may wish to have students use interactive geometry software to explore the composition of a shape under two parallel line reflections.

NOTE The solution to Problem 5 is on page T212.

**The Reflection-Rotation
Connection** Recall that a **rotation** is a
transformation that "turns" all points in the
plane about a fixed center point through a
specified angle. That is, if points P' and Q'
are the images of points P and Q under a
counterclockwise rotation about point C, then
$CP = CP'$, $CQ = CQ'$, and $m\angle PCP' = m\angle QCQ'$.

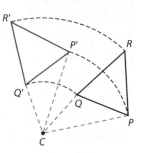

In Problems 6 and 7, you will investigate connections between rotations and
line reflections.

6 The diagram below shows $\triangle A'B'C'$ the image of $\triangle ABC$ under a
composition of two reflections across intersecting lines, first a
reflection across ℓ and then a reflection across m.

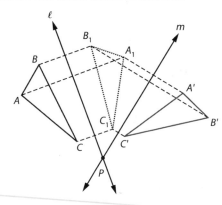

a. Explain why $\triangle A'B'C' \cong \triangle ABC$.

b. How does $\triangle A'B'C'$ appear to be related to $\triangle ABC$ by position?

c. A portion of the
above diagram is
reproduced here.

   i. Explain why
     $PA = PA'$ and
     $PB = PB'$.

   ii. Explain why
     $m\angle A'PB' = m\angle APB$.

   iii. Explain why
     $m\angle APA' = m\angle BPB'$.

d. Suppose X is a point
on ℓ ($X \neq P$) and X' is
the image of X under
the composition of a reflection across line ℓ followed by a
reflection across line m. Draw a diagram. Explain why it is
also the case that $m\angle XPX' = m\angle APA'$.

(5) **a.** The composition of two reflections across parallel lines is a translation because the image points P' and Q' are related to P and Q so that $\overline{PP'} \parallel \overline{QQ'}$ and $PP' = QQ'$ (definition of a translation—points move along parallel lines the same distance).

b. The magnitude is twice the distance between the parallel reflection lines. The direction is perpendicular to the reflection lines.

c. There are an infinite number of correct drawings for Part c. In every case, the reflection lines must be perpendicular to $\overleftrightarrow{TT'}$ and have distance between them of $\frac{1}{2}TT'$. Two examples are shown below.

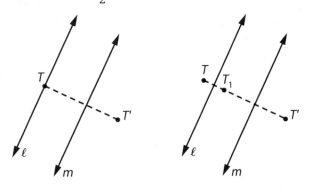

(6) **a.** $\triangle A_1B_1C_1 \cong \triangle ABC$ since $\triangle A_1B_1C_1$ is the reflected image of $\triangle ABC$ across line ℓ (Problem 2, page 210). Similarly, $\triangle A'B'C'$ is the reflected image of $\triangle A_1B_1C_1$ across line m, so $\triangle A'B'C' \cong \triangle A_1B_1C_1$. Thus, $\triangle A'B'C' \cong \triangle ABC$.

b. $\triangle A'B'C'$ appears to be a rotated image of $\triangle ABC$.

c. **i.** A line segment and its reflected image have the same length (Problem 1, page 210). Performing two line reflections in succession does not change the length of a line segment.

ii. An angle and its reflected image are congruent (Problem 2 Part c, page 210). Performing two line reflections in succession on an angle does not change the angle measure.

iii. Since $m\angle A'PB' = m\angle APB$, $m\angle A'PB' + m\angle BPA' = m\angle APB + m\angle BPA'$ (adding $m\angle BPA'$ to each of two equal measures). So, $m\angle APA' = m\angle BPB'$ (angle addition).

d. Show $m\angle APA' = m\angle XPX'$.
$m\angle APX = m\angle A_1PX_1 = m\angle A'PX'$ (angle measure is preserved under line reflection).
$m\angle APX + m\angle XPA' = m\angle XPA' + m\angle A'PX'$.

So, by angle addition, $m\angle APA' = m\angle XPX'$.

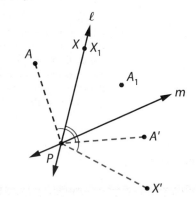

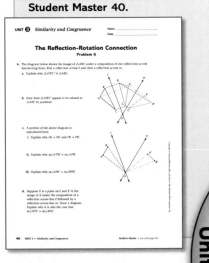
Unit 3

7 Look back at your work in Parts c and d of Problem 6.

a. Explain why the composition of reflections across two intersecting lines is a rotation about the point of intersection.

b. How would you describe the *directed angle* of the rotation?

c. In the diagram below, points S' and T' are the images of points S and T under a rotation about a point C.

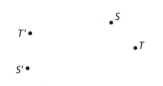

On a copy of the diagram, find two lines so that the composition of reflections across those lines maps S to S' and T to T'. You might start by finding a line ℓ so that the reflection of point S across ℓ is point S'.

d. What is the center and directed angle of the rotation?

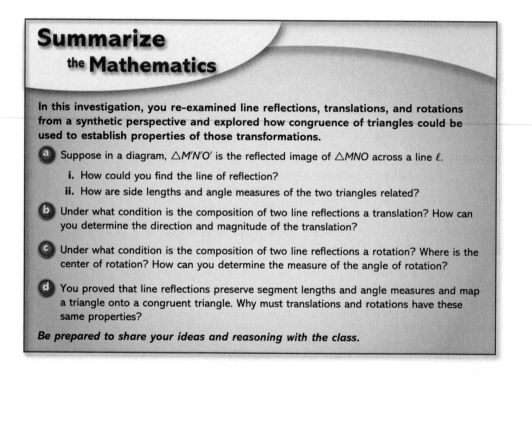

Summarize
the Mathematics

In this investigation, you re-examined line reflections, translations, and rotations from a synthetic perspective and explored how congruence of triangles could be used to establish properties of those transformations.

a Suppose in a diagram, $\triangle M'N'O'$ is the reflected image of $\triangle MNO$ across a line ℓ.

  i. How could you find the line of reflection?

  ii. How are side lengths and angle measures of the two triangles related?

b Under what condition is the composition of two line reflections a translation? How can you determine the direction and magnitude of the translation?

c Under what condition is the composition of two line reflections a rotation? Where is the center of rotation? How can you determine the measure of the angle of rotation?

d You proved that line reflections preserve segment lengths and angle measures and map a triangle onto a congruent triangle. Why must translations and rotations have these same properties?

Be prepared to share your ideas and reasoning with the class.

7 **a.** When A and B were reflected across two lines ℓ and m that intersected at point P, the definition on page 212 for a rotation about point P was satisfied. All points in the plane are turned about a fixed point P through a specified angle. In this case, $PA = PA'$, $PB = PB'$, and $m\angle APA' = m\angle BPB'$.

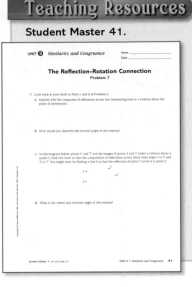
b. In Problem 6, the angle of rotation was a clockwise rotation the measure of $\angle APA'$ or $\angle BPB'$, which is twice the measure of the angle between ℓ and m in the direction from ℓ to m.

c. Draw $\overline{SS'}$ and its perpendicular bisector ℓ. Reflect T across ℓ to T_1. Draw m as the perpendicular bisector of $\overline{T_1T'}$. S' is on m because distance is preserved across line reflections. $ST = S'T_1 = S'T'$. The intersection of ℓ and m is C.

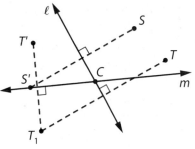

A second method follows. S and S' are on a circle with center C, and T and T' are on another circle with center C. So to find C, construct the perpendicular bisectors of $\overline{SS'}$ and $\overline{TT'}$ as shown at the right. These lines intersect at C. Then draw $\overline{CS'}$ and $\overline{CS}$. The angle of rotation is a counterclockwise rotation the measure of $\angle SCS'$.

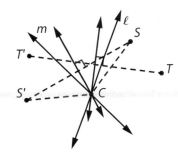

Now draw lines ℓ and m between $\overleftrightarrow{CS'}$ and $\overleftrightarrow{CS}$ intersecting at C with angle size $\frac{1}{2}m\angle SCS'$. A simpler example is to let ℓ be $\overleftrightarrow{CS}$ and m be the angle bisector of $\angle SCS'$.

d. The center is the intersection of lines ℓ and m. The angle of rotation is a counterclockwise rotation of magnitude $m\angle S'CS$.

Unit 3

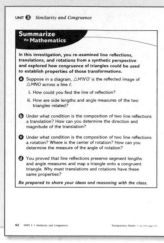

Summarize
the Mathematics

a i. ℓ is the perpendicular bisector of the segment formed by any point M, N, or O and its image.

ii. The corresponding angles and sides are congruent.

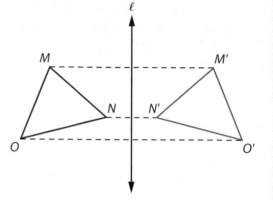

b When the two lines of reflection are parallel, the composition of reflections across these lines is a translation. The direction of the translation is perpendicular to the reflection lines, moving points in the direction from the first reflection line toward the second. The magnitude is twice the distance between the two parallel lines of reflection.

c When the two lines of reflection intersect, the composition of reflections across these lines is a rotation. The center of rotation is the point of intersection of the two lines of reflection. The magnitude is twice the measure of the directed angle between the first line of reflection and the second one.

d Translations and rotations are compositions of two line reflections. Since each reflection preserves segment lengths, angle measures, and maps triangles onto congruent triangles, the composition of two reflections has the same properties.

Teacher Notes

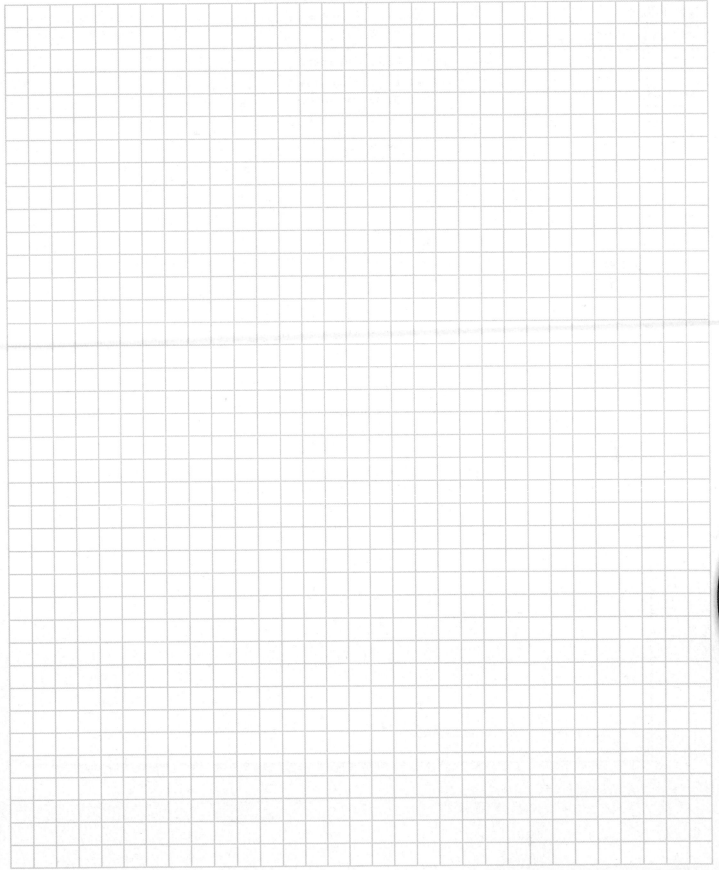

✔ Check Your Understanding

Using a copy of the diagram below, draw the image of △ABC under the composition of successive reflections across line ℓ, line m, and line n. Label the final image triangle △A'B'C'.

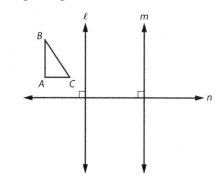

a. Explain why △A'B'C' ≅ △ABC.

b. Compare the clockwise/counterclockwise orientation of the corresponding vertices of the two triangles. What explains this fact?

c. How would you describe this transformation?

d. Draw segments $\overline{AA'}$ and $\overline{BB'}$. What appears to be true about the midpoints of those segments? Is the same true for the midpoint of $\overline{CC'}$?

e. How could you use Problem 6 on page 177 to prove that your observation in Part d is true for any point P and its image P' under this composite transformation? Start by drawing a new diagram showing lines ℓ, m, and n. Mark a point P and locate its image P'.

✓ Check Your Understanding

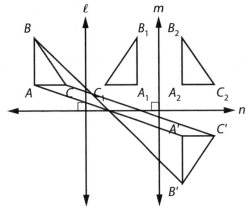

a. Each time a triangle is reflected across a line, it is mapped onto a congruent triangle. So, $\triangle ABC \cong \triangle A'B'C'$.

b. In the given triangle, the vertices A, B, and C are labeled in clockwise order. In $\triangle A'B'C'$, the vertices A', B', and C' are labeled in counterclockwise order. The orientation of a figure is reversed with each line reflection. Since $\triangle ABC$ and $\triangle A'B'C'$ are related by a composition of three line reflections, the orientation is reversed.

c. This transformation is a glide-reflection, a composition of a translation that maps $\triangle ABC$ to $\triangle A_2B_2C_2$ and a reflection across the line n which is parallel to the direction of the translation. (See Course 2, page 224.)

d. The midpoints appear to be on n.

e. **Prove:** If P is reflected across two parallel lines ℓ and m and then across a line n perpendicular to ℓ and m as shown in the diagram, then the midpoint M of $\overline{PP'}$ lies on line n.

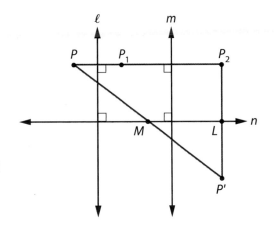

Proof: Consider $\triangle PP_2P'$. Point L lies on line n and is the midpoint of side $\overline{P_2P'}$ since P' is the reflected image of P_2 across n. Line n is parallel to $\overline{PP_2}$ because it is perpendicular to m, which is perpendicular to $\overline{PP_2}$. Since line n is parallel to one side of $\triangle PP_2P'$ and intersects a second side $(\overline{P_2P'})$ at the midpoint, n intersects the third side $(\overline{P'P})$ at the midpoint M (Midpoint Connector Theorem for Triangles).

Applications

1 Prove, if possible, that $\triangle ABD \cong \triangle CBD$ under each set of conditions below.

    a. $\overline{AB} \cong \overline{BC}$ and $\angle ABD \cong \angle CBD$.

    b. $\overline{BD}$ is the perpendicular bisector of $\overline{AC}$.

    c. $\overline{BD} \perp \overline{AC}$ and $m\angle A = m\angle C$.

    d. $AB = BC$ and D is the midpoint of $\overline{AC}$.

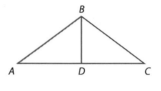

2 Suppose you are given the following information about the figure shown at the right.

$$\overline{ST} \cong \overline{SP} \text{ and } \overline{TO} \cong \overline{PO}$$

Can you conclude that $\triangle STO \cong \triangle SPO$? Write a proof or give a counterexample.

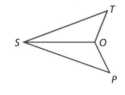

3 For the four lines shown, $\overleftrightarrow{AB} \parallel \overleftrightarrow{DE}$ and C is the midpoint of $\overline{BD}$.

    a. Prove that $\triangle ABC \cong \triangle EDC$.

    b. Using your work in Part a, explain why you also can conclude that C is the midpoint of $\overline{AE}$.

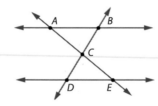

4 Hutchins Lake is a long, narrow lake. Its length is represented by $\overline{AB}$ in the diagram shown below. Dmitri designed the following method to determine its length. First, he paced off and measured $\overline{AC}$ and $\overline{BC}$. Then, using a transit, he made $m\angle PCA = m\angle ACB$. He then marked point D on $\overrightarrow{CP}$ so that $DC = BC$, and he measured $\overline{AD}$.

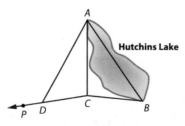

Hutchins Lake

    a. Dmitri claimed $AB = AD$. Is he correct? Justify your answer.

    b. Andrea claimed she could find the length AB of the lake without sighting $\triangle ADC$. Suppose $AC = 500$ m, $BC = 200$ m, and $m\angle ACB = 100°$. What is the length of Hutchins Lake?

On Your Own

Applications

1 a. Conditions: $\overline{AB} \cong \overline{BC}$ and $\angle ABD \cong \angle CBD$

Proof: $\overline{BD}$ is common to $\triangle ABD$ and $\triangle CBD$. So, $\triangle ABD \cong \triangle CBD$ (SAS).

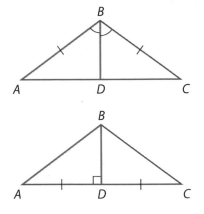

b. Conditions: $\overline{BD} \perp \overline{AC}$ and $\overline{AD} \cong \overline{CD}$

Proof: $\overline{BD}$ is common to both triangles. $\angle ADB \cong \angle CDB$ (right angles). So, $\triangle ABD \cong \triangle CBD$ (SAS).

c. Conditions: $\overline{BD} \perp \overline{AC}$ and $m\angle A = m\angle C$

Proof: $\angle ADB \cong \angle CDB$ (right angles) and $\overline{BD} \cong \overline{BD}$. So, $\triangle ABD \cong \triangle CBD$ (AAS).

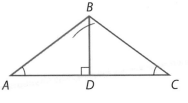

d. Conditions: $AB = BC$ and D is the midpoint of $\overline{AC}$.

Proof: $\overline{AD} \cong \overline{DC}$ and $\overline{BD} \cong \overline{BD}$. So, $\triangle ABD \cong \triangle CBD$ (SSS).

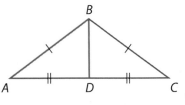

2 We are given that $\overline{ST} \cong \overline{SP}$ and $\overline{TO} \cong \overline{PO}$. $\overline{SO}$ is congruent to itself. So, $\triangle STO \cong \triangle SPO$ (SSS).

3 a. We are given that $\overleftrightarrow{AB} \parallel \overleftrightarrow{DE}$ and C is the midpoint of $\overline{BD}$. Since $\overleftrightarrow{AB}$ and $\overleftrightarrow{DE}$ are cut by transversal $\overleftrightarrow{BD}$, $\angle ABC \cong \angle EDC$ (alternate interior angles). C is the midpoint of $\overline{DB}$, so $\overline{CB} \cong \overline{DC}$ (definition of midpoint). $\angle ACB \cong \angle ECD$ (vertical angles). $\triangle ABC \cong \triangle EDC$ (ASA).

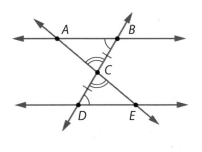

b. You can conclude that C is the midpoint of $\overline{AE}$ because $\overline{AC}$ and $\overline{CE}$ are corresponding parts of the congruent triangles and so are congruent.

4 a. Since $DC = BC$, $m\angle DCA = m\angle BCA$, and $AC = AC$, $\triangle DCA \cong \triangle BCA$ (SAS Congruence Theorem). Dmitri is correct since the procedure produced two congruent triangles, $\triangle ABC$ and $\triangle ADC$, and $\overline{AB} \cong \overline{AD}$ by CPCTC.

b. $AB^2 = AC^2 + BC^2 - 2(AC)(BC)(\cos 100°)$
$= 500^2 + 200^2 - 2(500)(200)(\cos 100°) \approx 324{,}730$ m
$AB \approx 570$ m

Reasoning about Congruent Triangles

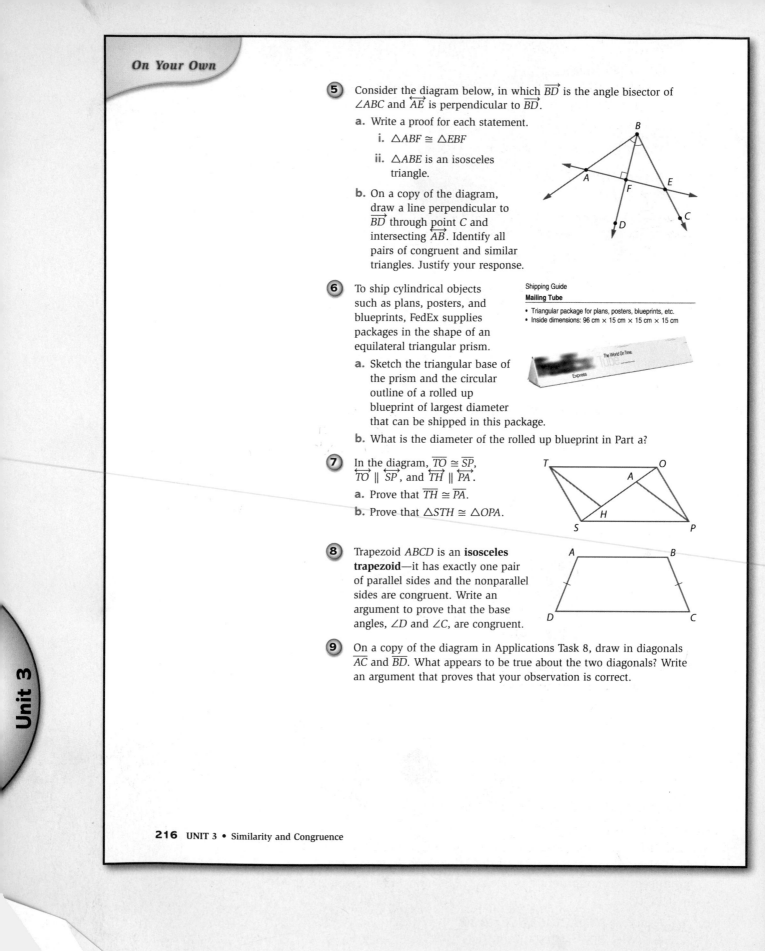

5 Consider the diagram below, in which $\overrightarrow{BD}$ is the angle bisector of ∠*ABC* and $\overleftrightarrow{AE}$ is perpendicular to $\overrightarrow{BD}$.

  a. Write a proof for each statement.

    i. △*ABF* ≅ △*EBF*

    ii. △*ABE* is an isosceles triangle.

  b. On a copy of the diagram, draw a line perpendicular to $\overrightarrow{BD}$ through point *C* and intersecting $\overleftrightarrow{AB}$. Identify all pairs of congruent and similar triangles. Justify your response.

6 To ship cylindrical objects such as plans, posters, and blueprints, FedEx supplies packages in the shape of an equilateral triangular prism.

Shipping Guide
Mailing Tube
• Triangular package for plans, posters, blueprints, etc.
• Inside dimensions: 96 cm × 15 cm × 15 cm × 15 cm

  a. Sketch the triangular base of the prism and the circular outline of a rolled up blueprint of largest diameter that can be shipped in this package.

  b. What is the diameter of the rolled up blueprint in Part a?

7 In the diagram, $\overline{TO} \cong \overline{SP}$, $\overrightarrow{TO} \parallel \overleftrightarrow{SP}$, and $\overleftrightarrow{TH} \parallel \overleftrightarrow{PA}$.

  a. Prove that $\overline{TH} \cong \overline{PA}$.

  b. Prove that △*STH* ≅ △*OPA*.

8 Trapezoid *ABCD* is an **isosceles trapezoid**—it has exactly one pair of parallel sides and the nonparallel sides are congruent. Write an argument to prove that the base angles, ∠*D* and ∠*C*, are congruent.

9 On a copy of the diagram in Applications Task 8, draw in diagonals $\overline{AC}$ and $\overline{BD}$. What appears to be true about the two diagonals? Write an argument that proves that your observation is correct.

5 **a.** **i.** **Prove:** $\triangle ABF \cong \triangle EBF$

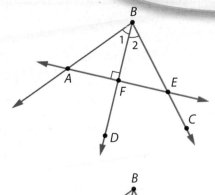

$\overline{BF} \cong \overline{BF}$ (common side)
$\angle AFB \cong \angle EFB$ (right angles)
$\angle 1 \cong \angle 2$ (definition of angle bisector)
$\triangle ABF \cong \triangle EBF$ (ASA)

ii. **Prove:** $\triangle ABE$ is an isosceles triangle.

$\overline{AB} \cong \overline{BE}$ (CPCTC from part i)
So, $\triangle ABE$ is an isosceles triangle. (definition)

b. $\angle 1 \cong \angle 2$ (base angle of isosceles triangle). $\overleftrightarrow{AE} \parallel \overleftrightarrow{HC}$ because both lines are perpendicular to the same line $\overleftrightarrow{BG}$. $\angle 1 \cong \angle 4$ and $\angle 2 \cong \angle 3$ (corresponding angles), hence all four numbered angles are congruent.

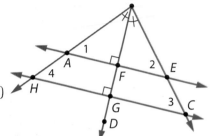

Similar Triangles	**Congruent Triangles**
$\triangle AFB \sim \triangle HGB$ (AA)	$\triangle AFB \cong \triangle EFB$ (ASA, SAS or AAS)
$\triangle AFB \sim \triangle CGB$ (AA)	$\triangle HGB \cong \triangle CGB$ (ASA or AAS)
$\triangle EFB \sim \triangle HGB$ (AA)	
$\triangle EFB \sim \triangle CGB$ (AA)	
$\triangle ABE \sim \triangle HBC$ (AA)	

6 **a.** From the Check Your Understanding on page 203, we know that the center P of the incircle joined to a vertex and the midpoint of a side containing that vertex forms a 30°-60° right triangle (see diagram).

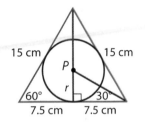

b. $\tan 30° = \dfrac{r}{7.5}$

$r \approx 4.33$ cm

$d = 2r \approx 8.66$ cm

7 **a.** Since $\overleftrightarrow{TO} \parallel \overleftrightarrow{SP}$, we know $\angle TOS \cong \angle PSO$ (alternate interior angles). Since $\overleftrightarrow{TH} \parallel \overleftrightarrow{PA}$, we know $\angle THO \cong \angle PAS$ (alternate interior angles). We were given $\overline{TO} \cong \overline{SP}$. So, $\triangle THO \cong \triangle PAS$ by the AAS Congruence Theorem. Therefore, $\overline{TH} \cong \overline{PA}$ (CPCTC).

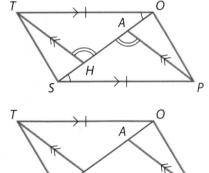

b. From Part a, quadrilateral *TOPS* is a parallelogram, so opposite sides $\overline{TS}$ and $\overline{OP}$ are congruent. Since $\triangle THO \cong \triangle PAS$, $\overline{HO} \cong \overline{AS}$. Subtracting length HA from both HO and AS shows that $SH = OA$. Also from Part a, we know that $\overline{TH} \cong \overline{PA}$. So, $\triangle STH \cong \triangle OPA$ by the SSS Congruence Theorem. (Other proofs using parallel lines can be constructed.)

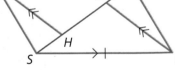

8 **ASSIGNMENT NOTE** Be sure to assign or discuss this task.

Given: *ABCD* is an isosceles trapezoid with $\overline{AB} \parallel \overline{DC}$ and $\overline{AD} \cong \overline{BC}$.

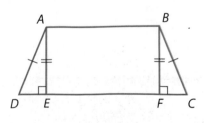

Prove: $\angle D \cong \angle C$

Construct the altitudes from A and B to $\overline{DC}$. $\overleftrightarrow{AB} \parallel \overleftrightarrow{DC}$, $\overline{AE} \perp \overline{AB}$ and $\overline{BF} \perp \overline{AB}$ (alternate interior angles), so *ABFE* is a rectangle and $\overline{AE} \cong \overline{BF}$. So, $\triangle AED \cong \triangle BFC$ (HL). $\angle D \cong \angle C$ (CPCTC).

> **NOTE** The solution to Task 9 is on page T217.

Unit 3

10 At the right is the par 2 miniature golf green reproduced from Investigation 4. You were able to show that if point H' is the reflection image of the hole H across side ℓ, then a putt aimed at point P will produce the indicated path of the ball.

The path of the ball has another important property that has physical applications. Of all paths from point B to line ℓ to point H, the path $\overline{BP} + \overline{PH}$ has minimal length.

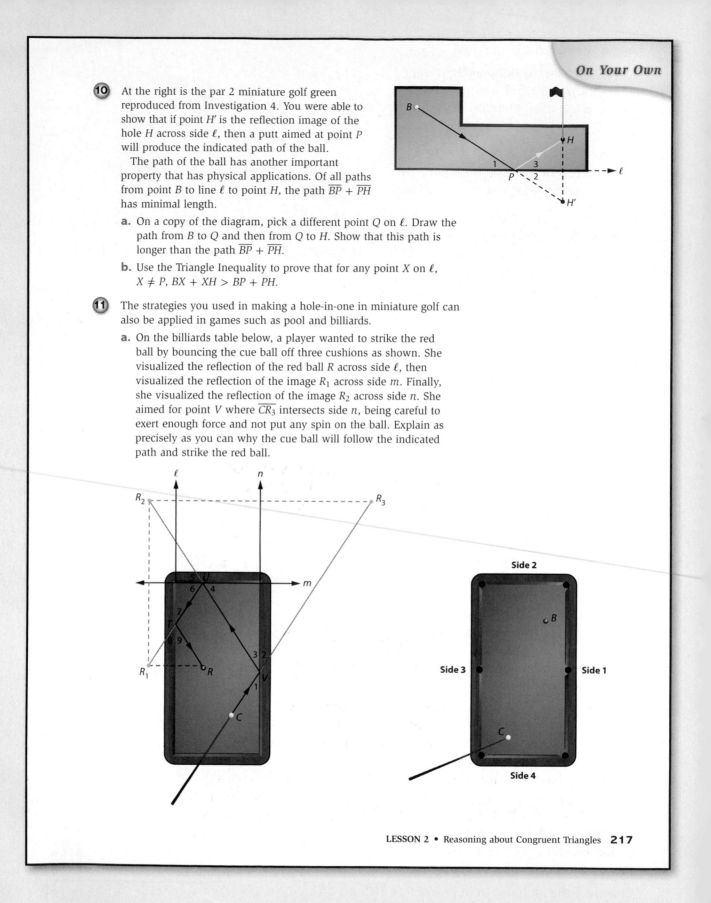

  a. On a copy of the diagram, pick a different point Q on ℓ. Draw the path from B to Q and then from Q to H. Show that this path is longer than the path $\overline{BP} + \overline{PH}$.

  b. Use the Triangle Inequality to prove that for any point X on ℓ, $X \neq P$, $BX + XH > BP + PH$.

11 The strategies you used in making a hole-in-one in miniature golf can also be applied in games such as pool and billiards.

  a. On the billiards table below, a player wanted to strike the red ball by bouncing the cue ball off three cushions as shown. She visualized the reflection of the red ball R across side ℓ, then visualized the reflection of the image R_1 across side m. Finally, she visualized the reflection of the image R_2 across side n. She aimed for point V where $\overline{CR_3}$ intersects side n, being careful to exert enough force and not put any spin on the ball. Explain as precisely as you can why the cue ball will follow the indicated path and strike the red ball.

Unit 3

3 • Similarity and Congruence

6

9 The diagonals appear to be congruent.

Given: *ABCD* is an isosceles trapezoid with $\overline{AB} \parallel \overline{DC}$ and $\overline{AD} \cong \overline{BC}$.

Prove: $\overline{AC} \cong \overline{BD}$

$\angle D \cong \angle C$ (base angles of an isosceles trapezoid are congruent; Task 8).
$\overline{DC} \cong \overline{CD}$ (common side of triangle). So,
$\triangle ADC \cong \triangle BCD$ (SAS) and $\overline{AC} \cong \overline{BD}$ (CPCTC).

10 **a.** Students may show that $BQ + QH > BP + PH$ by measuring. Alternatively, they might indicate that the path of the ball, $\overline{BP} + \overline{PH}$, is the same length as $\overline{BP} + \overline{PH'}$. Since the shortest distance between two points is a straight line segment, $BQ + QH > BP + PH$.

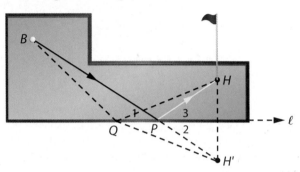

b. By the Triangle Inequality, $BX + XH' > BP + PH'$. Since XH' and PH' are reflected images of XH and PH, respectively, $XH' = XH$ and $PH' = PH$. So, $BX + XH > BP + PH$ (substitution).

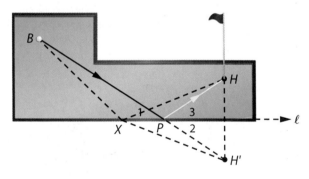

11 **a.** Angle measures are preserved by line reflections. The three numbered angles at V are the same measure since $\angle 1$ and $\angle 2$ are vertical angles formed by n and $\overrightarrow{CR_3}$ and $\angle 2$ and $\angle 3$ are reflected images of each other across n. Students may also use the fact that when the ball bounces off a side, the angles at which it strikes and leaves the side are congruent (principle of physics). The same reasoning applies to the angles at U and T. The cue ball will hit the red ball since it will first follow a path toward R_3, then a path toward R_2, then a path toward R_1, and finally, a path toward R.

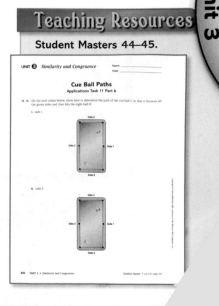

b. On copies of the pool table, show how to determine the path of
the cue ball *C* so that it bounces off the given sides and then hits
the eight ball *B*.

    i. side 1   **ii.** side 2

    iii. side 1, then side 2   **iv.** side 3, then side 2, then side 1

12 In 2007, the southeastern and southwestern regions of the United
States suffered severe drought due in part to climate changes. Some
communities turned to rivers as a source of water. But pumping water
from a river can be expensive. Two small, rural communities along the
Flint River in Georgia decided to pool their resources and build a
pumping station that would pipe water to both communities.

On a copy of the diagram, determine a location of the pumping
station that will use the minimum amount of pipe. Then explain
why the amount of pipe required is the minimum possible.

13 In each case below, $\triangle ABC \cong \triangle PQR$.

- On a copy of each pair of triangles, determine if you can map
  $\triangle ABC$ onto $\triangle PQR$ by a composition of line reflections. If so,
  find and label the appropriate line(s).

- In each case, identify the composite transformation as precisely
  as you can. If it is a rotation, give its center and directed angle
  of rotation. If it is a translation, give its magnitude and direction.

a.

b.

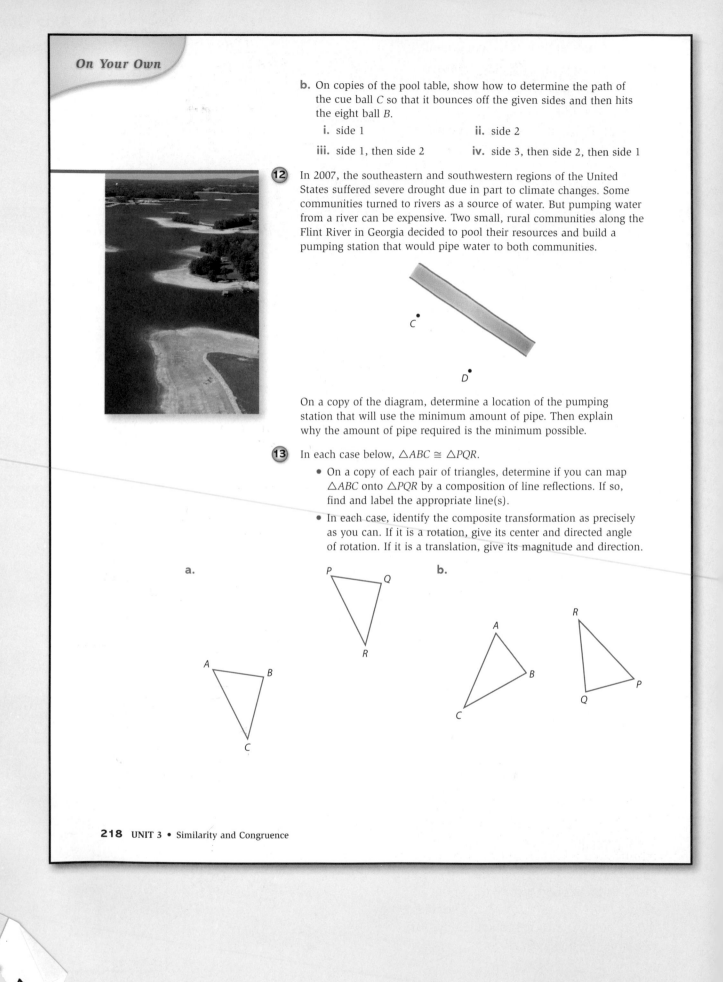

b. i.

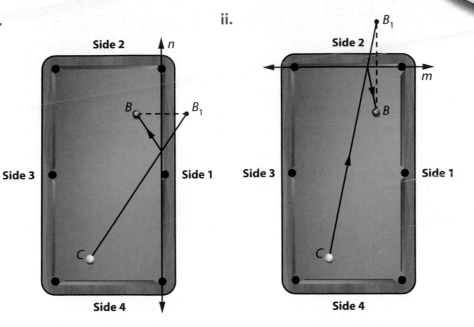

ii.

iii. First reflect B to B_1 across m, then reflect B_1 to B_2 across n. This establishes a path from C towards B_2 that bounces to a path towards B_1, and then towards B.

iv. As in part iii, reflect B across the last side (side 1) first, then continue to reflect the images across the sides in the reverse order in which the ball will strike them.

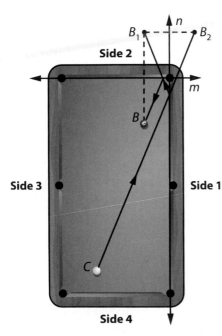

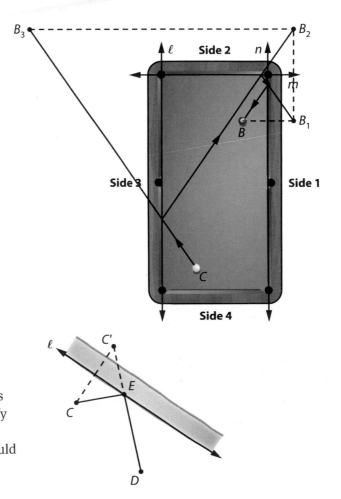

12 The reflection of C across ℓ locates C'. The point E where ℓ and $\overline{C'D}$ intersect is the location for a pumping station that requires the least amount of pipe. Students should use the Triangle Inequality to justify that this location gives the minimum amount of pipe. Alternatively, students could reflect point D across ℓ to solve this task. (See the solution to Task 10.)

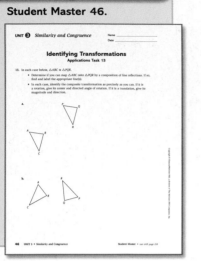
13 One possible pair of lines is provided for each part below.

a.

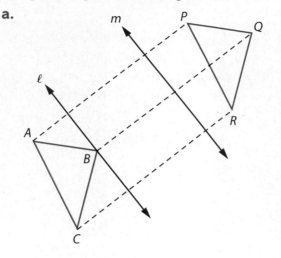

This is a translation along a line parallel to $\overleftrightarrow{AP}$. The magnitude is twice the distance from ℓ to m. (In any correct diagram, the lines of reflection should be perpendicular to $\overline{AP}$, $\overline{BQ}$, and $\overline{CR}$, and the distance between the lines of reflection should be half the length of any of these three segments.)

b.

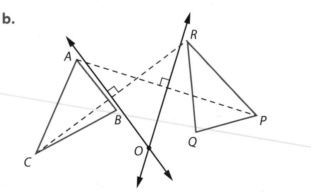

This is a rotation. The center is O the intersection of the perpendicular bisectors of $\overline{AP}$, $\overline{CR}$, and $\overline{BQ}$. Only two bisectors are needed to locate O. The rotation is a clockwise rotation through an angle whose measure is equal to m$\angle AOP$, m$\angle BOQ$, and m$\angle COR$.

Connections

14　**a.** SSS congruence conjecture for parallelograms: If three sides of one parallelogram are congruent to three sides of a second parallelogram, then the parallelograms are congruent.

　　False: Two parallelograms can have corresponding sides congruent without having angles congruent.

　b. SAS congruence conjecture for parallelograms: If two consecutive sides and the included angle of one parallelogram are congruent to the corresponding sides and included angle of a second parallelogram, then the parallelograms are congruent.

　　This conjecture is *true*. The SAS similarity conjecture for parallelograms is true for any scale ratio *k*, hence it is true for *k* = 1. See Applications Task 7, page 182. Here is a separate proof:

　　Prove: □*ABCD* ≅ □*WXYZ*

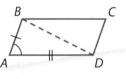

　　□*ABCD* and □*WXYZ* with $\overline{AB} \cong \overline{WX}$, $\overline{AD} \cong \overline{WZ}$, and ∠*A* ≅ ∠*W* (given information).

　　Since each diagonal of a parallelogram divides the parallelogram into two congruent triangles, △*ABD* ≅ △*CDB* and △*WXZ* ≅ △*YZX*. But △*ABD* ≅ △*WXZ* (SAS). So, all four triangles are congruent. From this, you can show that all corresponding sides and angles of the two parallelograms are congruent. So, □*ABCD* ≅ □*WXYZ*.

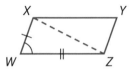

　　　Alternatively, students might draw upon properties of parallelograms to do this proof, such as opposite sides and angles are congruent.

　c. ASA congruence conjecture for parallelograms: If two consecutive angles and the included side of one parallelogram are congruent to the corresponding angles and included side of a second parallelogram, then the parallelograms are congruent.

　　False: Two parallelograms can have corresponding angles congruent and one pair of sides congruent, but the other pair of sides (consecutive to the congruent pair) need not be congruent.

　d. AAS congruence conjecture for parallelograms: If two angles and a nonincluded side of one parallelogram are congruent to the corresponding two angles and side of a second parallelogram, then the parallelograms are congruent.

　　False: See the counterexample at the right.

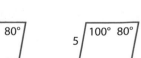

Connections

14. In Investigation 1, you used conditions for similarity of triangles and a scale factor of 1 to establish four sets of conditions that are sufficient to prove that two triangles are congruent: SSS, SAS, ASA, and AAS.

   a. Rewrite the SSS Congruence Theorem, replacing the word "triangles" with "parallelograms." Prove or disprove that your statement about two parallelograms is a theorem.

   b. Follow the directions in Part a for the SAS Congruence Theorem.

   c. Follow the directions in Part a for the ASA Congruence Theorem.

   d. Follow the directions in Part a for the AAS Congruence Theorem.

15. Two points determine a line. Explain and provide an illustration that shows why three noncollinear points determine a circle.

16. Find the coordinates of the centroid C of $\triangle PQR$.

   a. For each median, how does the distance from the vertex to point C compare to the length of the median from that vertex?

   b. Use interactive geometry software to test if the relationship you found in Part a holds for other triangles. Write a statement summarizing your findings.

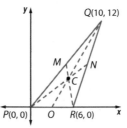

17. In Investigation 2, you saw that a cardboard triangle can be balanced on the tip of a pencil placed at the centroid of the triangle.

   a. Cut a triangle from poster board or cardboard. Draw a median of the triangle. Can you balance the triangle on the edge of a ruler placed along the median?

   b. Your work in Part a suggests that a median divides a triangle into two triangles of equal area. Write a proof of this statement.

15 Any three noncollinear points determine a triangle because the points in pairs determine the three sides of the triangle. As shown in Problem 2 on page 201, a circle can be circumscribed about any triangle. The point of concurrency of the perpendicular bisectors of the sides of a triangle locates the circumcenter of the triangle.

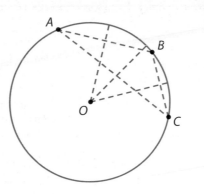

NOTE The solution to Task 14 is on page T218B.

16 The coordinates of M and N are $M(5, 6)$ and $N(8, 6)$. The equation of $\overleftrightarrow{PN}$ is $y = \frac{3}{4}x$. The equation of $\overleftrightarrow{MR}$ is $y = -6(x - 6) = -6x + 36$. Point C is the intersection of these two lines.

So, solve the system:

$$\begin{cases} y = -6x + 36 \\ y = \frac{3}{4}x \end{cases}$$

$$\frac{3}{4}x = -6x + 36$$

$$\frac{27}{4}x = 36$$

$$x = \frac{16}{3}$$

$$y = \left(\frac{3}{4}\right)\left(\frac{16}{3}\right) = 4$$

So, $C\left(\frac{16}{3}, 4\right)$. Check that this point also lies on $\overline{QO}$. The equation of $\overleftrightarrow{QO}$ is $7y = 12x - 36$. $(7)(4) = 12\left(\frac{16}{3}\right) - 36$ is true.

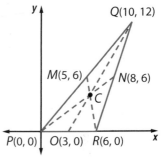

a. The distance from the vertex to the point C is two-thirds the length of the median. Students can verify this using the distance formula or note the change in x and y values and use similar triangles. See the diagram at the right for one case. The distance from the vertex to C is twice the distance from C to the midpoint of the opposite side.

Thus, the distance from the vertex to the point C is $\frac{2}{3}$ the length of the median from that vertex.

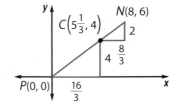

b. In any triangle, the distance from a vertex to the centroid is $\frac{2}{3}$ the length of the median drawn from that vertex. Interactive geometry software will confirm this relationship for other triangles. The solution to Extensions Task 30 provides a proof.

17 a. The triangle should balance.

b. Given: $\triangle ABC$ with median $\overline{AD}$

Prove: The areas of $\triangle ADC$ and $\triangle ADB$ are the same.

Construct the altitude $\overline{AE}$ to $\overleftrightarrow{BD}$.

The area of $\triangle ADC = \frac{1}{2}(AE)(CD)$.

The area of $\triangle ABD = \frac{1}{2}(AE)(BD)$.

Since $BD = CD$, the two areas are the same.

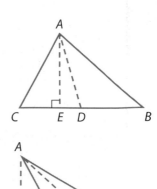

18 In Problem 7 of Investigation 3, you likely used the Midpoint Connector Theorem for Triangles to prove the Midpoint Connector Theorem for Quadrilaterals.

If the midpoints of the sides of a quadrilateral are connected in order, the resulting quadrilateral is a parallelogram.

Consider now how you could prove the statement using coordinate methods.

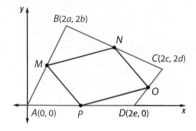

a. Why was the coordinate system placed so that vertex *A* is at the origin and side $\overline{AD}$ is on the *x*-axis?

b. Why were the coordinates of vertices *B*, *C*, and *D* chosen to be (2*a*, 2*b*), (2*c*, 2*d*), and (2*e*, 0), respectively?

c. Write a coordinate proof of the Midpoint Connector Theorem for Quadrilaterals.

d. Describe a second strategy for proving this theorem using coordinates.

19 Use interactive geometry software or paper and pencil to explore special cases of the Midpoint Connector Theorem for Quadrilaterals on page 206.

a. Draw a square and name it *ABCD*. Find the midpoints of the sides. Connect them in order to obtain quadrilateral *EFGH*.

   i. What special kind of quadrilateral does quadrilateral *EFGH* appear to be?

   ii. How would you justify your conjecture?

b. Draw a rectangle and name it *ABCD*. Find the midpoints of the sides. Connect them in order to obtain quadrilateral *EFGH*.

   i. What special kind of quadrilateral does quadrilateral *EFGH* appear to be?

   ii. How would you justify your conjecture?

c. Draw a rhombus and name it *ABCD*. Find the midpoints of the sides. Connect them in order to obtain quadrilateral *EFGH*.

   i. What special kind of quadrilateral does quadrilateral *EFGH* appear to be?

   ii. How would you justify your conjecture?

Reflections

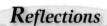

20 How could you generalize the definition of congruence of triangles (page 196) to a definition of *congruence of polygons*?

18 **a.** This placement forces some of the coordinates to be zero which should make computations for distance and slope easier.

b. Choosing multiples of two avoids fractional or decimal coordinates. It makes the midpoint coordinates (a, b), (c, d), and $(e, 0)$ rather than coordinates such as $\left(\frac{1}{2}a, \frac{1}{2}b\right)$.

c–d. Student proofs should use one of the sets of sufficient conditions for parallelograms. (See Problem 2 on page 205 and Problem 7 on page 206.) One example is provided. Show both pairs of opposite sides are parallel.

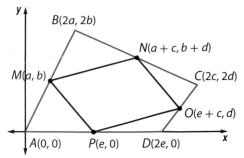

Slope of $\overline{MN}$ is $\dfrac{(b+d)-b}{(a+c)-a} = \dfrac{d}{c}$

Slope of $\overline{PO}$ is $\dfrac{d-0}{(e+c)-e} = \dfrac{d}{c}$

Slope of $\overline{MP}$ is $\dfrac{b}{a-e}$

Slope of $\overline{NO}$ is $\dfrac{(b+d)-d}{(a+c)-(e+c)} = \dfrac{b}{a-e}$

Since opposite sides have the same slope, they are parallel and *ABCD* is a parallelogram.

TECHNOLOGY TIP There are various ways to create a sketch of the quadrilaterals specified in Task 19 using *CPMP-Tools*. Two common approaches are outlined below:

Option 1: (1) Choose the ![button] button, draw any quadrilateral. (2) With the quadrilateral selected, choose the ![button] button to construct midpoints of all sides. (3) Choose the ![button] button, draw a quadrilateral whose vertices are the midpoints of Step 2. (4) Use the ![button] button to select each quadrilateral, then use the "Measurements" menu to obtain length and angle measures.

Option 2: (1) Choose the ![button] button to draw a line, then the ![.P] button to draw a point not on the line. (2) Choose the ![button] button and hold down the Shift key as you click on both objects to select them. (3) Use the ![button] and/or ![button] buttons to construct parallels and/or perpendiculars to the given line and point until a parallelogram has been created. (4) Use the ![button] button to construct points at intersections of selected lines. (5) Choose the ![button] button to draw a parallelogram with vertices at the constructed points. (6) Start at Step 2 of Option 1 to complete sketch.

Once quadrilaterals *ABCD* and *DEFG* have been constructed, students can use the length and angle measurements to guide their investigation as they drag the vertices of the original quadrilateral until each case (square, rectangle, rhombus) has been considered. As with a paper-and-pencil exploration, students should be able to make conjectures about the type of quadrilateral formed with approximate measures of angles and sides.

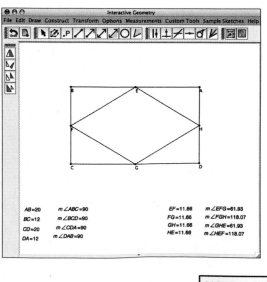

NOTE Solutions for Task 19 are on page T220A.

Unit 3

19 **a.** **i.** *EFGH* appears to be a square or a rhombus. (The measurements produced by geometry software for the angles and sides of *EFGH* may differ slightly. You can use this fact as an example of why in mathematics a formal proof is needed.)

    ii. To justify that *EFGH* is a square, you might consider the congruent triangles formed at the vertices of square *ABCD* (SAS). This would allow you to conclude that the sides of *EFGH* are all congruent. The measure of each angle of *EFGH* is
$180° -$ (*sum of the two acute angles of the congruent triangles*) $= 90°$.

b. **i.** *EFGH* appears to be a rhombus.

    ii. To justify, you need only determine that all four sides of *EFGH* are congruent. This can be done by showing the triangles formed at the vertices of rectangle *ABCD* are congruent (SAS).

c. **i.** *EFGH* appears to be a rectangle.

    ii. By the Midpoint Connector Theorem for Quadrilaterals, *EFGH* is a parallelogram. To determine if *EFGH* is a rectangle, you need to determine that one angle of *EFGH* is a right angle. Since opposite angles of a parallelogram are congruent and consecutive angles are supplementary, all angles of *EFGH* would then be right angles.

There is more than one way to justify that one of the angles of *EFGH* is a right angle. One possibility is described here.

Since $\triangle ADE$ is isosceles, $m\angle AEH = \frac{1}{2}(180° - m\angle A) = 90° - \frac{1}{2} m\angle A$.

Similarly, $m\angle BEF = 90° - \frac{1}{2} m\angle B$.

Since the sum of the measures of the three angles formed at *H* is $180°$, $m\angle HEF = 180° - m\angle AEH - m\angle BEF$.

So, $m\angle HEF = 180° - \left(90° - \frac{1}{2} m\angle A\right) - \left(90° - \frac{1}{2} m\angle B\right) = \frac{1}{2} m\angle A + \frac{1}{2} m\angle B$.

Since $\angle A$ and $\angle B$ are supplementary, $m\angle HEF$ is $\frac{1}{2}(180°) = 90°$.

Reflections

20 **a.** Two polygons are congruent if and only if they are similar with a scale factor of 1.

Teacher Notes

21 In this unit, you have reasoned with "corresponding angles" in the contexts of similarity and congruence of triangles and in the context of parallel lines cut by a transversal. Draw sketches illustrating the different meanings of "corresponding angles."

22 Given two angles, there is a variety of conditions that would allow you to conclude, without measuring, that the angles are congruent. For example, if you know the angles are vertical angles, then you know they are congruent. What other conditions will allow you to conclude two angles are congruent? List as many as you can.

23 The Midpoint Connector Theorem for Quadrilaterals is an amazing result. It was first proved by a French mathematician, Pierre Varignon (1654–1722). Here is a more recent unexpected "point connector" result.

   a. On a copy of the diagram at the right, continue to draw segments parallel to the sides of the triangle. What happens?

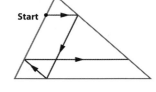

   b. What was the total number of segments drawn? Can you explain why this happens?

   c. Is there a "start" point for which there will be fewer segments drawn? If so, where is the point located? How many segments will there be?

24 The diagram below can be used to prove properties of parallelograms using coordinates.

   a. Determine the coordinates of vertex *C*.

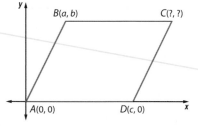

   b. Look back at Problem 3 (pages 205–206) of Investigation 3. From the list, pick two properties of parallelograms that you proved using congruent triangles. For each property, describe how you could also prove the property using coordinate methods.

25 In this lesson, you re-examined congruence of triangles as a special case of similarity of triangles. The following statement relates similarity to congruence in terms of a size transformation.

> *Two figures are similar if one is congruent to a size transformation of the other.*

Is this description of similarity consistent with the definition of similarity in Lesson 1? Explain.

21 Corresponding angles were used in connection with similar and congruent triangles and polygons.

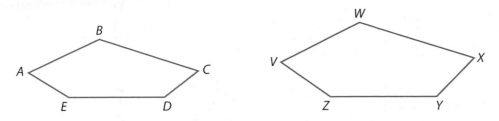

Corresponding pairs of angles above are: $\angle A$ and $\angle V$, $\angle B$ and $\angle W$, $\angle C$ and $\angle X$, $\angle D$ and $\angle Y$, and $\angle E$ and $\angle Z$.

Corresponding angles were also used in connection with parallel lines cut by a transversal as shown below. The corresponding angle pairs are: $\angle 1$ and $\angle 2$, $\angle 3$ and $\angle 4$, $\angle 5$ and $\angle 6$, and $\angle 7$ and $\angle 8$.

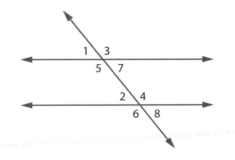

22 Two angles are congruent if they are:
- Vertical angles
- Right angles
- Angles with equal measures
- Corresponding, alternate interior, or alternate exterior angles formed by parallel lines cut by a transversal
- Corresponding angles in similar or congruent polygons
- Opposite angles in a parallelogram

23 **a.** Drawing two additional lines leads you back to the starting point.

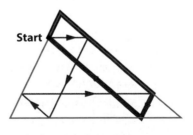

b. Total number of lines drawn: 6
There are two parallel lines for each side of the triangle.
    Since parallelograms are formed (as shown in red in the diagram), the opposite congruent sides determine that you end up back at the starting point.

c. If you start at the midpoint of one of the sides of the triangle, only three segments will be drawn.

24 **a.** $C(a + c, b)$

b. For each property below, one possible plan for proof is provided.

Property: Each diagonal divides the parallelogram into two congruent triangles.

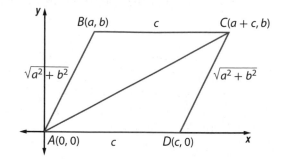

Proof Plan: Use the distance formula to show that the lengths $AB = DC$ and $AD = BC$. Draw diagonal $\overline{AC}$. Triangles ABC and CDA have a common side, the diagonal, thus they are congruent (SSS). Repeat using the other diagonal.

Property: Opposite angles are congruent.

Proof Plan: Use coordinates to show that the tangent ratios for $\angle A$ and $\angle C$ are the same. $\tan A = \dfrac{b}{a}$, $\tan C = \dfrac{b}{a}$, so $m\angle A = m\angle C$. Repeat for $\angle ABC$ and $\angle ADC$.

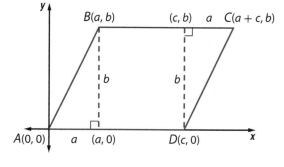

Property: Consecutive angles are supplementary.

Proof Plan: Use tangent ratios $\left(\dfrac{b}{a}\right)$ to show that $\angle A$ and $\angle EDC$ are the same. Since $m\angle A = m\angle EDC$ (corresponding angles of parallel lines) and $m\angle ADC = 180° - m\angle EDC$

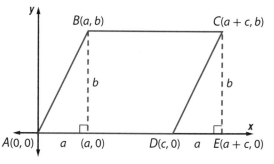

(linear pair), $m\angle ADC = 180° - m\angle A$. So, these consecutive angles are supplementary. Similar arguments show other pairs of consecutive angles are supplementary.

Alternatively, use coordinates to show that opposite angles are congruent as in the previous plan. Then show that since the sum of all four angles is 360°, the sum of two consecutive angles is 180°.

Property: The diagonals bisect each other.

Proof Plan: Write an expression for the coordinates of the midpoint of each diagonal and determine that they are the same. Both midpoints have coordinates $\left(\dfrac{a + c}{2}, \dfrac{b}{2}\right)$.

25 The definition of similarity in Lesson 1 is: "Two polygons with the same number of sides are similar provided their corresponding angles have the same measure and the ratios of lengths of corresponding sides is a constant."

We showed on pages 177 and 178 that size transformations preserve angle measure and change lengths by the scale factor k of the transformation. So, given two polygons, if one can be transformed to a third polygon that is congruent to the second polygon, then the two given polygons would be similar by the same scale factor.

For example, given $\triangle ABC$ and $\triangle XYZ$, if $\triangle ABC \sim \triangle A'B'C'$ with scale factor k from $\triangle ABC$ to $\triangle A'B'C'$, and $\triangle A'B'C' \cong \triangle XYZ$, then $\triangle ABC \sim \triangle XYZ$ with scale factor k from $\triangle ABC$ to $\triangle XYZ$.

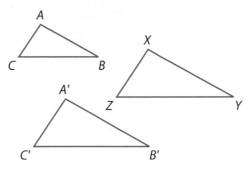

Extensions

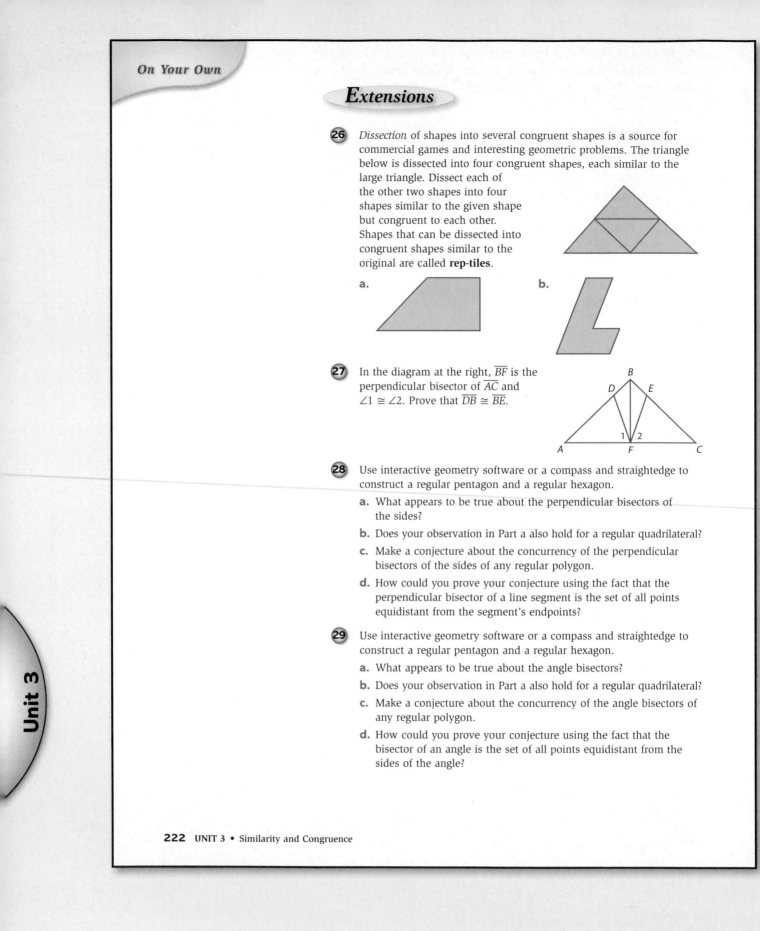

26 *Dissection* of shapes into several congruent shapes is a source for commercial games and interesting geometric problems. The triangle below is dissected into four congruent shapes, each similar to the large triangle. Dissect each of the other two shapes into four shapes similar to the given shape but congruent to each other. Shapes that can be dissected into congruent shapes similar to the original are called **rep-tiles**.

a.

b.

27 In the diagram at the right, $\overline{BF}$ is the perpendicular bisector of $\overline{AC}$ and $\angle 1 \cong \angle 2$. Prove that $\overline{DB} \cong \overline{BE}$.

28 Use interactive geometry software or a compass and straightedge to construct a regular pentagon and a regular hexagon.

a. What appears to be true about the perpendicular bisectors of the sides?

b. Does your observation in Part a also hold for a regular quadrilateral?

c. Make a conjecture about the concurrency of the perpendicular bisectors of the sides of any regular polygon.

d. How could you prove your conjecture using the fact that the perpendicular bisector of a line segment is the set of all points equidistant from the segment's endpoints?

29 Use interactive geometry software or a compass and straightedge to construct a regular pentagon and a regular hexagon.

a. What appears to be true about the angle bisectors?

b. Does your observation in Part a also hold for a regular quadrilateral?

c. Make a conjecture about the concurrency of the angle bisectors of any regular polygon.

d. How could you prove your conjecture using the fact that the bisector of an angle is the set of all points equidistant from the sides of the angle?

Extensions

26 a.

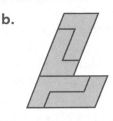

b.

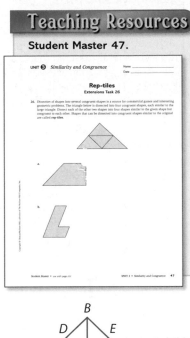
27 **Prove:** $\overline{DB} \cong \overline{BE}$

Statement	**Reason**
(1) $AF = CF$	$\overline{BF}$ is the perpendicular bisector of $\overline{AC}$ (given).
(2) $AB = CB$	B is on the perpendicular bisector, so is equidistant from the endpoints of $\overline{AC}$.
(3) $\triangle ABC$ is isosceles	Definition of isosceles triangle
(4) $\angle A \cong \angle C$	Base angles of isosceles triangles are congruent
(5) $\angle 1 \cong \angle 2$	Given
(6) $\triangle ADF \cong \triangle CEF$	ASA Congruence Theorem
(7) $\overline{AD} \cong \overline{CE}$	CPCTC
(8) $AD + DB = AB$ $CE + BE = BC$	Segment length addition
(9) $\overline{DB} \cong \overline{BE}$	By Step 2, $AB = CB$, then subtract equal lengths from Step 7 to get $DB = BE$ and thus congruence.

Alternatively, after Step 6, prove $\triangle DFB \cong \triangle EFB$; then $\overline{DB} \cong \overline{BE}$ (CPCTC).

28
a. The perpendicular bisectors of the sides of a regular hexagon appear to coincide at a single point, and this also seems to be true for a regular pentagon.

b. Yes, the conjecture in Part a holds for a regular quadrilateral (a square).

c. Given any regular polygon, the perpendicular bisectors of its sides coincide at a single point.

INSTRUCTIONAL NOTE
Students may find it helpful to see pages 398–403 of Course 1 (Unit 6, Lesson 2, Investigation 1) on regular polygons.

Unit 3

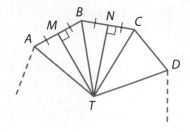

d. You could reason as for a triangle (Problem 6, page 198), by drawing perpendicular bisectors of two consecutive sides of the polygon, and labeling their intersection T. You need to show that T lies on the perpendicular bisectors of all sides of the polygon. To do this, divide the polygon into triangles by drawing all segments that join T to the vertices of the polygon, then show all these triangles are congruent. (In the diagram, $\overline{TM}$ and $\overline{TN}$ are the perpendicular bisectors of sides $\overline{AB}$ and $\overline{BC}$.) Since T is equidistant from A and B, and T is equidistant from B and C, it follows that $TA = TB = TC$. You need to show that $TC = TD$. Since all sides of the regular polygon are congruent, $\triangle ABT \cong \triangle CBT$ (SSS), and $\angle ABT \cong \angle CBT$ (CPCTC) implies $m\angle CBT = \frac{1}{2}m\angle B$. Since $\triangle BTC$ is isosceles, $m\angle BCT = m\angle CBT = \frac{1}{2}m\angle B$. Since all angles of the polygon are congruent, it follows that $m\angle BCT = \frac{1}{2}m\angle C$, and hence $m\angle DCT = \frac{1}{2}m\angle C$. So, $\triangle BCT \cong \triangle DCT$ (SAS), and so $TC = TD$ (CPCTC). This shows that T is on the perpendicular bisector of $\overline{CD}$. Repeating the argument on the next consecutive pair of triangles, and so on, will establish that all vertices are equidistant from T, and hence T lies on the perpendicular bisectors of all sides of the polygon. An alternate argument would be to also draw segments that join T to the midpoint of each side of the polygon and show that all consecutive triangles formed are right triangles, so that these segments are the perpendicular bisectors of the sides of the polygon.

29 **a.** The angle bisectors of a regular hexagon appear to coincide at a single point, and this also seems to be true for a regular pentagon.

b. Yes, the conjecture in Part a holds for a regular quadrilateral (a square).

c. Given any regular polygon, the angle bisectors coincide at a single point.

INSTRUCTIONAL NOTE
Be sure that in the proof plans for Task 28 Part d and Task 29 Part d, students do not inadvertently assume that the pairs of perpendicular bisectors all intersect at the same point, or that angle bisectors all intersect at the same point. The special properties of a regular polygon—all angles are congruent and all sides are congruent—must be part of the proof, since the concurrency of perpendicular bisectors of sides and the concurrency of angle bisectors are not true in general, except for triangles. A follow-up exercise could be to ask students if a polygon has all angles congruent, are the perpendicular bisectors of the sides concurrent? (For quadrilaterals, the answer is yes.) And, if a polygon has all sides congruent, are the angle bisectors concurrent? (For quadrilaterals, the answer is yes.)

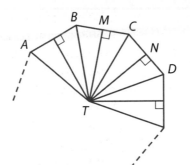

d. You could begin by drawing
   bisectors of two consecutive
   angles of the polygon, and labeling
   their intersection *T*. You need to
   show that *T* lies on all the angle
   bisectors of the polygon. To do
   this, divide the polygon into right
   triangles by drawing all segments
   that join *T* to the vertices of the
   polygon, and drawing from *T* a
perpendicular segment to each side of the polygon. Then show all
these triangles are congruent. (In the diagram, $\overline{TB}$ and $\overline{TC}$ are angle
bisectors of $\angle B$ and $\angle C$, respectively, and $\overline{TM}$ and $\overline{TN}$ are
perpendicular to $\overline{BC}$ and $\overline{CD}$, respectively.) You need to show that $\overline{TD}$
is an angle bisector. Since all angles of the regular polygon are
congruent, the bisectors split $\angle B$ and $\angle C$ into angles that are all
congruent. $\triangle BMT \cong \triangle CMT$ (AAS), so $BM = MC$; *M* is the midpoint
of $\overline{BC}$. Also, $MC = NC$ ($\overline{TC}$ is the angle bisector). Since all sides of the
regular polygon are congruent, *N* is the midpoint of $\overline{CD}$. $\triangle NCT \cong \triangle NDT$
(SAS), hence $\angle NCT \cong \angle NDT$. So, $m\angle NDT = \frac{1}{2}m\angle C = \frac{1}{2}m\angle D$. Thus, $\overline{TD}$
is the bisector of $\angle D$. Repeating the argument on the next consecutive
pair of right triangles, and so on, will establish that *T* lies on all the
angle bisectors of the regular polygon. (Note that along the way, the
segments drawn from *T* perpendicular to the sides have been shown to
be bisectors of the sides, so that *T* is also on all the perpendicular
bisectors of the sides of the polygon.)

30 Coordinate methods can be used to prove that the medians of a triangle are concurrent, and that the distance from each vertex to the point of concurrency is $\frac{2}{3}$ the length of the median.

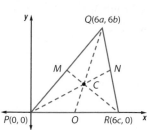

a. Why do you think the coordinates of points P, Q, and R were chosen as shown?

b. To prove that the medians are concurrent, you might proceed as follows.

   i. Verify that the equation for $\overleftrightarrow{PN}$ is $y = \frac{b}{a+c}x$. That the equation for $\overleftrightarrow{QO}$ is $y = \frac{2b}{2a-c}(x-3c)$.

   ii. What does the following CAS display tell you?

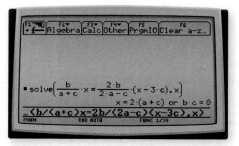

   iii. Verify that the point of intersection of $\overleftrightarrow{PN}$ and $\overleftrightarrow{QO}$ is also on $\overrightarrow{MR}$. What can you conclude?

c. Show that the distance from each vertex to the point of concurrency is $\frac{2}{3}$ the length of the median.

31 Look back at Connections Task 14. What conditions that ensure congruence of two parallelograms could be modified with additional side or angle information to provide a test of congruence of two general quadrilaterals? Write an argument justifying your congruence condition for general quadrilaterals.

32 The two quadrilaterals below are not drawn to scale. In Parts a and b, determine if the given information is sufficient to guarantee the two quadrilaterals are congruent. Explain your reasoning. If quadrilateral *ABCD* is not congruent to quadrilateral *PQRS*, what is the least amount of additional information you would need to conclude the two quadrilaterals are congruent?

a. Is *quadrilateral ABCD* ≅ *quadrilateral PQRS* if these four conditions are satisfied?

- $\overline{AD} \cong \overline{PS}$
- $\overline{BC} \cong \overline{QR}$
- $\overline{AB}$ is parallel to $\overline{CD}$.
- $\overline{PQ}$ is parallel to $\overline{RS}$.

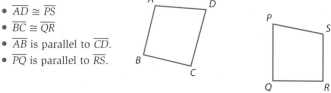

30 **a.** We need to prove that the distance from the vertex to the point of concurrency is $\frac{2}{3}$ the length of the median, so these coordinates might help eliminate fractions in the computation.

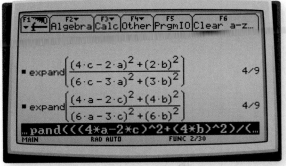

$Q(6a, 6b)$

$M(3a, 3b)$ $N(3a + 3c, 3b)$

C

$P(0, 0)$ $O(3c, 0)$ $R(6c, 0)$ x

b. **i.** $\overleftrightarrow{PN}$: $y = \dfrac{3b}{3a + 3c}x = \dfrac{b}{a + c}x$

$\overleftrightarrow{QO}$: $y = \dfrac{6b}{6a - 3c}(x - 3c) = \dfrac{2b}{2a - c}(x - 3c)$

ii. The **solve(** command produced the x-coordinate of the point where $\overleftrightarrow{PN}$ and $\overleftrightarrow{QO}$ intersect, $x = 2(a + c)$. (The two expressions would also be equal if b, c, or both b and c are zero.)

iii. The y-coordinate can be found by substitution.

$y = \dfrac{b}{a + c} \cdot 2(a + c) = 2b$. So, point C has coordinates $(2a + 2c, 2b)$. To verify that it is on $\overleftrightarrow{MR}$, write the equation of $\overleftrightarrow{MR}$: $y = \dfrac{3b}{3a - 6c}(x - 6c) = \dfrac{b}{a - 2c}(x - 6c)$. Then evaluate this linear equation for $x = 2a + 2c$ to see if $y = 2b$.

$y = \dfrac{b}{a - 2c}(2a + 2c - 6c) = \dfrac{b}{a - 2c}(2a - 4c)$

$= \dfrac{b}{a - 2c} \cdot 2(a - 2c) = 2b$

A CAS could be used for this task as shown at the right.

The conclusion is that the medians of a triangle are concurrent.

c. Applying the distance formula:

$\dfrac{PC}{PN} = \dfrac{\sqrt{(2a + 2c)^2 + (2b)^2}}{\sqrt{(3a + 3c)^2 + (3b)^2}} = \dfrac{2\sqrt{(a + c)^2 + (b)^2}}{3\sqrt{(a + c)^2 + (b)^2}} = \dfrac{2}{3}$

$\dfrac{RC}{RM} = \dfrac{\sqrt{(4c - 2a)^2 + (2b)^2}}{\sqrt{(6c - 3a)^2 + (3b)^2}} = \dfrac{2}{3}$

$\dfrac{QC}{QO} = \dfrac{\sqrt{(4a - 2c)^2 + (4b)^2}}{\sqrt{(6a - 3c)^2 + (6b)^2}} = \dfrac{2}{3}$

To reduce the computation, you can find the distances squared as shown in the display at the right.

NOTE Solutions to Tasks 31 and 32 and on page T224.

Unit 3

b. Is *quadrilateral ABCD* ≅ *quadrilateral PQRS* if these three conditions are satisfied?

- ∠A ≅ ∠P
- ∠C ≅ ∠R
- $\overline{AD} \cong \overline{PS}$

33 In Investigation 4, you proved that a triangle and its image under a line reflection or a composition of two (three) line reflections are congruent. In this task, you will justify the following striking result.

If △ABC ≅ △A′B′C′, then there is a congruence-preserving transformation that maps △ABC onto △A′B′C′ and this transformation is the composition of at most three line reflections.

Study the steps below to find the possible lines of reflection for a transformation that will map △ABC onto △A′B′C′ by successive reflections across those lines.

Step 1

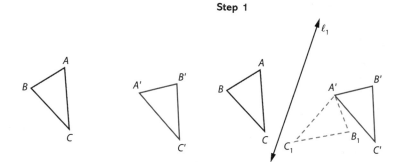

Step 2 **Step 3**

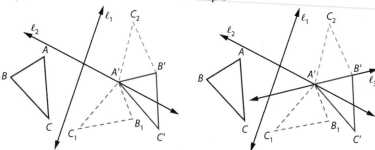

a. In Step 1, △A′B₁C₁ is the reflection image of △ABC across line ℓ₁.

- How was line ℓ₁ chosen?
- How is A′B₁ related to A′B?

b. In Step 2, ℓ₂ was chosen to be the perpendicular bisector of $\overline{B_1B'}$.

- Why was ℓ₂ chosen that way?
- The diagram shows that point A′ is on ℓ₂. Why must that be the case?
- How is A′C₂ related to A′C?

31 The SAS Congruence Theorem for parallelograms can be modified in two different ways. Both can be proved by drawing appropriate diagonals and showing triangles are congruent. Two general quadrilaterals are congruent if three corresponding sides and the two included angles formed by those sides are congruent. (SASAS)

Two general quadrilaterals are congruent if four pairs of corresponding sides are congruent and one pair of corresponding angles is congruent. (SASSS)

32 a. Since $\overline{AB}$ is not necessarily congruent to $\overline{PQ}$, the four conditions do not ensure that the quadrilaterals are congruent. There are four possible quadrilaterals that could be congruent to $ABCD$ (see the diagram): $PQRS$, PQR_1S, $PQRS_1$, PQR_1S_1. To conclude the two quadrilaterals are congruent, you would need to have $\overline{AB} \cong \overline{PQ}$, $\overline{CD} \cong \overline{SR}$, and one pair of corresponding angles congruent.

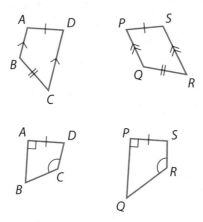

b. The conditions do not ensure the quadrilaterals are congruent. You can see this by visualizing quadrilateral $PQRS$ changing shape by increasing the length of $\overline{PQ}$ and $\overline{SR}$ without changing the given measurements.

To conclude the two quadrilaterals are congruent, the least amount of information you would need to know is that $\overline{CD} \cong \overline{RS}$.

33 a. • ℓ_1 is the perpendicular bisector of $\overline{AA'}$.
   • We were told that $\triangle A'B'C'$ is the image of $\triangle ABC$ across successive line reflections. Since line reflections preserve distance, $AB = A'B_1 = A'B'$.

b. • Choosing ℓ_2 in this manner will map $A'B_1$ onto $A'B'$ leaving only one more vertex C to transform.
   • Since $A'B_1 = A'B'$, point A' is equidistant from the endpoints of $\overline{B_1B'}$ and so must be on the perpendicular bisector ℓ_2.
   • $A'C_2 = A'C'$. $\overline{A'C_2}$ is the result of reflecting $\overline{AC}$ twice, and reflections preserve distance. $AC = A'C'$, so $A'C_2 = A'C'$.

c. • Choosing ℓ_3 in this manner will map C_2 onto C'.
   • Since $A'C_2 = A'C'$, point A' is on the perpendicular bisector ℓ_3 of $\overline{C_2C'}$. Similarly, $B'C_2 = B'C'$ and so B' is also on ℓ_3.

d. The reflection of A across ℓ_1 was A'. Since A' is on ℓ_2 and ℓ_3, A' remains A' under line reflections ℓ_2 and ℓ_3.
   $B \xrightarrow{\ell_1} B_1 \xrightarrow{\ell_2} B' \xrightarrow{\ell_3} B'$ (ℓ_2 is the perpendicular bisector of $\overline{B_1B'}$ and B' is on ℓ_3.)
   $C \xrightarrow{\ell_1} C_1 \xrightarrow{\ell_2} C_2 \xrightarrow{\ell_3} C'$ (ℓ_3 is the perpendicular bisector of $\overline{C_2C'}$.)

e. ℓ_2 should be chosen as the perpendicular bisector of $\overline{C_1C'}$.

f. You would not need a third line reflection; two line reflections would be sufficient.

ASSIGNMENT NOTE
Applications Task 13 should be completed prior to Extensions Task 33.

Unit 3

c. In Step 3, ℓ_3 was chosen to be the perpendicular bisector of $\overline{C_2C'}$.

   • Why was ℓ_3 chosen that way?

   • The diagram shows that points A' and B' are on ℓ_3. Why must that be the case?

d. Why is A' the reflection image of point A across line ℓ_1, then line ℓ_2, and then line ℓ_3? Why is B' the reflection image of point B under the composition of these three line reflections? Why is C' the reflection image of point C under this composition of line reflections?

e. Suppose in Step 1, the reflection image of point B across ℓ_1 was point B'. How should ℓ_2 in Step 2 be chosen?

f. Suppose in Step 2, the reflection image of point C_1 was point C'. How should ℓ_3 in Step 3 be chosen?

g. How does your work in Parts a–f justify this fundamental theorem of congruence-preserving transformations?

34 An **equilic quadrilateral** is a quadrilateral with a pair of congruent opposite sides that, when extended, meet to form a 60° angle. The other two sides are called *bases*.

a. Quadrilateral $ABCD$ is equilic with bases $\overline{AB}$ and $\overline{CD}$ and $\overline{AD} \cong \overline{BC}$.

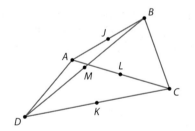

   • Could base $\overline{AB}$ be parallel to base $\overline{CD}$? Explain your reasoning.

   • Could $\overline{AB} \cong \overline{CD}$? Explain.

   • Find $m\angle D + m\angle C$.

   • Find $m\angle A + m\angle B$.

b. Suppose you have an equilic quadrilateral $ABCD$ with $\overline{AD} \cong \overline{BC}$ and diagonals $\overline{AC}$ and $\overline{BD}$. Points J, K, L, and M are midpoints of bases $\overline{AB}$ and $\overline{CD}$ and diagonals $\overline{AC}$ and $\overline{BD}$, respectively. How are the four points J, K, L, and M related? Prove you are correct.

c. Draw an equilic quadrilateral $ABCD$ with $\overline{AD} \cong \overline{BC}$ and $AB < CD$. Draw an equilateral triangle on base $\overline{AB}$ that shares no points with the interior of quadrilateral $ABCD$. Label the third vertex P. How are points P, C, and D related? Prove your claim.

g. The steps showed that at most three line reflections across perpendicular bisectors of corresponding vertices and their images results in a mapping of A to A', B to B', and C to C'. So, $\triangle ABC$ is mapped onto $\triangle A'B'C'$.

NOTE Solutions to Task 33 Parts c–f are on page T224.

34 **a.** • Yes, $\overline{AB}$ and $\overline{CD}$ could be parallel. The shape would be an isosceles trapezoid.

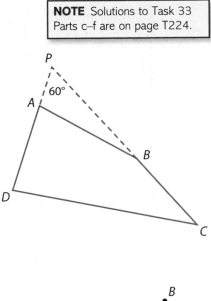

   • No, $\overline{AB}$ and $\overline{CD}$ could not be congruent. If they were, the quadrilateral would be a parallelogram, and the congruent opposite sides would not meet to form a 60° angle.

   • Extending $\overline{AD}$ and $\overline{BC}$ would give a triangle with base angles D and C and a third angle of measure 60°. Thus, $m\angle D + m\angle C = 180° - 60° = 120°$.

   • Subtract the sum $m\angle D + m\angle C$ from the sum of all interior angle measures to get $m\angle A + m\angle B = 360° - 120° = 240°$. Alternatively, $m\angle A + m\angle B$ is the sum of the exterior angle measures of $\triangle APB$, which is $60° + m\angle PBA + 60° + m\angle PAB = 120° + (180° - 60°) = 240°$.

b. The four points are the vertices of rhombus $JLKM$. By the Midpoint Connector Theorem:

$$MJ = \frac{1}{2}AD \text{ (using } \triangle BDA)$$

$$LK = \frac{1}{2}AD \text{ (using } \triangle CDA)$$

$$JL = \frac{1}{2}BC \text{ (using } \triangle ABC)$$

$$MK = \frac{1}{2}BC \text{ (using } \triangle DBC)$$

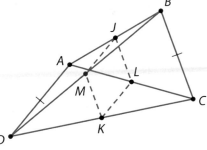

Since $\overline{BC} \cong \overline{AD}$ and $\frac{1}{2}BC = \frac{1}{2}AD$, all the sides of $JLKM$ are equal and $JLKM$ is a rhombus.

c. Points P, C, and D are vertices of an equilateral triangle.

Proof: We are interested in $m\angle PAD$ and $m\angle PBC$, since they are included angles of two pairs of congruent sides ($AD = CB$ and $BP = AP$). If these two angles can be shown to be congruent, then $\triangle PAD$ and $\triangle PBC$ are also congruent.

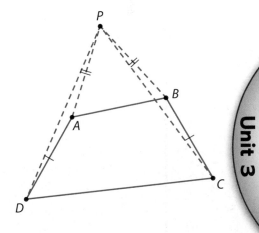

From Part a, we know
$m\angle DAB + m\angle CBA = 240°$
$\qquad\quad m\angle DAB = 240° - m\angle CBA$.

We also know
$m\angle PBC = m\angle PBA + m\angle ABC$
$\qquad\quad = 60° + m\angle ABC$.

Now,
$m\angle PAD = 360° - m\angle DAB - m\angle PAB$
$\qquad\quad = 360° - m\angle DAB - 60°$
$\qquad\quad = 300° - m\angle DAB$
$\qquad\quad = 300° - (240° - m\angle CBA)$
$\qquad\quad = 60° + m\angle ABC$
$\qquad\quad = m\angle PBC$.

Thus, $\triangle PAD \cong \triangle PBC$ by SAS. So $\overline{DP} \cong \overline{CP}$ by CPCTC. Also by CPCTC, $\angle DPA \cong \angle CPB$. $m\angle APC + m\angle CPB = m\angle APB = 60°$, so $m\angle APC + m\angle DPA = 60°$. Thus, $\triangle DPC$ is isosceles with a 60° angle, so $\triangle DPC$ is equilateral.

Review

35 If $1,000 < x < 2,000$, place the following expressions in order from smallest to largest.

$$\sqrt{x} \qquad \frac{x}{5} \qquad \frac{5}{x} \qquad x^2 \qquad \frac{x+3}{5} \qquad \frac{5}{x+2} \qquad |x|$$

36 For each table of values, determine if the relationship is linear, exponential, or quadratic. Then find a rule that matches the relationship in the table.

a.

x	0	1	2	3	4	5
y	297	99	33	11	$3\frac{2}{3}$	$1\frac{2}{9}$

b.

x	0	3	6	9	12	15
y	99	115	131	147	163	179

c.

x	2	3	4	5	6	7
y	18	15.5	13	10.5	8	5.5

37 Why is the length of the perpendicular segment to a line drawn from a point not on a line the shortest distance from the point to the line?

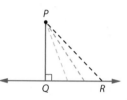

38 Find the length of the line segment that connects each pair of points. Express your answer in simplest radical form.

a. $(3, 6)$ and $(11, 10)$

b. $(5, -4)$ and $(0, -1)$

c. (a, b) and $(a, 0)$

39 Consider $\triangle XYZ$ with $m\angle Y = 90°$ and $\sin X = \frac{3}{5}$.

a. Find $m\angle X$.

b. Sketch two different triangles that each meet the given conditions. Identify the lengths of all sides of your triangles.

c. Are the two triangles you drew in Part b similar? Explain your reasoning.

40 Rewrite each expression in a simpler equivalent form.

a. $-\frac{2}{5}(14x + 12) + \frac{1}{5}(3x - 6)$

b. $\frac{8x + 10}{2} + 6x - 15$

c. $x(10 - x) - 3(x + 4) + 12$

Review

35 $\frac{5}{x+2}, \frac{5}{x}, \sqrt{x}, \frac{x}{5}, \frac{x+3}{5}, |x|, x^2$

36 **a.** Exponential; $y = 297\left(\frac{1}{3}\right)^x$

    b. Linear; $y = \frac{16}{3}x + 99$

    c. Linear; $y = -2.5x + 23$

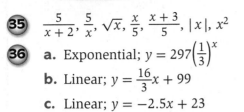 **Just in Time**

37 As shown in the diagram, any point R other than the point Q where the perpendicular meets the line forms right $\triangle PQR$ with right angle at Q. $\overline{PR}$ is the hypotenuse of the right triangle and thus longer than $\overline{PQ}$.

38 **a.** $4\sqrt{5}$ **b.** $\sqrt{34}$ **c.** $\sqrt{b^2} = |b|$

39 **a.** $m\angle X = \sin^{-1}\left(\frac{3}{5}\right) \approx 36.9°$

    b. Responses may vary, but $\frac{YZ}{XZ} = \frac{3}{5}$.

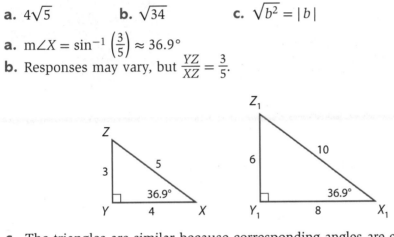

    c. The triangles are similar because corresponding angles are congruent.

40 **a.** $-5x - 6$

    b. $10x - 10$

    c. $-x^2 + 7x$

41 The suggested serving size for a certain cereal is $1\frac{1}{4}$ cups.

a. How much cereal would you need if you wanted to have 15 servings?

b. Georgia has 25 cups of cereal. How many servings does she have?

c. A box of cereal weighs 10 ounces and contains 9 servings. What does 1 cup of cereal weigh?

d. Write a symbolic rule that describes the relationship between the weight of the cereal and the number of servings.

42 The histogram below represents the number of sit-ups that the 60 eleventh-grade students at Eisenhower High School were able to complete in one minute.

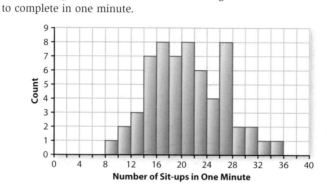

a. Jeremy did 29 sit-ups. What is his percentile ranking within this group of eleventh graders?

b. Stephanie was only at the 40th percentile. How many sit-ups was Stephanie able to do?

43 Graph the solution set to each system of inequalities. On your graphs, identify the coordinates of the points of intersections of the graphs.

a. $4x + 8y < 40$
$x - 2y > 8$

b. $y \geq -3$
$y \leq x^2 - 5$

44 Suppose a data set x_1, x_2, x_3, x_4, x_5, has mean $\bar{x}$ and standard deviation s.

a. If a constant c is added to each of the five values, what is the mean of the transformed values? What is the standard deviation of the transformed values?

b. If each of the five values is multiplied by a positive constant d, what is the mean of the transformed values? What is the standard deviation of the transformed values?

c. How would the data transformation in Part a affect the median? The interquartile range?

d. How would the data transformation in Part b affect the median? The interquartile range?

41   **a.** $18\frac{3}{4}$ cups

     b. 20 servings

     c. $\frac{10}{9}$ ounces per serving and $1\frac{1}{4}$ cups per serving

$$\frac{\frac{10}{9}}{\frac{5}{4}} = \frac{x}{1}$$

$$x = \frac{40}{45} = \frac{8}{9} \text{ ounces in 1 cup}$$

     d. Weight w is $\frac{10}{9}$ of the number of servings n.

$$w = \frac{10}{9}n$$

🕐 Just in Time

42   **a.** Counting Jeremy, 56 out of 60 students, or 93%, did 29 or fewer sit-ups. So, Jeremy is at about the 93rd percentile.

     b. Solving $\frac{x}{60} = 0.40$, $x = 24$. So, Stephanie was the 24th student from the bottom in the number of sit-ups. This means she did 18 or 19 sit-ups.

43   The graphs below shade out the nonfeasible region, so the unshaded area is the solution.

     a. 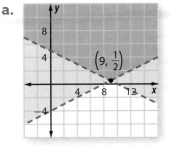   **b.**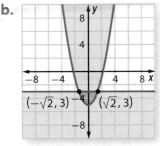

🕐 Just in Time

44   **a.** The transformed mean is c more than the original mean. So, $\bar{x}_T = \bar{x} + c$. The standard deviation of the transformed values is the same as the standard deviation s of the original set of five values.

     b. The transformed mean $\bar{x}_T$ is $\dfrac{dx_1 + dx_2 + dx_3 + dx_4 + dx_5}{5} = d\bar{x}$.

       Thus, $\bar{x}_T$ is d times the mean of the original set of values. The standard deviation of the transformed values is

$$s_T = \sqrt{\frac{(dx_1 - d\bar{x})^2 + (dx_2 - d\bar{x})^2 + (dx_3 - d\bar{x})^2 + (dx_4 - d\bar{x})^2 + (dx_5 - d\bar{x})^2}{5}}.$$

       s_T is d times the standard deviation of the original set of five values.

     c. The median of the transformed values would be c more than the original median value. The IQR would be the same for both sets of values.

     d. Both the median and the IQR would be d times the original median and IQR.

Unit 3

45 Match each of the following histograms of test scores in three classes, I, II, and III, to the best description of class performance.

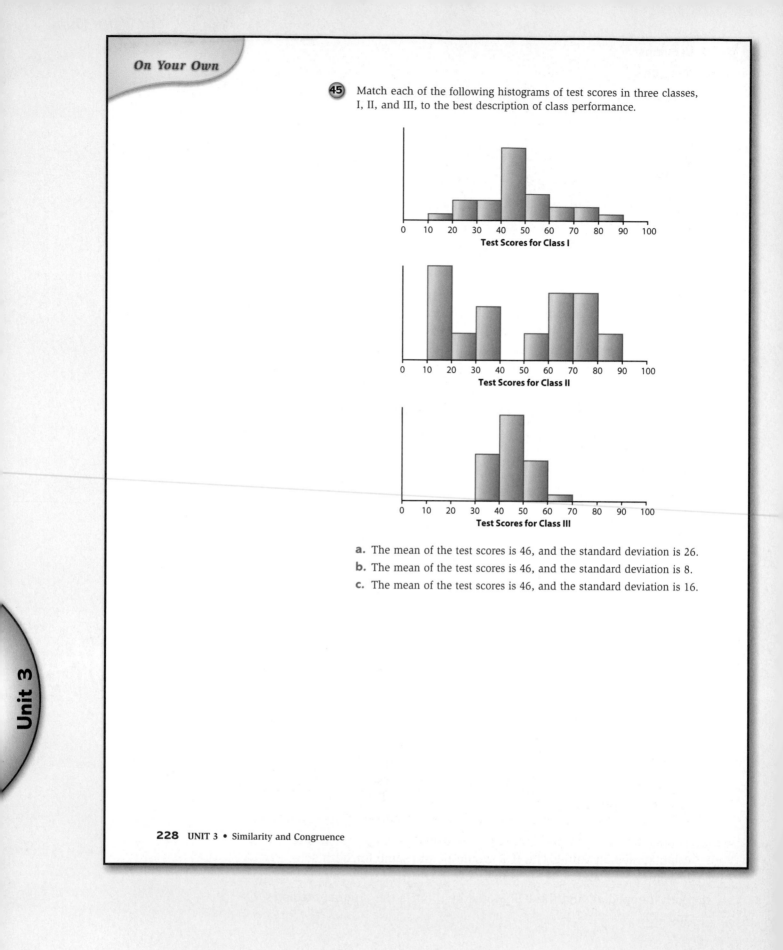

Test Scores for Class I

Test Scores for Class II

Test Scores for Class III

a. The mean of the test scores is 46, and the standard deviation is 26.
b. The mean of the test scores is 46, and the standard deviation is 8.
c. The mean of the test scores is 46, and the standard deviation is 16.

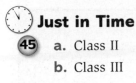

Just in Time

45 **a.** Class II

 b. Class III

 c. Class I

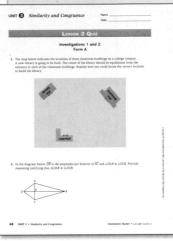

LESSON 3

Looking Back

In this unit, you re-examined similarity and congruence as related ideas and as tools for solving problems. In Lesson 1, you used the Law of Cosines and the Law of Sines to deduce sufficient conditions on side lengths or angle measures to ensure similarity of triangles. You used similarity to explain the design of mechanisms, calculate inaccessible heights and distances, and prove important geometric relationships and properties of size transformations.

In Lesson 2, you used similarity conditions for triangles to justify sufficient conditions for congruence of triangles that you discovered and used without proof in your previous work. You used congruence of triangles to locate special centers of triangles and to investigate and prove properties and conditions for congruence of (special) parallelograms. You also re-examined and proved properties of congruence-preserving transformations and then used those transformations to solve problems.

The tasks in this final lesson will help you review and organize your knowledge of key ideas and strategies for reasoning with similarity and congruence.

1. When a rectangular photograph is to be enlarged to fit the width of a given column of type in a newspaper or magazine, the new height can be found by extending the width to the new measure and drawing a perpendicular as shown. The point at which the perpendicular meets the extended diagonal determines the height of the enlargement. Explain as precisely as you can why this method works.

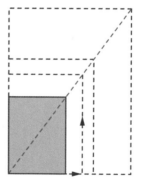

Looking Back

In this lesson, students are asked to employ their skills in a variety of situations. Remind the groups that when something is proved, it can be used in later proofs. This is especially important in Task 4 Part a where students can draw on the diagonal properties of a rectangle; Task 5 Part b using the fact that the perpendicular bisectors of a triangle intersect at a point equidistant from the vertices; and Task 7 Part b using the congruent base angles of an isosceles triangle or the Midpoint Connector Theorem for Quadrilaterals. Sharing responsibility for some proofs, such as Task 3 Part c, will improve the progress through the lesson.

1 Using the diagram at the right, $\triangle DGF \sim \triangle DCB$. (AA Similarity Theorem—angle D is common to both triangles.) The scale factor relating $\triangle DGF$ to $\triangle DCG$ is $\frac{DG}{DC}$. The diagonal and the perpendicular define height of the similar triangles.

Alternatively, a size transformation with center D and scale factor $\frac{DG}{DC}$ determines the point F on $\overrightarrow{DB}$ that is the corner of the enlarged rectangle.

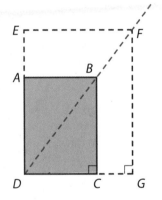

In the diagram below, $\triangle ABC$ is a right triangle and $\overline{BD}$ is an altitude to side $\overline{AC}$.

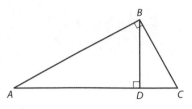

a. Prove that $(AB)^2 = (AC)(AD)$.

b. Find a similar expression for $(BC)^2$.

c. Use your work in Parts a and b to provide another proof of the Pythagorean Theorem.

3 In the diagram below, $\overline{PR}$ and $\overline{QS}$ are diagonals of quadrilateral $PQRS$, and interest at point T. $\overline{PS} \cong \overline{QR}$, $\overline{PT} \cong \overline{QT}$, and $\overline{ST} \cong \overline{RT}$.

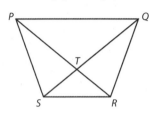

a. Identify and name eight triangles in the diagram.

b. Which pairs of the eight triangles seem to be congruent? Name each pair.

c. Using the given information, prove or disprove that each identified pair of triangles are congruent.

d. Which of the remaining pairs of triangles are similar? Provide an argument to support your answer.

e. What can you conclude about $\overline{PQ}$ and $\overline{SR}$ when you know the given information? Write a proof for your claim.

2 **a. Prove:** $(AB)^2 = (AC)(AD)$

$\angle ADB \cong \angle ABC$ (right angles). $\angle A$ is common to both triangles. So, $\triangle ADB \sim \triangle ABC$ (AA). $\triangle ABC$ is related to $\triangle ADB$ by a scale factor $\dfrac{AB}{AD}$ which is the same value as $\dfrac{AC}{AB}$. So, $\dfrac{AB}{AD} = \dfrac{AC}{AB}$ and thus, $(AB)^2 = (AC)(AD)$.

b. $\triangle BDC \sim \triangle ABC$ (AA) by scale factor $\dfrac{BC}{DC}$.

$\dfrac{BC}{DC} = \dfrac{AC}{BC}$

So, $(BC)^2 = (AC)(DC)$.

c. $(AB)^2 + (BC)^2 = (AC)(AD) + (AC)(DC)$

$$= (AC)(AD + DC)$$
$$= (AC)(AC)$$
$$= (AC)^2$$

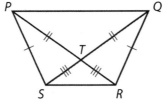

INSTRUCTIONAL NOTE
If students completed Applications Task 5 on page 181, you could refer them to that task before they begin Task 2.

3 **a.** $\triangle PSR$, $\triangle QSR$, $\triangle PTS$, $\triangle STR$, $\triangle QTR$, $\triangle PTQ$, $\triangle PQR$, $\triangle PQS$

b. $\triangle PSR$ and $\triangle QRS$
$\triangle PTS$ and $\triangle QTR$
$\triangle SPQ$ and $\triangle RQP$

c. Prove: $\triangle PTS \cong \triangle QTR$

$\overline{PS} \cong \overline{QR}$, $\overline{PT} \cong \overline{QT}$, and $\overline{ST} \cong \overline{RT}$ are given as initial information. Thus, $\triangle PTS \cong \triangle QTR$ by the SSS Congruence Theorem.

Prove: $\triangle SPQ \cong \triangle RQP$

From the initial information, you know $\overline{PS} \cong \overline{QR}$. Also $\overline{PQ} \cong \overline{PQ}$. $SQ = ST + TQ$ and $RP = RT + TP$. Since the addends are equal ($RT = ST$ and $TP = TQ$), $SQ = RP$. Thus, $\triangle SPQ \cong \triangle RQP$ by the SSS Congruence Theorem.

Prove: $\triangle PSR \cong \triangle QRS$

These triangles can be proven congruent using the same tactic that was used in the proof above.

d. The remaining pair of similar triangles is $\triangle STR$ and $\triangle QTP$.

Prove: $\triangle STR \sim \triangle QTP$

$\angle PTQ \cong \angle RTS$ since they are vertical angles. Since it is given that $\overline{PT} \cong \overline{QT}$ and $\overline{ST} \cong \overline{RT}$, $\dfrac{PT}{RT} = \dfrac{QT}{ST} = k$ (or $PT = k \cdot RT$ and $QT = k \cdot ST$). Thus, $\triangle STR \sim \triangle QTP$ by the SAS Similarity Theorem.

e. Conclusion: $\overline{PQ}$ is parallel to $\overline{SR}$.

Since $\triangle STR \sim \triangle QTP$, the alternate interior angles, $\angle TSR$ and $\angle TQP$, are congruent. So, $\overline{PQ} \parallel \overline{SR}$.

Unit 3

④ Civil engineers, urban planners, and design engineers are frequently confronted with "traffic center" problems. In mathematical terms, these problems often involve locating a point *M* that is equidistant from three or more given points or for which the sum of the distances from *M* to the given points is as small as possible. In the first two parts of this task, you are to write and analyze a synthetic proof and a coordinate proof of the following theorem:

The midpoint of the hypotenuse of a right triangle is equidistant from its vertices.

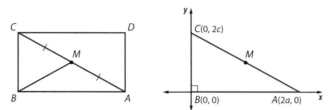

a. In the diagram on the left, $\triangle ABC$ is composed of two consecutive sides and a diagonal of rectangle *ABCD*. Using that diagram, write a synthetic proof that if *M* is the midpoint of $\overline{AC}$, then $MA = MB = MC$.

b. Using the diagram on the right, write an analytic proof that if *M* is the midpoint of $\overline{AC}$, then $MA = MB = MC$.

c. For the proof in Part b, why were the coordinates of points *A* and *C* assigned $(2a, 0)$ and $(0, 2c)$ rather than simply $(a, 0)$ and $(0, c)$, respectively?

⑤ Suppose cities *A*, *B*, and *C* are connected by highways $\overline{AB}$, $\overline{BC}$, and $\overline{AC}$ as shown.

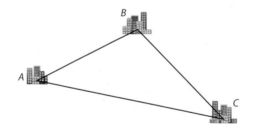

a. On a copy of $\triangle ABC$, find the location for a proposed new airport that would be the same distance from each of the existing highways.

b. Explain why your proposed location meets the constraints.

Unit 3

4 **a.** **Given:** Rectangle $ABCD$ with M the midpoint of $\overline{AC}$

Prove: $MA = MB = MC$

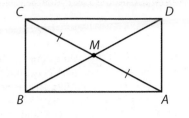

Statement	Reason
(1) $MA = MC$	Definition of midpoint
(2) Draw diagonal $\overline{BD}$ that intersects $\overline{AC}$ at M. So, $MB = MD$.	Property of rectangle: diagonals bisect each other
(3) $AC = BD$	Property of rectangle: diagonals are congruent
(4) $\frac{1}{2}AC = \frac{1}{2}BD$	Multiplication Property of Equality
(5) $MA = MB = MC$	Step 1 and Step 4

b. If M is the midpoint of $\overline{AC}$, then its coordinates must be $\left(\frac{2a}{2}, \frac{2c}{2}\right) = (a, c)$.

By the distance formula,

$MB = \sqrt{a^2 + c^2}$

$MA = \sqrt{(2a - a)^2 + (0 - c)^2}$

$\quad = \sqrt{a^2 + c^2}$

$MC = \sqrt{(0 - a)^2 + (2c - c)^2}$

$\quad = \sqrt{a^2 + c^2}$

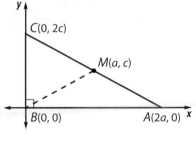

Therefore, all three segments have equal length.

c. Assigning $2a$ and $2c$ as the x- and y-coordinates eliminates fractions when using the midpoint formula.

5 **a.** Locate P, the intersection of the perpendicular bisectors of the three sides of $\triangle ABC$.

b. P is equidistant from A, B, and C. This was proved in Problem 1 on page 201.

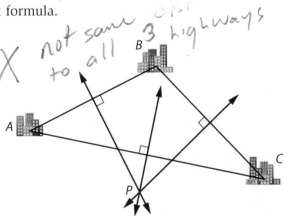

✗ not same dist to all 3 highways

Unit 3

6 On a copy of the billiards table, sketch the path of the cue ball as it rebounds from $\overline{AB}$, from $\overline{BC}$, from $\overline{CD}$, from $\overline{AD}$, and from $\overline{AB}$ again. (This assumes that the ball has enough speed to travel the whole path, of course!) Label the points where the ball strikes the cushions R, S, T, and U, respectively.

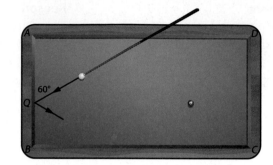

a. At what angle does the ball leave $\overline{AB}$ the second time? Explain your reasoning.

b. What appears to be true about $\overline{QR}$ and $\overline{ST}$? Write a proof of your conjecture.

c. Suppose you wanted to bank the cue ball off $\overline{BC}$ rather than $\overline{AB}$ in order to strike the red ball. At what point on the cushion $\overline{BC}$ would you aim?

  • On a copy of the billiards table, draw the path of the cue ball.

  • Prove that if the ball has no spin and sufficient speed, it will follow the drawn path and strike the red ball.

d. Is it possible, for each side of the table, to bank the cue ball off that side and strike the red ball? Explain.

e. If you were to try to hit the red ball by banking the cue ball off two sides, which pair of sides would you use? Why? Draw the path of the cue ball. Justify that it will hit the red ball.

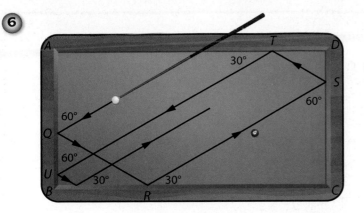

Teaching Resources

Student Masters 61–63.

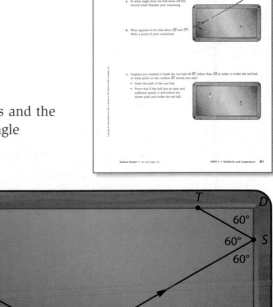

a. The ball leaves $\overline{AB}$ for the second time at 60°. Using triangles and the fact that the sides of the tables are parallel lets us find the angle measures as given in the diagram above.

b. $\overline{QR}$ and $\overline{ST}$ are parallel.

Using the fact that the angle the ball hits the cushion and the angle it rebounds are the same measure, angle measures can be determined as shown in the diagram at the right. Since $\angle QRS$ and $\angle RST$ are supplementary and interior angles on the same side of the transversal, $\overleftrightarrow{QR} \parallel \overleftrightarrow{ST}$.

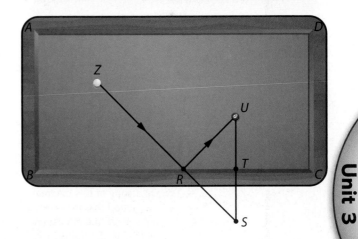

c. • See the diagram at the right.

• Let S be the reflection of U across $\overleftrightarrow{BC}$. Draw $\overline{ZS}$ and let R be the intersection of $\overline{ZS}$ with $\overline{BC}$. $RT = RT$, $UT = TS$ (line reflection preserves distance), and $\angle RTU \cong \angle RTS$ ($\overline{US}$ is perpendicular to $\overline{BC}$ and $\overline{RT}$). So, $\triangle RTU \cong \triangle RTS$ (SAS). Since $\triangle RTU \cong \triangle RTS$, $\angle URT \cong \angle SRT$ (CPCTC) and the ball will hit U, the preimage of S.

NOTE Solutions to Task 6 Parts d and e are on page T233.

Unit 3

7 The display below suggests that if the midpoints of the sides of an isosceles trapezoid are connected in order, a special parallelogram is formed.

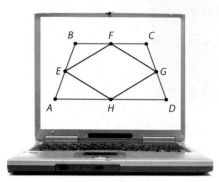

a. Make and test conjectures about the type of parallelogram that is formed.

b. Prove your conjecture using synthetic methods. Using coordinate methods.

c. Which proof method in Part b seems to be the better approach for this problem? Why?

8 In July 2006, a tsunami, triggered by an undersea earthquake, struck the coasts of India and Indonesia, destroying villages. Tidal waves damaged bridges. A new bridge connecting villages *V* and *W* positioned as shown below is to be constructed across the river.

a. If river conditions permit, why should a bridge $\overline{XY}$ be constructed perpendicular to the banks of the river?

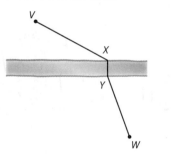

b. The diagram shows one possible location of the bridge. Write an expression for the length of the path from village *V* to village *W*.

c. On a copy of this diagram, find the image *V'* of point *V* under the translation that maps point *X* onto point *Y*. How could you use point *V'* to find a location for the bridge so that the path from point *V* to the bridge and then to point *W* is of minimum length? Why would that make sense?

d. Explain why your location of the bridge provides a shorter path than the path in the diagram. Why is it shorter than the path for any other possible location of the bridge?

d. You can bank the cue ball off any side as shown in the diagram below.

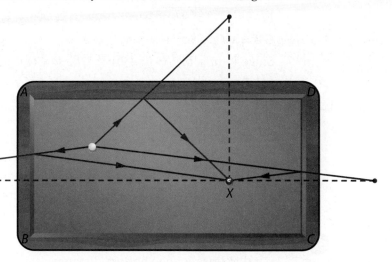

e. Responses may vary. One likely choice is shown below. This path is shorter than others and thus leaves less room for error if the angle is slightly miscalculated. It may also be easier to visualize the composite reflections in this case. The cue ball will hit the red ball because the path satisfies the law of physics—the angle of incidence equals the angle of reflection.

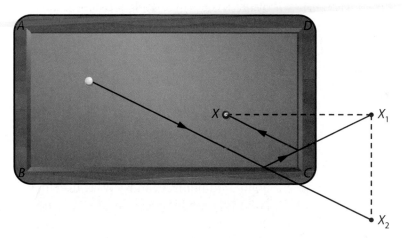

7 **a.** The parallelogram is a rhombus.

b. **Synthetic Method:**
$\angle A \cong \angle D$ (base angles of isosceles trapezoid—Applications Task 8 of Lesson 2 on page 216)
$AH = DH$ (midpoint of $\overline{AD}$)
$AE = DG$ (each half the length of two congruent segments, $\overline{AB}$ and $\overline{CD}$)
$\triangle AEH \cong \triangle DGH$ (SAS)
$\overline{EH} \cong \overline{GH}$ (CPCTC)
$EFGH$ is a parallelogram (Midpoint Connector Theorem for Quadrilaterals) and has two consecutive sides congruent and thus is a rhombus.

Coordinate Method:

$EH = \sqrt{(-(a+b))^2 + c^2}$

$GH = \sqrt{(a+b)^2 + c^2}$

Since $(-(a+b))^2 = (a+b)^2$,
$EH = GH$.

Parallelogram *EFGH* has
two consecutive sides
congruent and thus is
a rhombus.

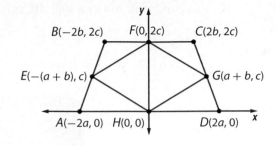

c. Responses will vary. They may depend on how successful students
were with these proofs. This is an opportunity to discuss the value of
strategically placing figures on coordinate axes.

8 a. The perpendicular between two
parallel lines is the shortest distance
from a point on one line to the
other line.

b. $VX + XY + YW$

c. Draw $\overline{V'W}$. Point *A*, the intersection
of $\overline{V'W}$ with the riverbank on the side
of the river where *W* is located, is the
location for the bridge. $V'W$ is the
shortest distance between V' and *W*
and $V'V = XY$ which is the shortest
distance across the river. The
shortest path from *V* to *W* is then
$VB + BA + AW$.

   Alternatively, the same bridge
location would result if W' is the image
of *W* under the translation that maps
point *Y* to point *X*, and $\overline{VW'}$ is drawn.
Point *B* is the intersection of $\overline{VW'}$ with
the riverbank on *V*'s side of the river.

d. Draw $\overline{V'Y}$. By the Triangle Inequality,
$V'Y + YW > V'W$. $V'Y = VX$ and
$V'V = XY$ (translations preserve
segment length). Also, $VB = V'A$ since
$VBAV'$ is a parallelogram ($\overline{VV'} \cong \overline{BA}$
and $\overline{VV'} \parallel \overline{BA}$). So, the original path
$VX + XY + YW = V'Y + V'V + YW$.
Since $V'Y + YW > V'W = V'A + AW$,
$V'Y + V'V + YW > V'A + AW + VV' =$
$VB + BA + AW$.

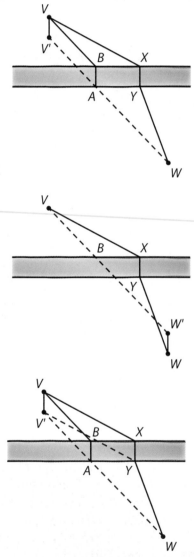

Teacher Notes

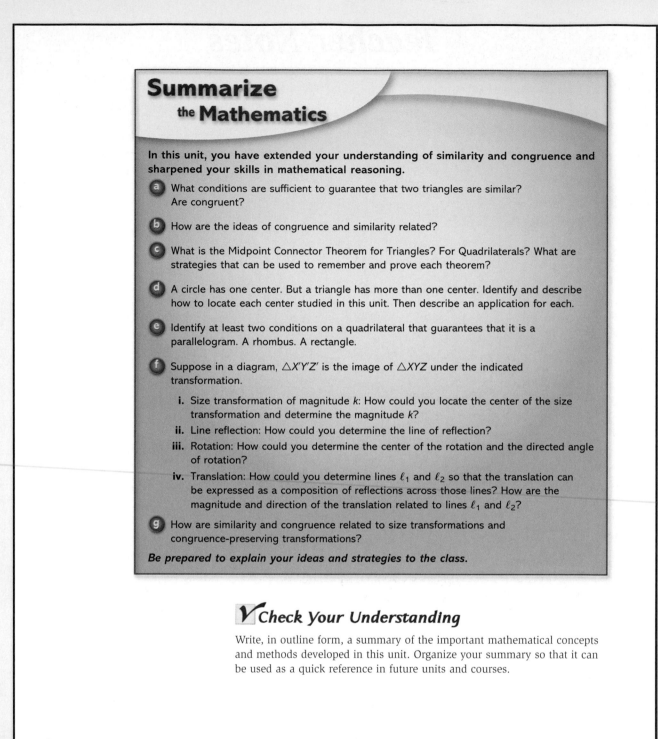

Summarize
the Mathematics

In this unit, you have extended your understanding of similarity and congruence and sharpened your skills in mathematical reasoning.

a What conditions are sufficient to guarantee that two triangles are similar? Are congruent?

b How are the ideas of congruence and similarity related?

c What is the Midpoint Connector Theorem for Triangles? For Quadrilaterals? What are strategies that can be used to remember and prove each theorem?

d A circle has one center. But a triangle has more than one center. Identify and describe how to locate each center studied in this unit. Then describe an application for each.

e Identify at least two conditions on a quadrilateral that guarantees that it is a parallelogram. A rhombus. A rectangle.

f Suppose in a diagram, $\triangle X'Y'Z'$ is the image of $\triangle XYZ$ under the indicated transformation.

   i. Size transformation of magnitude k: How could you locate the center of the size transformation and determine the magnitude k?

   ii. Line reflection: How could you determine the line of reflection?

   iii. Rotation: How could you determine the center of the rotation and the directed angle of rotation?

   iv. Translation: How could you determine lines ℓ_1 and ℓ_2 so that the translation can be expressed as a composition of reflections across those lines? How are the magnitude and direction of the translation related to lines ℓ_1 and ℓ_2?

g How are similarity and congruence related to size transformations and congruence-preserving transformations?

Be prepared to explain your ideas and strategies to the class.

✔ Check Your Understanding

Write, in outline form, a summary of the important mathematical concepts and methods developed in this unit. Organize your summary so that it can be used as a quick reference in future units and courses.

Summarize
the Mathematics

Teaching Resources

Transparency Masters 64–65.

UNIT 3 *Similarity and Congruence*

Summarize
the Mathematics

In this unit, you have extended your understanding of similarity and congruence and sharpened your skills in mathematical reasoning.

a What conditions are sufficient to guarantee that two triangles are similar? Are congruent?

b How are the ideas of congruence and similarity related?

c What is the Midpoint Connector Theorem for Triangles? For Quadrilaterals? What are strategies that can be used to remember and prove each theorem?

d A circle has one center. But a triangle has more than one center. Identify and describe how to locate each center. Then describe an application for each.

e Identify at least two conditions on a quadrilateral that guarantees that it is a parallelogram. A rhombus. A rectangle.

64 UNIT 3 • Similarity and Congruence   Transparency Master • *see unit page 234*

a Two triangles are similar in the following instances.
- Two pairs of corresponding angles have the same measure (AA).
- The ratios of the lengths of corresponding sides are a constant (SSS).
- The lengths of two sides of one triangle are a multiple, k, of the lengths of corresponding sides of the other triangle and the included angles have the same measure (SAS).

Two triangles are congruent in the following instances:
- They are similar with scale factor 1.
- The three sides of one triangle are congruent to the corresponding sides of the other triangle (SSS).
- Two angles and the included side of one triangle are congruent to the corresponding two angles and included side of the other triangle (ASA).
- Two sides and the included angle of one triangle are congruent to the corresponding two sides and included angle of the other triangle (SAS).
- Two angles and a nonincluded side of one triangle are congruent to the corresponding two angles and side of the other triangle (AAS).

b Similarity of polygons is the general notion in which corresponding angles are congruent and corresponding sides are a constant multiple of each other (corresponding sides are proportional). When the multiple is one, then the figures are congruent. Most generally, two geometric figures are similar if they have the same shape, or the same shape and same size (thus, also congruent).

c The Midpoint Connector Theorem for Triangles: If a line segment joins the midpoints of two sides of a triangle, then it is parallel to the third side of the triangle and half the length of that side. Similar triangles were used to prove this theorem. The scale factor from the larger triangle to the smaller triangle was one-half.

The Midpoint Connector Theorem for Quadrilaterals: If the midpoints of consecutive sides of any quadrilateral are connected in order, the resulting quadrilateral is a parallelogram.

This theorem was proved by drawing the diagonals of the quadrilateral and applying the Midpoint Connector Theorem for Triangles.

d Centers of triangles:
The circumcenter is the intersection point of the perpendicular bisectors of the sides of the triangle. It is the center of the circle that circumscribes the triangle. Since this point is equidistant from each vertex, it is used in applications when the goal is to identify a location the same distance from three noncollinear points such as placing a distribution center equidistant from three stores that carry a product.

The incenter is the intersection of the angle bisectors of the triangle. It is the center of the inscribed circle. This point is helpful for applications where you want a location to be equidistant from three nonparallel lines.

The centroid is the point of intersection of the medians of a triangle. The centroid locates the center of gravity of a triangle. This might be used to locate the place to best support a triangular weight with a beam.

(e) A quadrilateral is a parallelogram if any of the following conditions hold.

- Both pairs of opposite sides are congruent.
- One pair of opposite sides are congruent and parallel.
- Both pairs of opposite sides are parallel.
- The diagonals bisect each other.
- Consecutive angles are supplementary.
- Opposite angles are congruent.

A quadrilateral is a rhombus if it is a parallelogram with two consecutive sides congruent. So, any of the conditions above could be used with this additional condition. In addition, a quadrilateral is a rhombus if the diagonals are perpendicular bisectors of each other.

A quadrilateral is a rectangle if it is a parallelogram with one right angle. So, this condition added to any of the parallelogram conditions guarantees a rectangle. In addition, a quadrilateral is a rectangle if:

- all angles are congruent.
- the diagonals bisect each other and are congruent.

(f) **i.** To find the center of the size transformation, draw the lines connecting points and their images. The intersection point of these lines is the center. The scale factor is the distance from the center to any image point divided by the distance of its preimage point to the center.

ii. To find the line of refection, draw the segment connecting a point and its image and construct the perpendicular bisector of that segment. The perpendicular bisector is the line of reflection.

iii. To find the center of the rotation, take two distinct points and draw the segments that join these points to their images. Construct the perpendicular bisectors of these two segments. The intersection of these two perpendicular bisectors is the center C of the rotation. The angle size is $m\angle PCP'$ where P is any point except C and P' is the image of P under the rotation. The direction of the angle is from the preimage point to the image point.

iv. Lines ℓ_1 and ℓ_2 are perpendicular to the segment formed by a point T and its image T'. One easy way to identify these lines is to draw $\overline{TT'}$ and ℓ_1 perpendicular to $\overline{TT'}$ at T. (The reflected image of T across ℓ_1 is T. Next draw ℓ_2, the perpendicular bisector of $\overline{TT'}$. The magnitude of the translation is TT', twice the distance between ℓ_1 and ℓ_2. The direction is from T to T'. Any two lines ℓ_1 and ℓ_2 that are perpendicular to $\overleftrightarrow{TT'}$ such that the distance between ℓ_1 and ℓ_2 is half the length TT' will produce the desired translation as a composition of reflections across ℓ_1 and then ℓ_2.

(g) Size transformations preserve angle measure and thus map polygons to similar polygons. Congruence-preserving transformations are line reflections, rotations, translations, and glide-reflections. Since these transformations preserve distance and angle measures, they map a polygon onto a congruent polygon.

✓ Check Your Understanding

You may wish to have students use the Teaching Master, *Similarity and Congruence* Unit Summary, to help them organize the information. Above all, this should be something that is useful to the individual student.

Practicing for Standardized Tests

Each Practicing for Standardized Tests master presents 10 questions in the multiple-choice format of test items similar to how they often appear in standardized tests. Answers are provided below.

Answers to Practice Set 3

1. (c)	**2.** (a)	**3.** (d)	**4.** (e)	**5.** (e)
6. (c)	**7.** (d)	**8.** (a)	**9.** (b)	**10.** (e)

Teaching Resources

Student Masters 66–68.

Assessment Masters 69–90.

Student Masters 91–92.

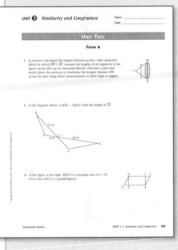

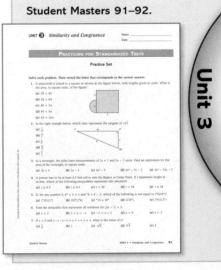

Unit 3

UNIT 4

SAMPLES AND VARIATION

Taking political polls and manufacturing car parts do not seem similar at first glance. However, both involve processes that have variation in the outcomes. When Gallup takes a poll, different samples of voters would give slightly different estimates of the president's popularity. When Ford Motor Company builds a car, body panels will vary slightly in their dimensions even if they are made by the same machine.

In this unit, you will investigate how understanding this variability helps both pollsters and manufacturers improve their products. The statistical methods they use can be effectively applied to any area in which there is variation in the process, essentially every area of human endeavor. The essential knowledge and skills required for this work are developed in three lessons of this unit.

Lessons

1 Normal Distributions

Describe characteristics of a normal distribution, compute and interpret a z-score, and estimate probabilities of events that have a normal distribution.

2 Binomial Distributions

Construct a binomial distribution and predict whether it will be approximately normal, compute the mean and standard deviation of a binomial distribution, and identify rare events.

3 Statistical Process Control

Recognize when the mean and standard deviation change in a plot over time, use control charts and the tests for out-of-control behavior, understand why it is best to watch a process for awhile before trying to adjust it, compute the probability of a false alarm, and use the Central Limit Theorem.

SAMPLES AND VARIATION

Unit Overview

Following the ideas of American W. Edwards Deming, considered by many to be the father of Japanese industry's use of quality control, statistical methods are used increasingly in American industry to improve the quality of products. Companies that are committed to the improvement of their products require that the methods be understood by everyone, from employees on the shop floor to those in the executive suite. Called quality control, statistical process control, quality improvement, and other names, the techniques used are highly mathematical. In this unit, students will study the mathematics behind these methods. New topics include standardized values, binomial distributions, odds, and the Central Limit Theorem and topics covered in additional depth include percentiles, expected value, probability distributions, the standard deviation, normal distributions, the Multiplication Rule of Probability, and the Addition Rule of Probability.

Samples and Variation provides students with experience in thinking about and working with the variation in measurements. The first and second lessons involve students in thinking about the shape, mean, and standard deviation of normal and binomial distributions and in using the standard deviation as a unit of measure that can be used to describe location in a normal distribution. Students may be surprised to discover the variety of situations in which approximately normal distributions occur.

The mean and the standard deviation are the most useful measures of center and spread for distributions that are roughly symmetrical and have no outliers. The mean, standard deviation, and normal distribution are natural partners. Students will explore the relationships among the three in the first lesson. In the second lesson, they will explore the relationship between the normal and binomial distributions.

The third lesson introduces students to control charts, which display samples of measurements taken over time. When the measurements come from a distribution that is approximately normal (or, the mean of sets of measurements are approximately normal), there are criteria for defining when an industrial manufacturing process goes "out of control." These criteria are based on probabilistic arguments and are the foundation for the quality control tests that are used in industry. In particular, students study tests taken from the influential *Western Electric Statistical Quality Control Handbook*.

Unit Objectives

- Understand the standard deviation as a measure of variability and the normal distribution as a model of variability
- Use the number of standard deviations from the mean (standardized value) as a measure of position
- Construct binomial distributions and determine the probability of events in binomial situations
- Use a random sample to decide whether a given proportion p is plausible as the proportion of successes in the population from which the sample came
- Construct and interpret control charts
- Understand the Central Limit Theorem and how it is applied to statistical process control

Short Path in Course 2 Unit 8, *Probability Distributions*

If your students have not studied the probability unit in Course 2 of *Core-Plus Mathematics*, they should complete the short path of that unit outlined on page T74A of this *Teacher's Guide* before beginning this unit.

CPMP-Tools

CPMP-Tools statistics software features and custom tools applicable to this unit are: Simulation, Distribution of Sample Means, Binomial Distributions, and Control Chart. The statistics tools have been developed with features that allow students to do a simulation and compare results to either a binomial or normal theoretical distribution. More detailed instructions for each tool are included at point of use in this *Teacher's Guide*. A few sample screens are shown below.

The "Binomial Distributions" custom tool allows students to vary the number of successes and the probability of a success on each trial to see how the shape, center, and spread of the distribution are affected.

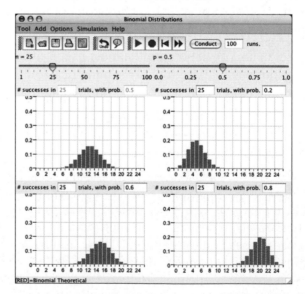

The following screen displays the Nickel Weights marked with 1, 2, and 3 standard deviations from the mean and the normal theoretical distribution with mean and standard deviation of the sample of nickel weights superimposed on the histogram.

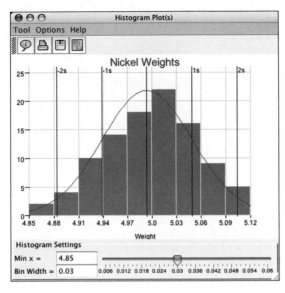

Built in data sets for use in this unit are:

Probability and Statistics:
Scope and Sequence Courses 1–3

As your students finish Course 3 of the *Core-Plus Mathematics* curriculum, they will have learned a great deal about statistics and probability. Among the fundamental ideas studied were shapes of distributions, measures of center (mean and median), and measures of variation (standard deviation, interquartile range). Interpretation of graphical displays including histograms, box plots, and scatterplots was emphasized.

Other topics studied include correlation and least-squares regression, experimental design and the randomization test, simulation, the geometric distribution, the multiplication and addition rules of probability, and the normal distribution.

In this unit, topics include standardized scores, the binomial distribution, control charts, and the Central Limit Theorem. This knowledge will be useful to them in science labs, in social science courses, and in interpreting the reports of surveys and experiments that they hear and read daily in the media.

Students who have completed Course 3 are exceptionally well prepared to take Advanced Placement Statistics. The AP Statistics syllabus includes all of the topics listed above except control charts.

Lesson Objectives	On Your Own Assignments*	Suggested Pacing	Materials
Lesson 1 *Normal Distributions* • Describe characteristics of a normal distribution • Understand that the number of standard deviations from the mean is a measure of location • Use standardized values and a table of the normal distribution to find probabilities	**After Investigation 1:** A1, A2 or A3, C9, C10, R15, E20, Rv24–Rv26 **After Investigation 2:** A4, A5, choose two of C11–C13, choose two of R16–R18, E21 or E22, Rv27–Rv28 **After Investigation 3:** Choose two of A6–A8, C14, R19, E23, Rv29–Rv31	6 days (including assessment)	• Rulers with millimeter markings (one per student) • *CPMP-Tools* Data Analysis • Unit Resources
Lesson 2 *Binomial Distributions* • Use simulation to construct an approximate binomial distribution • Predict the shape of a binomial distribution • Use the formulas for the expected value and standard deviation of a binomial distribution • Use standardized values to find probabilities of events in binomial situations • Use a random sample to decide whether a given proportion p is plausible as the proportion of successes in the population from which the sample came	**After Investigation 1:** A1, A2, A3 or A4, C7–C9, R12, choose two of E17, E18, or E21, Rv22–Rv24 **After Investigation 2:** A5, A6, C10, C11, R13, R14, R15 or R16, E19 or E20, Rv25–Rv28	5 days (including assessment)	• Unit Resources • *CPMP-Tools* Simulation "Binomial Distributions" custom tool
Lesson 3 *Statistical Process Control* • Recognize when the mean and standard deviation change on a plot-over-time • Use control charts and tests for out-of-control behavior • Compute the probability of a false alarm on a set of readings, that is, the probability that a test will give an out-of-control signal for a process that is under control • Understand the Central Limit Theorem and how it is applied to statistical process control	**After Investigation 1:** A1, A2, C9, R14, R15, Rv25–Rv28 **After Investigation 2:** A3, A4, A5 or A6, C10, C11, choose two of R16–R18, E21 or E22, Rv29, Rv30 **After Investigation 3:** A7, A8, C12, C13, R19, R20, E23 or E24, Rv31, Rv32	6 days (including assessment)	• Unit Resources • *CPMP-Tools* "Control Chart" custom tool Distribution of Sample Means
Lesson 4 *Looking Back* • Review and synthesize the major objectives of the unit		2 days (including assessment)	• Unit Resources

* When choice is indicated, it is important to leave the choice to the student.

Note: *It is best if Connections tasks are discussed as a whole class after they have been assigned as homework.*

Unit 4

Teacher Notes

Normal Distributions

Jet aircraft, like Boeing's latest 787 Dreamliner, are assembled using many different components. Parts for those components often come from other manufacturers from around the world. When different machines are used to manufacture the same part, the sizes of the produced parts will vary slightly. Even parts made by the same machine have slight variation in their dimensions.

Variation is inherent in the manufacturing of products whether they are made by computer-controlled machine or by hand. To better understand this phenomenon, suppose your class is working on a project making school award certificates. You have decided to outline the edge of a design on each certificate with one long piece of thin gold braid.

Certificate of Distinction

This certificate is awarded to

_____

to recognize achievement in

_____

on this day,_____.

Normal Distributions

This lesson introduces students to the normal distribution and its characteristics. In a normal distribution, most values are clustered near the mean with values trailing off at each end of the distribution. In a normal distribution, the mean and median are the same, and the distribution is symmetric around the mean. Students are given three benchmarks for the distribution: 68%, 95%, and 99.7% of a normal distribution are within one, two, and three standard deviations of the mean, respectively.

In Lessons 2 and 3, students will learn how the normal distribution is used in making decisions.

Lesson Objectives

- Describe characteristics of a normal distribution
- Understand that the number of standard deviations from the mean is a measure of location
- Use standardized values and a table of the normal distribution to find probabilities

Lesson Launch

In discussing the Think About This Situation, a teacher in western Michigan found that the opening TATS on measuring perimeter hooks students and sets them up well for understanding the variability in measurement studied in this unit and seeing the need for quality control. Although it does take some time for all students to complete the measuring, it is worth the time spent.

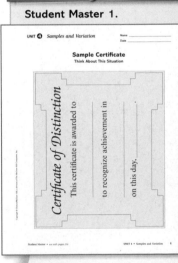

Teaching Resources

Student Master 1.

UNIT 4 *Samples and Variation*   Name
                                        Date

Sample Certificate
Think About This Situation

Certificate of Distinction

This certificate is awarded to

to recognize achievement in

on this day,

Unit 4

The shape of the distribution does not become apparent until you have at least 30 measurements. So if you have a small class, you may want to combine results with those of other classes or students from previous years. Alternatively, you can use these measurements from the 131 students of a Wisconsin high school. The distribution has a mean of about 768 mm with a standard deviation of about 34. Because of the very low values from a few students, the median of 772 may be the best estimate of the true perimeter. (Your students' measurements can be quite different if you are using a photocopy of the certificate.)

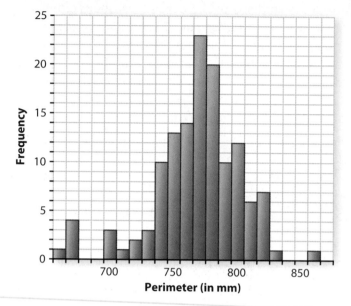

CPMP-Tools You may wish to use the *CPMP-Tools* "Estimate Center and Spread" custom tool on your class data or the data set of certificate measurements already provided in the Data Analysis software. This is a Course 1 custom tool that can be found in the Course 3 software under Data Analysis, Custom Tools, Other Custom Tools. More information about this custom tool is on page T118 in the Course 1, Part A *Teacher's Guide*. The displays below show this custom tool using the built-in certificate data.

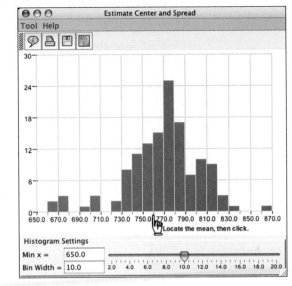

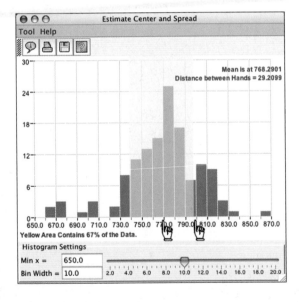

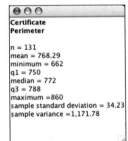

Unit 4

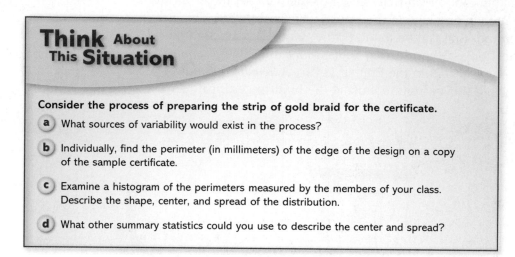

Think About **This Situation**

Consider the process of preparing the strip of gold braid for the certificate.

a What sources of variability would exist in the process?

b Individually, find the perimeter (in millimeters) of the edge of the design on a copy of the sample certificate.

c Examine a histogram of the perimeters measured by the members of your class. Describe the shape, center, and spread of the distribution.

d What other summary statistics could you use to describe the center and spread?

In this lesson, you will explore connections between a normal distribution and its mean and standard deviation and how those ideas can be used in modeling the variability in common situations.

Investigation 1 — Characteristics of a Normal Distribution

Many naturally occurring measurements, such as human heights or the lengths or weights of supposedly identical objects produced by machines, are **approximately normally distributed**. Their histograms are "bell-shaped," with the data clustered symmetrically about the mean and tapering off gradually on both ends, like the shape below.

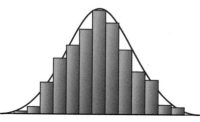

When measurements can be modeled by a distribution that is approximately normal in shape, the mean and standard deviation often are used to summarize the distribution's center and variability. As you work on the problems in this investigation, look for answers to the following question:

How can you use the mean and standard deviation to help you locate a measurement in a normal distribution?

Unit 4

Think About This Situation

a Variability would exist in measuring the perimeter, in measuring the braid against the ruler, in the rulers themselves, in how tightly the braid was stretched as it was being cut, and even in the width of the scissors used to cut the braid.

b Measurements will vary. They are supposed to vary, so be sure students do not compare measurements at this stage.

Discuss the strategies students used to find the perimeter. If students decided to take advantage of the symmetry, they saved time by measuring only part of the perimeter. Their estimates may have larger error built in; because with fewer measurements, there is less of a "canceling effect" of over- and under-measuring.

c While the distribution will depend on the individual measurements from Part b, the shape should be approximately normal. Students may be surprised at how much variation there is in their measurements. Some of the variation may be due to out-and-out mistakes, such as misuse of the ruler. But most variation will be due to the judgments and estimates that students made in the measurement process.

d You could use median and interquartile range (IQR) or the mean and standard deviation.

Investigation 1 Characteristics of a Normal Distribution

Students have learned that it is important to describe a set of data with a measure of variability, as well as with a measure of center. In this investigation, students first will review estimating the standard deviation from the fact that about two-thirds of the values in a normal distribution lie within one standard deviation of the mean. They then will learn that in a normal distribution:

68% of the values lie within one standard deviation of the mean.

95% of the values lie within two standard deviations of the mean.

99.7% of the values lie within three standard deviations of the mean.

Repeated measurements of the same thing are often normally distributed, as are many physical characteristics. (Karl Gauss, an eighteenth-century mathematician, became interested in the normal distribution, sometimes called the Gaussian distribution, when he found that repeated astronomical measurements were normally distributed.) The standard deviation is the measure of spread associated with a normal distribution.

COLLABORATION SKILL
Help our group check our solutions.

POSSIBLE MISCONCEPTION
Be aware that students tend to use the 68%-95%-99.7% rule on all distributions, not just the normal distributions for which it is valid. Reflections Task 18 will remind them that they should use this rule only on distributions that they know are approximately normal.

In Course 1, *Patterns in Data*, you estimated the mean of a distribution by finding the balance point of a histogram. You estimated the standard deviation of a normal distribution by finding the distance to the right of the mean and to the left of the mean that encloses the middle 68% (about two-thirds) of the values. Use this knowledge to help analyze the following situations.

a. The histogram below shows the political points of view of a sample of 1,271 voters in the United States. The voters were asked a series of questions to determine their political philosophy and then were rated on a scale from liberal to conservative. Estimate the mean and standard deviation of this distribution.

Political Philosophy

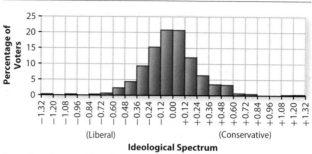

Source: Romer, Thomas, and Howard Rosenthal. 1984. Voting models and empirical evidence. *American Scientist*, 72: 465–473.

b. In a science class, you may have weighed something by balancing it on a scale against a standard weight. To be sure a standard weight is reasonably accurate, its manufacturer can have it weighed at the National Institute of Standards and Technology in Washington, D.C. The accuracy of the weighing procedure at the National Institute of Standards and Technology is itself checked about once a week by weighing a known 10-gram weight, NB 10. The histogram below is based on 100 consecutive measurements of the weight of NB 10 using the same apparatus and procedure. Shown is the distribution of weighings, in micrograms below 10 grams. (A microgram is a millionth of a gram.) Estimate the mean and standard deviation of this distribution.

NB 10 Weight

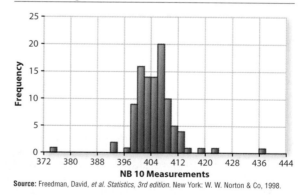

Source: Freedman, David, *et al. Statistics, 3rd edition.* New York: W. W. Norton & Co, 1998.

Although the approximately normal distributions in this investigation look different, they do have the same general shape. To transform one into another, all you have to do is translate so that the means coincide and then stretch or shrink the distribution so that the standard deviations are the same. If you know a distribution is normal and you have its mean and standard deviation, then the distribution is uniquely determined. See Extensions Task 22 on pages 256 and 257.

INSTRUCTIONAL NOTE You may need to remind students that they are to estimate the mean and standard deviation by looking at the histograms. They are not supposed to enter numbers into their calculators. The mean is the balance point, and the standard deviation is roughly the distance from the mean on both sides that "captures" the middle two-thirds of the values.

1
  a. The mean is about 0 and the standard deviation is about 0.24.
  b. A good estimate of the mean is 404 or 405. It is actually 404.60. A good estimate of the standard deviation is 6 or 7. It is actually 6.467.

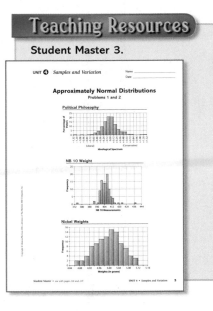

Teaching Resources

Student Master 3.

UNIT 4 *Samples and Variation*

Approximately Normal Distributions
Problems 1 and 2

Political Philosophy

NB 10 Weight

Nickel Weights

2 The data below and the accompanying histogram give the weights, to the nearest hundredth of a gram, of a sample of 100 new nickels.

Nickel Weights (in grams)

4.87	4.92	4.95	4.97	4.98	5.00	5.01	5.03	5.04	5.07
4.87	4.92	4.95	4.97	4.98	5.00	5.01	5.03	5.04	5.07
4.88	4.93	4.95	4.97	4.99	5.00	5.01	5.03	5.04	5.07
4.89	4.93	4.95	4.97	4.99	5.00	5.02	5.03	5.05	5.08
4.90	4.93	4.95	4.97	4.99	5.00	5.02	5.03	5.05	5.08
4.90	4.93	4.96	4.97	4.99	5.01	5.02	5.03	5.05	5.09
4.91	4.94	4.96	4.98	4.99	5.01	5.02	5.03	5.06	5.09
4.91	4.94	4.96	4.98	4.99	5.01	5.02	5.04	5.06	5.10
4.92	4.94	4.96	4.98	5.00	5.01	5.02	5.04	5.06	5.11
4.92	4.94	4.96	4.98	5.00	5.01	5.02	5.04	5.06	5.11

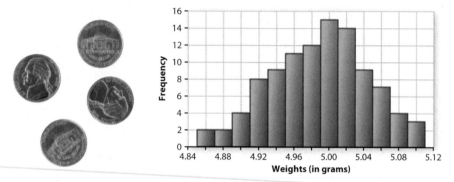

a. The mean weight of this sample is 4.9941 grams. Find the median weight from the table above. How does it compare to the mean weight?

b. Which of the following is the standard deviation?

0.0253 grams   0.0551 grams   0.253 grams   1 gram

c. On a copy of the histogram, mark points along the horizontal axis that correspond to the mean, one standard deviation above the mean, one standard deviation below the mean, two standard deviations above the mean, two standard deviations below the mean, three standard deviations above the mean, and three standard deviations below the mean.

d. What percentage of the weights in the table above are within one standard deviation of the mean? Within two standard deviations? Within three standard deviations?

e. Suppose you weigh a randomly chosen nickel from this collection. Find the probability that its weight would be within two standard deviations of the mean.

2 **a.** The median located in the table is 5. It is about the same as the mean.

b. The standard deviation is 0.0551 grams.

c. Students should place tick marks at 4.8288, 4.8839, 4.9390, 5.0492, 5.1043, and 5.1594 as shown below.

TECHNOLOGY NOTE These data are in *CPMP-Tools*.

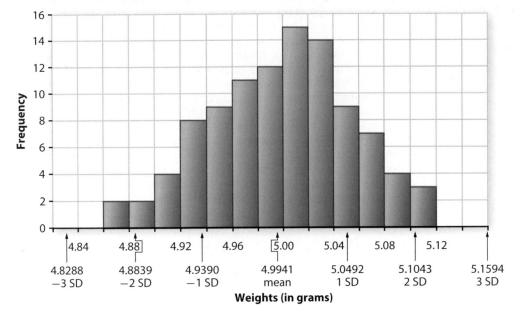

d. $\frac{67}{100}$, or 67% of the nickels are within one standard deviation of the mean.

$\frac{95}{100}$, or 95% of the nickels are within two standard deviations of the mean.

100% of the nickels are within three standard deviations of the mean.

e. 0.95

Unit 4

In Problems 1 and 2, you looked at distributions of real data that had an *approximately* normal shape with mean $\bar{x}$ and standard deviation s. Each distribution was a sample taken from a larger population that is more nearly normal. In the rest of this investigation, you will think about theoretical populations that have a perfectly normal distribution.

The symbol for the *mean of a population* is μ, the lower-case Greek letter "mu." The symbol for the *standard deviation of a population* is σ, the lower case Greek letter "sigma." That is, use the symbol μ for the mean when you have an entire population or a theoretical distribution. Use the symbol $\bar{x}$ when you have a sample from a population. Similarly, use the symbol σ for the standard deviation of a population or of a theoretical distribution. Use the symbol s for the standard deviation of a sample.

All normal distributions have the same overall shape, differing only in their mean and standard deviation. Some look tall and skinny. Others look more spread out. All normal distributions, however, have certain characteristics in common. They are symmetric about the mean, 68% of the values lie within one standard deviation of the mean, 95% of the values lie within two standard deviations of the mean, and 99.7% of the values lie within three standard deviations of the mean.

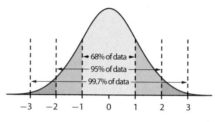

3. Suppose that the distribution of the weights of newly minted coins is a normal distribution with mean μ of 5 grams and standard deviation σ of 0.10 grams.

   a. Draw a sketch of this distribution. Then label the points on the horizontal axis that correspond to the mean, one standard deviation above and below the mean, two standard deviations above and below the mean, and three standard deviations above and below the mean.

   b. Between what two values do the middle 68% of the weights of coins lie? The middle 95% of the weights? The middle 99.7% of the weights?

   c. Illustrate your answers in Part b by shading appropriate regions in copies of your sketch.

3 **a.**

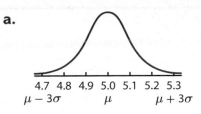

4.7 4.8 4.9 5.0 5.1 5.2 5.3
$\mu - 3\sigma$ μ $\mu + 3\sigma$

b. 68% of the coins weigh between 4.9 and 5.1 grams.
95% of the coins weigh between 4.8 and 5.2 grams.
99.7% of the coins weigh between 4.7 and 5.3 grams.

c.

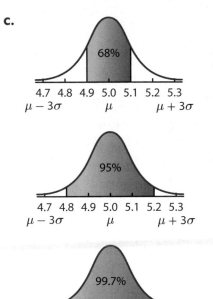

68%

4.7 4.8 4.9 5.0 5.1 5.2 5.3
$\mu - 3\sigma$ μ $\mu + 3\sigma$

95%

4.7 4.8 4.9 5.0 5.1 5.2 5.3
$\mu - 3\sigma$ μ $\mu + 3\sigma$

99.7%

4.7 4.8 4.9 5.0 5.1 5.2 5.3
$\mu - 3\sigma$ μ $\mu + 3\sigma$

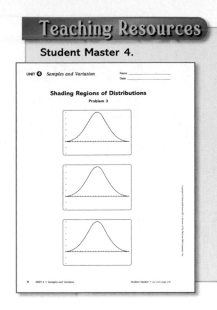

Unit 4

④ Answer the following questions about normal distributions. Draw sketches illustrating your answers.

a. What percentage of the values in a normal distribution lie above the mean?

b. What percentage of the values in a normal distribution lie more than two standard deviations from the mean?

c. What percentage of the values in a normal distribution lie more than two standard deviations above the mean?

d. What percentage of the values in a normal distribution lie more than one standard deviation from the mean?

⑤ The weights of babies of a given age and gender are approximately normally distributed. This fact allows a doctor or nurse to use a baby's weight to find the weight percentile to which the child belongs. The table below gives information about the weights of six-month-old and twelve-month-old baby boys.

Weights of Baby Boys

	Weight at Six Months (in pounds)	Weight at Twelve Months (in pounds)
Mean μ	17.25	22.50
Standard Deviation σ	2.0	2.2

Source: Tannenbaum, Peter, and Robert Arnold. *Excursions in Modern Mathematics.* Englewood Cliffs, New Jersey: Prentice Hall. 1992.

a. On separate axes with the same scales, draw sketches that represent the distribution of weights for six-month-old boys and the distribution of weights for twelve-month-old boys. How do the distributions differ?

b. About what percentage of six-month-old boys weigh between 15.25 pounds and 19.25 pounds?

c. About what percentage of twelve-month-old boys weigh more than 26.9 pounds?

d. A twelve-month-old boy who weighs 24.7 pounds is at what percentile for weight? (Recall that a value x in a distribution lies at, say, the 27th **percentile** if 27% of the values in the distribution are less than or equal to x.)

e. A six-month-old boy who weighs 21.25 pounds is at what percentile?

4   **a.** 50%   **b.** 5%

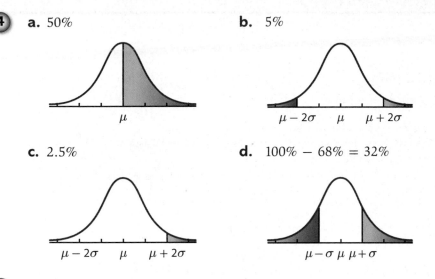

c. 2.5%   **d.** $100\% - 68\% = 32\%$

5   **a.** The shapes are similar because both distributions are approximately normal. The distribution of weights at twelve months has a higher mean and is spread out slightly more than the distribution at six months.

Distribution of Weights of Baby Boys (in pounds)

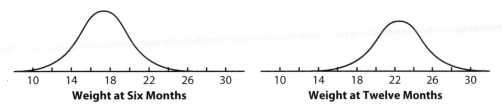

b. 15.25 pounds is one standard deviation below the mean, and 19.25 pounds is one standard deviation above the mean. Thus, about 68% of the weights of six-month-old boys falls between these weights.

c. 26.9 pounds is two standard deviations above the mean, so about 2.5% of twelve-month-old boys weigh more than 26.9 pounds.

d. 24.7 pounds is one standard deviation above the mean, so about 84% of the weights are below this. The baby is at the 84th percentile.

e. This weight is two standard deviations above the mean. Thus, the baby is at about the 97th percentile.

(It is interesting that while the distribution of weights of babies of a given age is approximately normally distributed, the distribution of adults' weights is skewed right.)

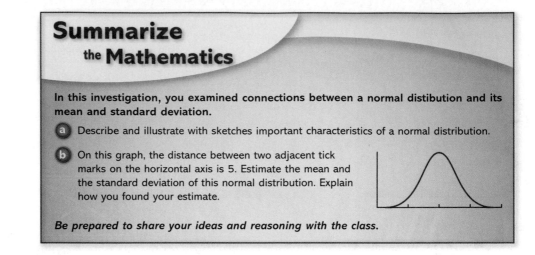

Summarize
the Mathematics

In this investigation, you examined connections between a normal distibution and its mean and standard deviation.

a Describe and illustrate with sketches important characteristics of a normal distribution.

b On this graph, the distance between two adjacent tick marks on the horizontal axis is 5. Estimate the mean and the standard deviation of this normal distribution. Explain how you found your estimate.

Be prepared to share your ideas and reasoning with the class.

✓ Check Your Understanding

Scores on the Critical Reading section of the SAT Reasoning Test are approximately normally distributed with mean μ of 502 and standard deviation σ of 113.

a. Sketch this distribution with a scale on the horizontal axis.

b. What percentage of students score between 389 and 615 on the verbal section of the SAT?

c. What percentage of students score over 615 on the verbal section of the SAT?

d. If you score 389 on the verbal section of the SAT, what is your percentile?

Investigation 2   Standardized Values

Often, you are interested in comparing values from two different distributions. For example: Is Sophie or her brother Pablo taller compared to others of their gender? Was your SAT score or your ACT score better? Answers to questions like these rely on your answer to the following question, which is the focus of this investigation:

How can you use standardized values to compare values from two different normal distributions?

Note that the two parts of this STM ask students to think about the connections between a normal distribution and its mean and standard deviation. In Part a, they mark the mean and standard deviations from the mean on a graph. In Part b, they estimate the mean and standard deviation from the graph. One effective approach for this particular STM is to have pairs of students briefly discuss the two parts and then summarize as a full class. Students can then write complete responses to the STM informed by the class discussion.

Summarize
the Mathematics

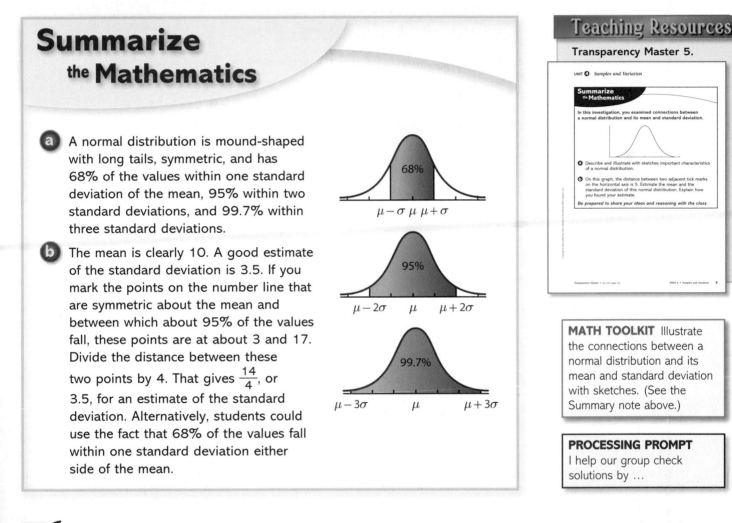

a A normal distribution is mound-shaped with long tails, symmetric, and has 68% of the values within one standard deviation of the mean, 95% within two standard deviations, and 99.7% within three standard deviations.

b The mean is clearly 10. A good estimate of the standard deviation is 3.5. If you mark the points on the number line that are symmetric about the mean and between which about 95% of the values fall, these points are at about 3 and 17. Divide the distance between these two points by 4. That gives $\frac{14}{4}$, or 3.5, for an estimate of the standard deviation. Alternatively, students could use the fact that 68% of the values fall within one standard deviation either side of the mean.

Teaching Resources

Transparency Master 5.

UNIT ❹ *Samples and Variation*

Summarize
the Mathematics

In this investigation, you examined connections between a normal distribution and its mean and standard deviation.

❶ Describe and illustrate with sketches important characteristics of a normal distribution.

❷ On this graph, the distance between two adjacent tick marks on the horizontal axis is 5. Estimate the mean and the standard deviation of this normal distribution. Explain how you found your estimate.

Be prepared to share your ideas and reasoning with the class.

MATH TOOLKIT Illustrate the connections between a normal distribution and its mean and standard deviation with sketches. (See the Summary note above.)

PROCESSING PROMPT
I help our group check solutions by …

✔ *Check Your Understanding*

a.

276 389 502 615 728
$\mu - 2\sigma$ μ $\mu + 2\sigma$

b. 68% because these scores are one standard deviation from the mean

c. Half of 32%, or 16%

d. 16th percentile

NOTE SAT verbal scores are rounded to the nearest ten when reported to students. The numbers in this task are unrounded.

Unit 4

① Examine the table below, which gives information about the heights of young Americans aged 18 to 24. Each distribution is approximately normal.

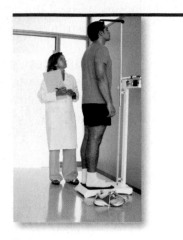

Heights of American Young Adults (in inches)

	Men	Women
Mean μ	68.5	65.5
Standard Deviation σ	2.7	2.5

   a. Sketch the two distributions. Include a scale on the horizontal axis.

   b. Alexis is 3 standard deviations above average in height. How tall is she?

   c. Marvin is 2.1 standard deviations below average in height. How tall is he?

   d. Miguel is 74" tall. How many standard deviations above average height is he?

   e. Jackie is 62" tall. How many standard deviations below average height is she?

   f. Marina is 68" tall. Steve is 71" tall. Who is relatively taller for her or his gender, Marina or Steve? Explain your reasoning.

The **standardized value** tells how many standard deviations a given value lies from the mean of a distribution. For example, in Problem 1 Part b, Alexis is 3 standard deviations above average in height, so her standardized height is 3. Similarly, in Problem 1 Part c, Marvin is 2.1 standard deviations below average in height, so his standardized height is -2.1.

② Look more generally at how standardized values are computed.

   a. Refer to Problem 1, Parts d and e. Compute the standardized values for Miguel's height and for Jackie's height.

   b. Write a formula for computing the standardized value z of a value x if you know the mean of the population μ and the standard deviation of the population σ.

③ Now consider how standardizing values can help you make comparisons. Refer to the table in Problem 1.

   a. Find the standardized value for the height of a young woman who is 5 feet tall.

   b. Find the standardized value for the height of a young man who is 5 feet 2 inches tall.

   c. Is the young woman in Part a or the young man in Part b shorter, relative to his or her own gender? Explain your reasoning.

In this investigation, students will learn how to use the standard deviation as the unit of measurement in measuring how far a value is from the mean of a normal distribution.

NOTE Standardized values sometimes are called *z*-scores.

1 **a. Heights of American Young Adults** (in inches)

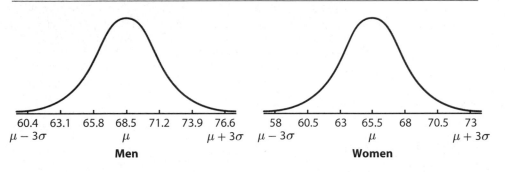

b. $65.5" + 3(2.5") = 73"$

c. $68.5" - 2.1(2.7") = 62.83"$

d. $\dfrac{74 - 68.5}{2.7} = 2.04$ standard deviations above average

e. $\dfrac{62 - 65.5}{2.5} = -1.4$, or 1.4 standard deviations below average

f. Marina is $\dfrac{68 - 65.5}{2.5} = 1$ standard deviation above average.

Steve is $\dfrac{71 - 68.5}{2.7} \approx 0.926$ standard deviations above average.

Marina is relatively taller than Steve because her height is farther above the mean as measured by the standard deviation for the appropriate distribution.

2 **a.** Miguel: $z = \dfrac{74 - 68.5}{2.7} \approx 2.04$

Jackie: $z = \dfrac{62 - 65.5}{2.5} = -1.4$

b. $z = \dfrac{x - \mu}{\sigma}$

INSTRUCTIONAL NOTE
Be sure all students have the correct formula in Part b before they go on to Problem 3.

3 **a.** $z = \dfrac{60 - 65.5}{2.5} \approx -2.2$

b. $z = \dfrac{62 - 68.5}{2.7} \approx -2.41$

c. The young man is relatively shorter because he is farther below the mean of his distribution as measured by the standard deviation than the young woman is from the mean of her distribution.

(4) In an experiment about the effects of mental stress, subjects' systolic blood pressure and heart rate were measured before and after doing a stressful mental task. Their systolic blood pressure increased an average of 22.4 mm Hg (millimeters of Mercury) with a standard deviation of 2. Their heart rates increased an average of 7.6 beats per minute with a standard deviation of 0.7. Each distribution was approximately normal.

Suppose that after completing the task, Mario's blood pressure increased by 25 mm Hg and his heart rate increased by 9 beats per minute. On which measure did he increase the most, relative to the other participants? (Source: Mental Stress-Induced Increase in Blood Pressure Is Not Related to Baroreflex Sensitivity in Middle-Aged Healthy Men. *Hypertension*. 2000. vol. 35)

Summarize the Mathematics

In this investigation, you examined standardized values and their use.

a What information does a standardized value provide?

b What is the purpose of standardizing values?

c Kua earned a grade of 50 on a normally distributed test with mean 45 and standard deviation 10. On another normally distributed test with mean 70 and standard deviation 15, she earned a 78. On which of the two tests did she do better, relative to the others who took the tests? Explain your reasoning.

Be prepared to share your ideas and reasoning with the class.

✔Check Your Understanding

Refer to Problem 1 on page 243. Mischa Barton claims to be 5 feet 9 inches tall. Justin Timberlake claims to be 6 feet 1 inch tall. Who is taller compared to others of their gender, Mischa Barton or Justin Timberlake? Explain your reasoning.

④ Blood pressure: $z = \dfrac{25 - 22.4}{2} = 1.3$

Heart rate: $z = \dfrac{9 - 7.6}{0.7} \approx 2$

Both Mario's blood pressure and heart rate increased more than average. But relative to the other participants, Mario's heart rate increased more.

Summarize the Mathematics

ⓐ A standardized value tells you how many standard deviations from the mean the original value lies. Further, if the standardized value is positive, the value lies above the mean. If it is negative, the value lies below the mean.

ⓑ Standardizing values helps make comparisons between original values from two normal distributions that have different means and/or standard deviations.

ⓒ For the first test, $z = \dfrac{50 - 45}{10} = 0.5$. For the second test, $z = \dfrac{78 - 70}{15} \approx 0.53$. Kua's standardized value and percentile ranking are higher for the second test. So she did better on it, relative to the other students.

✔Check Your Understanding

Their standardized values are as follows.

Mischa Barton: $z = \dfrac{69 - 65.5}{2.5} \approx 1.4$

Justin Timberlake: $z = \dfrac{73 - 68.5}{2.7} \approx 1.67$

Justin Timberlake is taller compared to other young men than Mischa Barton is compared to other young women. He is 1.67 standard deviations above average, and she is only 1.4 standard deviations above average.

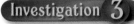

Investigation 3 — Using Standardized Values to Find Percentiles

In the first investigation, you were able to find the percentage of values within one, two, and three standard deviations of the mean. Your work in this investigation will extend to other numbers of standard deviations and help you answer the following question:

> *How can you use standardized values to find the location of a value in a distribution that is normal, or approximately so?*

The following table gives the proportion of values in a normal distribution that are less than the given standardized value z. By standardizing values, you can use this table for any normal distribution. If the distribution is not normal, the percentages given in the table do not necessarily hold.

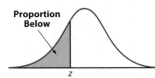

Proportion
Below

z

Proportion of Values in a Normal Distribution that Lie Below a Standardized Value z

z	Proportion Below	z	Proportion Below	z	Proportion Below	z	Proportion Below
−3.5	0.0002	−1.7	0.0446	0.1	0.5398	1.9	0.9713
−3.4	0.0003	−1.6	0.0548	0.2	0.5793	2.0	0.9772
−3.3	0.0005	−1.5	0.0668	0.3	0.6179	2.1	0.9821
−3.2	0.0007	−1.4	0.0808	0.4	0.6554	2.2	0.9861
−3.1	0.0010	−1.3	0.0968	0.5	0.6915	2.3	0.9893
−3.0	0.0013	−1.2	0.1151	0.6	0.7257	2.4	0.9918
−2.9	0.0019	−1.1	0.1357	0.7	0.7580	2.5	0.9938
−2.8	0.0026	−1.0	0.1587	0.8	0.7881	2.6	0.9953
−2.7	0.0035	−0.9	0.1841	0.9	0.8159	2.7	0.9965
−2.6	0.0047	−0.8	0.2119	1.0	0.8413	2.8	0.9974
−2.5	0.0062	−0.7	0.2420	1.1	0.8643	2.9	0.9981
−2.4	0.0082	−0.6	0.2743	1.2	0.8849	3.0	0.9987
−2.3	0.0107	−0.5	0.3085	1.3	0.9032	3.1	0.9990
−2.2	0.0139	−0.4	0.3446	1.4	0.9192	3.2	0.9993
−2.1	0.0179	−0.3	0.3821	1.5	0.9332	3.3	0.9995
−2.0	0.0228	−0.2	0.4207	1.6	0.9452	3.4	0.9997
−1.9	0.0287	−0.1	0.4602	1.7	0.9554	3.5	0.9998
−1.8	0.0359	0.0	0.5000	1.8	0.9641		

Using Standardized Values to Find Percentiles

If the distribution is approximately normal and you know how many standard deviations a given value is from its mean, then you can use the table on page 245 to estimate what proportion of values in the distribution are less than the given value.

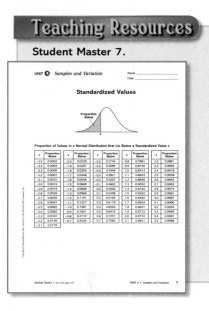
What Is the Difference Between $z < 1.3$ and $z \leq 1.3$?

Students have been taught to be careful about the difference between, say, $x < 1.3$ and $x \leq 1.3$. So, they naturally might expect that there is a difference between the probability that $z < 1.3$ and the probability that $z \leq 1.3$. However, because z is defined for all real numbers and so is a continuous random variable, these probabilities are equal. In the diagram below, the only difference between the region that represents $z < 1.3$ and the region that represents $z \leq 1.3$ is that the line segment above $z = 1.3$ is included in the region for $z \leq 1.3$ but not in the region for $z < 1.3$. A line segment has no width and so contributes nothing to the area. (In other words, the probability that $z = 1.3$ is 0. This does not mean that the event of getting $z = 1.3$ is impossible, however.) Thus, the shaded region represents both probabilities. From the table, both probabilities are equal to 0.9032.

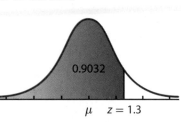

For an alternative explanation, see mathforum.org/library/drmath/view/62719.html.

If you would like to use a table of the standard distribution that has more precision, you can download the AP Statistics Course Description at www.collegeboard.com/prod_downloads/ap/students/statistics/ap-stats-0607.pdf. You will have to adjust the answers in this *Teacher's Guide* if you use a different table.

1 Use the table to help answer the following questions. In each part, draw sketches that illustrate your answers.

    a. Suppose that a value from a normal distribution is two standard deviations below the mean. What proportion of the values are below it? What proportion are above it?

    b. If a value from a normal distribution is 1.3 standard deviations above the mean, what proportion of the values are below it? Above it?

    c. Based on the table, what proportion of values are within one standard deviation of the mean? Within two standard deviations of the mean? Within three standard deviations of the mean?

2 Reproduced below is the table of heights of Americans aged 18 to 24.

Heights of American Young Adults (in inches)

	Men	Women
Mean μ	68.5	65.5
Standard Deviation σ	2.7	2.5

    a. Miguel is 74 inches tall. What is his percentile for height? That is, what percentage of young men are the same height or shorter than Miguel?

    b. Jackie is 62 inches tall. What is her percentile for height?

    c. Abby is 5 feet 8 inches tall. What percentage of young women are between Jackie (Part b) and Abby in height?

    d. Gabriel is at the 90th percentile in height. What is his height?

    e. Yvette is at the 31st percentile in height. What is her height?

3 All 11th-grade students in Pennsylvania are tested in reading and math on the Pennsylvania System of School Assessment (PSSA). The mean score on the PSSA math test in 2006–2007 was 1,330 with standard deviation 253. You may assume the distribution of scores is approximately normal. (Source: www.pde.state.pa.us/a_and_t/cwp/view.asp?A=3&Q=129181)

    a. Draw a sketch of the distribution of these scores with a scale on the horizontal axis.

    b. What PSSA math score would be at the 50th percentile?

    c. What percentage of 11th graders scored above 1,500?

    d. Javier's PSSA score was at the 76th percentile. What was his score on this test?

a. 0.0228 $1 - 0.0228 = 0.9772$

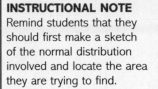

b. 0.9032 $1 - 0.9032 = 0.0968$

c. 0.6826; 0.9544; 0.9974

2 **a.** Miguel's standardized height is $\frac{74 - 68.5}{2.7} \approx 2.0$. This gives a percentile for height of about 97th.

b. Jackie's standardized height is $\frac{62 - 62.5}{2.5} \approx -1.4$. This gives a percentile for height of about 8th.

c. Abby's standardized height is $z = \frac{68 - 65.5}{2.5} = 1$. Her percentile is about the 84th. So, $84 - 8$ or 76% of young women are between Jackie and Abby in height. (Without rounding, the percentage is 76.05%.)

d. His standardized height is closest to 1.3. Solving $1.3 = \frac{x - 68.5}{2.7}$, Gabriel's height is about 72.01".

e. Her standardized height is closest to −0.5. Solving $-0.5 = \frac{x - 65.5}{2.5}$, Yvette's height is about 64.25".

3 **a.** See the distribution at the right.

b. 1,330

c. $z = \frac{1,500 - 1,330}{253} \approx 0.7$

So, $1 - 0.7580$, or 24.2%, of 11th graders had scores above 1,500.

d. His standardized value is about 0.7. Solving $0.7 = \frac{x - 1,330}{253}$, Javier's score was about 1,507.

Unit 4

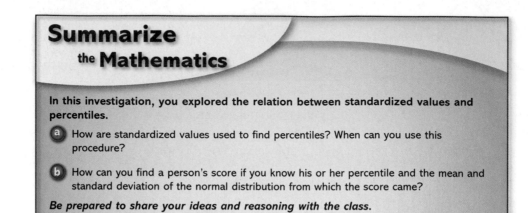

Summarize
the Mathematics

In this investigation, you explored the relation between standardized values and percentiles.

a How are standardized values used to find percentiles? When can you use this procedure?

b How can you find a person's score if you know his or her percentile and the mean and standard deviation of the normal distribution from which the score came?

Be prepared to share your ideas and reasoning with the class.

✓ Check Your Understanding

Standardized values can often be used to make sense of scores on aptitude and intelligence tests.

a. Actress Brooke Shields reportedly scored 608 on the math section of the SAT. When she took the SAT, the scores were approximately normally distributed with an average on the math section of about 462 and a standard deviation of 100.

   i. How many standard deviations above average was her score?

   ii. What was Brooke Shields' percentile on the math section of the SAT?

b. The IQ scores on the Stanford-Binet intelligence test are approximately normal with mean 100 and standard deviation 15. Consider these lines from the movie *Forrest Gump*.

> **Mrs. Gump:** Remember what I told you, Forrest. You're no different than anybody else is. Did you hear what I said, Forrest? You're the same as everybody else. You are no different.
>
> **Principal:** Your boy's … different, Miz Gump. His IQ's 75.
>
> **Mrs. Gump:** Well, we're all different, Mr. Hancock.

   i. How many standard deviations from the mean is Forrest's IQ score?

   ii. What percentage of people have an IQ higher than Forrest's IQ?

Summarize
the Mathematics

(a) Compute the standardized value z using the formula $z = \dfrac{x - \mu}{\sigma}$. Then find this value of z in the table on page 245. The corresponding "proportion below" gives the percentile. You can use this procedure only if the distribution from which the value came is normal.

(b) First, find the percentile (proportion below) in the table on page 245 and get the corresponding value of z. Substitute that value of z, along with the mean and standard deviation of the distribution, into the formula $z = \dfrac{x - \mu}{\sigma}$. Solve for x.

MATH TOOLKIT Using an example of your choice, explain the following.

(1) the purpose of standardized values

(2) the formula for computing a standardized value

(3) how a standardized value is used to find percentiles

(4) when you can use this procedure

Then give an example of how to find a score when you know the percentile, mean, and standard deviation of the normal distribution from which the score came.

✔Check Your Understanding

a. **i.** Her score was $\dfrac{608 - 462}{100} = 1.46$ standard deviations above average.

   ii. Her percentile was about 93.

b. **i.** Forrest's standardized IQ is $\dfrac{75 - 100}{15} \approx -1.7$.
   His IQ is 1.7 standard deviations below the mean.

   ii. $1 - 0.0446 \approx 95.54\%$

On Your Own

Applications

1 Thirty-two students in a drafting class were asked to prepare a design with a perimeter of 98.4 cm. A histogram of the actual perimeters of their designs is displayed below. The mean perimeter was 98.42 cm.

Design Perimeters

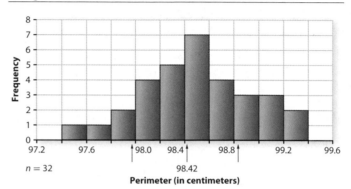

$n = 32$

Perimeter (in centimeters)

a. What might explain the variation in perimeters of the designs?

b. The arrows mark the mean and the points one standard deviation above the mean and one standard deviation below the mean. Use the marked plot to estimate the standard deviation for the class' perimeters.

c. Estimate the percentage of the perimeters that are within one standard deviation of the mean. Within two standard deviations of the mean.

d. How do the percentages in Part c compare to the percentages you would expect from a normal distribution?

2 For a chemistry experiment, students measured the time for a solute to dissolve. The experiment was repeated 50 times. The results are shown in the chart and histogram at the top of the next page.

Unit 4

Applications

1 **a.** Variation could be caused by inaccuracies in the drawing or the measuring process.

b. A good estimate would be close to 0.45 cm.

c. Using the four bars within one standard deviation of the mean, the estimate is about $\frac{20}{32}$, or 62.5%. About 91% or 94% (29 or 30) of the values are within two standard deviations of the mean.

d. The percentages are a bit less than the 68% and 95% that you would expect from a normal distribution.

Dissolution Time (in seconds)

4	5	6	7	8	8	8	8	9	9
9	10	10	10	10	10	10	10	11	11
11	11	11	12	12	12	12	12	12	12
12	13	13	13	13	13	14	14	14	14
14	15	15	16	16	17	17	17	19	19

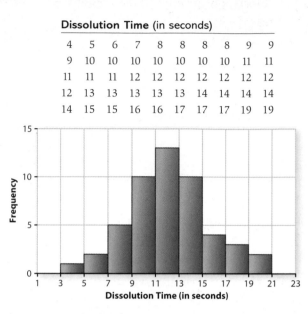

a. The mean time for the 50 experiments is 11.8 seconds. Find the median dissolution time from the table above. How does it compare to the mean dissolution time?

b. Which of the following is the best estimate of the standard deviation?

         1.32 seconds   3.32 seconds   5.32 seconds

c. On a copy of the histogram, mark points along the horizontal axis that correspond to the mean, one standard deviation above the mean, one standard deviation below the mean, two standard deviations above the mean, two standard deviations below the mean, three standard deviations above the mean, and three standard deviations below the mean.

d. What percentage of the times are within one standard deviation of the mean? Within two standard deviations? Within three standard deviations?

e. How do the percentages in Part d compare to the percentages you would expect from a normal distribution?

2 **a.** The mean is given as 11.8 seconds, and the median is 12. Again, the mean and the median are very close, which is what we would expect from a distribution that is nearly symmetric.

b. The standard deviation is about 3.32 seconds.

c. Students should place arrows at 1.84, 5.16, 8.48, 15.12, 18.44, and 21.76 as shown below.

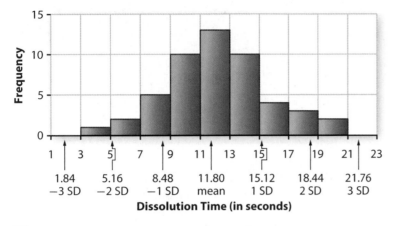

d. $\frac{35}{50}$, or 70%, of the times are within one standard deviation of the mean.

$\frac{46}{50}$, or 92%, of the times are within two standard deviations of the mean.

100% of the times are within three standard deviations of the mean.

e. They are close to the theoretical percentages of 68%, 95%, and 99.7%.

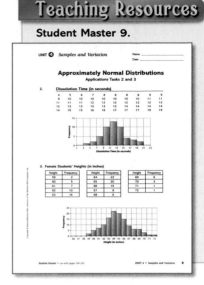

TECHNOLOGY NOTE
The data in Task 2 are actual data from a chemistry lab and are in *CPMP-Tools*.

3 The table and histogram below give the heights of 123 women in a statistics class at Penn State University in the 1970s.

Female Students' Heights

Height (in inches)	Frequency	Height (in inches)	Frequency
59	2	66	15
60	5	67	9
61	7	68	6
62	10	69	6
63	16	70	3
64	22	71	1
65	20	72	1

Source: Joiner, Brian L. 1975. Living histograms. *International Statistical Review 3*: 339–340.

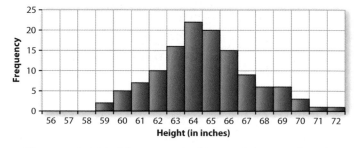

a. The mean height of the women in this sample is approximately 64.626 inches. Which of the following is the best estimate of the standard deviation?

0.2606 inches   0.5136 inches   2.606 inches   5.136 inches

b. On a copy of the histogram, mark points along the horizontal axis that correspond to the mean, one standard deviation above the mean, one standard deviation below the mean, two standard deviations above the mean, two standard deviations below the mean, three standard deviations above the mean, and three standard deviations below the mean.

c. What percentage of the heights are within one standard deviation of the mean? Within two standard deviations? Within three standard deviations?

d. Suppose you pick a female student from the class at random. Find the probability that her height is within two standard deviations of the mean.

3 **a.** The standard deviation is about 2.606 inches.

  b. Students should place arrows at 56.808, 59.414, 62.020, 67.232, 69.838, and 72.444 as shown below.

TECHNOLOGY NOTE These data are in *CPMP-Tools*.

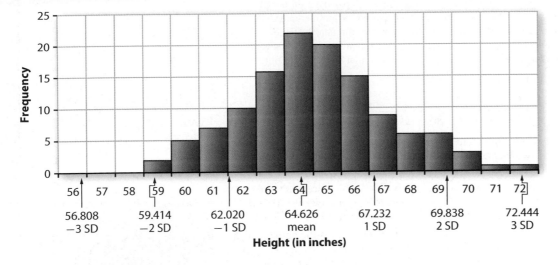

  c. Approximately $\frac{83}{123}$, or 67%, are within one standard deviation of the mean.

  Approximately $\frac{116}{123}$, or 94%, are within two standard deviations of the mean.

  Approximately 100% are within three standard deviations of the mean.

  d. 0.94

4 Suppose a large urban high school has 29 math classes. The number of students enrolled in each of the classes is displayed on the plot below. The outlier is a calculus class with only 7 students enrolled. One way to handle an outlier is to report a summary statistic computed both with and without it. If the two values are not very different, it is safe to report just the value that includes the outlier.

Math Class Enrollment

a. Justina computed the mean twice, with and without the outlier. The two means were 35.97 and 37.00. Which mean was computed with the outlier?

b. Justina also computed the standard deviation twice, with and without the outlier. The two standard deviations were 3.25 and 6.34. Which standard deviation was computed with the outlier?

c. How many standard deviations from the mean is the enrollment in the class with 43 students when the calculus class is included in computing the mean and standard deviation? When the calculus class is not included in the calculations?

d. Suppose five students drop out of each class. What will be the new mean and standard deviation if the calculus class is included in the computations?

5 Runners in the Boston Marathon compete in divisions determined by age and gender. In a recent marathon, the mean time for the 18- to 39-year-old women's division was 225.31 minutes with standard deviation 26.64 minutes. The mean time for the 50- to 59-year-old women's division was 242.58 minutes with standard deviation 21.78 minutes. In that marathon, a 34-year-old woman finished the race in 4:00:15, and a 57-year-old woman finished the race in 4:09:08 (hours:minutes:seconds).

a. How many standard deviations above the mean for her division was each runner?

4 **a.** The mean will be larger if the smallest class size is removed. Thus, the mean with the calculus class is 35.97, and the mean without it is 37.00.

b. The standard deviation will be smaller if the smallest class size is removed. Thus, the standard deviation with the outlier (the calculus class) is 6.34.

c. With the outlier: $\frac{43 - 35.97}{6.34} \approx 1.11$

Without the outlier: $\frac{43 - 37.00}{3.25} \approx 1.85$

d. The new mean will be five students less, or 30.97. The new standard deviation will be the same as the old standard deviation, 6.34.

5 **a.** The 34-year-old woman was $\frac{240.25 - 225.31}{26.64} \approx 0.56$ standard deviations above the mean time for her division. The 57-year-old woman was $\frac{249.13 - 242.58}{21.78} \approx 0.30$ standard deviations above the mean time for her division. Thus, the 57-year-old did better relative to her age because a low standardized time (runner ran relatively faster in her age group) is better than a high standardized time (runner ran relatively slower in her age group). (This is valid even if the distributions of times are not approximately normal as long as the distributions are about the same shape.)

> **INSTRUCTIONAL NOTE**
> Whether the two summary statistics are "very different" depends, as always, on the context of the situation and on the purpose of computing a summary statistic.

b. Write a formula that gives the number of standard deviations from the mean for a time of x minutes by a woman in the 18- to 39-year-old division.

c. Write a formula that gives the number of standard deviations from the mean for a time of x minutes by a woman in the 50- to 59-year-old division.

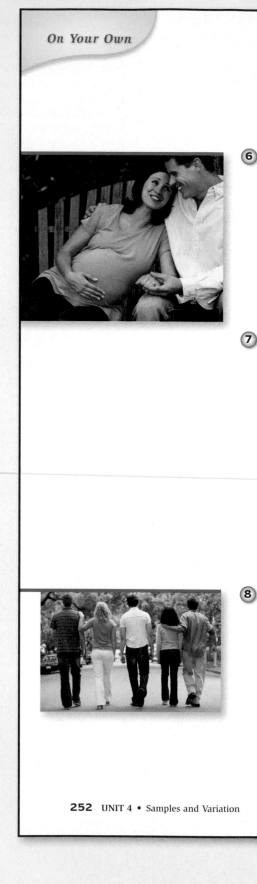

(6) The length of a human pregnancy is often said to be 9 months. Actually, the length of pregnancy from conception to natural birth varies according to a distribution that is approximately normal with mean 266 days and standard deviation 16 days.

a. Draw a sketch of the distribution of pregnancy lengths. Include a scale on the horizontal axis.

b. What percentage of pregnancies last less than 250 days?

c. What percentage of pregnancies are longer than 298 days?

d. To be in the shortest 2.5% of pregnancies, what is the longest that a pregnancy can last?

e. What is the median length of pregnancy?

(7) Scores on the mathematics section of the SAT Reasoning Test are approximately normally distributed with mean 515 and standard deviation 114. Scores on the mathematics part of the ACT are approximately normally distributed with mean 21.0 and standard deviation 5.1.

a. Sketch graphs of the distribution of scores on each test. Include a scale on the horizontal axis.

b. What percentage of the SAT scores lie above 629? Above what ACT score would this same percentage of scores lie?

c. What ACT score is the equivalent of an SAT score of 450?

d. Find the percentile of a person who gets an SAT score of 450.

e. One of the colleges to which Eliza is applying accepts either SAT or ACT mathematics scores. Eliza scored 680 on the mathematics part of the SAT and 27 on the mathematics section of the ACT. Should she submit her SAT or ACT mathematics score to this college? Explain your reasoning.

(8) Many body dimensions of adult males and females in the United States are approximately normally distributed. Approximate means and standard deviations for shoulder width are given in the table below.

U.S. Adult Shoulder Width (in inches)

	Men	Women
Mean μ	17.7	16.0
Standard Deviation σ	0.85	0.85

a. What percentage of women have a shoulder width of less than 15.5 inches? Of more than 15.5 inches?

b. What percentage of men have a shoulder width between 16 and 18 inches?

b. The time of x minutes is $\dfrac{x - 225.31}{26.64}$ standard deviations from the mean.

c. The time of x minutes is $\dfrac{x - 242.58}{21.78}$ standard deviations from the mean.

6 **a.** See the sketch at the right.

b. 250 days is one standard deviation below the mean. So, about 16% of pregnancies last less than 250 days. (If students use the table on page 245, they will get 15.87%.)

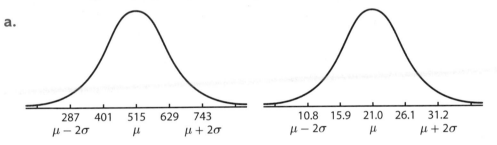

Pregnancy Length (in days)

c. 298 days is two standard deviations above the mean. So, approximately 2.5% (2.28% using the table) of pregnancies last longer than 298 days.

d. The shortest 2.5% of pregnancies are more than two standard deviations below the mean or less than 234 days.

e. In a normal distribution, the median and mean are equal. So, the median length of pregnancy is 266 days.

7 **a.**

b. An SAT score of 629 is one standard deviation above the mean, so about 16% of the scores are above this. (If students use the table on page 245, they will get 15.87%.) One standard deviation above the mean for an ACT score is 26.1.

c. An SAT score of 450 has $z = \dfrac{450 - 515}{114} \approx -0.5702$. To find the equivalent ACT score, solve $-0.5702 = \dfrac{x - 21}{5}$ to get 18.1.

d. From Part c, an SAT score of 450 has $z \approx -0.6$. Using the table, the proportion of scores below 450 is 0.2743. So, the percentile is about the 27th.

e. Ellen's 680 on the SAT is $\dfrac{680 - 515}{114} \approx 1.45$ standard deviations above the mean. Her ACT score is $\dfrac{27 - 21}{5.1} \approx 1.18$ standard deviations above the mean. So, she should submit the SAT score.

8 **a.** $z = \dfrac{15.5 - 16.0}{0.85} \approx -0.6$. The percentage of women with shoulder widths less than 15.5 inches is about 27.43%. The percentage of women with shoulder widths more than 15.5 inches is about $100\% - 27.43\%$, or 72.57%.

b. The standardized value for a man's shoulder width of 18 inches is approximately 0.4, which corresponds to a proportion of about 0.6554. The standardized value for a man's shoulder width of 16 inches is -2, which corresponds to a proportion of about 0.0228. So, about $0.6554 - 0.0228 = 0.6326$, or 63.26%, of men have shoulder widths between 16 and 18 inches.

Unit 4

c. What percentage of American women have a shoulder width more than 17.7 inches, the average shoulder width for American men?

d. What percentage of men will be uncomfortable in an airplane seat designed for people with shoulder width less than 18.5 inches? What percentage of women will be uncomfortable?

e. If you sampled 100,000 men, approximately how many would you expect to be uncomfortable in an airline seat designed for people with shoulder width less than 18.5 inches? If you sampled 100,000 women, approximately how many would you expect to be uncomfortable in an airline seat designed for people with shoulder width less than 18.5 inches?

Connections

9 Three very large sets of data have approximately normal distributions, each with a mean of 10. Sketches of the overall shapes of the distributions are shown below. The scale on the horizontal axis is the same in each case. The standard deviation of the distribution in Figure A is 2. Estimate the standard deviations of the distributions in Figures B and C.

Figure A   **Figure B**   **Figure C**

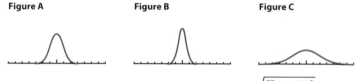

10 How is the formula for the standard deviation $s = \sqrt{\dfrac{\Sigma(x - \overline{x})^2}{n - 1}}$ like the distance formula?

11 If a set of data is the entire population you are interested in studying, you compute the population standard deviation using the formula:

$$\sigma = \sqrt{\frac{\Sigma(x - \mu)^2}{n}}$$

If you are looking at a set of data as a sample from a larger population of data, you compute the standard deviation using this formula:

$$s = \sqrt{\frac{\Sigma(x - \overline{x})^2}{n - 1}}$$

a. For a given set of data, which is larger, σ or s? Explain your reasoning.

b. Does it make much difference whether you divide by n or by $n - 1$ if $n = 1,000$? If $n = 15$?

c. A sample tends to have less variability than the population from which it came. How does the formula for s, the standard deviation for a sample, account for this fact?

c. A woman whose shoulder width is the average for men would have a z-score of $\frac{17.7 - 16.0}{0.85} = 2$. The proportion of women with shoulder widths less than 17.7 inches is 0.975 (or, using the table, 0.9772). Because $1 - 0.975 = 0.025$, the percentage of American women with shoulder widths larger than the average for American men is about 2.5% (or, using the table, 2.28%).

d. For men, $z = \frac{18.5 - 17.7}{0.85} \approx 0.9$. Using the table, the proportion of men with shoulder widths less than 18.5 inches is 0.8159. Since $1 - 0.8159 = 0.1841$, the percentage of adult males that will be uncomfortable is about 18.41%. For women, $z = \frac{18.5 - 16.0}{0.85} \approx 2.9$. Using the table, about $1 - 0.9981$, or 0.19%, of adult women will be uncomfortable.

e. $100,000(0.1841) = 18,410$ men
$100,000(0.0019) = 190$ women

Connections

9 The standard deviation for Figure B is approximately 1 because it is about half the standard deviation of Figure A. The standard deviation for Figure C is approximately 5 because it is about 2.5 times the standard deviation of Figure A.

10 Both involve finding the sum of squared differences and then taking the square root. The main difference is dividing by $n - 1$ in the formula for the standard deviation, which makes it a type of average.

If you think of the values in the sample as a point in space, $(x_1, x_2, \ldots, x_n)$, then the standard deviation (if you ignore dividing by $n - 1$) gives the distance between that point and the point of the mean, $(\bar{x}, \bar{x}, \ldots, \bar{x})$. That is, the standard deviation really is a Euclidean distance between two points.

11 **NOTE** Theoretically, you would use σ (dividing by n) for the standard deviation of a population and for the standard deviation of a theoretical distribution. You would use the sample standard deviation s when computing the standard deviation of a sample taken from a larger population. In practice, s is almost always used with real data, even when you have the entire population of values, and σ is used only for the standard deviation of a theoretical distribution.

Usually, the standard deviation of a sample is computed in order to estimate the standard deviation of the population. But random samples tend to have less variability than the population from which they came. If you divide by n to compute the sample standard deviation, then it tends, on average, to be smaller than the population standard deviation. Dividing by $n - 1$ makes the variance (the square of the standard deviation) an unbiased estimate of the variance of the population. In other words, the average value of the variances of all possible samples from a given population (dividing by $n - 1$) is exactly equal to the variance of the population. (It is impossible to get an unbiased estimate of both the standard deviation and the variance at the same time.)

For a proof that s^2 is an unbiased estimator of σ^2, see "Why $n - 1$ in the Formula for the Sample Standard Deviation?" by Stephen A. Book, *The College Mathematics Journal* 10 (1979): 330–333.

a. s is larger. The only difference in the two formulas is that you divide by n to compute σ and by $n - 1$ to compute s. Since dividing by a smaller number makes the quotient larger, s always is larger than σ.

b. If n is large, the values of s and σ are almost the same. Even if n is not very large, s and σ do not vary a lot. Compare the computations below where in all cases $\sum(x - \bar{x})^2 = 1{,}500$.

$$\sigma = \sqrt{\frac{1{,}500}{15}} = 10 \qquad\qquad s = \sqrt{\frac{1{,}500}{14}} \approx 10.35$$

$$\sigma = \sqrt{\frac{1{,}500}{1{,}000}} \approx 1.2247 \qquad\qquad s = \sqrt{\frac{1{,}500}{999}} \approx 1.2254$$

c. Dividing by $n - 1$ rather than by n inflates the standard deviation a bit (more when n is smaller than when n is larger). Thus, because samples tend to have less variability than the population, the value of s should be closer to the true standard deviation σ of the population than if you divided by n.

Teacher Notes

12 Suppose a normal distribution has mean 100 and standard deviation 15. Now suppose every value in the distribution is converted to a standardized value.

a. What is true about the mean of the standardized values?

b. What is true about the standard deviation of the standardized values?

13 In a normal distribution, about 5% of the values are more than two standard deviations from the mean. If a distribution is not approximately normal, is it possible to have more than 5% of the values two or more standard deviations from the mean? In this task, "standard deviation" refers to the population standard deviation σ, as defined in Task 11.

a. Make up two sets of numbers and compute the percentage that are two or more standard deviations from the mean. Your objective is to get the largest percentage that you can.

b. What is the largest percentage of numbers that you were able to find in Part a? Compare your results to those of other students completing this task.

14 The formula for Pearson's correlation that you studied in the Course 2 *Regression and Correlation* unit is

$$r = \frac{1}{n-1} \sum \left(\frac{x - \bar{x}}{s_x} \right) \left(\frac{y - \bar{y}}{s_y} \right).$$

Here, n is the sample size, $\bar{x}$ is the mean of the values of x, $\bar{y}$ is the mean of the values of y, s_x is the standard deviation of the values of x, and s_y is the standard deviation of the values of y.

a. Use this formula to find the correlation between x and y for the following pairs of numbers.

x	y
1	1
2	2
3	6

b. Explain the meaning of the correlation in the context of standardized values.

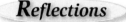
Reflections

15 Why do we say that distributions of real data are "approximately" normally distributed rather than say they are normally distributed?

Unit 4

12 **a.** Standardizing will subtract 100 from every value and divide the difference by 15. Thus, by the rules of transformations studied in the Course 1 *Patterns in Data* unit, the new mean will be equal to the old mean minus 100 and then divided by 15, or $\frac{100 - 100}{15} = 0$. Alternatively, the new mean is

$$\frac{\left(\frac{x_1 - 100}{15}\right) + \left(\frac{x_2 - 100}{15}\right) + \cdots + \left(\frac{x_n - 100}{15}\right)}{n} = \frac{(x_1 + x_2 + \cdots + x_n) - n \cdot 100}{15n}$$

$$= \frac{\frac{(x_1 + x_2 + \cdots + x_n)}{n} - 100}{15}$$

$$= \frac{100 - 100}{15}$$

$$= 0$$

b. Standardizing will subtract 100 from every value, which does not change the standard deviation, and divide the difference by 15. Thus, the new standard deviation will be equal to the old standard deviation divided by 15, or 1.

13 **a.** Responses will vary. The set {0, 5, 5, 5, 5, 5, 5, 5, 10} has a mean of 5 and a standard deviation s of 2.36. Two of the nine values (or 22.2%) are more than two standard deviations from the mean. It is difficult to get a larger percentage.

b. The largest percentage must be less than 25%. (This is true by Chebyshev's inequality that says that the proportion of values in any distribution that lie k or more standard deviations from the mean is less than or equal to $\frac{1}{k^2}$.)

14 **a.** For these numbers, $\bar{x} = 2$, $s_x = 1$, $\bar{y} = 3$, $s_y = 2.6458$. It is easiest to organize the work in a table.

x	y	$\dfrac{x - \bar{x}}{s_x}$	$\dfrac{y - \bar{y}}{s_y}$	$\left(\dfrac{x - \bar{x}}{s_x}\right)\left(\dfrac{y - \bar{y}}{s_y}\right)$
1	1	−1	−0.7559	0.7559
2	2	0	−0.3780	0
3	6	1	1.1339	1.1339

$$r = \frac{1}{n - 1} \sum \left(\frac{x - \bar{x}}{s_x}\right)\left(\frac{y - \bar{y}}{s_y}\right) = \frac{1}{3 - 1}(1.8898) = 0.9449$$

b. The correlation coefficient is the average product of the standardized values of x and the standardized values of y (with the exception that we divide by $n - 1$ rather than by n when computing the average).

Reflections

15 A normal distribution is the (theoretical) distribution under the continuous normal curve. No distribution of real data can be continuous and smooth because it has a finite number of values.

Unit 4

16 Under what conditions will the standard deviation of a data set be equal to 0? Explain your reasoning.

17 Consider the weights of the dogs in the following two groups.

  • the dogs pulling a sled in a trans-Alaska dog sled race

  • the dogs in a dog show, which includes various breeds of dogs

  a. Which group would you expect to have the larger mean weight? Explain your reasoning.

  b. Which group would you expect to have the larger standard deviation? Explain your reasoning.

18 Is it true that in all symmetric distributions, about 68% of the values are within one standard deviation of the mean? Give an example to illustrate your answer.

19 ACT and SAT scores have an approximately normal distribution. Scores on classroom tests are sometimes assumed to have an approximately normal distribution.

  a. What do teachers mean when they say they "grade on a curve"?

  b. Explain how a teacher might use a normal distribution to "grade on a curve."

  c. Under what circumstances would you want to be "graded on a curve"?

Extensions

20 The producers of a movie did a survey of the ages of the people attending one screening of the movie. The data are shown in the table.

  a. Compute the mean and standard deviation for this sample of ages. Do this without entering each of the individual ages into a calculator or computer software. (For example, do not enter the age "14" thirty-eight times).

  b. In this distribution, what percentage of the values fall within one standard deviation of the mean? Within two standard deviations of the mean? Within three standard deviations of the mean?

  c. Compare the percentages from Part b to those from a normal distribution. Explain your findings in terms of the shapes of the two distributions.

Saturday Night at the Movies

Age (in years)	Frequency
12	2
13	26
14	38
15	32
16	22
17	10
18	8
19	8
20	6
21	4
22	1
23	3
27	2
32	2
40	1

16 For the standard deviation to be zero, each deviation, $x - \bar{x}$, must be zero. Thus, each value must be equal to the mean. In other words, all values in the data set must be the same.

17 **a.** All of the dogs pulling a sled will be large dogs, while dogs in a dog show of various breeds will be small, medium, and large. The dog sled team will have the greater mean weight.

b. The dogs pulling the sled all will be fairly hefty dogs. The dogs of various sizes in the dog show would have the larger standard deviation as their weights and will vary more from the mean weight.

18 This is not true. For example, in the distribution {4, 5, 6}, which has mean 5 and standard deviation 1, all of the values are within one standard deviation of the mean.

> **INSTRUCTIONAL NOTE**
> Task 18 reminds students that the rule that 68% of the values lie within one standard deviation of the mean can be counted on only for a distribution that is approximately normal.

19 **a.** This often means that the number of As is the same as the number of Fs. Similarly, the number of Bs is the same as the number of Ds. There would be more Cs than any other grade and fewer As and Fs.

b. A teacher could give the 68% of the students whose scores fell within one standard deviation of the mean a C, the 13.5% between one and two standard deviations above the mean a B, the 13.5% between one and two standard deviations below the mean a D, the 2.5% more than two standard deviations above the mean an A, and the 2.5% more than two standard deviations below the mean an F.

c. On a difficult test where all students scored very low, most students would prefer to have the teacher grade on the curve rather than have all students fail the test. But in general, as the average high school grade nowadays is above C, the grading scheme in Part b would probably lower the grades of most students. For example, in a class of 30 students, if the teacher follows the percentages in Part b, the distribution would have 0.75 As, 4.05 Bs, 20.4 Cs, 4.05 Ds, and 0.75 Fs. This is far fewer As and Bs than is typical.

Extensions

20 **a.** The mean age is 16 years, and the standard deviation is 3.7 years. The mean can be found using the formula $\bar{x} = \dfrac{\Sigma xf}{n}$, where n is 165 and each value of x is multiplied by its frequency f. The corresponding formula for the standard deviation is $s = \sqrt{\dfrac{\Sigma(x - \bar{x})^2 f}{n - 1}}$. Many calculators and computer software will calculate these values if you put the values in one list and their frequencies in another.

b. The percentage of ages that fall within one, two, and three standard deviations of the mean are approximately 87.3%, 97%, and 98%, respectively.

> **INSTRUCTIONAL NOTE**
> Task 20, like Task 18, reminds students of the rule that 68% of the values lie within one standard deviation of the mean can be counted on only for a distribution that is approximately normal.

> **NOTE** The solution to Task 20 Part c is on page T256.

Unit 4

21 In 1903, Karl Pearson and Alice Lee collected the heights of 1,052 mothers. Their data are summarized below. A mother who was exactly 53 inches tall was recorded in the 53–54 inches row.

Heights of Mothers (in inches)

Height	Number of Mothers	Height	Number of Mothers
52–53	1	62–63	183
53–54	1	63–64	163
54–55	1	64–65	115
55–56	2	65–66	78
56–57	7	66–67	41
57–58	18	67–68	16
58–59	34	68–69	7
59–60	80	69–70	5
60–61	135	70–71	2
61–62	163		

Source: Pearson, Karl and Alice Lee. 1903. On the laws of inheritance in man. *Biometrika*: 364.

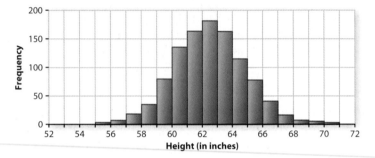

a. Is this distribution of heights approximately normal? Why or why not?

b. Collect the heights of 30 mothers. How does the distribution of your sample compare to the distribution of heights from mothers in 1903?

c. What hypothesis might you make about heights of mothers today? Design a plan that you could use to test your hypothesis.

22 The equation of the curve that has the shape of a normal distribution is:

$$y = \frac{1}{\sigma\sqrt{2\pi}}\, e^{-\frac{1}{2}\left(\frac{x-\mu}{\sigma}\right)^2}$$

In this formula, μ is the mean of the normal distribution, σ is the standard deviation, and the number e is approximately equal to 2.71828.

a. Use your calculator or computer software to graph the normal curve that has a mean of 0 and a standard deviation of 1.

b. Describe what happens to the curve if you increase the mean. Describe what happens if you increase the standard deviation.

c. The ages are not normally distributed. This can best be seen from the plot of the data. The histogram is not symmetric. For example, only $\frac{67}{165}$, or approximately 40.6%, of the ages lie at or above the mean. The 87.3% of ages within one standard deviation of the mean is quite a bit more than the 68% of ages that would be within one standard deviation of the mean in a normal distribution.

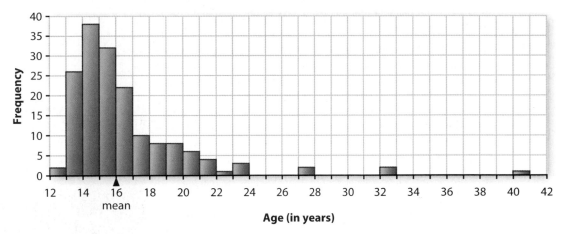

21 **a.** Yes. The distribution is mound-shaped, symmetric, clustered about the mean, and tapers off at the ends of the distribution.

b. The mothers will probably be taller, in general, than those in 1903.

c. Students might conjecture that mothers today are taller. They might also conjecture that the heights are still about the same. Their plan might include obtaining a larger sample of mothers. If they do not think of selecting the mothers randomly, ask them to consider whether mothers in some ethnic groups or age groups seem to be taller than in others. Also ask them to consider whether this would affect the results if students did not take a random sample.

> **INSTRUCTIONAL NOTE**
> For Task 21, students will need to collect the heights of 30 mothers. Students might do this as a group.

22 **a.** For $\mu = 0$ and $\sigma = 1$, $y = \frac{1}{\sqrt{2\pi}} e^{-\frac{x^2}{2}}$. Note that the curve approaches 0 asymptotically, never reaching it, as x increases or decreases.

b. If you increase the mean, the curve will be shifted right on the horizontal axis. If you increase the standard deviation, the curve will become wider.

TECHNOLOGY NOTE The screens on the next page show how you can use the *CPMP-Tools* CAS sliders to dynamically vary the mean *m* and standard deviation *s*.

c. Normal curves have two "bends," or **points of inflection**. One is on the left side of the curve where the graph changes from curved up to curved down. The other is on the right side of the curve where the graph changes from curved down to curved up. Estimate the point where the "bend" seems to occur in the curve in Part a. What relation does this point have to the mean and standard deviation?

23 Discuss whether the situations below are consistent with what you know about normal distributions and IQ tests. Recall that the mean and standard deviation for IQ tests are $\mu = 100$ and $\sigma = 15$. What could account for any inconsistencies that you see?

a. One of the largest K–12 districts in the country, educates between 700,000 and 800,000 children. In this district, there are special magnet schools for "highly gifted" children. The only way for a child in this district to be classified as highly gifted is to score 145 or above on an IQ test given by a school psychologist. Recently, at one gifted magnet school, there were 61 students in the sixth-grade class.

b. One way for a child to be identified as gifted in California is to have an IQ of 130 or above. A few years ago, a Los Angeles high school had a total enrollment of 2,830 students, of whom 410 were identified as gifted.

Review

24 Suppose that the cost of filling up a car with gasoline is a function of the number of gallons and can be found using the rule $C(g) = 2.89g$.

a. What does the 2.89 tell you about this situation?

b. What is the cost of 4.2 gallons of gas?

c. Find the value of g so that $C(g) = 19.65$. Then explain what your solution means in this context.

d. Is this relationship a direct variation, inverse variation, or neither? Explain.

25 In the diagram at the right, $\overline{BC}$ is the perpendicular bisector of $\overline{AD}$, and $AD = 20$ cm. If possible, complete each of the following tasks. If not possible, explain why not.

a. Prove that $\triangle ACB \cong \triangle DCB$.

b. Find the area of $\triangle ABD$.

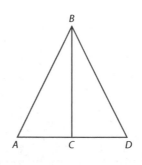

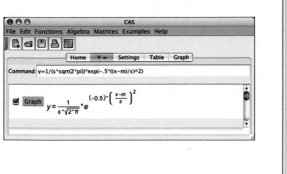

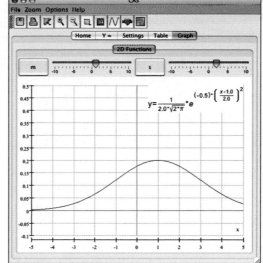

c. The inflection points occur at $x = 1$ and $x = -1$. So, the x values of the inflection points are one standard deviation from the mean.

23 a. From the table on page 245, you expect the proportion of children who have IQs of 145, or three standard deviations above the mean, to be about $1 - 0.9987 = 0.0013$.

There are about $\frac{750,000}{13} \approx 57,692$ sixth-graders in this school district. Notice that $0.0013(57,692) \approx 75$ students. Thus, the 61 looks about right, except that not all children with IQs above 145 are tested. Furthermore, many or most of those who are tested probably do not choose to go to a magnet school. Also, there are other similar magnets for sixth-graders. The assumptions about IQ scores do not account for this many highly gifted sixth-graders in one school.

b. You expect about 2.5% of children to have IQs of 130 or above. But $0.025(2,830) = 70.75$. There are far more gifted students than you would expect at this high school. There are other ways to be classified as gifted, which would raise the total, or perhaps this is a high school that the gifted children choose to attend. Or, perhaps the shape, mean, or standard deviation of IQ tests has changed.

Review

24 a. For every one-gallon increase, the cost of filling up the car increases by $2.89, or the price of gas is $2.89 per gallon.

b. $12.14

c. When the cost was $19.65, 6.8 gallons were bought.

d. The relationship is a direct variation since it can be expressed in the form $y = kx$ with $k = 2.89$.

25 a. $\overline{AC} \cong \overline{CD}$ because $\overline{BC}$ is the perpendicular bisector of $\overline{AD}$. $\angle ACB \cong \angle DCB$ because both are right angles. The triangles have a common side, $\overline{BC}$. So, $\triangle ACB \cong \triangle DCB$ by SAS.

b. This is not possible since neither the length of $\overline{BC}$ (the height) nor the length of either $\overline{AB}$ or $\overline{BD}$ are known.

26 Solve each inequality and graph the solution on a number line. Then describe the solution using interval notation.

a. $3(x + 7) \geq 5$ b. $10 - 8x < 4(8 - 4x)$

c. $2x \geq 5x - 3$ d. $x^2 > 4$

e. $x^2 - 5x < 0$

27 Rewrite each expression in factored form.

a. $3x^2 + 9x$ b. $2x^2 + 9x + 4$

c. $x^2 - 64$ d. $x^2 - 12x - 45$

28 Try to answer each of the following using mental computation only.

a. What is 25% of 400?

b. What is 60% of 80?

c. 20 is what percent of 50?

d. 180 is what percent of 270?

e. 6 is 20% of what number?

f. 14 is 2% of what number?

29 Given $\triangle XYZ$ with m$\angle X = 90°$ and $\sin Y = \frac{1}{2}$:

a. Find a set of possible exact side lengths for the triangle. Are your side lengths the only ones possible? If so, explain why. If not, explain why not.

b. Which of the following is the value for cos Z?

$$\frac{1}{2} \qquad \frac{2}{\sqrt{3}} \qquad \sqrt{3} \qquad \frac{\sqrt{3}}{2}$$

c. Find m$\angle Y$.

30 Rewrite each expression in simplest equivalent form.

a. $10 - 4(5x + 1)$ b. $(2x + 1)(3 - x) + 5(x + 3)$

c. $\frac{6x + 9}{3}$ d. $(4x + 5)^2$

31 Recall that two events A and B are independent if the occurrence of one of the events does not change the probability that the other occurs. For each situation, decide if it is reasonable to assume that the events are independent. Then find the probability of both events occurring.

a. Rolling a pair of dice one time

Event A: Getting doubles

Event B: Getting a sum that is even

b. Flipping a coin twice

Event A: Getting heads on the first flip

Event B: Getting heads on the second flip

Unit 4

26 **a.** $\left[-\frac{16}{3}, \infty\right)$

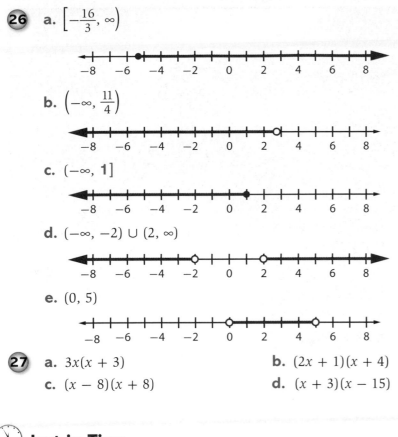

b. $\left(-\infty, \frac{11}{4}\right)$

c. $(-\infty, 1]$

d. $(-\infty, -2) \cup (2, \infty)$

e. $(0, 5)$

27 **a.** $3x(x + 3)$ **b.** $(2x + 1)(x + 4)$

     c. $(x - 8)(x + 8)$ **d.** $(x + 3)(x - 15)$

Just in Time

28 **a.** 100   **b.** 48

     c. 40%   **d.** $66\frac{2}{3}\%$

     e. 30   **f.** 700

29 **a.** One possibility is $XZ = 1$, $XY = \sqrt{3}$, $YZ = 2$. Any scalar multiple of these side lengths would also be correct because the triangles would all be similar and thus have the same angle measures.

     b. $\frac{1}{2}$

     c. $m\angle Y = 30°$

30 **a.** $-20x + 6$ **b.** $-2x^2 + 10x + 18$

     c. $2x + 3$ **d.** $16x^2 + 40x + 25$

Just in Time

31 **a.** These events are not independent. If you roll doubles, then you know the sum will be even.

$P(doubles \text{ and } even) = \frac{1}{6}$

     b. These events are independent. The outcome of the first flip does not affect the outcome of the second flip.

$P(heads \text{ and } heads) = \frac{1}{2} \cdot \frac{1}{2} = \frac{1}{4}$

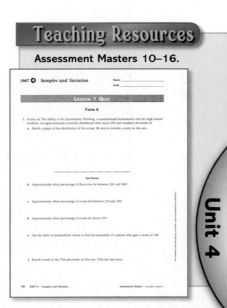

Teaching Resources

Assessment Masters 10–16.

Unit 4

Binomial Distributions

In the first lesson, you learned about properties of the normal distribution. This lesson is about binomial distributions. For example, suppose you flip a coin 10 times and count the number of heads. The binomial distribution for this situation gives you the probability of getting 0 heads, of getting 1 head, of getting 2 heads, and so on, up to the probability of getting 10 heads. A similar situation occurs when counting the number of successful free throw attempts for a specific basketball player in a game or season.

Consider the case of Candace Parker who played basketball for the University of Tennessee from 2005 to 2008. She is a versatile player usually playing forward, but she was listed on Tennessee's roster as forward, center, and guard. She played in 110 games and made 526 of her 738 attempted free throws. (Source: chicagosports.sportsdirectinc.com)

Binomial Distributions

This lesson is about binomial (success/failure) situations. Students will learn to solve problems such as estimating the probability of getting 65 or more heads if they flip a coin 100 times. They will learn whether such a result should make them conclude that the coin is not fair.

Lesson Objectives

- Use simulation to construct an approximate binomial distribution
- Predict the shape of a binomial distribution
- Use the formulas for the expected value and standard deviation of a binomial distribution
- Use standardized values to find probabilities of events in binomial situations
- Use a random sample to decide whether a given proportion p is plausible as the proportion of successes in the population from which the sample came

Lesson Launch

While discussing Candace Parker's record, bring up the issue of the misconception that there are hot and cold streaks in sports. (Students may not agree with this. But, in general, statisticians do not find more "streaks" and "slumps" in professional athletes than would be predicted by chance alone. If, for example, you have many people flipping coins, eventually, just by chance alone, you will get long streaks of heads and of tails.) Additional sources and information for interested students are listed below.

Also, indicate to students that they will be learning about one of the amazing connections of mathematics, which is, how the normal distribution can be used to model the binomial distribution and how this helps make decisions about probabilistic events.

Resources Related to Hot Streaks

Tversky, A., & Gilovich, T. "The Cold Facts about the Hot Hand in Basketball." *Chance*, Vol. 2, No. 1, 1989, pp. 16–21.

New York Times, Science Desk. "Hot Hands' Phenomenon: A Myth?" April 19, 1988, < www.dartmouth.edu/~chance/course/Syllabi/Princeton96/Hot_Hands.html >

Gilovich, T., Vallone, R., & Tversky, A. "The Hot Hand in Basketball: On the Misperception of Random Sequences." *Cognitive Psychology*, Vol. 17, 1985, pp. 295–314.

Schilling, M. F. "The Longest Run of Heads." *College Mathematics Journal*, Vol. 21, 1990, pp. 196–207.

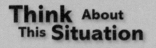

Think About This Situation

Suppose you were watching Candace Parker play basketball in 2008.

a) What is your best estimate of the probability that Candace Parker will make a single free throw?

b) How many free throws do you expect her to make in 20 attempts?

c) Suppose Candace Parker attempts 20 free throws in a series of games. Would you be surprised if she made all 20? If she made only 12?

d) How would you simulate 10 runs of the situation of Candace Parker attempting 20 free throws? What assumptions are you making that may be different from the real-life situation?

In this lesson, you will learn how to answer questions like those above by describing the shape, center, and spread of the distribution of the possible numbers of successes.

Investigation 1 — Shape, Center, and Spread

Repeating the same process for a fixed number of *trials* and counting the number of "successes" is a common situation in probability. For example, you might roll a pair of dice 50 times and count the number of doubles. Or, you might survey 500 randomly selected U.S. teens and count the number who play soccer. (Recall that getting a random sample of 500 U.S. teens is equivalent to putting the names of all U.S. teens in a hat and drawing out 500 at random.) These are called **binomial situations** if they have the four characteristics listed below.

- There are two possible outcomes on each trial called "success" and "failure."
- Each trial is independent of the others. That is, knowing what happened on previous trials does not change the probability of a success on the next trial. (If you take a relatively small random sample from a much larger population, you can consider the trials independent.)
- There is a fixed number of trials n.
- The probability p of a success is the same on each trial.

Your work in this investigation will help you answer the following question:

What are the shape, mean, and standard deviation of a distribution of the number of successes in a binomial situation?

Albright, S. C. "A Statistical Analysis of Hitting Streaks in Baseball." *Journal of the American Statistical Association*, Vol. 88, No. 424, December 1993, p. 1175.

Scheaffer, R. L., Gnanadesikan, M., Watkins, A. E., and Witmer, J. *Activity-Based Statistics*, 2nd Ed., Key Curriculum Press, 2004, "Streaky Behavior."

Think About This Situation

a $\frac{526}{738} \approx 0.713$

b 0.713 of 20, or 14.26.

c Yes, as making all 20 free throws is pretty unlikely for a 0.713 shooter. No, as making 12 is close to the expected number of 14.26.

d Using a random digit table or random digits generated from your calculator or computer, divide the digits into triples. Let 001–713 represent the event of Candace Parker making the shot and the other triples represent Candace Parker missing the shot. Alternatively, let 000–712 represent making the shot and 713–999 represent missing the shot. Select 20 sets of triples. Record the number of successes. Do this ten times.

You are assuming that the probability she makes each free throw is 0.713, no matter how she has done in previous shots. That is, she does not get rattled, for example, after missing a shot or two. This is approximately true in real-life basketball games with expert players, and so it is a useful model for getting approximate answers.

NOTE As can be seen by the 20 random digits at the right, letting 1 to 713 represent Candace Parker making a shot, she missed 5 of 20 shots. To simulate 10 runs of 20 free throws, you would repeat this simulation 9 more times. (To set a range of random numbers, select the #–# button on the left of the screen.)

Simulation

Tool Edit Build View Simulation Sample Simulations Help

Conduct 20 runs.

▼ Simulation Model
Start = 1
End = 1000

Outcome #	Integer 1...1000
1	538
2	90
3	540
4	525
5	631
6	412
7	936
8	737
9	784
10	80
11	345
12	195
13	758
14	585
15	686
16	501
17	926
18	108
19	292
20	585

Teaching Resources

Transparency Master 17.

UNIT 4 *Samples and Variation*

Think About This Situation

Suppose you were watching Candace Parker play basketball in 2008.

a What is your best estimate of the probability that Candace Parker will make a single free throw?

b How many free throws do you expect her to make in 20 attempts?

c Suppose Candace Parker attempts 20 free throws in a series of games. Would you be surprised if she made all 20? If she made only 12?

d How would you simulate 10 runs of the situation of Candace Parker attempting 20 free throws? What assumptions are you making that may be different from the real-life situation?

Transparency Master • use with page 260 UNIT 4 • *Samples and Variation* **17**

INSTRUCTIONAL NOTE
If students round 14.26, you may need to remind them that "expect" means on the average, and so the expected value may be a value that is impossible to obtain on a single run. Otherwise, this is brought to their attention after Problem 1 on page 261.

TECHNOLOGY NOTE
On the TI-83 and TI-84, use **randInt(1,1000)** or **randInt(0,999)**. The **randInt** command is found under MATH PRB. On the TI-Nspire, **randInt** is found under Calculator, Menu, Probability, Random, Integer.

Unit 4

Investigation 1 Shape, Center, and Spread

In this investigation, students will learn how to construct a binomial distribution for a given probability of success p and number of trials n and to estimate the distribution's shape, mean, and standard deviation.

Note on Characteristics of a Binomial Situation

Students may wonder why the second and fourth characteristics of a binomial situation (listed on page 260 of the student text) are both needed.

Does not a fixed value of p indicate that trials are independent? No, it does not. For example, suppose you observe six members of a family next Saturday and count the number who go to a theme park. The family plans to go to the theme park on Saturday if the weather is good. The probability of good weather is 0.8. Here, there are a fixed number of trials (people), 6. Each person either will go to the theme park (a success), or they will not go. The probability of a success on each trial is 0.8. However, the trials are not independent. If on Saturday, you find out that the first member of the family went to the theme park, you know that the others did, too. So, the probability of a success on the second trial becomes 1.

Does the fact that the trials are independent indicate a fixed value of p? Again, the answer is no. For example, suppose you are going to spin a penny ten times and count the number of heads. After three spins, your penny rolls under the sofa, so you take another penny out of your pocket for the remaining seven spins. In this case, the trials are independent, but the probability of a head on the first three spins will not be exactly equal to the probability of a head on the last seven spins as the two pennies will be balanced a bit differently due to wear and difference in manufacture.

You may wish to introduce students to the acronym "BINS" to help them remember the characteristics of a binomial situation. They will need to use these characteristics often in this lesson.

B: "**Bi**," two possible outcomes
I: **I**ndependent trials
N: Fixed **N**umber of trials
S: **S**uccess probability the **S**ame for each trial

Teacher Notes

1 Determine whether each of the following situations is a binomial situation by identifying:

- the two possible outcomes on each trial
- whether the trials are independent
- the number of trials
- the probability of a success on each trial

a. You flip a coin 20 times and count the number of heads.

b. You roll a six-sided die 60 times and count the number of times you get a 2.

c. About 51% of the residents of the U.S. are female. You take a randomly selected sample of 1,200 U.S. residents and count the number of females. (Source: *Gender: 2000, Census 2000 Brief*, September 2001, page 1.)

d. In 2005, 60% of children lived in areas that did not meet one or more of the Primary National Ambient Air Quality Standards. You select 75 children at random from the U.S. and count the number who live in areas that do not meet one or more of these standards. (Source: *America's Children: Key National Indicators of Well-Being 2007*, page 30.)

e. The player with the highest career free throw percentage in NBA history is Mark Price who made 2,135 free throws out of 2,362 attempts. Suppose Mark Price shoots 20 free throws and you count the number of times he makes his shot. (Source: www.nba.com/statistics/)

Recall that in probability, **expected value** means the *long-run average* or *mean* value. For example, if you flip a coin 7 times, you might get 3 heads, you might get 4 heads, and you might get more or fewer. Over many sets of 7 flips, however, the average or **expected number** of heads will be 3.5. So, you can say that you *expect* to get 3.5 heads if you flip a coin 7 times.

2 In the Course 2 *Probability Distributions* unit, you learned that if the probability of a success on each trial of a binomial situation is p, then the expected number of successes in n trials is np.

a. What formula gives you the expected number of failures?

b. For the binomial situations in Problem 1, what are the expected number of successes and the expected number of failures?

You can use statistics software or a command on your calculator to simulate a binomial situation. For example, suppose you want to simulate flipping a coin 100 times and counting the number of heads. From the calculator Probability menu, select **randBin(**. Type in the number of trials and the probability of a success, **randBin(100,.5)** and press **ENTER**. The calculator returns the number of successes in 100 trials when the probability of a success is 0.5. The "Random Binomial" feature of simulation software like in *CPMP-Tools* operates in a similar manner.

3 Give the calculator or software command that you would use to simulate each of the binomial situations in Problem 1. Then do one run and record the number of successes.

1 Each of these is a binomial situation.

   a. The outcomes are *heads* (success) or *tails*. The trials are independent as the probability of getting a head does not change depending on what has happened before. There are 20 trials, and the probability of a success is $\frac{1}{2}$.

   b. The outcomes are *2* (success) or *not 2*. The trials are independent as the probability of getting a 2 does not change depending on what has happened before. There are 60 trials, with probability of success $\frac{1}{6}$.

   c. The outcomes are *female* (success) or *male*. You can consider the trials independent because of the large number of U.S. residents and the relatively small sample size. There are 1,200 trials, and the probability of a success is 0.51.

   d. The outcomes are *child lives in an area that does not meet the standards* (success) or *child lives in an area that meets the standards*. As in Part c, you can consider the trials independent because of the large number of U.S. children and the relatively small sample size. There are 75 trials. The probability of a success is 0.60.

   e. The outcomes are *makes it* (success) or *misses it*. The trials are independent if you assume that Price is a typically consistent professional athlete. There are 20 trials, and the probability of a success is $\frac{2,135}{2,362}$, or about 0.904.

2   **a.** $n(1-p)$

  b.

Part	Expected Successes	Expected Failures
a	10	10
b	10	50
c	612	588
d	12	63
e	18.08	1.92

3 Number of successes will vary.

  a. randBin(20,.5)

  b. randBin(60,1/6)

  c. randBin(1200,.51)

  d. randBin(75,.60)

  e. randBin(20,2135/2362)

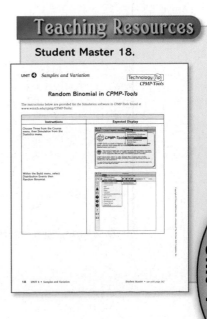

4. Suppose you flip a coin 100 times and count the number of heads.

   a. What is the expected number of heads?

   b. If everyone in your class flipped a coin 100 times and counted the number of heads, how much variability do you think there would be in the results?

   c. Use the **randBin** function of your calculator or the "Random Binomial" feature of simulation software to simulate flipping a coin 100 times. Record the number of heads. Compare results with other members of your class.

   d. Perform 200 runs using the software or combine calculator results with the rest of your class until you have the results from 200 runs. Make a histogram of this **approximate binomial distribution**. What is its shape?

   e. Estimate the expected number of heads and the standard deviation from the histogram. How does the expected number compare to your answer from Part a?

In Problem 4, you saw a binomial distribution that was approximately normal in shape. In the next problem, you will examine whether that is the case with all binomial distributions.

5. According to the 2000 U.S. Census, about 20% of the population of the United States are children, age 13 or younger. (Source: *Age: 2000, Census 2000 Brief*, October 2001 at www.census.gov/prod/2001pubs/c2kbr01-12.pdf) Suppose you take a randomly selected sample of people from the United States. The following graphs show the binomial distributions for the number of children in random samples varying in size from 5 to 100.

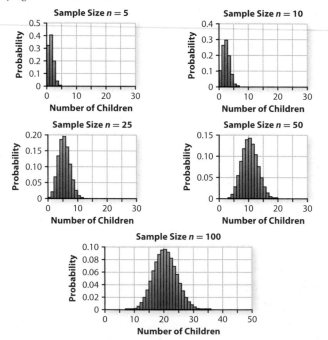

Unit 4

4 TECHNOLOGY NOTE *CPMP-Tools* You can conduct 200 runs of flipping a coin 100 times and counting the heads by using the "Simulation" feature. Choose Build, Distribution Events, Random Binomial and conduct 200 runs with $n = 100$ and $p = 0.5$. Choose View, Graph to see a screen similar to the one below.

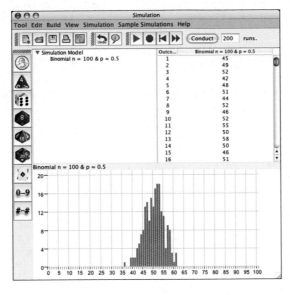

TECHNOLOGY NOTE: CALCULATOR You may need to remind students how to set the viewing window for a histogram or remind them they can use the **ZoomStat** command. For this histogram, Xscl = 3 works well. The calculator command, **randBin(100,.5,200)→L1**, simulates flipping a coin 100 times, counting the number of successes, repeating this 200 times, and storing the numbers of successes in List 1. This can take as many as 10 minutes depending on the calculator. You may want to have a student start his or her calculator ahead of time. On the TI-Nspire, it took less than 5 seconds.

Alternatively, enter the combined class results in a data sheet of *CPMP-Tools* in order to use the "Estimate Center and Spread" custom tool under "Other Custom Tools." (See the Course 1 Unit 2 *Teacher's Guide* or *CPMP-Tools* Course 1 Help documentation for more information on this custom tool.) In Problem 7, students will use the formula for the standard deviation of a binomial distribution and check their estimate from the simulation done in Problem 4.

a. 50

b. Students' estimates of variability will vary. (Have students compare their estimate here with class results in Part e.)

c. Results will vary. One class of 30 students got the following numbers of heads, which range from 39 to 60.

> 44, 52, 55, 46, 49, 60, 45, 46, 54, 51, 56, 44, 52, 54, 48,
> 45, 53, 56, 52, 54, 42, 49, 58, 54, 48, 53, 39, 53, 46, 50

d. Results will vary, but the histogram below gives the results of 200 runs from one class. The shape is approximately normal.

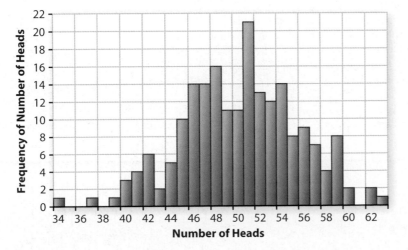

e. The expected number of heads should be about 50. The standard deviation should be about 5.

a. The histogram for a sample size of 5 has six bars, one for 0 successes, one for 1 success, one for 2 successes, one for 3 successes, one for 4 successes, and a very short bar for 5 successes.

    i. Why are there more bars as the sample size increases?

    ii. How many bars should there be for a sample size of n?

    iii. Why can you see only 7 bars on the histogram for a sample size of 10?

b. Use the histograms on the previous page to help answer the following questions.

    i. What happens to the shape of the distribution as the sample size increases?

    ii. What happens to the expected number of successes as the sample size increases?

    iii. What happens to the standard deviation of the number of successes as the sample size increases?

6 As you saw in Problem 5, not all binomial distributions are approximately normal. Statisticians have developed a *guideline* that you can use to decide whether a binomial distribution is approximately normal.

> *The shape of a binomial distribution will be approximately normal if the expected number of successes is 10 or more and the expected number of failures is 10 or more.*

a. Write the guideline about when a binomial distribution can be considered approximately normal using two algebraic inequalities where n is the number of trials and p is the probability of a success.

b. In each of the following situations, decide if the sample size is large enough so that the binomial distribution will be approximately normal.

    i. The five distributions in Problem 5

    ii. 100 flips of a coin and counting the number of heads

    iii. Rolling a die 50 times and counting the number of 3s

    iv. Randomly selecting 1,200 U.S. residents in Problem 1 Part c

    v. Randomly selecting 75 children in Problem 1 Part d

7 One of the reasons the standard deviation is such a useful measure of spread is that the standard deviation of many distributions has a simple formula. The **standard deviation of a binomial distribution** is given by:

$$\sigma = \sqrt{np(1 - p)}$$

a. Suppose you flip a coin 100 times and count the number of heads. Use this formula to compute the standard deviation of the binomial distribution.

b. Compare your answer in Part a to the estimate from your simulation in Problem 4 Part e.

5 **a.** **i.** There are more bars as the sample size increases because there are more possible numbers of children in the sample, 0 children through n children.

   ii. For a sample size of n, there should be $n + 1$ bars (0 through n children).

   iii. You can see only 7 bars for a sample size of 10 because the probability of getting more than 6 children is so small that the other bars do not show up on the histogram. They are there, but the probability in each case is close to 0.

   b. **i.** As the sample size increases, the distribution becomes more approximately normal.

   ii. As the sample size increases, the expected number of successes increases. In this case, the expected number of successes is $n \cdot (0.2)$.

   iii. As the sample size increases, the standard deviation of the number of successes also increases. This should make sense to students because the number of bars increases.

INSTRUCTIONAL NOTE The Law of Large Numbers says that as the number of trials increases, the proportion of successes tends to get closer to p. However, the *number* of successes tends to get more spread out as the number of trials increases. Students examined this fact in Course 1 Unit 8, *Patterns in Chance*, Lesson 2, Reflections Task 17 on page 578.

6 **a.** $np \geq 10$

   $n(1 - p) \geq 10$

   b.

INSTRUCTIONAL NOTE
Encourage students to use number sense to recognize that, in many cases, the computations for np and $n(1 - p)$ do not need to be done to conclude whether or not they are greater than or equal to 10. (FYI: The AP Statistics exam requires the computation to receive full credit.) Also, notice that in Parts b–f, the conclusions about normality are the same that one would arrive at by examining each histogram.

Part	n	np	$n(1-p)$	Approximately Normal
i	5	1	4	no; both are less than 10
	10	2	8	no; both are less than 10
	25	5	20	no; the expected number of successes is less than 10
	50	10	40	yes; both are greater than or equal to 10
	100	20	80	yes; both are greater than or equal to 10
ii	100	50	50	yes; both are greater than or equal to 10
iii	50	8.33	41.67	no; the expected number of successes is less than 10
iv	1,200	612	588	yes; both are greater than or equal to 10
v	75	45	30	yes; both are greater than or equal to 10

7 **a.** $\sigma = \sqrt{100(0.5)(1 - 0.5)} = 5$

   b. The estimated standard deviation from Problem 4 Part e should be about equal to the theoretical standard deviation of 5.

(8) Suppose you plan to spin a spinner, like the one shown, 60 times and count the number of times that you get green.

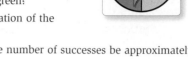

a. If p represents the probability of getting green on a single spin, what is the value of p? What does $1 - p$ represent?

b. In 60 spins, what is the expected number of times that you will get green?

c. What is the standard deviation of the number of greens?

d. Will the distribution of the number of successes be approximately normal? If so, make a sketch of this distribution, marking values of the mean and one, two, and three standard deviations from the mean on the x-axis.

e. Would you be surprised to get 13 greens? 20 greens? Use standardized values in your explanations.

f. In Problem 5, you learned that as the number of trials for a binomial distribution increases, the standard deviation of the number of successes increases. Suppose you increase the number of spins to 240.

   i. Compute the standard deviation of this distribution.

   ii. Describe the relationship between the standard deviation for 240 spins and the standard deviation for 60 spins.

   iii. How can you recognize this relationship by examining the formula for the standard deviation of a binomial distribution?

(9) About 60% of children ages 3 to 5 are read to daily by a family member. (Source: *America's Children: Key National Indicators of Well-Being 2007*, page 51.) Suppose you take a random sample of 75 children this age.

a. Describe the shape. Compute the mean and standard deviation of the binomial distribution for this situation.

b. Using the expected number and standard deviation, describe the number of children you might get in your sample who are read to daily by a family member.

c. Out of the 75 children in your sample, suppose you get 42 children who are read to daily by a family member. Compute the standardized value for 42 children. Use this standardized value to estimate the probability of getting 42 or fewer children who are read to daily by a family member.

d. Out of the 75 children in your sample, suppose you get 50 children who are read to daily by a family member. Compute the standardized value for 50 children. Use this standardized value to estimate the probability of getting 50 or more children who are read to daily by a family member.

8 **a.** $p = \frac{1}{4}$

$1 - p$ represents the probability of getting a color other than green on a single spin.

b. One fourth of 60 spins, or 15 times

c. $\sigma = \sqrt{np(1-p)} = \sqrt{60(0.25)(0.75)} \approx 3.35$

d. Yes, because both the expected number of successes, 15, and the expected number of failures, 45, are 10 or more.

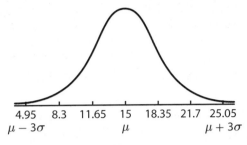

4.95	8.3	11.65	15	18.35	21.7	25.05
$\mu - 3\sigma$			μ			$\mu + 3\sigma$

e. You would not be surprised to get 13 greens because that is less than one standard deviation from the mean. $z = \dfrac{x - \mu}{\sigma} \approx \dfrac{13 - 15}{3.35} \approx -0.597$

You would not be surprised to get 20 greens because that is less than two standard deviations from the mean. $z = \dfrac{x - \mu}{\sigma} \approx \dfrac{20 - 15}{3.35} \approx 1.493$

f. **i.** $\sigma = \sqrt{np(1-p)} = \sqrt{240(0.25)(0.75)} \approx 6.7$

ii. The standard deviation for 240 spins is twice that for 60 spins.

iii. You can see from the formula $\sqrt{np(1-p)}$ that the sample size n is a factor of the value under the square root sign. Thus, when you quadruple the sample size, the standard deviation doubles. Showing this symbolically, the standard deviation changes from

$$\sigma = \sqrt{np(1-p)} \text{ to } \sqrt{4np(1-p)} = 2\sqrt{np(1-p)} = 2\sigma.$$

9 **a.** $\mu = np = 45$

$\sigma = \sqrt{75(0.6)(0.4)} \approx 4.24$

The distribution is approximately normal because $np = 75(0.6) \geq 10$ and $n(1-p) = 75(0.4) \geq 10$.

b. If you take a random sample of 75 children aged 3 to 5, you expect to get 45 who are read to daily by a family member, give or take 4.24.

c. $z = \dfrac{42 - 45}{4.24} \approx -0.71$. Using the table on page 245, the probability is about 0.2420.

d. $z = \dfrac{50 - 45}{4.24} \approx 1.18$. Using the table on page 245, the probability is about $1 - 0.8849 = 0.1151$.

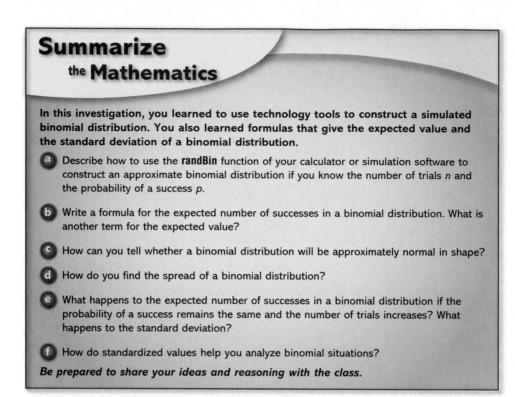

Summarize
the Mathematics

In this investigation, you learned to use technology tools to construct a simulated binomial distribution. You also learned formulas that give the expected value and the standard deviation of a binomial distribution.

a Describe how to use the **randBin** function of your calculator or simulation software to construct an approximate binomial distribution if you know the number of trials *n* and the probability of a success *p*.

b Write a formula for the expected number of successes in a binomial distribution. What is another term for the expected value?

c How can you tell whether a binomial distribution will be approximately normal in shape?

d How do you find the spread of a binomial distribution?

e What happens to the expected number of successes in a binomial distribution if the probability of a success remains the same and the number of trials increases? What happens to the standard deviation?

f How do standardized values help you analyze binomial situations?

Be prepared to share your ideas and reasoning with the class.

✓Check Your Understanding

About 66.2% of all housing units in the U.S. are owner-occupied. (Source: quickfacts.census.gov/qfd/states/00000.html) Suppose you randomly select 120 housing units from the U.S.

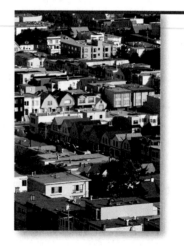

a. What is the expected number of owner-occupied units?

b. Is the binomial distribution of the number of owner-occupied units approximately normal?

c. What is the standard deviation of this binomial distribution? What does it tell you?

d. Would you be surprised to find that 65 of the housing units are owner-occupied? To find that 90 of the housing units are owner-occupied? Explain.

e. Compute a standardized value for 72 owner-occupied units. Use this standardized value to estimate the probability of getting 72 or fewer owner-occupied units.

f. Explain how to use your calculator to simulate taking a random sample of 120 housing units from the U.S. and determining how many are owner-occupied.

Although this STM has six parts to discuss, the ideas are highly connected. As you discuss responses, build the connections among expected number of successes, expected number of failures, the rule that tells whether a binomial distribution will be approximately normal, and the mean and the standard deviation of a binomial distribution. Students should also recognize that the standardized values are of the form $\frac{value - mean}{SD}$ for either an approximately normal binomial distribution or a normal distribution.

Summarize
the Mathematics

a To perform one run, use the command **randBin(n,p)**. The calculator will return the number of successes in one run of *n* trials, where the probability of success on each trial is *p*. Repeat this many times until you can estimate the shape, mean, and standard deviation of the sampling distribution. Alternatively, students may describe how they used simulation software such as *CPMP-Tools* to construct the distribution.

b The expected number of successes in a binomial distribution may be found using *np*. The mean is another term for the expected value, so $\mu = np$.

c Use the rule that both *np* and *n*(1 − *p*) have to be greater than or equal to 10. If either one is less than 10, the distribution will be skewed (to the right if *p* < 0.5 and to the left if *p* > 0.5).

d The standard deviation is commonly used to measure spread and is given by $\sigma = \sqrt{np(1 - p)}$.

e The expected number of successes increases and the standard deviation increases.

f When the binomial distribution is approximately normal, you can find the proportion of times that you get *x* or fewer successes (or *x* or more) by computing the standardized value for *x*: $z = \frac{x - np}{\sqrt{np(1 - p)}}$.
Then use the table on page 245 to find the proportion associated with this *z*.

Teaching Resources

Transparency Master 20.

UNIT ❹ *Samples and Variation*

Summarize
the Mathematics

In this investigation, you learned to use technology tools to construct a simulated binomial distribution. You also learned formulas that give the expected value and the standard deviation of a binomial distribution.

ⓐ Describe how to use the **randBin** function of your calculator or simulation software to construct an approximate binomial distribution if you know the number of trials *n* and the probability of a success *p*.

ⓑ Write a formula for the expected number of successes in a binomial distribution. What is another term for the expected value?

ⓒ How can you tell whether a binomial distribution will be approximately normal in shape?

ⓓ How do you find the spread of a binomial distribution?

ⓔ What happens to the expected number of successes in a binomial distribution if the probability of a success remains the same and the number of trials increases? What happens to the standard deviation?

ⓕ How do standardized values help you analyze binomial situations?

Be prepared to share your ideas and reasoning with the class.

20 UNIT 4 • Samples and Variation   Transparency Master • see unit page 265

PROCESSING PROMPT
I made sure _____
                        (name)
was included by ... .

MATH TOOLKIT Summarize what you know about a binomial distribution if you know the number of trials *n* and the probability of a success *p*. Include information about the shape, the expected value, and standard deviation of the distribution. Provide an example that shows how you can use standardized values to help you analyze binomial situations.

Summarize the Mathematics, *page 265*

Teacher: In this investigation, you learned how to recognize when a situation is a binomial situation. Wasn't it interesting to see the different contexts: sports statistics, games that might involve spinners or dice, and health and well-being statistics? We used technology to simulate some of these situations and learned formulas to help analyze the situations. Take a few minutes to discuss Parts a–d in your groups. You need not write complete sentence responses at this time, but you may make some notes about your discussion if you wish. *(Teacher gives students 5 or 10 minutes to discuss the first four parts.)*

Teacher: Alanna, you were helping your group answer Part a that asks how you use technology to construct an approximate binomial distribution when you know specific *n* and *p*. Please do that using the technology display for the whole class while you explain the process.

Alanna: Look. If the binomial distribution is, say, 100 trials with probability of 0.4 on each trial, the command **randBin(100,.4)** will give the number of successes for the 100 trials. See, I got 38 successes this time. To make a distribution, we would need to do this many times and make a histogram that contains all of the runs.

Teacher: Isaac, if Alanna performed 50 runs of the simulation, how would you decide if that was enough runs?

Isaac: Well, 50 is not many, but you would look to see if the shape of the distribution was settling down and if you could estimate the mean and standard deviation from the histogram. That is what was nice about the software simulations. You could get hundreds of runs in a few seconds.

Teacher: So, how did you set up the software simulation?

Isaac: You just needed to enter the number of trials and probability of success. Then pick a number of runs to do. You could do more runs later if you wanted to.

Teacher: So, to use either type of technology for simulation, we needed only to know the number of trials *n* and the probability of a success on each trial *p*.

Teacher: If we use *E* for expected number of successes, what formula can we write to show how to compute the expected number of successes? Quincey?

Quincey: $E = np$

Teacher: What other mathematical term describes the expected number of successes? And, can we write the formula in a second way using this term?

Quincey: Oh, that is the mean. We could write $\mu = np$.

Teacher: Does anyone want to add to our discussion at this point or ask questions? *(No response.)* Let's write these two equations here on the board. *(The teacher writes $E = np$ and $\mu = np$.)* We are up to Part c of the STM. How can you tell whether a binomial situation will be approximately normal?

Carson: You use the 10 or greater rule. *(The teacher waits for either Carson or others to be more specific.)*

Aquil: Yeah, he means that both *n* times *p* and *n* times 1 minus *p* must be greater than or equal to 10.

Teacher: Okay, let's write these rules as inequalities again. Carson, please write the rules on the board. *(He writes $np \geq 10$ and $n(1 - p) \geq 10$.)* Recall that *n* stands for the number of trials and *p* the probability of a success on each trial. For the next question, I want each of you to think quietly of your answer and then I will call on someone to provide a response. Here goes: If we think of the expression *np* as a whole, what does it represent? *(The teacher waits and then calls on David.)*

David: *np* is the expected number of successes.

Hudson: We said that was also called the mean.

Teacher: What about $n(1 - p)$ then? As a whole, what does it represent?

Henrietta: That is the expected number of failures.

Teacher: Why do you think that?

Henrietta: Well, $1 - p$ is the probability of a failure. So, multiply that times the number of trials and you have the number of failures you can expect.

Teacher: So, how could we express criteria for deciding whether or not a binomial distribution is approximately normal using these ideas? Cecilia?

Cecilia: You need to check to see if the expected number of successes and the expected number of failures are 10 or more.

Teacher: Good thinking, class. Now we said a few minutes ago that *np*, or the expected number of successes, was also the mean of the binomial distribution. How do you find the standard deviation of the distribution? As you think about the answer to this question, consider the last few minutes of our discussion. Talk about this in your groups for a minute. Again, the question is: "How do you find the standard deviation of a binomial distribution?" *(Teacher waits.)* Let's hear from the group at table 4.

Ivan: You do *np* times 1 minus *p* and then take the square root of that number.

Juan: Another way to say that is the square root of the product of expected number of successes times the probability of a failure.

Teacher: Let's write the formula for the standard deviation of a binomial distribution under the formula for the mean that is on the board. Now take a few minutes to discuss Parts e and f in your groups. Explain how you know your answer to Part d is correct by referring to the formulas on the board. *(Teacher gives students about 2–3 minutes to discuss.)* Table 3 people, please come up to the board to explain your thinking on Part e. As the number of trials increases and the probability of success remains the same, what happens to the expected number of successes and the standard deviation of the binomial distribution? Use these formulas to help explain your answers. *(The group members indicate that both the expected number of successes and the standard deviation are increasing. They refer to the formulas for verification.)*

Teacher: Are there any additional comments or questions? *(The teacher accepts the answer that both are increasing but wonders if some students have thought more deeply about this question.)*

Terry: Our group discussed the fact that the rate of increase for the expected number of successes as n increases is a constant rate, but that is not true for the standard deviation increase. We remembered the problem that asked us to look at what happened if the number of spins went from 60 to 240—Problem 8 Part f. That was a 4 times increase in the number of trials. The standard deviation only doubled. So, the increases going on with the standard deviation are slower than the increases for the expected number of successes.

Penny: That is because of the square rooting going on.

Teacher: Does that make sense to others? *(Students agree.)* It often seems helpful when you refer back to your work in the investigation to explain thinking during our STM discussions. Good job! Now the final part of this STM, "How do the standardized values help you analyze binomial situations?" Adam, your turn.

Adam: $z = \dfrac{x - np}{\sqrt{np(1 - p)}}$

Teacher: Class, does Adam have the formula correct? *(Students indicate agreement.)* Adam, what does the x represent and what does that formula for z help us find?

Adam: Well, you want to find out the probability of getting x or fewer successes. So, you calculate z using the formula. Next, find that number in the standardized values table. The number to the right of it tells you the probability that you have x or fewer successes.

Teacher: Any clarifications or changes needed to Adam's answer?

Maya: Well, you could find the probability of x or more successes also but doing 1 minus the probability of x or fewer successes.

Teacher: Good discussion. One more thought, is it appropriate to use the table with standardized scores for all binomial distributions? Look back at page 245 for a minute as you consider your answer.

Tony: Oh, I know! That table was for normal distributions. So, we need to use our "rule of ten" to see if the binomial situation we have is approximately normal. That is why we have the rule! I didn't really get why we cared about the np and $n(1 - p)$ being 10 or more before.

Teacher: In the next investigation, we will use what we have learned here to make decisions about situations that seem a little suspicious. Stay tuned.

✔Check Your Understanding

a. 66.2% of 120 is 79.44 housing units.

b. The shape will be approximately normal because both $np = 120(0.662)$ and $n(1 - p) = 120(1 - 0.662)$ are 10 or greater.

c. $\sigma = \sqrt{np(1 - p)} = \sqrt{120(0.662)(1 - 0.662)} \approx 5.182$. If you take a random sample of 120 U.S. housing units, about 68% of the time you will find that between $79.44 - 5.182 = 74.258$ and $79.44 + 5.182 = 84.622$ of them are owner-occupied. Alternatively, you will find that about 95% of the time, between $79.44 - 2(5.182) = 69.076$ and $79.44 + 2(5.182) = 89.804$ of them are owner-occupied.

d. Yes, because 65 is more than two standard deviations from the mean of 79.44. Yes, because 90 also is more than two standard deviations from the mean of 79.44. This means that numbers of owner-occupied housing units this extreme would happen less than 5% of the time with a random sample.

e. $z = \dfrac{72 - 79.44}{5.182} \approx -1.44$. Using the table on page 245, the probability is about 0.0808.

f. Use the command **randBin(120,.662)**.

Teacher Notes

Investigation 2 — Binomial Distributions and Making Decisions

Sometimes things happen that make you suspicious. For example, suppose your friend keeps rolling doubles in Monopoly. Knowing about binomial distributions can help you decide whether you should look a little further into this suspicious situation. As you work on problems in this investigation, look for an answer to the following question:

> *How do you decide whether a given probability of success is a plausible one for a given binomial situation?*

1. Suppose that while playing Monopoly, your friend rolls doubles 9 times out of 20 rolls.

    a. What is the expected number of doubles in 20 rolls?

    b. What is the standard deviation of the number of doubles? Is your friend's number of doubles more than one standard deviation above the expected number? More than two?

    c. It does seem like your friend is a little lucky. The following histogram shows the binomial distribution for $n = 20$ and $p = \frac{1}{6}$. This is the theoretical distribution with the probability of getting each number of doubles shown on the vertical axis. Should you be suspicious of the result of 9 doubles in 20 rolls?

20 Rolls of the Dice

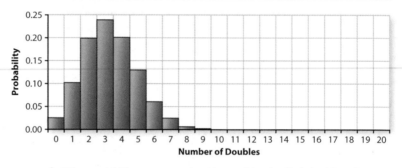

    d. What would be your reaction if your friend rolled doubles all 20 times after you started counting? Use the Multiplication Rule to find the probability that 20 doubles in a row will occur just by chance.

Binomial Distributions and Making Decisions

In this investigation, students learn to recognize which events are likely and which are unlikely (rare events) to happen in a binomial situation. They learn to use the results from a random sample to decide whether it is plausible that a given proportion is the correct proportion of successes for the binomial population from which the sample was taken.

Note About "Rare Event" Although used more and more often, "rare event" is not a term found in all textbooks. Here, it is used to identify an event that rarely occurs because it is one of the events in the outer 2.5% of the lower tail or the outer 2.5% of the upper tail of the distribution from which the sample was taken. Thus, rare events by definition occur 5% of the time. However, the reason for identifying them is that such an extreme event may have occurred for some reason other than just rare luck. That is, you should suspect that your event does not really belong to this distribution. For example, you suspect the dice are not fair and do not have probability $\frac{1}{6}$ of throwing doubles, or you suspect that the correct percentage of children is not 0.20.

①
   a. $20\left(\frac{1}{6}\right) = 3\frac{1}{3}$

   b. $\sigma = \sqrt{np(1-p)} = \sqrt{20\left(\frac{1}{6}\right)\left(\frac{5}{6}\right)} = 1\frac{2}{3}$, or about 1.67. Getting 9 doubles is much more than two standard deviations above the mean (about 3.4 standard deviations above the mean).

   c. You definitely should be suspicious. Getting 9 or more doubles just by chance is almost impossible.

   d. You would be convinced you should take a close look at the dice your friend is using. Rolling doubles 20 times out of 20 tries is almost impossible. Using the Multiplication Rule, the probability of getting 20 doubles out of 20 rolls just by chance is $\left(\frac{1}{6}\right)^{20} \approx 0.00000000000000027$.

(2) Recall that a **rare event** is one that lies in the outer 5% of a distribution. In a waiting-time distribution, rare events typically must be in the upper 5% of the distribution. In binomial distributions, rare events are those in the upper 2.5% or lower 2.5% because it is unlikely to get either an unusually large number of successes or an unusually small number of successes. Use the histogram in Problem 1 to determine which of the following are rare events if you roll a pair of dice 20 times.

a. Getting doubles only once

b. Getting doubles seven times

When a distribution is approximately normal, there is an easy way to identify rare events. You learned in the previous lesson that about 95% of the values in a normal distribution lie within two standard deviations of the mean. Thus, for a binomial distribution that is approximately normal, rare events are those more than two standard deviations from the mean.

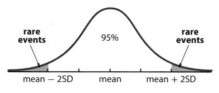

(3) Suppose you roll a pair of dice 100 times and count the number of times you roll doubles. The binomial distribution for this situation appears below.

100 Rolls of the Dice

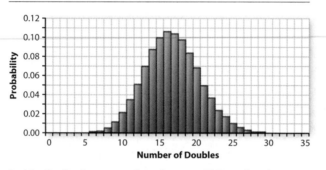

a. Is this distribution approximately normal? How does it compare to the distribution in Problem 1 on page 266?

b. Look at the tails of the histogram. Approximately what numbers of doubles would be rare events?

c. Use the histogram to estimate the expected value and standard deviation of the number of doubles in 100 rolls. Then use the formulas to calculate the expected value and standard deviation.

d. Using the values you calculated in Part c, determine which numbers of doubles would be rare events in 100 rolls of the dice. Are they the same as those you identified in Part b?

② **a.** This is not a rare event. Getting 1 or fewer doubles in 20 rolls happens about 10% + 2.5% = 12.5% of the time, so this outcome is not in the lower 2.5% of the distribution.

b. This is not a rare event as getting 7 doubles in 20 rolls is not in the upper 2.5% of the distribution. If you picture adding the heights of bars 8 and 9 to bar 7, the total probability is greater than 0.025.

③ **a.** The distribution is approximately normal. This is apparent by looking at the histogram or you can verify that the expected number of successes is $np = 100\left(\frac{1}{6}\right) \geq 10$ and the expected number of failures is $n(1 - p) = 100\left(\frac{5}{6}\right) \geq 10$. Compared to the distribution in Problem 1, it is more approximately normal, more symmetric, and looks smoother because it has more bars.

b. Looking at the outer 2.5% in each tail, rare events would be 10 doubles or fewer or 24 doubles or more.

c. A good estimate of the mean is 16 or 17 and a good estimate of the standard deviation is 3 or 4. From the formulas, $\mu \approx 16.67$ and $\sigma \approx 3.73$.

d. Rare events would be more than 16.67 + 2(3.73) = 24.13 doubles or fewer than 16.67 − 2(3.73) = 9.21 doubles. Rare events are almost the same as identified in Part b.

According to the 2000 U.S. Census, about 20% of the residents of the United States are children, age 13 or younger. (Source: *Age: 2000, Census 2000 Brief*, October 2001.) The binomial distribution shows the number of children in 1,000 random samples. Each sample was of size $n = 100$ U.S. residents.

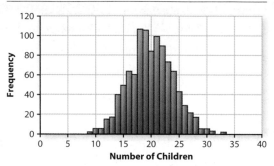

a. Is this distribution approximately normal? What are the mean and standard deviation?

b. Using the mean and standard deviation you calculated in Part a, determine which numbers of children would be rare events in a random sample of 100 U.S. residents.

c. Suppose you take a randomly selected sample of 100 residents of your community and find that there are 35 children.

   i. Would getting 35 children be a rare event if it is true that 20% of the residents in your community are children?

   ii. Would this sample make you doubt that 20% is the correct percentage of residents who are children? If so, the result is called *statistically significant*.

⑤ Look back at the process you used to analyze the result of getting 35 children in the random sample of 100 residents in the previous problem. Review the steps that you took to help you decide whether the event of 35 children was statistically significant.

Step 1. You want to decide whether it is plausible that the given value of p is the right one for your population. State this value of p.

Step 2. For the given value of p and your sample size (number of trials), verify that the binomial distribution is approximately normal. Compute its mean and standard deviation.

Step 3. Take a random sample from your population.

④　**a.** The shape is approximately normal. Students' estimates should be
$\mu \approx 20$ and $\sigma \approx 4$. Using the formulas, $\mu = np = 100(0.2) = 20$,
and $\sigma = \sqrt{np(1-p)} = \sqrt{100(0.2)(0.8)} = 4$.

b. Rare events would be more than $20 + 2(4) = 28$ children or fewer
than $20 - 2(4) = 12$ children.

c.　**i.** Yes, this would be a rare event because 35 is more than 28.

ii. Yes, this should raise some doubt because getting 35 (or more)
children in a random sample of 100 residents when the
population has only 20% children is very unlikely and calls
for some explanation.

NOTE ON THE TERMINOLOGY *RARE EVENT* AND *STATISTICALLY*
SIGNIFICANT Suppose we are thinking of a binomial population with a given
proportion of successes *p*.

- If we know for sure that our sample came from a population with the given
proportion of successes *p* and the number of successes in our sample is
in the lower 2.5% or upper 2.5% of the distribution, then we say that a
rare event occurred.

- If we *do not* know whether our sample came from a population with the given
proportion of successes *p* and the number of successes in our sample is in the
lower 2.5% or upper 2.5% of that distribution, then we use the term *statistically*
significant. This means that we do not find it plausible that the correct probability
of a success for the population from which that sample was taken is *p*.

- If a result from a sample is fairly close to what we would expect under the
assumption that *p* is the correct proportion of successes in the population, then
the result is not statistically significant and would not be a rare event. We
conclude that *p* is plausible for the proportion of successes in the population
from which the sample was taken.

⑤　**a.** Use the guideline $np \geq 10$ and $n(1-p) \geq 10$. The definition of rare
event relies on the fact that in a normal distribution, only 5% of
the values lie more than 2 standard deviations from the mean. In
other words, to use the table on page 245 to estimate probabilities
in a binomial situation, the binomial distribution has to be
approximately normal.

b. $\mu = np$; $\sigma = \sqrt{np(1-p)}$

c. Use the formula $z = \dfrac{x - \mu}{\sigma} = \dfrac{\text{number of successes} - np}{\sqrt{np(1-p)}}$.

d. If you have a statistically significant result and you are sure that you
have a random sample and that you received correct responses from
those you surveyed, you conclude that the given value of *p* is not
the correct one for your population. If the result is not statistically
significant, conclude that it is plausible that the given value of *p* is the
correct one for your population (but other values would be equally
plausible as well).

INSTRUCTIONAL NOTE
Problem 5 summarizes the
thinking behind statistical
inference.

Unit 4

Step 4. Determine how many standard deviations the number of successes in your sample is from the mean of the binomial distribution for the given p. Include a sketch of the situation.

Step 5. If the number of successes in your sample is more than two standard deviations from the mean, declare it **statistically significant**. If you have a random sample, there are two reasons that a statistically significant result could occur.

- You have the right value of p for your population but a rare event occurred.

- You have the wrong value of p for your population.

What makes the practice of statistics challenging is that it is usually impossible to know for sure which is the correct conclusion. However, it is unlikely to get a rare event (probability only 0.05) if you have the right p for your population. Thus, you conclude that the value of p is not the right one for your population.

a. How do you verify that the distribution is approximately normal? Why did you need to determine whether or not the distribution is approximately normal?

b. How do you compute the mean and standard deviation?

c. How do you find the number of standard deviations that your number of successes lies from the mean?

d. What should you conclude if you have a statistically significant result? What should you conclude if you do not have a statistically significant result?

6 About 51% of the residents of the U.S. are female. Tanner takes a random sample of 1,200 people from his community and finds that 640 of the 1,200 are female. From this, he concludes that in his community, the percentage of females is greater than 51%. Use the five steps from Problem 5 to help you decide if you agree with Tanner's conclusion.

7 In 2000, 16% of children lived in areas that did not meet one or more of the Primary National Ambient Air Quality Standards. Suppose that of a randomly selected sample of 100 children hospitalized for asthma, 29 live in an area that does not meet one or more of the Primary National Ambient Air Quality Standards. Is this a statistically significant result? What conclusion should you reach? (Source: *America's Children: Key National Indicators of Well-Being*, 2002, page 12.)

6 **State the value of p.** Here, you want to determine if it is plausible that 51% of all residents of Tanner's community are female. So, $p = 0.51$.

NOTE Solutions to Problem 5 are on page 1268.

Check normality and compute the mean and standard deviation. If you take a random sample of 1,200 people from the residents of the U.S., the distribution of the number of females you will get is approximately normal because both $np = 1{,}200(0.51) = 612$ and $n(1 - p) = 1{,}200(0.49) = 588$ are 10 or more.

$\mu = np = 1{,}200(0.51) = 612$ and
$\sigma = \sqrt{np(1 - p)} = \sqrt{1{,}200(0.51)(0.49)} \approx 17.32$.

Verify that you have a random sample. This was stated in the problem.

Determine how many standard deviations the number of successes from the sample is from the mean. Getting 640 girls in a random sample of 1,200 U.S. residents is $z = \dfrac{640 - 612}{17.32} \approx 1.62$ standard deviations from the mean.

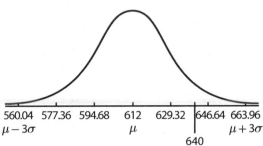

560.04 577.36 594.68   612   629.32 646.64 663.96
$\mu - 3\sigma$ μ $\mu + 3\sigma$
640

State a conclusion. Getting 640 females is less than 2 standard deviations from the mean, so this outcome is not statistically significant. In Tanner's community, the proportion of girls is consistent with the national proportion of 0.51. There is no reason to suspect that the 51% does not hold in this community.

Unit 4

NOTE You may notice that this source gives a much lower percent that live in areas with poor air quality than the source on page 261. You may wish to read more about this issue from the sources.

(7) **State the value of p.** Here, you want to determine if it is plausible that 16% of all children hospitalized for asthma live in an area that does not meet one or more of the Primary National Ambient Air Quality Standards. So, $p = 0.16$.

Check normality and compute the mean and standard deviation. If you take a random sample of 100 children from the U.S., the distribution of the number of children who lived in areas that do not meet the standards is approximately normal because both $np = 100(0.16) = 16$ and $n(1 - p) = 100(0.84) = 84$ are 10 or more.

$$\mu = np = 100(0.16) = 16 \text{ and } \sigma = \sqrt{np(1 - p)} = \sqrt{100(0.16)(0.84)} \approx 3.67.$$

Verify that you have a random sample. This was stated in the problem.

Determine how many standard deviations the result from the sample is from the mean. Getting 29 successes in the sample is $z = \dfrac{29 - 16}{3.67} \approx 3.54$ standard deviations from the mean.

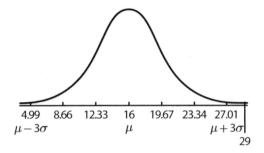

State a conclusion. Getting 29 children who live in areas that do not meet the air quality standards is more than 2 standard deviations above the mean, so this is a statistically significant outcome. Conclude that children with asthma are more likely to live in areas that do not meet the air quality standards. That is, the 16% simply does not apply to the population of children hospitalized with asthma.

It is also possible (but not probable) that the proportion of children hospitalized for asthma who live in areas that do not meet the standard is really 16%, but a rare event occurred with this particular sample.

The overall conclusion is that you do have evidence that the proportion who live in areas that do not meet the air quality standards is higher in children hospitalized with asthma. The alternative would be to conclude that a rare event occurred, but the probability of that is small.

Teacher Notes

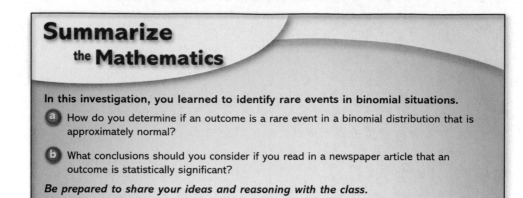

Summarize
the Mathematics

In this investigation, you learned to identify rare events in binomial situations.

a How do you determine if an outcome is a rare event in a binomial distribution that is approximately normal?

b What conclusions should you consider if you read in a newspaper article that an outcome is statistically significant?

Be prepared to share your ideas and reasoning with the class.

✔Check Your Understanding

According to a U.S. Department of Education report (*The Condition of Education 2003*, page 43. nces.ed.gov/pubs2003/2003067_3.pdf), about 62% of high school graduates enroll in college immediately after high school graduation. Suppose you take a random sample of 200 high school graduates and count the number who enroll in college immediately after graduation.

a. What is the expected number who enroll? The expected number who do not? Is this sample size large enough that the binomial distribution for this situation will be approximately normal?

b. Complete this sentence using the mean and standard deviation. If you select 200 high school graduates at random, you expect that ___ graduates enroll in college immediately after high school graduation, give or take ___ graduates.

c. Sketch this distribution. Include a scale on the *x*-axis that shows the mean and the points one and two standard deviations from the mean.

d. Suppose you want to see whether 62% is a plausible percentage for your community. You take a random sample of 200 high school graduates from your community and find that 135 enroll in college immediately after graduation. Is this statistically significant? What is your conclusion?

e. Suppose your random sample found 100 enrolled in college immediately after graduation. Is this statistically significant? What is your conclusion?

Unit 4

Summarize
the Mathematics

a You compute a standardized value *z* so you can see whether the outcome is more than two standard deviations from the mean. If so, it is a rare event under the assumption that the sample was random and the population proportion is as specified.

b You should consider at least four possible conclusions.

1. The proportion of successes in the population is not equal to the given proportion *p* that they were considering.

2. Their sampling procedure did not generate a random sample.

3. They did not get the correct response from the people in their sample.

4. The proportion of successes in the population is equal to the given proportion *p* they were considering, and they did take a random sample and get correct responses. But by chance, a rare event occurred.

MATH TOOLKIT Give an example of how you determine a rare event for a binomial distribution that is appropriately normal.

✓Check Your Understanding

a. The expected number who enroll is $200(0.62) = 124$. The expected number who do not enroll is $200(0.38) = 76$. The binomial distribution is approximately normal because both of these numbers are 10 or more.

b. If you select 200 high school graduates at random, you expect that 124 graduates enroll in college immediately after high school graduation, give or take,

$$\sigma = \sqrt{np(1-p)} = \sqrt{200(0.62)(0.38)} \approx 6.86 \text{ graduates.}$$

c.

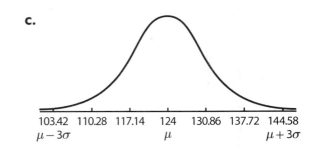

| 103.42 | 110.28 | 117.14 | 124 | 130.86 | 137.72 | 144.58 |
| $\mu - 3\sigma$ | | | μ | | | $\mu + 3\sigma$ |

d. Here, you want to decide if it is plausible that $p = 0.62$ is the correct proportion of all high school graduates in your community who enroll in college immediately after graduation. Getting 135 is less than two standard deviations from the expected number of 124. This is not statistically significant. Conclude that it is plausible that 62% of all high school graduates in your community enroll in college immediately after graduation. In other words, getting 135 is not unusual from a random sample of 200 high school graduates taken from a population where 62% enroll in college immediately after graduation.

e. Getting only 100 successes would be $z = \dfrac{100 - 124}{6.86} \approx -3.50$ standard deviations from the mean. This is statistically significant. You conclude that the proportion of all high school graduates in your community who enroll in college immediately after graduation is not 62%.

Applications

1 About 20% of the residents of the United States are children aged 13 and younger. Suppose you take a random sample of 200 people living in the United States and count the number of children.

  a. Will the binomial distribution for the number of children in a sample of this size be approximately normal? Why or why not?

  b. Compute the mean and the standard deviation of the binomial distribution for the number of children.

  c. Make a sketch of the distribution, including a scale on the x-axis that shows the mean and one, two, and three standard deviations from the mean.

  d. Use a standardized value to estimate the probability that your sample contains 45 or more children.

  e. The number of children in one sample is 1.94 standard deviations below average. How many children are in the sample?

  f. Suppose in your random sample of 200 people, 45 were children. Would you be surprised with that number of children? Explain.

2 Ty Cobb played Major League Baseball from 1905 to 1928. He holds the record for the highest career batting average (0.366). Suppose you pick 60 of his at bats at random and count the number of hits. (Source: baseball-almanac.com/hitting/hibavg3.shtml)

  a. Is the binomial distribution of the number of hits approximately normal?

  b. Compute the expected value and standard deviation of the binomial distribution of the number of hits in 60 at bats.

  c. Sketch this distribution. Include a scale on the x-axis that shows the mean and the points one and two standard deviations from the mean.

  d. Use a standardized value to estimate the probability that Cobb got 14 or fewer hits in this random sample of size 60.

  e. Suppose you were Cobb's coach. Would you have been concerned if Cobb got only 14 hits in his next 60 at bats?

On Your Own

Applications

(1) **a.** Yes, because both $np = 200(0.20) = 40$ and $n(1 - p) = 200(0.80) = 160$ are 10 or more.

b. $\mu = np = 200(0.20) = 40$

$\sigma = \sqrt{np(1 - p)} = \sqrt{200(0.20)(0.80)} \approx 5.66$

c.

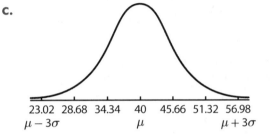

23.02 28.68 34.34 40 45.66 51.32 56.98
$\mu - 3\sigma$ μ $\mu + 3\sigma$

d. $z = \dfrac{45 - 40}{5.66} \approx 0.88$. Using the table on page 245, the probability is about $1 - 0.8159 = 0.1841$.

e. 1.94 standard deviations below average is $40 - 1.94(5.66) \approx$ 29 children.

f. The fact that the expected number is 40 does not mean you will get 40 children each time you take a random sample of 200 people. Sometimes you get fewer, and sometimes you get more. In this case, getting 45 is not very far from the expected number of 40. In fact, there is an 18% chance of getting this many children or even more in a sample this size.

(2) **a.** Yes, because both $np = 60(0.366) = 21.96$ and $n(1 - p) = 60(0.634) = 38.04$ are 10 or more.

b. $\mu = np = 60(0.366) = 21.96$

$\sigma = \sqrt{np(1 - p)} = \sqrt{60(0.366)(0.634)} \approx 3.73$

c.

10.77 14.5 18.23 21.96 25.69 29.42 33.15
$\mu - 3\sigma$ μ $\mu + 3\sigma$

d. $z = \dfrac{x - \mu}{\sigma} \approx \dfrac{14 - 21.96}{3.73} \approx -2.13$. From the table, the probability is about 0.0179.

e. Yes, because 14 hits is more than two standard deviations below the number of hits you would expect in 60 at bats. While such a small number of hits will happen to Cobb just by chance on rare occasions, it bears watching by the coach.

Unit 4

Binomial Distributions **T271**

3 A library has 25 computers, which must be reserved in advance. The library assumes that people will decide independently whether or not to show up for their reserved time. It also estimates that for each person, there is an 80% chance that he or she will show up for the reserved time.

  a. If the library takes 30 reservations for each time period, what is the expected number of people who will show? Is it possible that all 30 will show?

  b. How many reservations should the library take so that 25 are expected to show? Is it possible that if the library takes this many reservations, more than 25 people will show?

  c. Suppose the library decides to take 30 reservations. Use the **randBin** function of your calculator to conduct 5 runs of a simulation that counts the number who show. Add your results to a copy of the frequency table and histogram below so that there is a total of 55 runs.

Computer Reservations

Number of People Who Show	Frequency (before)	Frequency (after)
19	0	
20	1	
21	2	
22	3	
23	5	
24	8	
25	9	
26	9	
27	7	
28	4	
29	2	
30	0	
Total Number of Runs	50	55

3 **a.** You expect $30(0.80) = 24$ to show. It is possible that all 30 will show.

    b. Solve $25 = n(0.80)$ to get $n = 31.25$. So, you should make 31 reservations. Yes, it is certainly possible that more than 25 people will show, as 25 is the number you expect.

    c. Use **randBin(30,.80)** five times. Each time, the function will give you the number of students who showed out of the 30 who made reservations. Results of the five runs will vary.

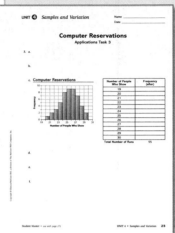

Teaching Resources

Student Master 23.

d. Describe the shape of the distribution.

e. Suppose the library takes 30 reservations. Based on the simulation, estimate the probability that more than 25 people show. Is 30 a reasonable number of reservations to take? Should the library take fewer than 30 reservations or is it reasonable to take more?

f. What assumption made in this simulation is different from the real-life situation being modeled?

④ Several years ago, a survey found that 25% of American pet owners carry pictures of their pets in their wallets. Assume this percentage is true, and you will be taking a random sample of 20 American pet owners and counting the number who carry pictures of their pets.

a. Describe how to conduct one run of a simulation using the **randBin** function of your calculator.

b. Predict the shape, mean, and standard deviation of the binomial distribution that you would get if you conduct a large number of runs.

c. Perform 10 runs of your simulation. Add your results to a copy of the following frequency table so that there is a total of 100 runs.

Number of People with Pictures of Their Pets	Frequency (before)	Frequency (after)
0	0	
1	2	
2	6	
3	12	
4	17	
5	18	
6	15	
7	10	
8	5	
9	3	
10	1	
11	1	
Total Number of Runs	90	100

d. Make a histogram of this distribution. Check your predictions in Part b.

e. Estimate the number of pet owners with pictures that would be rare events.

f. Patrick took a survey of 20 pet owners at the mall. Only one had a picture of a pet in his wallet. Does Patrick have any reason to doubt the reported figure of 25%?

d. The distribution is skewed left (towards the smaller numbers).

e. From the incomplete table with 50 runs, the estimate is
$$\frac{9 + 7 + 4 + 2 + 0}{50} = 0.44.$$

f. The assumption is that the people decide independently whether or not to show. In real life, for example, groups of students tend to do things together. A group of students that made reservations for the computers in the library might decide to do something else instead.

4

a. Use the **randBin(20,.25)** function. This will give the number of the 20 pet owners who carry a picture of their pet in their wallet.

b. The distribution will be skewed right (towards the larger values) because $np = 20(0.25) = 4$, which is less than 10. The mean should be at about $20(0.25) = 4$. The standard deviation should be about $\sigma = \sqrt{np(1 - p)} = \sqrt{20(0.25)(0.75)} \approx 1.94$.

c. Results from runs will vary.

d. A histogram of the 90 runs in the incomplete table appears below.

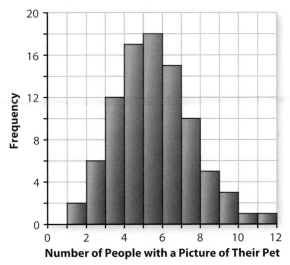

Number of People with a Picture of Their Pet

e. 1 or fewer, or 10 or more

f. If a random sample of 20 pet owners finds only one person with a picture of his or her pet, that would be a rare event if 25% of pet owners carry a picture of their pet. So, Patrick's result needs explaining. Perhaps the given percentage was not correct to begin with or perhaps it has changed. But it is also likely that Patrick was unlikely to be able to get a random sample of pet owners. Perhaps the percentage is different among pet owners at the mall than among all Americans. So, whether he has any reason to doubt the reported figure of 25% depends on how much he thinks his sample resembles a random sample of all pet owners.

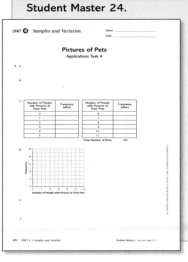

Teaching Resources

Student Master 24.

UNIT ❹ *Samples and Variation* Name _____
Date _____

Pictures of Pets
Applications Task 4

INSTRUCTIONAL NOTE
Task 4 offers an opportunity for your students to take their own survey.

5. According to the United States census, 66.2% of housing units are occupied by the owners. (Source: quickfacts.census.gov/qfd/states/00000.html) You want to see if this percentage is plausible for your county. Suppose you take a random sample of 1,100 housing units and find that 526 are owner-occupied. Is this a statistically significant result? What conclusion should you reach? Use the five steps in Problem 5 of Investigation 2 on pages 268 and 269 to help you decide.

6. You have inherited a coin from your eccentric uncle. The coin appears a bit strange itself. To test whether the coin is fair, you toss it 150 times and count the number of heads. You get 71 heads. What conclusion should you reach?

Connections

7. In Problem 5 (page 262) of Investigation 1, you examined the shape, center, and spread of binomial distributions with probability of success 0.2 and varying sample sizes. Use computer software like the "Binomial Distributions" custom tool to help generalize your findings from that problem (Part a) and to explore a related question (Part b).

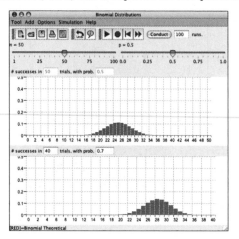

a. As n increases, but the probability of a success p remains the same, what happens to the shape, center, and spread of the binomial distribution for the number of successes?

b. As p increases from 0.01 to 0.99, but n remains the same (for example, $n = 50$), what happens to the shape, center, and spread of the binomial distribution for the number of successes?

(5) **State the value of p.** Here, you want to determine if it is plausible that 66.2% of all housing units in your county are owner-occupied. So, $p = 0.662$.

Check normality and compute the mean and standard deviation. If you take a random sample of 1,100 housing units from a population where 66.2% are owner-occupied, the distribution of the number of owner-occupied units is approximately normal because both $np = 1,100(0.662) = 728.2$ and $n(1 - p) = 1,100(1 - 0.662) = 371.8$ are much greater than 10.

$\mu = np = 1,100(0.662) = 728.2$ and
$\sigma = \sqrt{np(1 - p)} = \sqrt{1,100(0.662)(1 - 0.662)} \approx 15.689$.

Determine how many standard deviations the result from the sample is from the mean. $z = \dfrac{5206 - 728.2}{15.689} \approx -12.888$ standard deviations from the mean.

State a conclusion. The result from the sample is more than 2 standard deviations from the mean, and so this is statistically significant. It is almost impossible to get this few owner-occupied housing units in a random sample of 1,100 housing units from a population where 66.2% of housing units are owner-occupied. Thus, you should conclude that it is not plausible that the percentage of owner-occupied housing units is 66.2% in your county.

(6) **State the value of p.** Here, you want to determine if it is plausible that the coin is fair. So, $p = 0.5$.

Check normality and compute the mean and standard deviation. If you flip a fair coin 150 times, the distribution of the number of heads you will get is approximately normal because both $np = 150(0.5) = 75$ and $n(1 - p) = 150(1 - 0.5) = 75$ are greater than 10.

$\mu = np = 150(0.5) = 75$ and $\sigma = \sqrt{np(1 - p)} = \sqrt{150(0.5)(0.5)} \approx 6.124$.

Determine how many standard deviations the result from the sample is from the mean. $z = \dfrac{71 - 75}{6.124} \approx -0.653$ standard deviations from the mean.

State a conclusion. This is not a statistically significant result. It is quite plausible that your uncle's strange coin is fair. In other words, getting 71 heads in 150 flips of a fair coin would not be unusual, so you have no reason to suspect that the coin is unfair.

Connections

(7) **TECHNOLOGY NOTE** Students can explore these questions using the sliders for n and p that appear when you select the "Binomial Distributions" custom tool. Since the horizontal scale changes when n is changed, you may wish to have students show multiple distributions as displayed below. To obtain these from the "Binomial Distributions" custom tool, under the Add menu, choose either "Binomial with Editable n" or "Binomial with Editable p." The multiple display feature is also helpful to observe the symmetric nature of two histograms with the same sample size n and probabilities p and $1 - p$.

a. As the sample size n increases, the shape becomes more approximately normal and the mean and standard deviation of the number of successes increase.

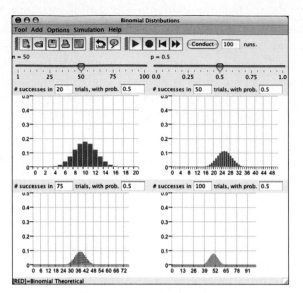

b. As the probability p increases but the number of successes remains constant, the shape of the distribution changes from skewed to the right to approximately normal to skewed to the left as shown below. As the probability increases, the mean of the distribution increases. The standard deviation, as p increases from 0.01 to 0.99, increases until $p = 0.5$ and then decreases.

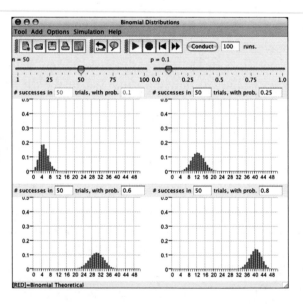

The "Binomial Distributions" custom tool includes a feature that runs a simulation of a binomial situation and superimposes the results of the simulation on the theoretical distribution as shown in the screen below at the left. The other screen shows the normal approximation to the binomial situation.

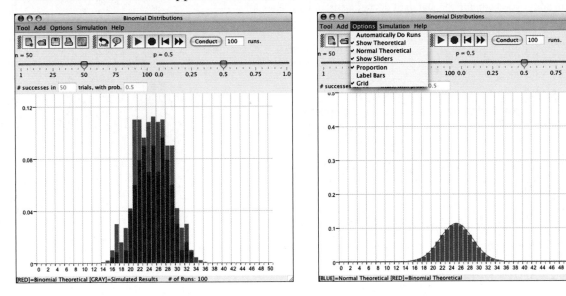

(8) Match each description of a binomial distribution in Parts a–d with its corresponding graph. It will help if you count the number of visible bars and if you compute the standard deviations from the values in Parts a–d.

   a. $p = 0.1, n = 40$
   b. $p = 0.2, n = 20$
   c. $p = 0.4, n = 10$
   d. $p = 0.8, n = 5$

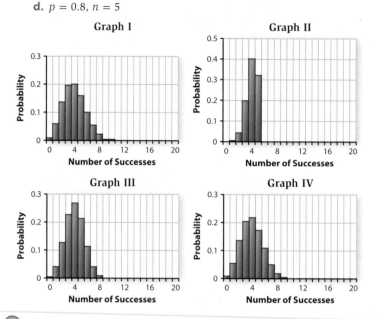

(9) In Investigation 1, you examined a simple formula for the standard deviation of a binomial distribution of the number of successes with n trials and probability of success p. In this task, you will further analyze the formula to make sure it gives the values you would expect.

   a. What do you think should be the standard deviation of the binomial distribution when $p = 1$? Does the formula give this value?

   b. What do you think should be the standard deviation of the binomial distribution when $p = 0$? Does the formula give this value?

   c. If you know the standard deviation of the binomial distribution with n trials and probability of success p, what is the standard deviation of the binomial distribution with n trials and probability of success $1 - p$? Why does this make sense?

   d. For a fixed number of trials n, what value of p will make the standard deviation, $\sqrt{np(1 - p)}$, the largest?

8 Note that all histograms are centered at $np = 4$, so students must make a decision based on spread.

Part	σ	Graph
a	1.9	I
b	1.8	IV
c	1.5	III
d	0.9	II

Looking at the histograms, the spreads from largest to smallest are I, IV, III, II. Also, the histogram in Graph II has to be the histogram for $n = 5$ because there are only six possible outcomes when $n = 5$. The histogram in Graph II is the only histogram with fewer than 6 visible bars.

9 **a.** When $p = 1$, the standard deviation should be 0 because all samples of size n will have n successes. Every trial is a success. The probability distribution table looks like this.

Number of Successes	Probability
0	0
1	0
⋮	⋮
n	1

That is, there will be no variability between the different samples. The formula gives this value, $\sigma = \sqrt{np(1 - p)} = \sqrt{n(1)(1 - 1)} = 0$.

b. When $p = 0$, the standard deviation should be 0 because all samples of size n will have 0 successes. No trial is a success. The probability distribution table looks like this.

Number of Successes	Probability
0	1
1	0
⋮	⋮
n	0

That is, there will be no variability between the different samples. The formula gives this value, $\sigma = \sqrt{np(1 - p)} = \sqrt{n(0)(1 - 0)} = 0$.

c. It is the same, $\sigma = \sqrt{n(1 - p)p} = \sqrt{np(1 - p)}$. This makes sense because the number of failures is n minus the number of successes. Because they differ by a constant, the variability in the number of successes should be the same as the variability in the number of failures.

d. Students may notice from recalling distributions they have seen that the variability is the largest for $p = 0.5$. From the formula, the largest value of $p(1 - p)$ occurs when $p = 0.5$. This can be proved by considering the graph of $y = p(1 - p) = p - p^2$. This is a parabola that opens down. The maximum occurs at the vertex when

$$p = -\frac{b}{2a} = \frac{1}{2}.$$

Unit 4

10 In Problem 6 of Investigation 1, you found that the sample size of 50 for rolling a die and counting the number of 3s was not large enough so that the binomial distribution can be considered approximately normal. What is the smallest sample size needed to be able to consider the binomial distribution for the situation of rolling a die and counting the number of 3s approximately normal?

11 About 60% of high school transcripts in the United States show that the student has taken a chemistry or physics course.

   a. Describe how to use the **randBin** function of your calculator to conduct a simulation to estimate the number of students who took a high school chemistry or physics course in a randomly selected group of 20 high school graduates.

   b. Conduct five runs of your simulation. Add your results to a copy of the frequency table and histogram below so there is a total of 400 runs.

Chemistry and Physics on Student Transcripts

Number Who Took Chemistry or Physics	Frequency (before)	Frequency (after)
6	3	
7	2	
8	17	
9	39	
10	51	
11	53	
12	80	
13	66	
14	39	
15	29	
16	13	
17	3	
Total Number of Runs	395	400

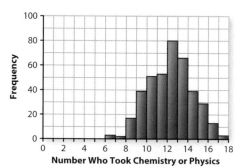

276 UNIT 4 • Samples and Variation

10 Solving $n\left(\frac{1}{6}\right) = 10$ gives $n = 60$.

11 **a.** Use **randBin(20,.60)**. This will return the number of students who took chemistry or physics in a random sample of 20 students from a population where 60% take chemistry or physics. Repeat this many times until the distribution takes shape.

b. Results from the five runs will vary.

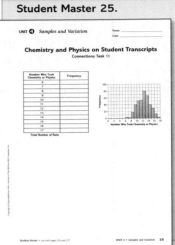

Teaching Resources

Student Master 25.

Unit 4

c. When 20 students are randomly selected, what is your estimate of the probability that fewer than half took chemistry or physics in high school?

d. Describe the shape of the distribution. According to the rule, should it be approximately normal?

e. Estimate the mean and standard deviation of this distribution from the histogram. Check your estimates using the formulas for the mean and standard deviation.

f. The histogram below shows the binomial distribution for the number of transcripts with chemistry or physics when 80 transcripts are selected at random, rather than 20. Describe how the shape, center, and spread of this histogram are different from those for sample sizes of 20.

Chemistry or Physics Enrollment

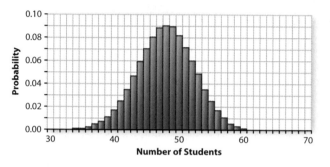

g. Is it more likely to find that fewer than half of the high school transcripts show that the student has taken a chemistry or physics course if you take a sample of size 20 or a sample of size 80? Explain why this should be the case.

Reflections

12 The following situations are not binomial situations. For each situation, list which of the four characteristics of a binomial situation on page 260 do not hold.

a. Roll a die 35 times. On each roll, note the number that appears on top.

b. Select five students from your classroom. Note whether each is male or female. The method of selection is to write the name of each student in your classroom on a slip of paper. Select a slip at random. Do not replace that slip. Select another slip at random. Do not replace that slip either. Select another slip at random. Continue until you have five names.

c. Using the incomplete table of 395 runs, the estimate is
$$\frac{3 + 2 + 17 + 39}{395} = \frac{61}{395}, \text{ or about } 0.154.$$

d. The distribution is skewed a bit left (towards the smaller numbers). Verifying this, $np = 20(0.60) = 12$ which is more than 10 but $n(1 - p) = 20(0.40) = 8$ is less than 10.

e. Good estimates of the mean are around 12 and good estimates of the standard deviation are around 2. Using the formulas,
$$\mu = np = 20(0.60) = 12 \text{ and } \sigma = \sqrt{np(1 - p)} = \sqrt{20(0.60)(0.40)} \approx 2.19.$$

f. As expected, with the same value of p, but a larger sample size, the distribution is more approximately normal with the sample size of 80. The mean number of students who have taken these courses is larger with a sample of size 80 than with a sample of size 20. The spread also is larger with a sample of size 80. As the sample size increases, the number of "successes" in the sample tends to have more variability. (But, by the Law of Large Numbers, the *proportion* of successes in the sample has *less* variability as the sample size increases.)

g. You can see from the histograms that you are much more likely to get fewer than half with the smaller sample size. Alternatively, according to the Law of Large Numbers, you expect the proportion from the larger sample to be closer to 60% with the proportion of successes from the smaller sample size.

Reflections

12 a. There are six possible outcomes, not just two categories of success and failure.

b. The draws are not independent because the probabilities for what happens on, for example, the fourth draw depend on what names have been previously drawn. Thus, the probability of getting, for example, a male changes as names are removed. The situation would be binomial if each slip of paper were replaced after each draw.

c. Place four new batteries in a calculator. Count the number that need to be replaced during 200 hours of use.

d. Flip a coin. Count the number of trials until you get a head.

e. Select 25 cars at random. Count the number of cars of each color.

13 Look back at the formulas for calculating the mean and standard deviation of a binomial probability distribution (pages 261 and 263). Consider a binomial situation with probability p.

a. If you double the sample size, what happens to the mean? To the standard deviation?

b. How does the mean vary with the sample size? How does the standard deviation vary with the sample size?

c. How are your answers to Parts a and b seen in the distributions on page 262?

14 Sports writers and commentators often speak of *odds* rather than probabilities. When you roll two dice, the odds of getting 7 as the sum are 6 to 30, or 1 to 5. That is, of 36 equally likely outcomes, 6 are successes and 30 are failures. Suppose you roll a pair of dice. Give both the probability and the odds of getting each of the following events.

a. a sum of 2

b. a sum of 8

c. an even sum

15 Suppose a person starts flipping a coin and gets heads on each flip.

a. How many heads do you think it would take before you were suspicious that the person had a two-headed coin? Before you were confident the person had a two-headed coin?

b. For your two answers in Part a, compute the probability that a person who begins to flip a fair coin will get this many heads in a row just by chance.

16 Statistics is sometimes defined as learning about a population by taking a sample from that population. Some people say you can prove anything with statistics. The truth is more nearly the opposite. You cannot *prove* anything with statistics. Explain why the second statement is the better one.

c. The probability it will last 200 hours will not be the same for each battery, but may depend on its location in the calculator. Also, the trials are probably not independent. If one battery has gone dead, it may strain the others and increase the probability that the others will give out at about the same time.

d. The number of flips is not fixed. (This is a waiting-time or geometric situation, not a binomial situation.)

e. There are many possible colors, not just two categories of success and failure.

13 a. If you double the sample size n, the mean np becomes $2np$. So, the mean doubles. The formula for the standard deviation is $\sigma = \sqrt{np(1-p)}$. When n is doubled, this becomes

$$\sqrt{(2n)p(1-p)} = \sqrt{2}\sqrt{np(1-p)}$$
$$= \sqrt{2}\,\sigma$$

So, the new standard deviation is $\sqrt{2}$ times the original one.

b. The mean varies directly with the sample size. The standard deviation varies directly with the square root of the sample size.

c. The mean is 1 in the first distribution. As the sample sizes change by a factor of 2, 5, 10, and 20, the mean changes by a factor of 2, 5, 10, and 20, respectively. You can observe that the standard deviation is increasing and that it seems to increase by less than the factors 2, 5, 10, and 20.

14 a. $\frac{1}{36}$; 1 to 35

b. $\frac{5}{36}$; 5 to 31

c. $\frac{18}{36}$, or $\frac{1}{2}$; 1 to 1

15 a–b. Responses will vary. Investigations have shown that people start to get suspicious after about five heads in a row. The probability of five heads in a row is $(0.5)^5 = 0.03125$. Such an investigation would make a good project for students.

16 When you take a sample from a population, you are seeing only part of the population. So, for example, if you take a random sample of 1,000 adults and find that all of them own a pair of black shoes, that does not allow you to say that the entire population of adults owns a pair of black shoes. There is always the uncertainty that results because you have not looked at the entire population. In fact, it is possible that very few adults in your population own black shoes and you happened to get the only 1,000 adults who do in your sample. That, however, is very unlikely.

That is, statistics is the science of making decisions based on what is likely and unlikely rather than making decisions based on what is possible. Almost any outcome is *possible* when you are dealing with random samples or with chance situations like rolling dice. So speaking in terms of what is possible does not get us very far. For decision making, we need to divide the possible outcomes into those that it is likely to get and those it is unlikely to get.

Extensions

17 Suppose you want to estimate the percentage of teens who count sheep in order to fall asleep. As the Law of Large Numbers tells you, the more teens you ask, the closer your estimate should be to the true percentage that you would get if you could ask all teens. (However, that is true only if you randomly select the teens you ask rather than, for example, asking only teens you know.)

Suppose that you want to be at least 95% sure that your estimate is off by no more than 3%. You can use the formula below to estimate the number of teens you need to ask. This formula gives the sample size n needed in order to be 95% certain that your estimate is within your margin of error E.

$$n = \frac{1}{E^2}$$

In your survey, you want to estimate the percentage of teens who count sheep. You want to be at least 95% sure your estimated percentage is within $E = 0.03$ (3%) of the true percentage. Substituting 0.03 into the formula gives

$$n = \frac{1}{(0.03)^2} = \frac{1}{0.0009} \approx 1,111.$$

You need to ask approximately 1,111 teens.

Being "at least 95% sure" means that out of every 100 surveys you perform, you expect that in 95 or more of them, your estimated percentage is within E of the true percentage.

a. Suppose you want to estimate the probability a loaded die lands with a 6 on top and be at least 95% sure that your estimated probability is within 5% of the actual probability. How many times should you toss the die?

b. Suppose you do a simulation to estimate a proportion. How many runs do you need to estimate the proportion to within 1%?

c. What is the margin of error associated with 200 runs of a simulation to estimate a proportion?

d. National polls often ask 1,200 randomly selected people questions such as whether they approve of the job the President is doing. What is the margin of error associated with a sample size of 1,200?

18 Use your graphing calculator or computer software to investigate the graph of the *sample size* function $n = \frac{1}{E^2}$ given in Extensions Task 17.

a. Should x or y represent the sample size? What does the other variable represent?

b. Graph this function.

c. Describe the shape of the graph of this function, including any symmetry.

d. Use the trace function to estimate the sample size needed for a margin of error of 2%. Of 3%. Of 8%.

Extensions

17 **NOTE** The formula $n = \frac{1}{E^2}$ for the sample size needed in order to estimate a proportion to within E with 95% confidence is a simplified version of the formula $n = 1.96^2 \cdot \frac{p(1-p)}{E^2}$. The simplification was obtained by estimating 1.96 with 2 and by using the fact that $p(1-p)$ has its maximum value when $p = 0.5$: $n = 1.96^2 \cdot \frac{p(1-p)}{E^2} \approx 2^2 \cdot \frac{0.5(1-0.5)}{E^2} = \frac{1}{E^2}$.

a. $n = \frac{1}{E^2} = \frac{1}{0.05^2} = 400$. You should perform at least 400 trials to be at least 95% sure that the estimated probability is within 5% of the actual probability.

b. $n = \frac{1}{E^2} = \frac{1}{0.01^2} = 10{,}000$ runs

c. $200 = \frac{1}{E^2}$; so, $E \approx 0.071$, or 7.1%. The margin of error associated with 200 trials is approximately 7.1%.

d. $1{,}200 = \frac{1}{E^2}$; so, $E \approx 0.029$, or 2.9%. The margin of error associated with 1,200 trials is approximately 2.9%.

18 a. Let y represent the sample size and x represent the margin of error.

b.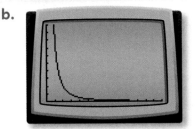

c. Because E and n cannot be negative, the graph lies in the first quadrant. It looks very much like the graph of $y = \frac{1}{x}$, except that it approaches the axes more quickly. It is symmetric about the line $y = x$.

d. The sample sizes needed are about 2,500, 1,111, and 156.

19 **Acceptance sampling** is one method that industry uses to control the quality of the parts it uses. For example, a recording company buys blank CDs from a supplier. To ensure the quality of these CDs, the recording company examines a sample of the CDs in each shipment. The company buys the shipment only if 5% or fewer of the CDs in the sample are defective. Assume that 10% of the CDs actually are defective.

"By a small sample we may judge the whole piece."
Miguel de Cervantes

a. Suppose the recording company examines a sample of 20 CDs from each shipment.

   i. Is this a binomial situation? If so, give the sample size and the probability of a "success."

   ii. Design and carry out a simulation of this situation.

   iii. What is your estimate of the probability that the shipment will be accepted?

b. Suppose the recording company examines a sample of 100 CDs from each shipment. Is a normal distribution a good model of the binomial distribution? If so, use it and a standardized value to estimate the probability that the shipment will be accepted.

20 Use the margin of error formula given in Extensions Task 17 to investigate the sample size needed to cut the margin of error in half.

a. What is the margin of error for a sample size of 100? What sample size would you need to cut this margin of error in half?

b. What is the margin of error with a sample size of 625? What sample size would you need to cut this margin of error in half?

c. In general, to cut a margin of error in half, how must the sample size change? Use the formula to justify your answer.

21 The Martingale is an old gambling system. At first glance, it looks like a winner. Here is how it would work for a player betting on red in roulette. The roulette wheel has 38 spaces, and 18 of these spaces are red. On the first spin of the wheel, Mr. Garcia bets $1. If red appears, he collects $2 and leaves. If he loses, he bets $2 on red on the second spin of the wheel. If red appears, he collects $4 and leaves. If he loses, he bets $4 on red on the third spin of the wheel, and so on. Mr. Garcia keeps doubling his bet until he wins.

a. If Mr. Garcia plays 76 times, how many times does he expect to win?

b. If Mr. Garcia wins on his first try, how much money will he be ahead? If he wins on his third try, how much money will he be ahead? If Mr. Garcia finally wins on his tenth try, how much money will he be ahead?

c. From the gambler's point of view, what are some flaws in this system? (From the gambler's point of view, there are flaws in *every* "system.")

19 **INSTRUCTIONAL NOTE** First, note that the percentage of defective CDs is higher than the recording company wants. The shipments *should* be rejected. The point of this task is to show that in a larger sample, the proportion of defective CDs tends to be closer to 10% than in a smaller sample. Larger samples, then, tend to result in rejected shipments more often than smaller samples.

a. i. Yes, this is a binomial situation with $n = 20$ and probability of success $p = 0.10$. Note that $np = 20(0.10) = 2$, so the normal approximation cannot be used for this problem.

ii. On the calculator, use the command **randBin(20,.10)** repeatedly to generate samples. Alternatively, students may use **randBin(20,.10,200)**, which will give the number of defective CDs in 200 samples of size 20 each, or the *CPMP-Tools* Simulation software: Build, Distribution Events, Random Binomial. Double-click $n = 100$ and $p = 0.5$ to change n and p.

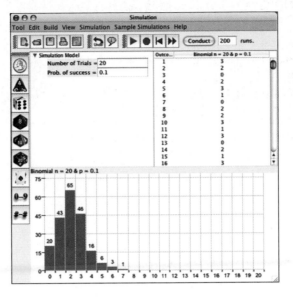

TECHNOLOGY NOTE
The exact probability given in Part a was found using the command **binomcdf(n,p,x)**, where x is the largest number of CDs that would result in rejecting a shipment. That is, this command gives the exact probability of getting x or fewer success in a binomial situation with n trials and probability of success p. Students will learn the formula used by this command, the binomial probability formula, in Course 4.

iii. The probability a shipment will be accepted is 0.39. Although the company will reject most shipments, as it should, a chance of 0.39 most likely will be an unacceptably high probability of accepting a shipment with too high a percentage of defective CDs. The company should either increase its sample size or not accept a shipment with any defective CD. (From the simulation above, the estimated probability that a shipment will be accepted is $\frac{20 + 43}{200} = 0.315$.)

b. This is a binomial situation with $n = 100$ and probability of success $p = 0.10$. A normal distribution can be used for this problem because both $np = 10$ and $n(1 - p) = 90$ are 10 or more. The mean is $\mu = np = 10$, and the standard deviation is $\sigma = \sqrt{np(1 - p)} = \sqrt{100(0.1)(0.9)} = 3$. The company accepts the shipment when there are 5% or fewer defective. This is 5 or fewer CDs. The standardized value for 5 CDs in the sample is $z = \frac{5 - 10}{3} = -1.7$. Using the table on page 245, the probability of 5 or fewer defective is about 0.0446. The company will almost always reject the shipment, as it should.

20 a. 0.10; 400   b. 0.04; 2,500

c. You must quadruple the sample size to cut the margin of error in half. To show this algebraically, suppose that $n = \frac{1}{E^2}$ is the sample size you need for a margin of error of E. If you want an error of $\frac{E}{2}$, you need a sample size of $\frac{1}{\left(\frac{E}{2}\right)^2} = \frac{1}{\left(\frac{E^2}{4}\right)} = 4\left(\frac{1}{E^2}\right) = 4n$, or 4 times the previous sample size of n.

NOTE Solutions for Task 21 Parts a–c are on page T281.

Unit 4

Review

22 Solve each of the following equations by reasoning with the symbols themselves.

a. $6x - x^2 = 5$

b. $3(x + 9)^2 = 75$

c. $4(3^x) = 108$

d. $(x + 3)(x - 2) = 10$

23 Suppose that you spin this spinner two times.

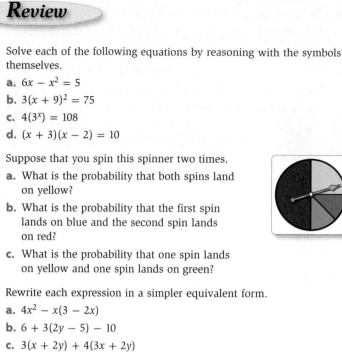

a. What is the probability that both spins land on yellow?

b. What is the probability that the first spin lands on blue and the second spin lands on red?

c. What is the probability that one spin lands on yellow and one spin lands on green?

24 Rewrite each expression in a simpler equivalent form.

a. $4x^2 - x(3 - 2x)$

b. $6 + 3(2y - 5) - 10$

c. $3(x + 2y) + 4(3x + 2y)$

d. $x(x + 1) - (x + 5)$

25 The length of a rectangle is three times its width. The area of the rectangle is 192 cm^2. Find the perimeter of the rectangle.

26 Determine if each statement is true or false. Explain your reasoning.

a. All rectangles are similar.

b. All circles are similar.

c. If $\triangle ABC \sim \triangle DEF$ with scale factor $\frac{3}{4}$ and $\triangle ABC$ is bigger than $\triangle DEF$, then the area of $\triangle DEF$ is $\frac{3}{4}$ the area of $\triangle ABC$.

d. If $\triangle XYZ$ is a right triangle with m$\angle Y = 90°$, then $\cos X = \sin Z$.

27 What is the difference between independent events and mutually exclusive events?

21 **a.** He expects to win 36 times out of 76 spins.

b. Mr. Garcia will be ahead $1 if he wins on his first try. If he wins his third try, he has bet a total of $1 + $2 + $4 = $7 and won $8, so is $1 ahead. If he does not win until the tenth try, he has bet $1 + $2 + $4 + $8 + $16 + $32 + $64 + $128 + $256 + $512 = $1,023 and won $1,024, so is $1 ahead.

c. The gambler is taking the chance of losing a large amount of money in order to win $1 since it is possible that the gambler will run out of money before the single win occurs. As shown in Part a, if Mr. Garcia is unlucky enough to require ten spins for his first win, he has had to bet $1,023 in order to win $1. (A further problem is that some casinos limit the amount a person can bet on each spin of the wheel.)

Review

22 **a.** $x = 1$ or $x = 5$ **b.** $x = -4$ or $x = -14$

    c. $x = 3$ **d.** $x = -\frac{1}{2} \pm \frac{\sqrt{65}}{2}$

Just in Time

23 **a.** $P(2 \text{ yellow}) = \frac{1}{4} \cdot \frac{1}{4} = \frac{1}{16}$

b. $P(\text{blue on first spin and red on second spin}) = \frac{1}{8} \cdot \frac{1}{2} = \frac{1}{16}$

c. $P(\text{yellow and green}) = \frac{1}{4} \cdot \frac{1}{8} + \frac{1}{8} \cdot \frac{1}{4} = \frac{2}{32} = \frac{1}{16}$

24 **a.** $6x^2 - 3x$ **b.** $6y - 19$

    c. $15x + 14y$ **d.** $x^2 - 5$

25 $(3w)(w) = 192$. So, $w = 8$ cm.
$P = 2(8 + 24) = 64$ cm

26 **a.** False. Here is a counterexample to the statement.

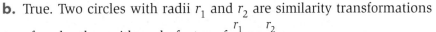

b. True. Two circles with radii r_1 and r_2 are similarity transformations of each other with scale factor of $\frac{r_1}{r_2}$ or $\frac{r_2}{r_1}$.

c. False. The area of $\triangle DEF$ is $\left(\frac{3}{4}\right)^2 = \frac{9}{16}$ the area of $\triangle ABC$.

d. True. Consider $\triangle XYZ$ as shown to the right. $\cos X = \frac{z}{y}$ and $\sin Z = \frac{z}{y}$. Thus, $\cos X = \sin Z$.

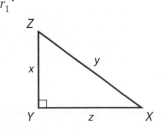

> **INSTRUCTIONAL NOTE**
> Review Task 26 Part d offers an opportunity to notice the "co" function (complementary angles) relationship between the sine and cosine functions.

27 Mutually exclusive events are two events that cannot occur on the same trial.

Independent events A and B are events such that the occurrence of one event does not change the probability of the second event occurring. Symbolically, this means that $P(A) = P(A \mid B)$ and $P(B) = P(B \mid A)$.

Unit 4

28 Without using a calculator or computer graphing tool, match each equation with the correct graph. Then use technology to check your answers. All graphs use the same scales.

a. $y = \dfrac{1}{x^2}$ **b.** $y = x^2 + 1$

c. $y = -x + 1$ **d.** $y = \dfrac{1}{x}$

e. $y = 2^x$ **f.** $y = x - 1$

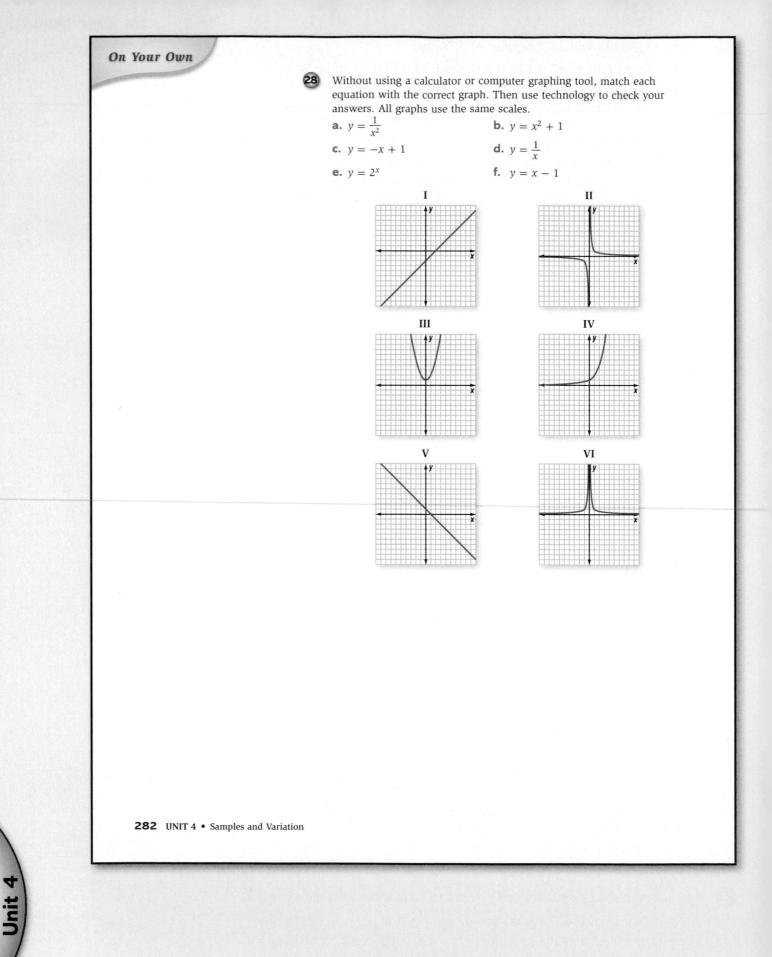

I II

III IV

V VI

28 a. VI   b. III

    c. V   d. II

    e. IV   f. I

Statistical Process Control

A major West Coast metal producer received the following complaint from a customer. The customer said that the metal he had recently received had an impurity in it. (The impurity was a trace element in the metal that affected how the metal performed.) Since this particular impurity had not been a problem in the past, the metal producer had not been monitoring it. The metal producer looked up the records on metal recently shipped to the customer. The percentage of the impurity in the metal for each week's shipment is given below in the table.

Metal Impurity

Week Ending	Percentage	Week Ending	Percentage	Week Ending	Percentage
4/7	0.000533	5/26	0.000721	7/14	0.002192
4/14	0.000472	6/2	0.000331	7/21	0.002205
4/21	0.000426	6/9	0.000537	7/28	0.002372
4/28	0.000481	6/16	0.000458	8/4	0.001866
5/5	0.000351	6/23	0.000420	8/11	0.002691
5/12	0.000471	6/30	0.000500	8/18	0.002721
5/19	0.000661	7/7	0.001976	8/25	0.002887

Source: From "Metal Impurity" by Lynda Finn. Copyright © Oriel Incorporated (formerly Joiner Associates), 1993. All rights reserved. Reprinted with permission.

Statistical Process Control

In this lesson, students will learn one way that industry uses statistical methods to maintain the quality of products and services. Control charts are ubiquitous in companies that are serious about providing a product that fits their customer's specifications and expectations.

In Investigation 1, students apply their knowledge of probability and the normal distribution to study the tests commonly used by industry to signal that a manufacturing process has gone out of control.

One of the more subtle points of this lesson is the fact that even though a process is under control, the tests will eventually signal that it is out of control. This is because rare events will happen, given enough time. For example, suppose we are monitoring the width of jar lids produced on a manufacturing line and find one that is more than three standard deviations from the mean. Test 1 (see page 290) signals that the process is out of control. Students will learn that this means one of two things, either

- the process has gone out of control, or
- the process has not gone out of control, but a rare event has occurred.

In Investigation 2, we will call the latter situation a false alarm and students will learn to compute the probability a false alarm will occur using a particular test when a process is under control.

In Investigation 3, students will learn the Central Limit Theorem and how it can be used in statistical process control.

Lesson Objectives

- Recognize when the mean and standard deviation change on a plot-over-time
- Use control charts and tests for out-of-control behavior
- Compute the probability of a false alarm on a set of readings, that is, the probability that a test will give an out-of-control signal for a process that is under control
- Understand the Central Limit Theorem and how it is applied to statistical process control

The metal producer graphed the data on a **plot over time**. This is called a **run chart** when used for an industrial process. The run chart is shown below.

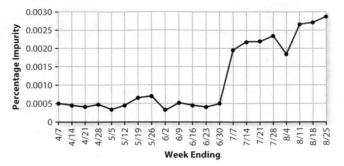

The metal producer checked with its supplier and found that the supplier had substituted a different raw material, which contained the impurity, in place of its regular raw material. The metal producer now routinely plots impurity levels of all types of impurities so that the customer will never again be the first to know.

Think About This Situation

Think about this example of variability in industrial production.

a When do you think the metal producer first started using the different raw material?

b The percentage of impurity varies even for raw material that comes from the same source. How could you estimate the variation in the percentage of impurity in shipments from the same source?

c Companies want to stop production as soon as possible after a process goes **out of control**. In the case of the metal producer, it was obvious when that happened. Often, a process goes out of control much more gradually. What should a company look for in a run chart to indicate its process might have gone out of control? Try to list several tests or rules that would signal that the process may have gone out of control.

In this lesson, you will explore some of the methods that industry uses to identify processes that have gone out of control.

Think About This Situation

Teaching Resources

Transparency Master 32.

UNIT 4 *Samples and Variation*

Think About This Situation

Think about this example of variability in industrial production.

a When do you think the metal producer first started using the different raw material?

b The percentage of impurity varies even for raw material that comes from the same source. How could you estimate the variation in the percentage of impurity in shipments from the same source?

c Companies want to stop production as soon as possible after a process goes **out of control**. In the case of the metal producer, it was obvious when that happened. Often, a process goes out of control much more gradually. What should a company look for in a run chart to indicate its process might have gone out of control? Try to list several tests or rules that would signal that the process may have gone out of control.

32 UNIT 4 • Samples and Variation   Transparency Master • use with page 284

a There is an abrupt change early in the week ending July 7. So, it is likely that the raw material was different at that time.

b You would have to measure the percentage of the impurity in many different batches when the process was under control and then summarize the variability in the percentages using the standard deviation or interquartile range.

c A student may suggest a rule like "the percentage goes up a little bit each time." That is the right idea for a rule, but students need to understand that their rules must be very explicit. Students need to define both what is meant by "a little bit" and how many times the percentage would need to go up for the rule to indicate an out-of-control process. Help students make their rules operational.

Investigation 1 Out of Control Signals

In this investigation, you will examine what the run chart of an out-of-control process can look like. You will then explore some of the tests employed by industry to signal that a process may have gone out of control. Think about answers to the following question as you work through this investigation:

> *What does a run chart look like when the process has gone out of control?*

1 At one factory, a process of filling milk containers is supposed to give a distribution of weights with mean 64 ounces and standard deviation 0.2 ounces. The following four run charts come from four different machines. For each machine, 30 milk containers were filled and the number of ounces of milk measured. Two of the four machines are out of control.

a. Which two machines appear to be out of control?

b. On which of these machines did the mean change?

c. On which of these machines did the standard deviation change?

Machine 1

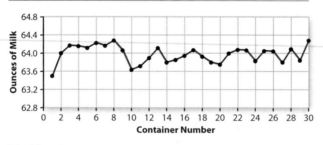

Machine 2

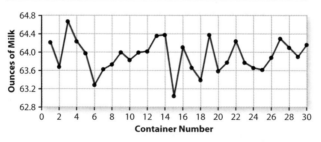

Investigation 1 · Out-of-Control Signals

In this investigation, students apply their knowledge of probability and the normal distribution to study the tests commonly used by industry to signal that a manufacturing process has gone out of control. Encourage students whose parents work in industrial settings to provide examples of run charts to bring to class. Some teachers have used this lesson as an opportunity for students to hear additional information about the use of statistical process control from community members.

It would be valuable to discuss Problems 1–5 and the eight tests shown on page 290 before students continue on to Problem 6.

Note on Tests 7 and 8 Two of the tests may cause your students some puzzlement. They may believe the process shown in Test 7 exhibits acceptable behavior. Test 7 gives an out-of-control signal because it detects a pattern that we would not expect for a process with the specified mean and standard deviation. This situation should be investigated promptly because decreased variation is usually beneficial. The cause should be identified and duplicated if possible. However, Test 7 can also indicate miscalculated control limits, incorrectly plotted points, or tampered data. In fact, Test 7 is not typically used in practice for the purpose of detecting an out-of-control process. Similarly, Test 8 is not typically used for that purpose.

Common Misconception About Test 4 If students have not had much experience with random behavior, Test 4 may also puzzle them. Its regular pattern of up-down-up is what many people think of as random. When in fact, it would rarely occur in a true random situation. It would be very unusual to pick fourteen digits at random and get a sequence like 2, 5, 3, 8, 6, 9, 1, 3, 2, 9, 0, 1, 0, 7, which alternates smaller, larger, smaller, … .

1   **a.** Machines 2 and 3 appear to be out of control.

    b. Machine 3

    c. Machine 2

Teaching Resources

Student Master 33.

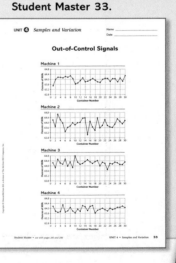

Machine 3

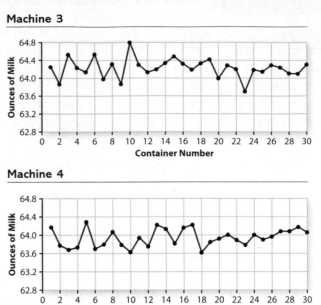

Machine 4

In Problem 1, you saw two ways that an out-of-control machine might behave. Since the people who monitor machines want to stop a machine as soon as possible after it has gone out of control, they have signs and patterns they look for in run charts.

2 Re-examine the data from the West Coast metal producer, reproduced below.

Metal Impurity

Week Ending	Percentage	Week Ending	Percentage	Week Ending	Percentage
4/7	0.000533	5/26	0.000721	7/14	0.002192
4/14	0.000472	6/2	0.000331	7/21	0.002205
4/21	0.000426	6/9	0.000537	7/28	0.002372
4/28	0.000481	6/16	0.000458	8/4	0.001866
5/5	0.000351	6/23	0.000420	8/11	0.002691
5/12	0.000471	6/30	0.000500	8/18	0.002721
5/19	0.000661	7/7	0.001976	8/25	0.002887

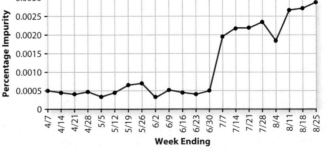

Teacher Notes

a. In the first 13 weeks of metal production, the percentage of the impurity was under control. That is, the percentage of the impurity varied a little from week to week but was of a level acceptable to the customer. Make a plot that displays the variability in these 13 percentages. Estimate the mean and standard deviation. Then compute the mean and standard deviation and compare to your estimates.

b. Now look at the percentage of impurity for the 14th week, which ended July 7. How many standard deviations from the mean computed in Part a is this percentage?

c. Assume that when the level of impurity is under control, the percentages of impurity are normally distributed with the mean and standard deviation that you calculated in Part a. If the level of impurity is under control, what is the probability of getting a percentage as high or higher than the one for July 7?

③ One commonly used test declares a process out of control when a single value is more than three standard deviations from the mean. This test assumes that the individual values are approximately normally distributed. If the process is in control, what is the probability that the next measurement will be more than three standard deviations from the mean?

④ Each of the run charts below was made from a process that was supposed to be normally distributed with a mean of 5 and a standard deviation of 1. The charts are based on displays produced using the statistical software Minitab.

a. UCL means "upper control limit." LCL means "lower control limit." How were these limits computed?

b. Using the test of three standard deviations or more from the mean, on which of the three charts is there a point where the process should be suspected to be out of control?

Chart 1

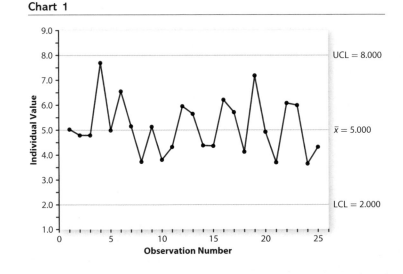

② INSTRUCTIONAL NOTE Because students know the effect on the mean and standard deviation of a set of data of transforming the values by multiplying by a constant, they might choose to code the data by multiplying by 1,000,000 and using integers like 533 in place of 0.000533.

a. Students might make a histogram or a stem-and-leaf plot to display the values. The stem-and-leaf plot below shows the ten-thousandth and hundred-thousandth places. Student estimates will vary, but students should estimate the mean around 0.0005% and a very small standard deviation ($\approx$ 0.0001%). The calculated value of the mean is 0.000489%, and the calculated value of the standard deviation is 0.000109%.

Metal Impurity

3	3 5
4	2 2 5 7 7 8
5	0 3 3
6	6
7	2

7 | 2 represents 0.000720%–0.000729%

b. $\dfrac{0.001976 - 0.000489}{0.000109} = \dfrac{1{,}976 - 489}{109} = 13.64$ standard deviations

c. The probability of getting a percentage as high or higher than the July 7 reading is very close to 0. (The proportion above 3.5 standard deviations is only 0.0002.) The process is out of control.

③ The probability is 0.003. Using the fact that 99.7% of the values are within three standard deviations of the mean, approximately 0.3% of the values are more than 3 standard deviations from the mean.

④ a. They are three standard deviations from the mean.
UCL $= \bar{x} + 3s = 5 + 3(1) = 8$ and LCL $= \bar{x} - 3s = 5 - 3(1) = 2$.

b. Chart 2 because the 15th observation is more than three standard deviations from the mean.

Chart 2

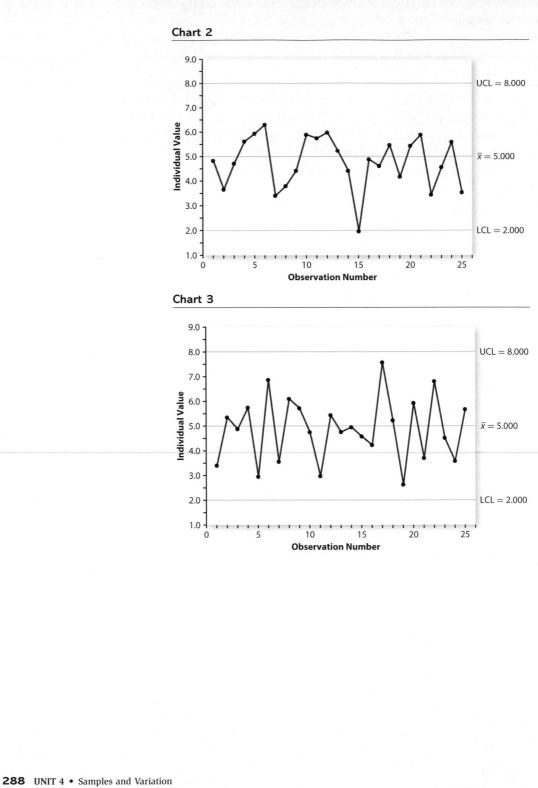

Chart 3

Teacher Notes

Unit 4

(5) The process documented on the run chart below is supposed to be normally distributed with a mean of 5 and a standard deviation of 1. The small "2" below the final point, where the process was stopped, indicates that the process may have gone out of control. Why do you think Minitab has declared the process out of control?

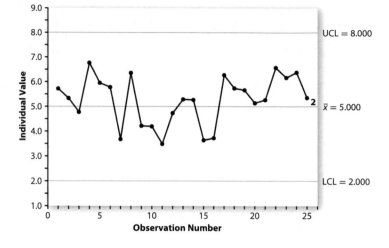

On the chart "Illustrations of Tests," which is reproduced on the next page, there are eight tests used by industry to signal that a process may have changed. The zones are marked off in standard deviations. For example, if a value falls in Zone A, it is more than two but less than three standard deviations from the mean $\bar{x}$. Each **x** marks the value at which a process is first declared out of control. Each of these tests assumes that the individual values come from a normal distribution.

5 Nine points in a row above the mean seems unlikely to have occurred just by chance. It is a good possibility that the mean of the process changed.

Unit 4

Illustrations of Tests

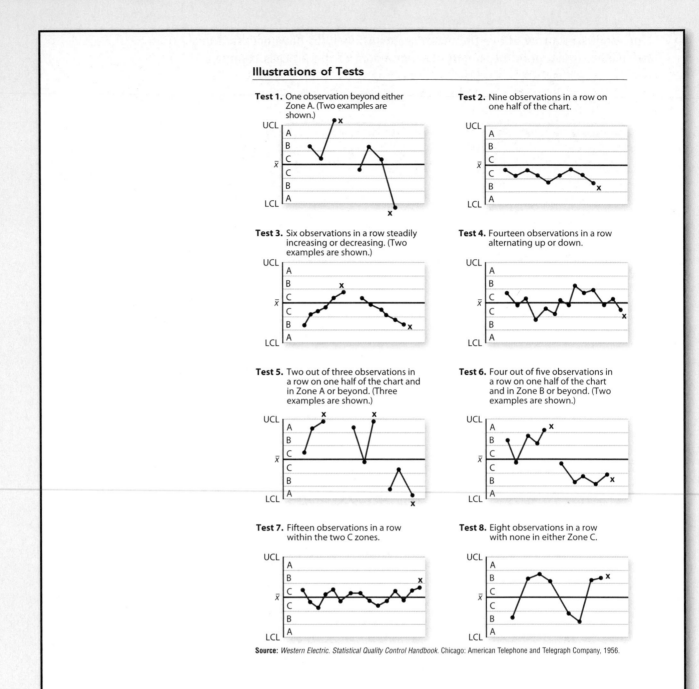

Test 1. One observation beyond either Zone A. (Two examples are shown.)

Test 2. Nine observations in a row on one half of the chart.

Test 3. Six observations in a row steadily increasing or decreasing. (Two examples are shown.)

Test 4. Fourteen observations in a row alternating up or down.

Test 5. Two out of three observations in a row on one half of the chart and in Zone A or beyond. (Three examples are shown.)

Test 6. Four out of five observations in a row on one half of the chart and in Zone B or beyond. (Two examples are shown.)

Test 7. Fifteen observations in a row within the two C zones.

Test 8. Eight observations in a row with none in either Zone C.

Source: *Western Electric. Statistical Quality Control Handbook.* Chicago: American Telephone and Telegraph Company, 1956.

CPMP-Tools As can be seen in the screens below, *CPMP-Tools* includes a "Control Chart" custom tool that can run the Western Electric tests for processes out of control. You can enter your own data or use the built-in data sets: Los Angeles Yearly Rainfall Averages, Apartment Temperatures, Manufactured Nails, and Gas Mileage.

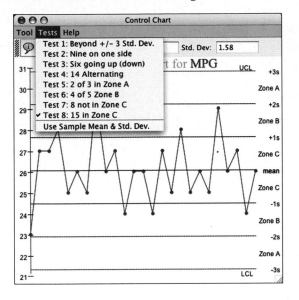

Unit 4

6 Match each of the eight tests to the best description.

   a. The observations are gradually getting larger (or smaller).

   b. One observation is very far from the mean.

   c. Two of three observations are unusually high (or low).

   d. Four of five observations are all somewhat high (or low).

   e. The mean seems to have decreased (or increased).

   f. The standard deviation seems to have decreased.

   g. The standard deviation seems to have increased.

   h. The process shows a non-random pattern that should be explained.

7 Look back at how these tests relate to your previous work in this investigation.

   a. What is the number of the test that signals when a single value is more than three standard deviations from the mean?

   b. Which test signaled the point marked "2" in Problem 5 (page 289)?

8 For each of the run charts below and on the next page, there is an **x** at the point when the process first was declared to be out of control. Give the number of the test used to decide that the process was out of control.

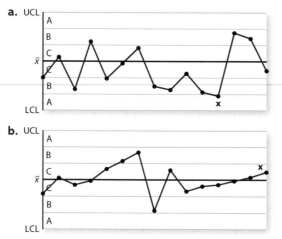

a.

b.

6 **a.** Test 3

   b. Test 1

   c. Test 5

   d. Test 6

   e. Test 2

   f. Test 7

   g. Test 8

   h. Test 4

7 **a.** Test 1

   b. Test 2

8 **a.** Test 6

   b. Test 3

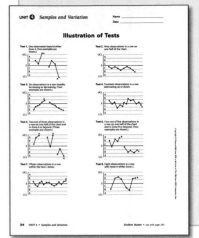

Teaching Resources

Student Master 34.

INSTRUCTIONAL NOTE
Some of the illustrations in the chart on page 290 contain one example (Tests 2, 4, 7, and 8), while others contain two (Tests 1, 3, and 6) or three examples (Test 5).

Unit 4

c.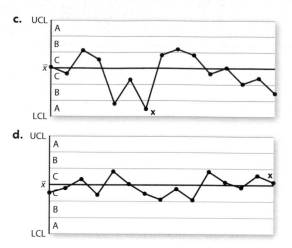

d.

9 Here is a run chart for a process that is supposed to have a normal distribution with mean 28 and standard deviation 2.

a. On a copy of the chart, identify and label the horizontal lines dividing the zones.

b. When did the process first go out of control? By which test?

c. Has the mean or the standard deviation changed?

The run charts that you have been examining are sometimes called Shewhart control charts. Dr. Walter A. Shewhart invented these charts in 1924 and developed their use while he worked for the Western Electric Company and Bell Laboratories. These charts provide a quick, visual check if a process has changed or gone "out of control." When there is change in an industrial process, the machine operator wants to know why and may have to adjust the machine.

Dr. Walter A. Shewhart

c. Test 5

d. Test 7

⑨ **a.**

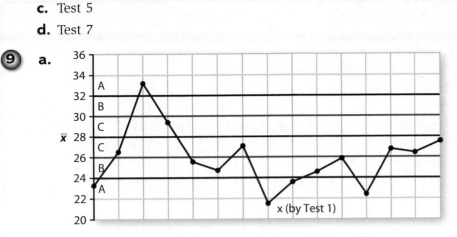

b. The process first went out of control at the eighth point by Test 1.

c. Test 1 may signal that either the mean or the standard deviation has changed. For this process, it appears that both the mean and standard deviation may have changed.

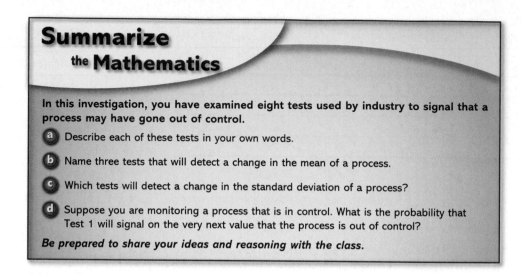

In this investigation, you have examined eight tests used by industry to signal that a process may have gone out of control.

a Describe each of these tests in your own words.

b Name three tests that will detect a change in the mean of a process.

c Which tests will detect a change in the standard deviation of a process?

d Suppose you are monitoring a process that is in control. What is the probability that Test 1 will signal on the very next value that the process is out of control?

Be prepared to share your ideas and reasoning with the class.

✔ Check Your Understanding

Examine each of the following run charts.

a. For this run chart, there is an asterisk (∗) below the observation at which the statistical software warned that the process may have gone out of control. Give the number of the test used.

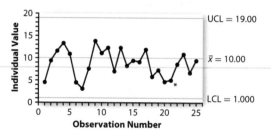

b. The process graphed on the run chart below is supposed to have a normal distribution with mean 8 ounces and standard deviation 1 ounce. Find the point at which the process should first be declared out of control. Give the number of the test used.

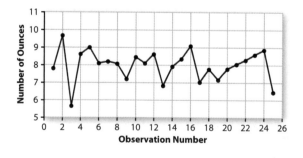

Summary

Having students describe the eight tests in their own words in Part a helps you to know that they understand them. It will also help make students more familiar with the rules. They need not write these descriptions. Stress again to students that the 68%-95%-99.7% rule can be used only with a normal distribution. In Investigations 2 and 3, we will assume that all of the values plotted on the control charts follow a normal distribution. Students should continue to state that as an assumption.

Summarize the Mathematics

a Students should discuss the tests in their own words.

b Tests 1, 2, 3, 4, 5, and 6 can all signal a change in the mean.

c Tests 1, 4, 7, and 8 can detect a change in the standard deviation.

d The probability is 0.003 if the values are normally distributed. So, this reading is possible, although a rare occurrence, when the process is in control.

✓Check Your Understanding

a. Test 4

b. The process should be declared out of control at the next to last point by Test 3.

Even a process that is under control exhibits variation. Consequently, the eight tests on page 290 occasionally will give an out-of-control signal, called a **false alarm**, for a process that is under control. For example, if you watch a process that is in control long enough, eventually one observation will be beyond one of the A zones, or six observations in a row will be steadily increasing, and so on. The tests have been designed so that false alarms occur very rarely. If you have been monitoring a process that is under control, the probability of a false alarm on the next set of observations is very small.

As you work through this investigation, look for answers to this question:

How can you find the probability of getting a false alarm?

① Assuming that the observations of a process are normally distributed, fill in the "Percentage of Observations in Zone" on a copy of the chart below. You can then refer to the chart when working on the remaining problems.

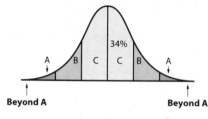

	Number of Standard Deviations from Mean	Percentage of Observations in Zone
Beyond Zone A		
UCL ——	3	
Zone A		
	2	
Zone B		
	1	
Zone C		
Mean ——	0	34%
Zone C		
	1	
Zone B		
	2	
Zone A		
LCL ——	3	
Beyond Zone A		

② Suppose a machine is filling cartons of ice cream and is under control. The operator uses only Test 1 to signal that the weight of the ice cream in the cartons may have gone out of control. What is the probability of a false alarm on the very next carton of ice cream being filled? Place your result in the appropriate row of a copy of the following table. Keep your table, as you will fill out some of the remaining rows in other problems.

Investigation 2 — False Alarms

If you observe a process long enough, eventually one of the eight tests will signal that the process is out of control, even if the process has been in control the entire time. That is, eventually, one of the rare events signaled by the tests will occur. In this investigation, students compute the probability that, when monitoring a process in control, an out-of-control signal will be given on the next set of observations by a particular test. Such an out-of-control signal for a process that is in control is called a *false alarm*.

When a test signals that the process is out of control, the operator does not know for sure whether the process has gone out of control or whether it is a false alarm. Depending on the costs of each action, the machine operator can do the following.

- immediately call a halt to production to see if something has gone out of adjustment
- watch the line for awhile to determine if a false alarm has occurred

Note on Reviewing the Multiplication Rule In order to find the probability of a false alarm, students must use the Multiplication Rule for independent events. You may want to review the Multiplication Rule before students start these problems. You might do this by recalling examples from prior units of study. (What is the probability of a 6 on one roll of a die? What is the probability of 6s occurring on each of the next two rolls?) Or you might want to use the context at hand by having students complete Connections Task 11 before starting this investigation. (If the process is in control, what is the probability that the next measurement will be in Zone A? What is the probability the next two consecutive measurements will be in Zone A?)

Note on the Assumption of Independence Many of the calculations for determining the probability of a false alarm use the Multiplication Rule for independent events. This use is legitimate only if the measurements are independent. Generally, independence cannot be attained in practice because two products coming off a production line close together in time tend to be more alike than two products that come off the line farther apart in time. Thus, the probabilities of a false alarm computed in this investigation are approximations to the real situation on a production line.

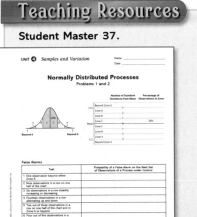

1

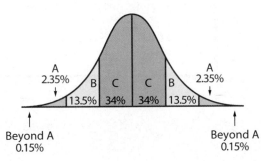

	Number of Standard Deviations from Mean	Percentage of Observations in Zone
UCL — Beyond Zone A	3	0.15%
Zone A		2.35%
Zone B	2	13.5%
Zone C	1	34%
Mean — Zone C	0	34%
Zone B	1	13.5%
Zone A	2	2.35%
LCL — Beyond Zone A	3	0.15%

A 2.35% | B 13.5% | C 34% | C 34% | B 13.5% | A 2.35%

Beyond A 0.15% | Beyond A 0.15%

Unit 4

Statistical Process Control **T294**

False Alarms

Test	Probability of a False Alarm on the Next Set of Observations of a Process Under Control
1 One observation beyond either Zone A	
2 Nine observations in a row on one half of the chart	
3 Six observations in a row steadily increasing or decreasing	
4 Fourteen observations in a row alternating up and down	
5 Two out of three observations in a row on one half of the chart and in Zone A or beyond	
6 Four out of five observations in a row on one half of the chart and in Zone B or beyond	
7 Fifteen observations in a row within the two C zones	
8 Eight observations in a row with none in either Zone C	

3 Now suppose the ice cream machine operator is using only Test 7. The machine continues to stay in control.

   a. What is the probability that a single observation will fall either within Zone C in the top half of the chart or within Zone C in the bottom half of the chart?

   b. What is the probability that the observations from each of the next 15 cartons filled will all fall within either of the two C zones? (In this and subsequent problems, you may assume that the observations are independent, although independence of measurements is rarely attained in practice even with processes that are under control. Nevertheless, your computations will be good approximations.)

   c. What is the probability that the ice cream machine operator will get a false alarm from the next 15 cartons being filled? Place your result in the appropriate row of your copy of the table, rounding to the nearest ten-thousandth.

4 Now suppose the ice cream machine operator is using only Test 2. The machine continues to stay in control.

   a. What is the probability that the next nine observations are all in the bottom half of the chart?

   b. What is the probability that the next nine observations are all in the top half of the chart?

   c. What is the probability that the next nine observations are all in the top half of the chart or all in the bottom half of the chart?

   d. What is the probability that the operator will get a false alarm from the next nine cartons being filled? Place your result in the appropriate row of your copy of the table, rounding to the nearest ten-thousandth.

(2) Test 1:

$1 - 0.997 = 0.003$

The probability is 0.003 that the weight of the next carton will be beyond either Zone A.

False Alarms

Test	Probability of a False Alarm on the Next Set of Observations of a Process under Control
1 One observation beyond either Zone A	0.003
2 Nine observations in a row on one half of the chart	0.0039 (from Problem 4 of Investigation 2)
3 Six observations in a row steadily increasing or decreasing	0.0028 (from OYO Task 21)
4 Fourteen observations in a row alternating up and down	0.0046 (from OYO Task 23)
5 Two out of three observations in a row on one half of the chart and in Zone A or beyond	0.0037 (from OYO Task 5)
6 Four out of five observations in a row on one half of the chart and in Zone B or beyond	0.0057 (from OYO Task 6)
7 Fifteen observations in a row within the two C zones	0.0031 (from Problem 3 of Investigation 2)
8 Eight observations in a row with none in either Zone C	0.0001 (from OYO Task 3)

INSTRUCTIONAL NOTE
The complete probability chart in Problem 2 for false alarms is included here, although students only find the probabilities for Tests 1, 2, and 7 during the investigation. Alert students to this. If you do not assign Extensions Tasks 21 and 23, you may wish to provide these probabilities to students.

(3) **a.** 0.68

   b. Using the Multiplication Rule for independent events, $(0.68)^{15} \approx 0.0031$.

   c. Approximately 0.0031. This result should be placed with Test 7 on the chart.

(4) **a.** $(0.5)^9 = 0.001953125$

   b. 0.001953125

   c. $2(0.001953125) \approx 0.0039$

   d. 0.0039. The result should be placed with Test 2 of the chart.

INSTRUCTIONAL NOTE
The Multiplication Rule for independent events is valid only when the events are independent. That is, to find the probability that event A and event B both happen, you can multiply the probability of A by the probability of B only if $P(A) = P(A \mid B)$.

5 A ceramic plate machine makes 20,000 plates in a year. It is under control. If the operator uses Test 1 only and measures every hundredth plate, what is the probability the operator will get through the year without having to stop the machine?

6 When computing the probabilities in Problems 3, 4, and 5, you used the Multiplication Rule for Independent Events. In real-life situations, the measurements will not be completely independent, even with processes that are under control. For example, when using Test 2, if the first measurement is in the bottom half of the chart, the next measurement will be slightly more likely to be in the bottom half of the chart than in the top half. Does this lack of independence mean that the probability of a false alarm when you use Test 2 in practice is greater or is less than the probability you computed in Problem 4?

The eight quality control tests were all devised so that, when you are monitoring a process that is in control, the probability of a false alarm on the next set of observations tested is about 0.005 or less. You will determine the probability of a false alarm for the remaining five tests on your chart in the On Your Own tasks.

Summarize the Mathematics

In this investigation, you examined the likelihood of a false alarm when using quality control tests.

a What is a false alarm? Why do false alarms occur occasionally if the process is under control?

b If you get an out-of-control signal, is there any way to tell for sure whether the process is out of control or whether it is a false alarm?

Be prepared to share your ideas and examples with the class.

✓ Check Your Understanding

A machine operator is using the following rule as an out-of-control signal; six observations in a row in Zone B in the top half of the chart or six observations in a row in Zone B in the bottom half of the chart. Assume the machine is in control.

a. What is the probability that the next six values are all in Zone B in the top half of the chart?

b. What is the probability that the operator gets a false alarm from the next six values?

⑤ The probability of Test 1 stopping the process on any one plate is 0.003, and the probability it does not is 0.997. The operator tests 200 plates. The probability that all 200 are less than three standard deviations from the mean is $(0.997)^{200} \approx 0.548$.

⑥ This lack of independence increases the probability of a false alarm when you use Test 2. If the measurements were independent, the probability that the next measurement would be in the same half of the chart as the previous measurement is $\frac{1}{2}$. However, with lack of independence, the probability the next measurement will be in the same half of the chart as the previous measurement is more than $\frac{1}{2}$.

Summarize
the Mathematics

a A false alarm occurs when a test signals that a process is out of control when it is actually in control. False alarms occur because even an event with a very small probability of occurring will happen eventually, if given enough opportunities.

b No, there is no way to tell for sure. But because the probability of getting an out-of-control signal is so small when the process is in control, it is usual to proceed as if the signal is correct.

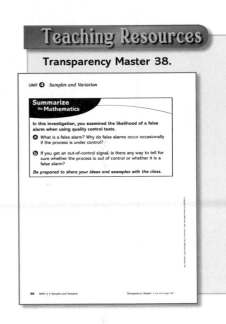
✔ Check Your Understanding

a. $(0.135)^6 \approx 0.000006$

b. $2(0.000006) = 0.000012$

3 **The Central Limit Theorem**

The use of control charts in the previous investigations required that the individual measurements be approximately normally distributed. However, the distribution of measurements of the parts coming off an assembly line may well be skewed. What can be done in that case?

As you work through this investigation, look for answers to the following question:

> *What is the Central Limit Theorem and how does it allow you*
> *to use control charts even when individual measurements*
> *come from a skewed distribution?*

1 Suppose that a process is under control. How would you find the probability of a false alarm on the next measurement when using Test 1 on page 290? Where did you use the assumption that the individual values are approximately normally distributed?

2 The eight tests illustrated on page 290 assume that observations come from a distribution that is approximately normal. For individual observations, this is not always the case. For example, suppose the carnival wheel below is designed to produce random digits from the set {0, 1, 2, 3, 4, 5, 6, 7, 8, 9}.

a. Suppose the wheel is operating correctly and produces digits at random.

   i. Describe the shape of the probability distribution of all possible outcomes.

   ii. What is the mean of the distribution?

   iii. What is the standard deviation of the distribution?

b. Can Test 1 ever signal that this process may be out of control? Explain. What about Test 5?

c. Since the distribution in Part a is not approximately normal, you should not use the eight tests on individual digits to check whether the wheel has gone out of control. Explore what you might do so you can use the tests.

   i. Use technology to produce 5 digits at random and find their mean.

In practice, many companies use control charts that are based on the mean of a random sample of measurements. For example, the machine operator might select 5 products at random from every 100, compute the mean of the 5, and plot that mean on the control chart. This is one way to produce the necessary normality and to have a more reasonable assessment of variation. In this investigation, students will learn how this is made possible by the Central Limit Theorem.

Notes on the Central Limit Theorem The term "Central Limit Theorem" was first used by George Polya in 1920. The term "limit" refers to the fact that the distribution of the sample mean becomes normal in the limit, as the sample size increases. The term "central" is indicative of the central importance of this theorem in the theory of statistics.

The distribution of the means of all possible samples taken from a finite distribution is called the sampling distribution of the sample mean. This sampling distribution has the following.

- the same mean as the population, $\mu_{\bar{x}} = \mu$
- a standard deviation equal to the standard deviation of the population divided by the square root of the sample size, $\sigma_{\bar{x}} = \dfrac{\sigma}{\sqrt{n}}$
- a shape that becomes more approximately normal with larger and larger sample sizes

It is this last property that is called the Central Limit Theorem. The *CPMP-Tools* "Distribution of Sample ..." custom tool, as well as other applets available on the Internet, can be used to illustrate the Central Limit Theorem. See page T298 for more information on this custom tool.

1 Using Test 1, any observation that is more than three standard deviations from the target mean gives an out-of-control signal. If the process is under control and the distribution of observations is approximately normal, the probability that this will happen on any one observation is very small, about 0.003.

This value is based on the percentage of values beyond three standard deviations for a normal distribution. This would not necessarily be the correct probability if the distribution had some other shape.

2 This problem introduces students to the Central Limit Theorem.

a. **i.** The shape is uniform. Each possible outcome has probability $\frac{1}{10}$.

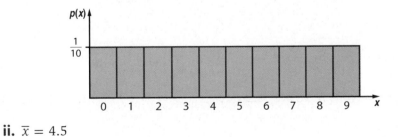

ii. $\bar{x} = 4.5$

iii. $\sigma \approx 2.87$

NOTE Solutions to Problem 2 Parts b and c are on page T298.

ii. Nela repeated part i 1,400 times using simulation software. That is, the software selected 5 digits at random and found the mean $\bar{x}$. Then the process was repeated until there were 1,400 means. What is the smallest mean Nela could have observed? The largest?

iii. The histogram below shows Nela's 1,400 means. About how many times did she get a mean of 2? Of 4.2?

Means of Samples of Five Random Digits

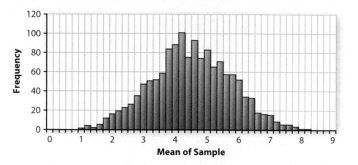

d. Use simulation software to conduct 1,500 runs of selecting 3 digits at random and calculating their means. Make a histogram of the distribution. Compare the shape and center of your histogram with Nela's histogram.

e. Repeat Part d selecting samples of 10 digits. Of 20 digits.

f. How could you use means to meet the normality assumption of the eight tests?

3 The following plot and table show the rainfall in Los Angeles for the 129 years from 1878 through 2006. The amount varies a great deal from year to year. (Source: National Weather Service)

Los Angeles Annual Rainfall 1878–2006

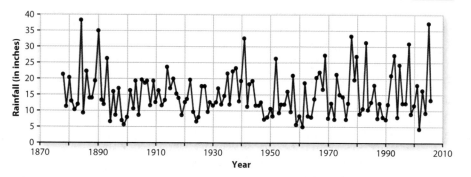

b. Neither Test 1 nor Test 5 would ever signal that the process was out of control, as all possible random digits are within two standard deviations of the mean. That is, an observation could never fall in or beyond Zone A.

c. **i.** Answers will vary. For example, if the random digits are 5, 4, 1, 4, and 9, then the mean is $\frac{23}{5}$, or 4.6.

ii. The smallest possible mean is $\frac{0+0+0+0+0}{5} = 0$.

The largest possible mean is $\frac{9+9+9+9+9}{5} = 9$.

(Neither of these happened in Nela's 1,400 trials in Part e.)

iii. Nela got a mean of 2 about 18 times and a mean of 4.2 about 101 times.

d. Answers will vary. The histograms should be centered near 4.5 and have a larger spread than Nela's histogram.

NOTE To conduct the simulation in *CPMP-Tools*, select Statistics, Simulation, 0–9, and then choose "Mean of" from the Build menu. Conduct 1,500 runs of the simulation for a mean of 3 random digits as shown in the second screen below. The graph can be turned on from the View menu.

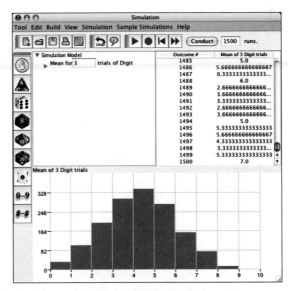

e. Answers will vary. Each histogram should be centered near 4.5. The larger the sample size, the smaller the spread and the more approximately normal.

f. You could plot the mean of consecutive groups of five random digits on a control chart. As we can see from Nela's histogram, these means are approximately normal with mean 4.5 and standard deviation of approximately 1.25. If, for example, Nela's next five digits were 9, 9, 8, 9, and 9, which have a mean of 8.8, she would declare the process out of control by Test 1.

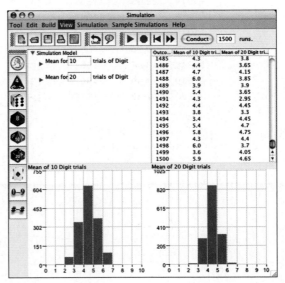

NOTE In Extensions Task 24, students will see that the standard deviation is $\frac{2.87}{\sqrt{5}}$.

Unit 4

Year	Rainfall (in inches)	Year	Rainfall (in inches)	Year	Rainfall (in inches)
1878	21.26	1921	13.65	1964	7.93
1879	11.35	1922	19.66	1965	13.69
1880	20.34	1923	9.59	1966	20.44
1881	13.13	1924	6.67	1967	22.00
1882	10.40	1925	7.94	1968	16.58
1883	12.11	1926	17.56	1969	27.47
1884	38.18	1927	17.76	1970	7.77
1885	9.21	1928	9.77	1971	12.32
1886	22.31	1929	12.66	1972	7.17
1887	14.05	1930	11.52	1973	21.26
1888	13.87	1931	12.53	1974	14.92
1889	19.28	1932	16.95	1975	14.35
1890	34.84	1933	11.88	1976	7.22
1891	13.36	1934	14.55	1977	12.31
1892	11.85	1935	21.66	1978	33.44
1893	26.28	1936	12.07	1979	19.67
1894	6.73	1937	22.41	1980	26.98
1895	16.11	1938	23.43	1981	8.98
1896	8.51	1939	13.07	1982	10.71
1897	16.88	1940	19.21	1983	31.25
1898	7.06	1941	32.76	1984	10.43
1899	5.59	1942	11.18	1985	12.82
1900	7.91	1943	18.17	1986	17.86
1901	16.29	1944	19.22	1987	7.66
1902	10.60	1945	11.59	1988	12.48
1903	19.32	1946	11.65	1989	8.08
1904	8.72	1947	12.66	1990	7.35
1905	19.52	1948	7.22	1991	11.99
1906	18.65	1949	7.99	1992	21.00
1907	19.30	1950	10.60	1993	27.36
1908	11.72	1951	8.21	1994	8.14
1909	19.18	1952	26.21	1995	24.35
1910	12.63	1953	9.46	1996	12.46
1911	16.18	1954	11.99	1997	12.40
1912	11.60	1955	11.94	1998	31.01
1913	13.42	1956	16.00	1999	9.09
1914	23.65	1957	9.54	2000	11.57
1915	17.05	1958	21.13	2001	17.94
1916	19.92	1959	5.58	2002	4.42
1917	15.26	1960	8.18	2003	16.49
1918	13.86	1961	4.85	2004	9.25
1919	8.58	1962	18.79	2005	37.25
1920	12.52	1963	8.38	2006	13.19

Hollywood Highland

NOTE ON L.A. RAINFALL There is little or no rain in Los Angeles in the summer, so rainfall is measured by a 12-month season that runs from July 1 through June 30, not by calendar year. The "year" given in the student text is the year that the season ended. For example, the year 2006, gives the rainfall for the July 1, 2005–June 30, 2006 season.

③ **NOTE ON SETTING THE CONTROL LIMITS FOR THE MEANS OF SAMPLES** The upper and lower control limits are set so that 99.7% of the sample means will fall between them when the process is under control. In other words, they are 3 standard deviations from the mean, or $3\frac{\sigma}{\sqrt{n}}$ from the mean. Here, σ is an estimate of the standard deviation of the population of all measurements and n is the number in the sample used to compute the mean. For Part d, $n = 3$.

CPMP-Tools The "Control Chart" custom tool of *CPMP-Tools* can be used for the built-in L.A. Rainfall data as shown below.

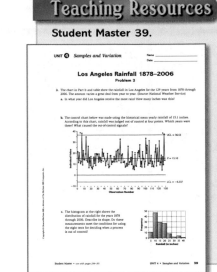
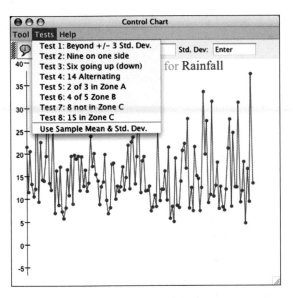

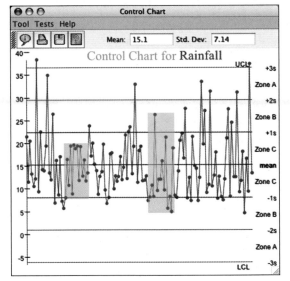

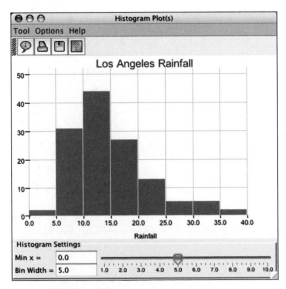

Unit 4

a. In what year did Los Angeles receive the most rain? How many inches was this?

b. The control chart below was made using the historical mean yearly rainfall of 15.1 inches. According to this chart, rainfall was judged out of control at four points. Which years were these? What caused the out-of-control signals?

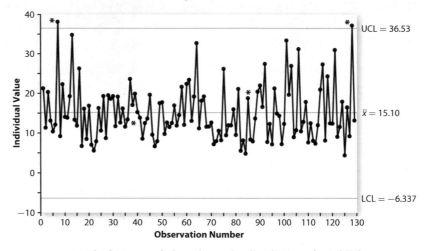

c. The histogram below shows the distribution of rainfall for the years 1878 through 2006. Describe its shape. Do these measurements meet the conditions for using the eight tests for deciding when a process is out of control?

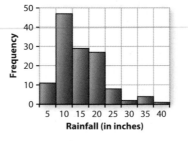

d. When individual measurements have a skewed distribution, quality control practitioners can plot the *means* of samples of measurements rather than plotting individual measurements. For example, the measurements of rainfall for the first three years were 21.26, 11.35, and 20.34 inches. The mean, $\bar{x}$, for these three years was 17.65 inches. That value is the first one plotted on the **x-bar chart** on the following page.

a. In 1884, when there was 38.18 inches

b. The tests signal that the process is out of control twice using Test 1 (one point beyond Zone A) at point 7 (1884) and at point 128 (2005), and twice using Test 4 (fourteen points in a row alternating up and down) at point 36 (1913) and at point 85 (1962).

c. The distribution of rainfall is skewed right and so does not meet the conditions for using the eight tests.

TECHNOLOGY NOTE These data are in *CPMP-Tools*.

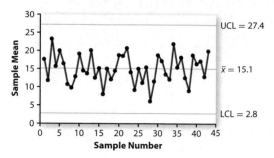

i. Using the table, find the value of the second mean plotted.

ii. Find the value of the last mean plotted.

iii. Does any mean give an out of control signal?

iv. Note that the middle line of the *x*-bar chart is at 15.1, the historical mean for individual years. Explain why 15.1 is also the mean of the values on the *x*-bar chart.

e. The histogram below shows the distribution of the sample means for consecutive samples of size 3. Are conditions now met for using the eight tests?

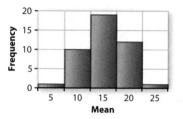

4 The two previous problems illustrated the **Central Limit Theorem**. Imagine taking repeated random samples of a fixed size from a non-normal distribution. The larger the sample size you use, the more approximately normal the distribution of sample means $\bar{x}$ tends to be. Typically, quality control practitioners use two to five measurements per sample. In general, the more skewed the distribution of individual measurements, the larger your sample size should be. Consider the strongly right-skewed population below, which has a mean of 2.

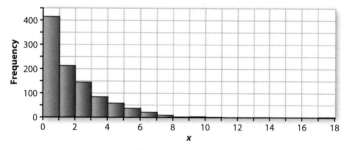

a. Using software like the "Distribution of Sample Means" custom tool, take 100 samples of size 1 from this skewed distribution. Describe the shape. Give the mean and standard deviation of the distribution of sample means.

d. i. $\dfrac{13.13 + 10.40 + 12.11}{3} = 11.88$

ii. $\dfrac{9.25 + 37.25 + 13.19}{3} \approx 19.90$

iii. No

iv. The mean of the individual measurements, x_{year}, is

$$\frac{x_{1878} + x_{1879} + x_{1880} + \cdots + x_{2004} + x_{2005} + x_{2006}}{129} = 15.1.$$

The mean of the means of groups of three is

$$\frac{\dfrac{x_{1878} + x_{1879} + x_{1880}}{3} + \dfrac{x_{1881} + x_{1882} + x_{1883}}{3} + \cdots + \dfrac{x_{2004} + x_{2005} + x_{2006}}{3}}{\dfrac{129}{3}} =$$

$$\frac{x_{1878} + x_{1879} + x_{1880} + x_{1881} + x_{1882} + x_{1883} + \cdots + x_{2004} + x_{2005} + x_{2006}}{129} = 15.1.$$

e. Yes, this distribution is approximately normal.

INSTRUCTIONAL NOTE
Using sets of consecutive measurements is not equivalent to taking random samples from the measurements, but consecutive measurements behave enough like random samples for tests based on means of consecutive measurements to work well.

④ The *CPMP-Tools* Distribution of Sample Means feature can be used with the built-in "Right-Skewed Population" data set to explore the shape, mean, and standard deviation of distributions of sample means for sample sizes of 1, 2, 5, 10, and 20. This feature is found in the Statistics menu of the Home screen and also from within Data Analysis (under the Statistics menu). The histograms below, constructed on the same scale, show simulated distributions of the sample mean for samples of sizes 1 and 10. Histogram settings are under the Options menu. The mean and standard deviation for each distribution of sample means can be found from the information button next to "runs".

a.

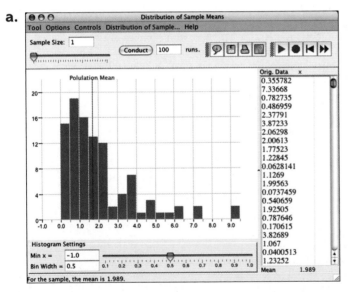

b. Repeat Part a for a sample size of 2. A sample size of 5. A sample size of 10. A sample size of 20.

c. Describe what happens to the mean and standard deviation of the distribution of the sample means as the sample size increases. Compare your observations with those of your classmates.

Summarize the Mathematics

In this investigation, you saw how the Central Limit Theorem can be used in situations when you want to use a control chart, but the distribution of measurements is not approximately normal.

a What is the Central Limit Theorem?

b How is the Central Limit Theorem used in statistical process control?

c Describe how the shape, center, and spread of the distribution of sample means is related to sample size.

Be prepared to explain your ideas and examples with the class.

✔Check Your Understanding

Your company has been successful in adjusting the machine that fills cereal boxes so that the mean weight in the boxes is 16.1 ounces. After filling several hundred boxes, it is obvious that the distribution of weights is somewhat skewed. So to ensure that you are warned if the process goes out of control, you decide to use an *x*-bar chart with samples of size 3. You set the upper control limit at 16.39 and the lower control limit at 15.81. Several days later, seven samples of the weights of three individual boxes were taken, as shown in the table.

Sample	Measurements
first	16.05, 16.27, 15.68
second	16.10, 15.80, 15.75
third	16.98, 16.12, 15.73
fourth	15.93, 15.92, 15.91
fifth	16.47, 16.04, 16.93
sixth	15.58, 15.90, 16.25
seventh	15.84, 15.60, 15.77

a. Compute the mean of each sample of size 3. Plot all seven means on an *x*-bar chart that shows the upper and lower control limits.

b. Has the process gone out of control?

c. Why were samples of size 3 used rather than size 1?

b.

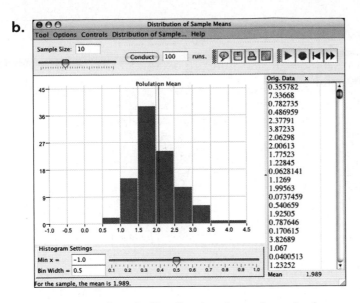

For the sample, the mean is 1.989.

Distribution of Sample Means

n = 100
mean = 2.02
minimum = 0.75
q1 = 1.63
median = 1.95
q3 = 2.32
maximum =4.09
sample standard deviation = 0.62
sample variance =0.39

c. The mean of each distribution is at about 2, the same as the mean of the population. The standard deviation decreases as the sample size increases. This makes sense because the sample mean should tend to be closer to the population mean with a larger sample size than with a smaller sample size. (In fact, the standard deviation of the distribution of sample means is equal to the standard deviation of the population divided by the square root of the sample size, if samples are taken with replacement. See Extensions Task 24 page 313.)

Summarize
the Mathematics

a The Central Limit Theorem is a statement about the shape of the distribution of the means of all possible samples of a fixed size taken from a finite population. It says that the shape becomes more and more approximately normal as the sample size increases. (If an infinite population is normal to begin with, the distribution of sample means is normal for all sample sizes.)

b The eight tests used with control charts depend on the condition that the distribution of measurements is approximately normal. This is needed so quality control practitioners know the probability of a false alarm. Even if individual measurements do not come from a distribution that is approximately normal, the means of groups of measurements of a fixed size will have an approximately normal distribution. Thus, the eight tests can be used.

c For the distribution of sample means, as *n* increases, the shape becomes more approximately normal, the means are all about the same as the population mean, and the standard deviation decreases.

MATH TOOLKIT Summarize your responses to the STM in your toolkit.

Unit 4

✔ Check Your Understanding

a. The means of the samples of size 3 are: 16.0000, 15.8833, 16.2767, 15.9200, 16.4800, 15.9100, and 15.7367.

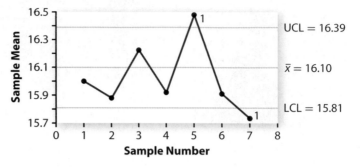

b. Yes, by Test 1 the process has gone out of control, at the fifth and seventh samples, where the means lie, respectively, above and below the control limits. (It appears that the standard deviation has increased.)

c. Sample size 1 distribution is the same as the population of sample means. For sample size 1, the standard deviation used to set control limits is not very accurate.

Teacher Notes

Applications

1. The thermostat in the Simpson's apartment is set at 70° Fahrenheit. Mrs. Simpson checks the temperature in the apartment every day at noon. The table and plot below give her observations over the last 25 days. She has been satisfied with the results and felt that the process was under control. However, at noon today, the temperature in her apartment was 63°F. Should Mrs. Simpson call building maintenance? Explain why or why not, in terms of statistical process control methods.

Temperature Observations

Day	Temp (in °F)	Day	Temp (in °F)	Day	Temp (in °F)
1	72	10	70	19	70
2	71	11	68	20	67
3	67	12	65	21	69
4	72	13	68	22	68
5	72	14	67	23	72
6	71	15	72	24	71
7	73	16	73	25	70
8	72	17	71		
9	69	18	70		

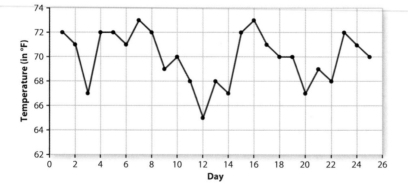

On Your Own

Applications

1 Yes, Mrs. Simpson should call maintenance. On previous days, the mean temperature was 70°F with a standard deviation of 2.16°F. Since $\frac{63 - 70}{2.16} \approx -3.2$, this morning's temperature was 3.2 standard deviations below the average. (Even if the temperatures are not normally distributed, this would be a fairly unusual occurrence.) The temperature of 63°F is out of control by Test 1. It is beyond the LCL as can be seen in the display below.

> **TECHNOLOGY NOTE**
> The temperature data are in *CPMP-Tools*.

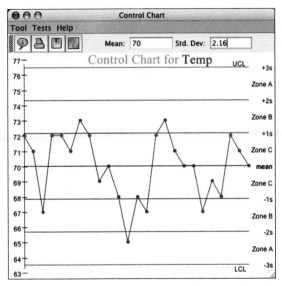

Unit 4

Statistical Process Control **T303**

(2) A person is running a machine that makes nails. The nails are supposed to have a mean length of 2 inches. But, as in all processes, the nails do not come out exactly 2 inches long each time. The machine is supposed to be set so the distribution of the lengths of the nails is normal and the standard deviation of the lengths of the nails is 0.03 inches.

a. Sketch the distribution of the lengths of the nails when the machine is under control. Mark the mean and one, two, and three standard deviations from the mean on the horizontal axis.

b. If the machine is set correctly, what percentage of the nails will be more than 2.06 inches long? Less than 1.94 inches long?

c. What percentage of the nails will be more than 2.09 inches long? Less than 1.91 inches long?

d. Suppose the machinist turns on the machine one morning after it has been cleaned. He finds these lengths in inches for the first ten nails, 2.01, 2.08, 1.97, 1.99, 1.92, 2.00, 2.03, 1.99, 1.97, and 1.95. Explain what your advice would be and why.

(3) In Investigation 2, Problems 2–4, you explored the probabilities of false alarms in the context of a machine filling cartons of ice cream with the process under control. Suppose now that the operator is using only Test 8 on page 290.

a. What is the probability that the next observation is not in either Zone C?

b. What is the probability that none of the next eight observations are in either Zone C?

c. What is the probability that the operator will get a false alarm from the next eight cartons being filled? Place your result in the appropriate row of your copy of the table from Investigation 2. Round your answer to the nearest ten-thousandth.

(4) The Ford Motor Company lists these four signals on its control charts.

- Any point outside of the control limits, more than three standard deviations from the mean

- Seven points in a row that are all above or all below the central line

- Seven points in a row that are either increasing or decreasing

- Any other obviously non-random pattern

Source: Ford Motor Company, *Continuing Process Control and Process Capability Improvement.* December, 1987.

a. Which of these tests is exactly the same as one of the tests (page 290) from the Western Electric handbook?

b. Assume that a manufacturing process is in control. If you are using only Ford's first test, what is the probability of a false alarm on the next observation?

2 **a.**

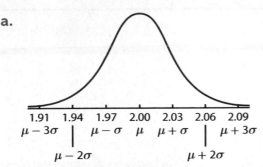

1.91 1.94 1.97 2.00 2.03 2.06 2.09
$\mu - 3\sigma$ | $\mu - \sigma$ μ $\mu + \sigma$ | $\mu + 3\sigma$
$\mu - 2\sigma$ $\mu + 2\sigma$

b. Since 95% of the nails will have lengths from 1.94 inches to 2.06 inches, 5% of them will be either longer than 2.06 inches or shorter than 1.94 inches. Since the distribution should be symmetric, 2.5% will be longer than 2.06 inches and 2.5% will be shorter than 1.94 inches.

c. $\frac{100\% - 99.7\%}{2} = 0.15\%$

0.15% will be more than 2.09 inches long, and 0.15% will be less than 1.91 inches long.

d. It does not look like the machine is out of adjustment. None of the eight tests signals that the process may be out of control. The machinist should continue working but keep watching the control chart.

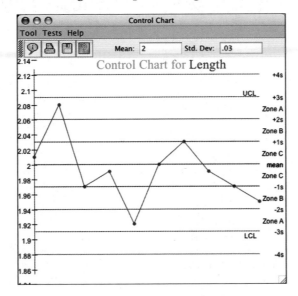

3 **a.** 0.32

b. $(0.32)^8 \approx 0.00011$

c. 0.0001. This result should be placed with Test 8 of the chart from page 291.

4 **a.** The first Ford test is the same as Test 1.

b. 0.003

c. Assume that a manufacturing process is in control. What is the probability of a false alarm on the next seven observations if you are using only Ford's second test?

d. Is Ford's second test more or less likely to produce a false alarm than the similar test from the Western Electric handbook? Explain.

e. Is Ford's third test more or less likely to produce a false alarm than the similar test from the Western Electric handbook? Explain.

5. Suppose that the ice cream machine in Investigation 2, Problem 2, is under control, and the operator is using only Test 5. You will now find the probability of a false alarm with the next three observations.

a. What is the probability that an observation will fall in Zone A at the top of the chart or beyond?

b. There are four ways that at least two of the next three observations can be in Zone A at the top of the chart or beyond. Three ways are described below. What is the fourth way?

- The first, second, and third observations are in Zone A or beyond.

- The first observation is not in Zone A or beyond. The second and third are.

- The first observation is in Zone A or beyond. The second is not, and the third is.

c. Find the probability of each of the four ways in Part b. Recall that two events are said to be **mutually exclusive** if it is impossible for both of them to occur on the same trial. Are these four ways mutually exclusive?

d. What is the probability that at least two of the next three observations will be in Zone A at the top of the chart or beyond?

e. What is the probability that at least two of the next three observations will be in Zone A at the bottom of the chart or beyond?

f. Are the events described in Parts d and e mutually exclusive?

g. What is the probability that the ice cream machine operator will get a false alarm from the next three cartons being filled? Place your result in your copy of the table from Investigation 2. Round your answer to the nearest ten-thousandth.

6. Suppose that the ice cream machine in Investigation 2, Problem 2, is under control and the operator is using only Test 6. Find the probability of a false alarm from the next five observations. Place your result in your copy of the table from Investigation 2, rounding to the nearest ten-thousandth.

c. $(0.5)^7 + (0.5)^7 = 0.015625$

d. Ford's test, which requires seven observations in a row, is more likely to produce a false alarm than Test 2, which requires nine observations. $(0.5)^7 > (0.5)^9$ (This is an opportunity for students to recall that when raising a number between 0 and 1 to a power, as the power increases, the value decreases. Alternatively, $f(x) = (0.5)^x$ is a decreasing function.)

e. Ford's test is less likely to produce a false alarm than Test 3, which requires only six observations in a row.

5 a. 0.025

b. The first and second observations are in Zone A or beyond; the third is not.

c. • $(0.025)(0.025)(0.025) \approx 0.000016$

   • $(0.975)(0.025)(0.025) \approx 0.000609$

   • $(0.025)(0.975)(0.025) \approx 0.000609$

   • $(0.025)(0.025)(0.975) \approx 0.000609$

   Yes, these four events are mutually exclusive. If one of them happens, none of the other three can happen.

d. Adding the probabilities in Part c, you get 0.001843.

e. 0.001843

f. Yes. If the observations are in the top half of the chart, they cannot also be in the bottom half of the chart.

g. $2(0.001843) \approx 0.0037$. This number should be placed with Test 5 on the table from page 295.

6 $2[(0.16)^5 + 5(0.16)^4(0.84)] \approx 0.0057$. This number should be placed with Test 6 on the table from page 295.

7 The distribution of the lengths of widgets made by a certain process is slightly skewed. Consequently, the company uses an *x*-bar chart with samples of size 2 to determine when the process may have gone out of control. When the process is in control, the mean is 3 cm. The lower and upper control limits of the *x*-bar chart are 2.97 and 3.03. One morning, eight samples of the lengths of two individual widgets were taken, as shown in the table.

Sample	Measurements (in cm)
first	3.00, 3.02
second	3.00, 2.98
third	3.01, 2.97
fourth	3.02, 3.00
fifth	2.98, 3.00
sixth	3.00, 3.00
seventh	3.01, 3.00
eighth	2.98, 3.00

a. Compute the mean of each sample of size 2. Plot all eight means on an *x*-bar chart that shows the upper and lower control limits.

b. Has the process gone out of control?

8 At the Web site www.fueleconomy.gov, people can report their vehicles' actual gas mileage and compare it to the EPA estimate.

a. The histogram below shows the overall gas mileage reported by the first 64 owners of a 2006 Honda Civic Hybrid to make a report. The EPA estimate for the 2006 Honda Civic Hybrid was 50 miles per gallon (mpg). Does it appear that vehicles are achieving that estimate, on average?

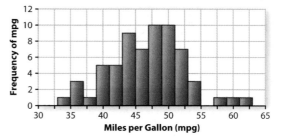

Unit 4

7 **a.** The means are: 3.008, 2.992, 2.987, 3.010, 2.990, 3.002, 3.004, and 2.989.

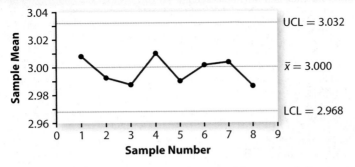

b. The process has not gone out of control by any of the tests.

8 **a.** No, the mean of the distribution of reported mpgs is less than 50 mpg. (In fact, it is about 46.7 mpg.)

b. The following histogram shows the means from 1,000 random samples of size 5 taken from the reported gas mileages in Part a. One of the samples had these mpg: 43.9, 53.9, 47.2, 45.0, and 46.9. Where is this sample represented on the histogram below?

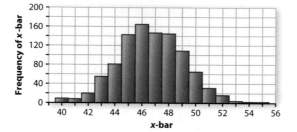

c. Describe how the shape, mean, and standard deviation of the distribution of sample means differ from that of the distribution of the individual mpgs. Is this what you would expect?

Connections

9 Suppose you are operating a machine that fills cereal boxes. The boxes are supposed to contain 16 ounces. The machine fills the boxes so that the distribution of weights is normal and the standard deviation is 0.2 ounces. You can adjust the mean.

a. If you set the machine so that the mean is 16 ounces, what percentage of customers will get a box of cereal that contains less than 16 ounces?

b. Explain where you would recommend setting the mean and why.

c. Suppose you are buying a new box-filling machine. All else being equal, should you buy one with a standard deviation of 0.2 ounces or 0.4 ounces? Explain your reasoning.

10 A paper clip machine makes 4,000,000 paper clips each month. The machinist measures every 10,000th paper clip to be sure the machine is still set correctly. When the machine is set correctly, the measurements follow a normal distribution. The machinist uses only Test 1 (one value more than three standard deviations from the mean). Suppose the machine remains set correctly for a month. How many times would you expect the operator to stop production anyway?

b. The mean of this sample is 47.38, so it is in the eighth bar from the left (above the tick mark for 47).

c. The shape is more approximately normal, the mean is still at about 46.7, and the standard deviation about half as large (in fact, going from about 5.5 to about 2.4).

Connections

9 a. Approximately 50% because the mean and median are equal in a normal distribution.

b. Responses may vary, but should be supported by a probability statement. For example, if you set the mean at 16.4 ounces, only 2.5% of the customers will get less than one pound. But half of the customers will get more than 0.4 ounces extra, and that is costly to the cereal company.

c. You should buy the one with the smaller standard deviation of 0.2 ounces. With 0.4 ounces, for Part b, you would have to set the mean at 16.8 ounces so that 97.5% of the customers would get at least a pound. However, in this case, half the customers would get more than 0.8 ounces extra of cereal.

10 The machinist will measure $\frac{4,000,000}{10,000} = 400$ paper clips. For approximately $400(0.003) = 1.2$ times, Test 1 will alert the operator to stop the machine.

11 Recall that two events are said to be **mutually exclusive** if it is impossible for both of them to occur on the same trial. Two events A and B are said to be **independent** if the probability that B occurs does not change depending on whether or not A occurred.

a. What is the rule for computing $P(A \text{ or } B)$ when A and B are mutually exclusive? For computing $P(A \text{ and } B)$ when A and B are independent?

b. If you pick one value at random from a normal distribution, what is the probability that it will be more than two standard deviations above the mean or more than two standard deviations below the mean?

c. If you pick one value at random from a normal distribution, what is the probability that it will be below the mean or more than two standard deviations above the mean?

d. If you pick five values at random from a normal distribution, what is the probability that all five values will be above the mean or all will be below the mean?

e. If you pick four values at random from a normal distribution, what is the probability that all four values will be more than two standard deviations above the mean?

f. If you pick five values at random from a normal distribution, what is the probability that all five values will be more than one standard deviation above the mean or all will be more than one standard deviation below the mean?

g. If you pick six values at random from a normal distribution, what is the probability that all six values will be below the mean?

h. If you select two values at random from a normal distribution, what is the probability that they both are more than two standard deviations above the mean or that they are both more than two standard deviations below the mean?

12 In the Course 2 *Probability Distributions* unit, you learned that the expected waiting time for a success in a waiting-time distribution is $\frac{1}{p}$, if p is the probability of a success on any one trial.

a. Suppose a machine operator is using only Test 1. If the process is under control, what is the expected number of items tested until Test 1 gives a false alarm? This is called the **average run length** or **ARL**.

b. If a machine operator uses both Test 1 and Test 2, is the ARL longer or shorter than if he or she uses just Test 1? Explain.

11 **a.** If two events A and B are mutually exclusive, $P(A \text{ or } B) = P(A) + P(B)$.
If the two events are independent, $P(A \text{ and } B) = P(A) \cdot P(B)$.

   b. 0.05

   c. $0.5 + 0.025 = 0.525$

   d. $(0.5)^5 + (0.5)^5 = 0.0625$

   e. $(0.025)^4 \approx 0.00000039$

   f. $(0.16)^5 + (0.16)^5 = 0.00021$

   g. $(0.5)^6 = 0.015625$

   h. $(0.025)^2 + (0.025)^2 = 0.00125$

12 **a.** The probability of a false alarm using only Test 1 is 0.003. So, the ARL
is $\frac{1}{0.003}$, or approximately 333 items.

   b. The probability of a false alarm is greater when you use more than
one test, so the ARL is shorter.

13 Here is a distribution that is *really* non-normal. Suppose that you take random samples of a fixed size *n* from this distribution and compute the mean. You do this several thousand times. This is exactly like making a binomial distribution except that instead of recording the number of successes in your sample, you record the number of successes divided by *n*, which gives the *proportion* of successes.

Outcome	Probability
0	0.1
1	0.9

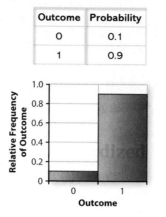

a. If the sample size is 1, what do you expect the resulting distribution to look like? Describe its shape and give its mean.

b. If the sample size is 2, what is the probability you get two 0s? Two 1s? One of each? Describe the shape and give the mean of the distribution of sample means.

c. How big does the sample size have to be before the distribution of sample means is approximately normal?

Reflections

14 A machinist is making video game tokens that are supposed to be 3.2 cm in diameter.

a. What might cause the mean diameter to change?

b. What might cause the standard deviation of the diameter to change while the mean stays the same?

15 Test 7 detects a *decrease* in variability. Why might a company want to detect a decrease in variability in the manufacturing of a product or in the processing of a service?

16 Why is it best if a machine operator does not use all eight tests but picks out just a few to use?

(13) **a.** It would look just like the histogram given in the student text. The mean is 0.9.

b. Using the Multiplication Rule for independent events, the probability that you get two 0s is $(0.1)(0.1) = 0.01$. The probability of two 1s is $(0.9)(0.9) = 0.81$. So, the probability of one 0 and one 1 is 0.18. The distribution of sample means for samples of size 2 is shown in this table.

Sample Mean	Probability
0	0.01
0.5	0.18
1	0.81

The shape is still skewed to the left (towards the smaller values), and the mean is still 0.9.

c. Using the guideline that both np and $n(1 - p)$ have to be at least 10, you need to solve the following system of inequalities.

$$n(0.9) \geq 10 \text{ and } n(1 - 0.9) \geq 10$$

The solutions are $n \geq 11.11$ and $n \geq 100$. So, you need a sample size of 100 or more.

Reflections

(14) **a.** The mean might change if the adjustment for the diameter of the tokens slips away from the required diameter, the operator does not set the adjustment quite right, the operator is not paying attention, and so on.

b. The standard deviation might decrease as the operator gets more skilled or if there is not enough oil, making the machine "tight." The standard deviation might increase if some parts get a bit loose or if a new, less-skilled operator takes over the machine.

(15) Decreased variation in a process is usually beneficial, and the cause should be identified and duplicated if possible. A decrease in variability means that the mean of the process can be pinpointed more precisely and the process adjusted so that the resulting products have little variability from the target mean. Smaller variability typically results when an operator gets more skillful or raw materials are more consistent.

(16) The more tests you use, the greater the chance of getting a false alarm (out-of-control signal when the process is actually in control). Too many false alarms will affect productivity.

17 If you pick six values at random from a distribution with unknown shape, what is the probability that all six values are more than the median? Can you answer this question for the mean? Explain.

18 A false alarm occurs when a machine is in control and a test warns that it may not be.

a. What could you call a situation for which the machine is not in control and no test has given a warning?

b. The following chart has four empty cells. Two of the cells should contain the words "correct decision." Another cell should contain the words "false alarm." The fourth cell should contain your new name from Part a. Write these words in the correct cells on a copy of the chart.

		Result of Test	
		Gives Alarm	**Does Not Give Alarm**
Condition of Machine	**In Control**		
	Not in Control		

19 The *x*-bar control chart below was made from a process that was entirely under control. Two hundred samples, each of size 5, were selected from a normal distribution with mean 0. The means of successive samples are plotted on the chart. There is one out-of-control signal, when the mean for sample 11 fell below the lower control limit. Does this mean that something is wrong or is it about what you would expect to happen?

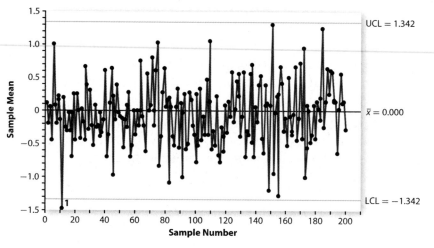

17 The probability that all six are above the median is $(0.5)^6 = 0.015625$. This question cannot be answered for the mean. Unless the distribution is known to be symmetric, we do not know what proportion of values are above the mean.

18 **a.** Responses will vary. False security is an appropriate term.

b.

		Result of Test	
		Gives Alarm	**Does Not Give Alarm**
Condition of Machine	**In Control**	False Alarm	Correct Decision
	Not in Control	Correct Decision	False Security

19 This is what you would expect to happen. A mean should fall outside the control limits about 0.003 of the time. Because there are 200 means, you would expect $0.003(200) = 0.6$, or about 1, of them to fall outside the control limits.

20 Look back at the distribution given in Problem 4 on page 301 of Investigation 3. Suppose 100 samples of fixed size 1, 2, 5, and 10 are taken from this population, which has mean 2. Match the sample size (1, 2, 5, or 10) with the histogram of the sample means (I, II, III, or IV).

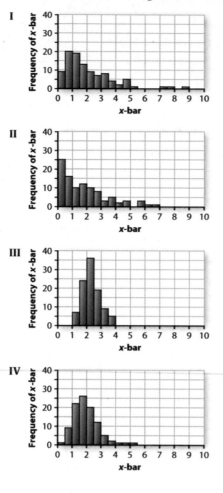

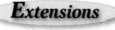

21 Suppose that the ice cream machine in Investigation 2, Problem 2, is under control and the operator is using only Test 3 from the chart on page 290. To find the probability of a false alarm, you can use the idea of permutations (ordered arrangements).

a. In how many different orders can the digits 1, 2, and 3 be listed?

b. In how many different orders can the digits 1, 2, 3, and 4 be listed?

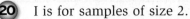

20 I is for samples of size 2.

II is for samples of size 1 as it is most like the population.

III is for samples of size 10 as it is the most approximately normal.

IV is for samples of size 5.

Extensions

21 **a.** They can be ordered: 123, 132, 231, 213, 312, and 321. There are six ways.

b. 24 ways. Students will probably need to list the orders. Encourage students to be systematic as they write their lists.

c. Compute 4! and 3! using the *factorial* function (!) on a calculator. Compare the calculator values of 4! and 3! to your answers in Parts a and b.

d. Use the factorial function to compute the number of different orders in which the digits 1, 2, 3, 4, 5, and 6 can be listed.

e. If the digits 1, 2, 3, 4, 5, and 6 are listed in a random order, what is the probability that they are in order from smallest to largest?

f. If the digits 1, 2, 3, 4, 5, and 6 are listed in a random order, what is the probability that they are in order from largest to smallest?

g. Are the two events described in Parts e and f mutually exclusive? If any six numbers are listed at random, what is the probability that they are in order from largest to smallest or in order from smallest to largest?

h. What is the probability that the ice cream machine operator will get a false alarm using only Test 3 with the next six cartons filled? Place your result in the appropriate row of your copy of the table from Investigation 2. Round your answer to the nearest ten-thousandth.

22 The probability of a false alarm using Test 8 is much smaller than the probability of a false alarm using any of the other tests. Describe how you could change Test 8 in order to make the probability of a false alarm closer to those of the other tests.

23 Suppose that the ice cream machine in Investigation 2, Problem 2, is under control and the operator is using only Test 4. In this task, you will use simulation to estimate the probability of a false alarm with the next fourteen observations.

a. First, describe a simulation to estimate the probability that if the digits 1, 2, 3, 4, and 5 are listed in a random order. They will alternate larger, smaller, larger, smaller, larger (for example: 5, 1, 3, 2, 4). Or, they will alternate smaller, larger, smaller, larger, smaller (for example: 4, 5, 2, 3, 1).

b. Perform your simulation 20 times. What is your estimate of the probability that the digits will alternate?

c. Make a listing of all 120 possible sequences of {1, 2, 3, 4, 5}. What is the theoretical probability that if these digits are listed at random, they will alternate?

c. The values should be the same. $4! = 24$ and $3! = 6$.

d. $6! = 720$

e. There is only one ordering from smallest to largest. So, the probability is $\frac{1}{6!} \approx 0.0014$.

f. $\frac{1}{720} \approx 0.0014$

g. Yes; $\frac{2}{720} \approx 0.0028$

h. The probability that the operator will get a false alarm from Test 3 is 0.0028. This result should be placed with Test 3 on the table from page 295.

22 From Applications Task 3, students found that the probability of a false alarm with Test 8 is about 0.0001, while that for the other tests are about 30 times greater. To make the probabilities more equal, you could change Test 8 by requiring only 5 observations in a row with none in either Zone C. Then the probability of a false alarm would be $(0.32)^5 \approx 0.003$.

23 **INSTRUCTIONAL NOTE** Students may need some help understanding why, for the purposes of this problem, selecting a random order for the digits from 1 to 5 is equivalent to randomly selecting five measurements from a normal distribution. They may notice that each digit is equally likely, while some measurements are less likely than others.

Suppose you randomly select five measurements from a normal distribution. To determine whether the measurements alternate in size, it is enough to know how those measurements are ranked by size. Every possible ranking by size of five measurements from a normal distribution is equally likely since there is no reason for the largest measurement to be selected third, for example, rather than second. Thus, if you replace the smallest measurement with a 1, the next smallest with a 2, and so on, every possible listing of the digits from 1 to 5 is equally likely. The simulation models this situation by randomly generating a possible listing of the digits from 1 to 5. This task is difficult to do theoretically.

ADDITIONAL RESOURCES

Comtet, Louis. *Advanced Combinatorics*. Boston: D. Reidel Publishing Company, 1974.

David, F. N., M. G. Kendall, and D. E. Barton. *Symmetric Functions and Allied Tables*. Cambridge: Cambridge University Press, 1966.

Sloane, N. J. A. *Encyclopedia of Integer Sequences*. San Diego: Academic Press, 1995. www.research.att.com/~njas/sequences

a. Students might suggest writing the digits 1, 2, 3, 4, and 5 on cards, shuffling the cards, writing the five digits out in the order they appear, and seeing if the digits alternate. Some students may use their calculators to select the order of the five digits.

b. Estimates will vary. (The theoretical probability is $\frac{32}{5!} \approx 0.267$. Since students use simulation with 20 trials, they will not get 0.267 exactly.)

NOTE The solution to Task 23 Part c is on page T313.

Teaching Resources

Student Master 43.

UNIT 4 *Samples and Variation*

Possible Sequences of {1, 2, 3, 4, 5}
Extensions Task 23

d. If you are able to share the work with others, design and carry out a simulation to estimate the probability that if the digits 1 through 14 are listed in a random order, they will alternate larger/smaller or smaller/larger. Place your result on the appropriate row of your copy of the table from Investigation 2, rounding to the nearest ten-thousandth.

24 When all possible random samples of a given size are taken from a population with standard deviation σ, the distribution of sample means has standard deviation equal to $\frac{\sigma}{\sqrt{n}}$. This is true if the samples are taken with replacement, meaning each item drawn is replaced before selecting the next one.

a. In Problem 4 of Investigation 3 (page 301) and in other problems, you noticed that the standard deviation of the distribution of sample means is smaller than the standard deviation of the population from which the random samples were taken. How are your observations explained by the above rule?

b. The population from Problem 4 has a standard deviation of about 1.93. Compare the population standard deviation to the standard deviation of the distribution of means you found for samples of size 1, 2, 5, 10, and 20.

c. The years of rainfall in Los Angeles in the table on page 299 have mean 15.1 and standard deviation 7.1. Show how the upper and lower control limits were computed in the chart in Problem 3 Part d on page 300.

Review

25 Imagine rolling a pair of tetrahedral dice.

a. Make a chart showing all possible outcomes for the sum when you roll a pair of tetrahedral dice.

b. If you roll a pair of tetrahedral dice, are the two events, getting a *sum of 5* and getting *doubles*, mutually exclusive? What is the probability that you get a sum of 5 or doubles?

c. There are 5! = 120, orderings of the digits 1 through 5. Making a list of all orderings is not difficult. But it is tedious, so you may choose to distribute the Teaching Master. Students can then count those orderings where the digits alternate larger, smaller, larger, smaller, larger or smaller, larger, smaller, larger, smaller. There are 32 of these, so the probability is $\frac{32}{120} \approx 0.267$.

d. Estimates will vary. The theoretical probability is $\frac{398,721,962}{14!} \approx 0.0046$. The estimate should be entered with Test 4 on the table from page 295.

24 a. $\frac{\sigma}{\sqrt{n}} < \sigma$ when $n > 1$ because we are dividing σ by a number greater than 1, $\sqrt{n}$.

b. $\frac{1.93}{\sqrt{1}} = 1.93$; $\frac{1.93}{\sqrt{2}} \approx 1.36$; $\frac{1.93}{\sqrt{5}} \approx 0.86$; $\frac{1.93}{\sqrt{10}} \approx 0.61$
Standard deviations should be about the same.

c. LCL $= 15.1 - 3 \cdot \frac{7.1}{\sqrt{3}} \approx 2.80$

UCL $= 15.1 + 3 \cdot \frac{7.1}{\sqrt{3}} \approx 27.4$

> **NOTE** If random samples are taken without replacement and the sample size is small compared to the size of the population (say, less than 10% of the population), it is approximately true that the distribution of sample means has standard deviation equal to $\frac{\sigma}{\sqrt{n}}$.

Review

25 a.

+	1	2	3	4
1	2	3	4	5
2	3	4	5	6
3	4	5	6	7
4	5	6	7	8

b. The two events are mutually exclusive.
P(*sum of 5 or doubles*) $= \frac{4}{16} + \frac{4}{16} = \frac{1}{2}$

26 Suppose it is true that "All graduates of Rio Grande High School must successfully complete three years of high school mathematics."

a. Write this statement in if-then form. What is the hypothesis? What is the conclusion?

b. If Alberto is a graduate of Rio Grande High School, what can you conclude? Explain your reasoning.

c. If Johanna was a student at Rio Grande High School and passed three years of high school mathematics, what can you conclude? Explain your reasoning.

27 Graph the solution set to each system of inequalities. Label the point of intersection of the boundary lines and the *x*- and *y*-intercepts of each line.

a. $x \geq 3$
   $2x + y \leq 6$

b. $4x + 3y > 30$
   $y < 2x - 5$

28 Without using technology tools, identify the *x*- and *y*-intercepts and the coordinates of the vertex of the graph of each quadratic function. Draw a sketch of the graph. Then check your work using technology.

a. $f(x) = (x + 3)(x - 5)$

b. $f(x) = 2x^2 - 6x$

c. $f(x) = x^2 - 4x + 3$

29 The coordinates of three vertices of $\square ABCD$ are $A(-2, 0)$, $B(1, 4)$, and $C(13, 9)$.

a. Find the coordinates of vertex *D*. Explain your reasoning, and verify that *ABCD* is a parallelogram.

b. Find the measures of all the angles in the parallelogram.

c. If the diagonals of the parallelogram intersect at point *E*, find the length of $\overline{AE}$.

30 Delaware Valley Car Rentals has rental locations in Port Jervis, Stroudsburg, and Easton. A customer who rents a car from Delaware Valley Car Rentals can return the car to any of the three locations. Company statistics show that of the cars rented in Port Jervis, 50% are returned to Port Jervis, 20% are returned to Stroudsburg, and 30% are returned to Easton. Of the cars rented in Stroudsburg, 25% are returned to Port Jervis, 40% to Stroudsburg, and 35% to Easton. Of the cars rented in Easton, 10% are returned to Port Jervis, 30% to Stroudsburg, and 60% to Easton.

a. Represent this information in a matrix in which the rows indicate the location in which the car was rented and the columns indicate where the car was returned. Use decimal values of the percentages.

26 **a. Hypothesis:** If a student graduated from Rio Grande High School,
     Conclusion: then he or she successfully completed three years of
             high school mathematics.

b. Alberto successfully completed three years of math. Since the
     hypothesis is true, you can make the conclusion.

c. You can conclude only that she successfully completed three years
     of math. She may not have graduated.

27 The shaded regions below indicate the solution. Some students may shade
     out the non-solutions as done in Unit 2.

a.   **b.**

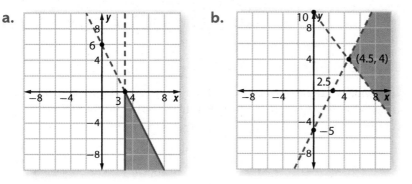

28 For each function, the vertex will lie on the line of symmetry. Finding the
     average of the two *x*-coordinates provides the *x* value for the vertex *v*.
     Finding $f(v)$ provides the *y*-coordinate of the vertex.

a. $f(x) = (x + 3)(x - 5)$ **b.** $f(x) = 2x(x - 3)$

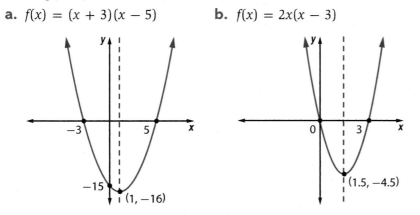

c. $f(x) = x^2 - 4x + 3 = (x - 3)(x - 1)$

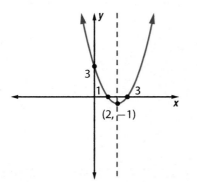

29 **a.** Students' methods will vary.

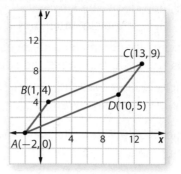

The fourth vertex is $D(10, 5)$. You move horizontally 12 units and vertically 5 units from B to C. So, making the same translation from A identifies D as $(-2 + 12, 0 + 5) = (10, 5)$. $\overline{AD} \parallel \overline{BC}$ because the $\frac{\Delta y}{\Delta x}$ is the same for both segments. The lengths of $\overline{AD}$ and $\overline{BC}$ are the same because they are both hypotenuses of right triangles with legs of length 12 and 5 units. Thus, $ABCD$ is a parallelogram.

b. Students' methods may vary. They might use the Law of Cosines by finding AD, AB, and BD. $AD = 13$, $AB = 5$, and $BD = \sqrt{82}$.

So, $m\angle BAD = \cos^{-1}\left(\frac{(\sqrt{82})^2 - (13)^2 - (5)^2}{(-2)(13)(5)}\right) \approx 30.5°$.

Alternatively, they might find $m\angle BAD$ as $\tan^{-1}\left(\frac{4}{3}\right) - \tan^{-1}\left(\frac{5}{12}\right)$. $m\angle BAD \approx 30.5°$. Thus, $m\angle C \approx 30.5°$ and $m\angle B = m\angle D \approx 149.5°$.

c. AC is $\sqrt{306}$ or approximately 17.49. Because the diagonals of a parallelogram bisect each other, AE is half that or about 8.75.

30 **a.**

		Returned to		
		PJ	S	E
Returned in	PJ	0.50	0.20	0.30
	S	0.25	0.40	0.35
	E	0.10	0.30	0.60

b. On one day, the company rents 20 cars in Port Jervis, 30 cars in Stroudsburg, and 45 cars in Easton. Use matrix multiplication to find the expected number of these cars that will be returned to each location.

c. Explain what the non-integer values in the matrix result might mean for this context.

31 Consider a circle with center at $(-3, 1)$ and radius 6.

a. Draw a sketch of the circle.

b. Recall that the general form for the equation of a circle is $(x - h)^2 + (y - k)^2 = r^2$, where (h, k) is the center of the circle and r is the radius. Write the equation for this circle.

c. Calculate the area of this circle.

d. Calculate the circumference of this circle.

e. Write an equation for a circle with the same center but with a circumference twice the circumference of this circle.

32 If $\cos \theta = -\frac{3}{5}$ and the terminal side of θ lies in Quadrant II, find $\sin \theta$ and $\tan \theta$.

b.

PJ S E

[20 30 45]; [20 30 45] ·

$$\begin{array}{c} \\ PJ \\ S \\ E \end{array} \begin{array}{ccc} PJ & S & E \\ \begin{bmatrix} 0.50 & 0.20 & 0.30 \\ 0.25 & 0.40 & 0.35 \\ 0.10 & 0.30 & 0.60 \end{bmatrix} \end{array} = \begin{array}{ccc} PJ & S & E \\ [22 & 29.5 & 43.5] \end{array}$$

You expect that 22 cars will be returned to Port Jervis, 29.5 cars to Stroudsburg, and 43.5 cars to Easton.

c. For example, the 29.5 means that if the situation of 20 cars rented in Port Jervis, 30 in Stroudsburg, and 45 in Easton were repeated many times, on average, 29.5 cars would be returned to Stroudsburg.

31 **a.**
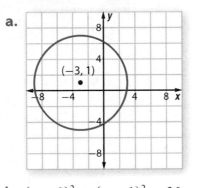

b. $(x + 3)^2 + (y - 1)^2 = 36$

c. $A = \pi(6)^2 \approx 113.1$ square units

d. $C = 2\pi(6) \approx 37.7$ units

e. $(x + 3)^2 + (y - 1)^2 = 144$

32 $\sin \theta = \dfrac{4}{5}$

$\tan \theta = -\dfrac{4}{3}$

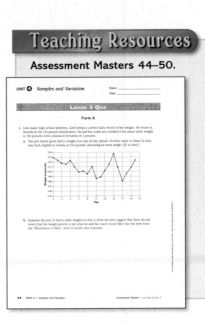

Looking Back

Y ou studied three basic tools in this unit: the normal distribution as a model of the variability in a distribution, the binomial distribution as a model of success/failure situations, and the control chart as a way to determine when an industrial process goes out of control.

The normal distribution is fundamental in characterizing variability for several reasons. As you learned in Lesson 1, many naturally occurring variables, such as human height, have an approximately normal distribution. As you learned in Lesson 2, if you have a large enough sample size, the binomial distribution is approximately normal in shape. As you learned in Lesson 3, the distribution of the means of random samples becomes more approximately normal as the sample size increases.

The following tasks will help you review and deepen your understanding of these basic ideas.

1. According to a U.S. Geological Survey report, the historical distribution of total rainfall for Guatemala averaged over 88 gauges at different stations during June, July, and August is approximately normal with a mean of 955 mm and a standard deviation of 257 mm. (Source: *June-July-August 2003 Rainfall Forecast Interpretation, Central America*, March 19, 2003)

   a. Sketch this distribution. Include a scale on the horizontal axis. Mark one, two, and three standard deviations from the mean.

   b. Would it be a rare event to have 500 mm of rainfall?

   c. In what percentage of years is the rainfall more than 1 meter? Explain.

   d. What amount of rainfall falls at the 25th percentile?

Looking Back

1 **a.**

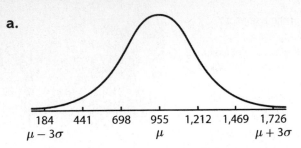

| 184 | 441 | 698 | 955 | 1,212 | 1,469 | 1,726 |

$\mu - 3\sigma$ μ $\mu + 3\sigma$

b. No. The standardized value for 500 mm is
$z = \dfrac{x - \mu}{\sigma} = \dfrac{500 - 955}{257} \approx -1.77$. This is less than
2 standard deviations from the mean so is not a rare event.

c. The standardized value for 1,000 mm is
$z = \dfrac{x - \mu}{\sigma} = \dfrac{1,000 - 955}{257} \approx 0.2$. From the table on
page 245, the proportion is $1 - 0.5793 = 0.4207$, or about
42% of the years.

d. The standardized value corresponding to a proportion of
0.25 is about -0.7. Solving $-0.7 = \dfrac{x - 955}{257}$, $x \approx 775$ mm.

2 The claim has been made that about 57% of drivers agree that travel would be safer if the minimum driving age for new drivers was raised from 16 to 18 years old. Suppose you take a random sample of 500 drivers and ask them if they agree. (Source: www.cnn.com/2003/US/05/27/dangerous.driving/index.html)

a. If the claim is correct, what is the expected number in your sample who will agree? The expected number who will disagree?

b. Is this sample size large enough that the binomial distribution for this situation will be approximately normal?

c. Compute the mean and standard deviation of the binomial distribution.

d. Sketch this distribution. Include a scale on the horizontal axis that shows the mean and the points one and two standard deviations from the mean.

e. If the claim is true, would it be a rare event to find only 270 people in your sample who agree? Why might that happen?

3 Suppose you kept track of the gas mileage for your vehicle over a 25-week span. You recorded the data as follows.

Gas Mileage

Week	Miles per Gallon	Week	Miles per Gallon
Feb 7	23	May 9	24
Feb 14	27	May 16	27
Feb 21	27	May 23	25
Feb 28	28	May 30	28
Mar 7	25	June 6	25
Mar 14	26	June 13	26
Mar 21	25	June 20	25
Mar 28	29.5	June 27	29
Apr 4	26	July 4	26
Apr 11	27	July 11	27
Apr 18	24	July 18	24
Apr 25	26	July 25	26
May 2	26		

a. Make a run chart for your vehicle's gas mileage. What does it tell you about the consistency of your vehicle's gas mileage?

b. Find the mean and standard deviation of the measurements of miles per gallon. Draw horizontal lines on the run chart representing the mean and one and two standard deviations from the mean. Was your vehicle's mileage unusual for any week in that time period?

Unit 4

2

a. The expected number in your sample of who will agree is $500(0.57) = 285$. The expected number who will disagree is $500(1 - 0.57) = 215$.

b. Yes, because both the expected number of successes, $np = 285$, and the expected number of failures, $n(1 - p) = 215$, are at least 10.

c. $\mu = np = 500(0.57) = 285$

$\sigma = \sqrt{np(1 - p)} = \sqrt{500(0.57)(1 - 0.57)} \approx 11.07 \approx 11$

d.

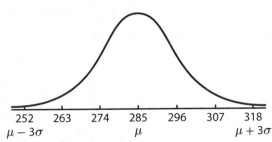

$$
\begin{array}{ccccccc}
252 & 263 & 274 & 285 & 296 & 307 & 318 \\
\mu - 3\sigma & & & \mu & & & \mu + 3\sigma
\end{array}
$$

e. No. The standardized value for 270 is

$z = \dfrac{x - \mu}{\sigma} = \dfrac{270 - 285}{11.07} \approx -1.355$. This is less than 2 standard deviations from the expected number of successes. Just by chance, you got 15 fewer successes in your sample than you expected. This is not a very big difference for a sample of 500 people.

3

a. The mileage was low the first week. Then it was relatively consistent except during the 8th and the 21st weeks, when it was higher than the other weeks.

> **TECHNOLOGY NOTE** These data are in *CPMP-Tools*.

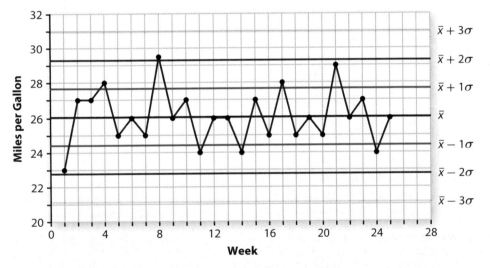

b. The mean was 26.06 mpg, and the population standard deviation was 1.55. Only during the 8th week was the mileage more than two standard deviations from the mean. We would expect such an event to happen in 5% of the weeks when gas mileage is in control, or about once out of 25 weeks.

c. To use the eight out-of-control tests, the data must be approximately normally distributed.

   i. Does that appear to be the case here? Explain.

   ii. How could you use the eight tests if the distribution had not been approximately normal?

d. Would you say fuel consumption of your vehicle is in control? If not, which test is violated?

e. Five weeks after July 25, you discovered that something seemed to be wrong with your vehicle, affecting its gas mileage. Write down two different sets of mileage data for those five weeks that would indicate you had a problem. Explain the test you were using and how it would apply to your data. Use a test only once.

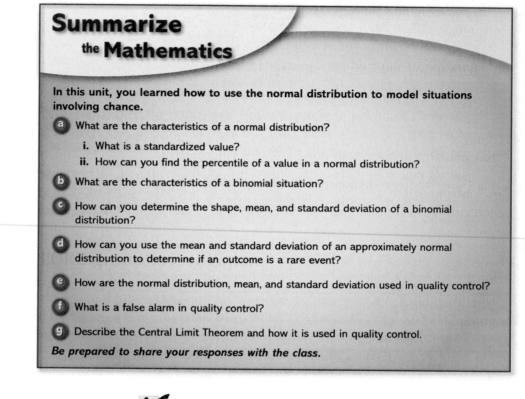

Summarize
the Mathematics

In this unit, you learned how to use the normal distribution to model situations involving chance.

a What are the characteristics of a normal distribution?

   i. What is a standardized value?

   ii. How can you find the percentile of a value in a normal distribution?

b What are the characteristics of a binomial situation?

c How can you determine the shape, mean, and standard deviation of a binomial distribution?

d How can you use the mean and standard deviation of an approximately normal distribution to determine if an outcome is a rare event?

e How are the normal distribution, mean, and standard deviation used in quality control?

f What is a false alarm in quality control?

g Describe the Central Limit Theorem and how it is used in quality control.

Be prepared to share your responses with the class.

✓Check Your Understanding

Write, in outline form, a summary of the important mathematical concepts and methods developed in this unit. Organize your summary so that it can be used as a quick reference in future units and courses.

c. **i.** Yes, the histogram below has about the right shape. The distribution is relatively symmetric.

ii. If the distribution had not been symmetric and mound-shaped, you would have to graph the means of equal-sized groups of individual mpgs rather than plotting individual mpgs. How many individual tanks of gas should be in each group depends on how badly non-normal the distribution of original measurements is.

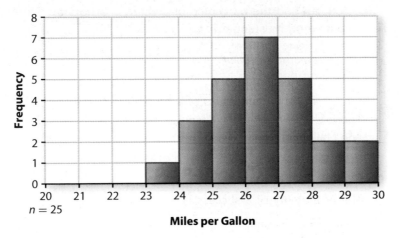

$n = 25$

Miles per Gallon

d. Fuel consumption seems to be in control. None of the tests is violated.

e. Since something seems to be "wrong" with the vehicle, it is probably getting lower gas mileage due to a mechanical problem, or perhaps there is a slow gas tank leak. For example, one reading of below 21.32 mpg would fail Test 1. Four out of five points less than 24.48 mpg (Test 6) or two out of three points in the set of five less than 22.9 mpg (Test 5) would also be indicators that the gas mileage had decreased.

Summarize
the Mathematics

a i. A standardized value is the number of standard deviations that a value lies from the mean of its distribution.

ii. You can find the percentile of a value in a normal distribution by computing its standardized value using the formula $z = \dfrac{value - mean}{standard\ deviation}$ and then looking up the percentile in the table on page 245.

b There are four characteristics of a binomial situation.

• There are two possible outcomes on each trial called "success" and "failure."

• Each trial is independent of the others.

• There is a fixed number of trials.

• The probability of a success is the same on each trial.

c To determine the shape, use the rule that the distribution is approximately normal if both np and $n(1 - p)$ are greater than or equal to 10. If either one is less than 10, the distribution will be skewed to the right if $p < 0.5$ and to the left if $p > 0.5$. The expected number of successes (mean) is found using np. The standard deviation is found by using $\sqrt{np(1 - p)}$.

d A rare event is one that is more than two standard deviations from the mean.

e The mean and standard deviation are used to determine the "zones" of a control chart. Six of the eight tests are based on the probability that a set of observations from a process that is in control will fall in various zones. These probabilities apply only if the observations are normally distributed. If the individual observations are not normally distributed, then you should plot the means of equal-sized groups of individual measurements.

f A false alarm happens when a test signals that a process is out of control, but the process is not out of control. The probabilities of false alarms are calculated by assuming the process is in control and then finding the probability that the next set of observations will give an out-of-control signal by that test.

g The Central Limit Theorem says that if you take repeated, independent, random samples of a fixed size (sampling with replacement) and form the distribution of the sample means, the distribution of the sample means becomes more approximately normal as the sample size increases. So, if the individual observations are not normally distributed, you can plot the means of equal-sized groups of individual measurements. The more skewed the original measurements, the larger the groups must be in order to get a distribution of sample means that is approximately normal.

✓ Check Your Understanding

You may wish to have students use the Teaching Master, *Samples and Variation Unit Summary*, to help them organize the information. Above all, this should be something that is useful to the individual student.

Practicing for Standardized Tests

Each Practicing for Standardized Tests master presents 10 questions in the multiple-choice format of test items similar to how they often appear in standardized tests. Answers are provided below.

Answers to Practice Set 4

1. (b) **2.** (a) **3.** (c) **4.** (b) **5.** (b)
6. (b) **7.** (d) **8.** (c) **9.** (c) **10.** (c)

Midterm Assessments

A bank of assessment tasks from which to construct a midterm exam that fits your particular class needs and emphases is provide in the *Unit 4 Resource Masters*, on the Course 3 *TeachersWorks Plus* CD, and on the Course 3 *ExamViewPro* CD. In addition to problems similar in form to those on quizzes and tests, the unit resources include several multiple-choice tasks for each unit and midterm projects.

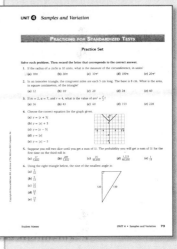
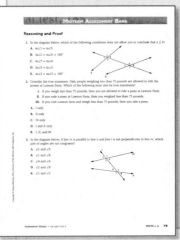

Glossary/Glosario

English	**Español**

A

Alternate exterior angles (p. 36) In the diagram, transversal *t* cuts lines ℓ and *m*, forming angles 1 through 8. Pairs of alternate exterior angles are ∠1 and ∠8, and ∠2 and ∠7. The angles in each pair are not between the lines and are on opposite sides of the transversal.

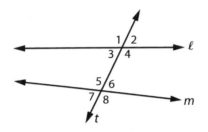

Ángulos alternos externos (pág. 36) En el diagrama, la transversal *t* corta las líneas ℓ y *m*. Los pares de ángulos alternos externos son ∠1 y ∠8, y ∠2 y ∠7. Los ángulos en cada par no están entre las líneas y están en lados opuestos de la transversal.

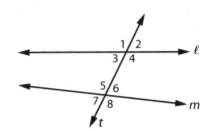

Alternate interior angles (p. 36) In the diagram, transversal *t* cuts lines ℓ and *m*, forming angles 1 through 8. Pairs of alternate interior angles are ∠3 and ∠6, and ∠4 and ∠5. The angles in each pair are between the two lines and on opposite sides of the transversal.

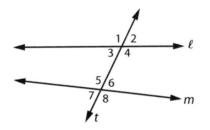

Ángulos alternos internos (pág. 36) En el diagrama, la transversal *t* corta las líneas ℓ y *m*, formando los ángulos 1 a 8. Los pares de ángulos alternos internos son ∠3 y ∠6, y ∠4 y ∠5. Los ángulos en cada par no están entre las rectas y están en lados opuestos de la transversal.

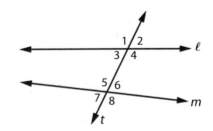

Amplitude (p. 434) Half the difference *maximum value − minimum value*, if they exist, in one cycle of a periodic graph.

Amplitud (pág. 434) Diferencia media entre *valor máximo − valor mínimo*, si existen, en un ciclo de una gráfica periódica.

Angular velocity (p. 421) The rate at which a rotating object such as a pulley, sprocket, or drive shaft turns.

Velocidad angular (pág. 421) La tasa a la que un objeto que rota, como una polea, rueda de engranaje o eje motor, gira.

Annual percentage rate or **APR** (p. 405) A standard way to state the effective annual interest rate on a loan.

Tasa anual porcentual o **TAP** (pág. 405) Forma estándar de enunciar la tasa de interés anual de un préstamo.

Annual percentage yield or **APY** (p. 473) The effective annual interest rate on an investment, taking into account the effect of *compounding interest*.

Renta anual porcentual o **RAP** (pág. 473) Tasa anual de interés de una inversión teniendo en cuenta el efecto del *interés compuesto*.

Glossary/Glosario

English	Español
Arc intercepted by an angle (p. 404) For an angle whose sides cut a circle at points A and B, the portion of the circle that lies in the interior of the angle, together with points A and B (the *endpoints of the arc*).	**Arco interceptado por un ángulo** (pág. 404) Para un ángulo cuyos lados cortan un círculo en los puntos A y B, la porción del círculo que se encuentra en el interior del ángulo, junto con los puntos A y B (*los extremos del arco*).
Arithmetic growth (p. 483) Growth that is modeled by an *arithmetic sequence*.	**Crecimiento aritmético** (pág. 483) Crecimiento basado en una *sucesión aritmética*.
Arithmetic sequence (p. 482) A sequence of numbers in which the difference between any two consecutive terms is a fixed nonzero constant. Symbolically, $a_n = a_{n-1} + d$.	**Sucesión aritmética** (pág. 482) Secuencia de números en los que la diferencia entre dos números consecutivos cualesquiera es una constante fija diferente a cero. Simbólicamente, $a_n = a_{n-1} + d$.
Arithmetic series (p. 493) A *series* whose terms are those of an *arithmetic sequence*.	**Serie aritmética** (pág. 493) *Serie* cuyos términos son los de una *sucesión aritmética*.
Attracting fixed point (p. 521) A *fixed point* such that function iteration sequences that start close to it converge to that point.	**Punto fijo de atracción** (pág. 521) Un *punto fijo* tal que las sucesiones de función de iteración que comienzan cercanas al mismo convergen en ese punto.
Average run length or **ARL** (p. 308) When using control charts, the expected number of items tested until a test gives a false alarm.	**Longitud media de recorrido** o **LMR** (pág. 308) En el uso de diagramas de control, el número esperado de artículos examinados hasta que la prueba da como resultado una falsa alarma.

· (B) ·

English	Español
Balance (p. 406) In the case of a loan, the money still owed.	**Saldo** (pág. 406) En el caso de un préstamo, el dinero que todavía se adeuda.
Binomial situation (p. 260) A probabilistic situation with a fixed number of independent trials, each with two possible outcomes, and the same probability of a success on each trial.	**Situación binomial** (pág. 260) Situación probabilística con un número fijo de pruebas independientes, cada una con dos resultados posibles y la misma probabilidad de éxito en cada prueba.

· (C) ·

English	Español
Central angle of a circle (p. 401) An angle of measure less than 180° whose vertex is at the center of the circle and whose sides contain radii of the circle.	**Ángulo central de un círculo** (pág. 401) Ángulo que mide menos de 180° cuyo vértice está en el centro del círculo y cuyos lados son radios del círculo.
Centroid of a Triangle (p. 203) The point of concurrency of the medians of a triangle.	**Centroide de un triángulo** (pág. 203) Punto de concurrencia de las medianas de un triángulo.
Chord of a circle (p. 397) A segment that joins two distinct points on a circle.	**Cuerda de un círculo** (pág. 397) Segmento que une dos puntos de un círculo.
Circle (p. 186) The set of all points in a plane that are equidistant from a given point O, called the *center* of the circle.	**Círculo** (pág. 186) Conjunto de todos los puntos de un plano que son equidistantes de un punto dado O, llamado *centro* del círculo.

Glossary/Glosario

English	Español

Circumcenter (p. 201) The point of concurrency of the perpendicular bisectors of the sides of a triangle; this is the center of the *circumcircle* (*circumscribed circle*) of the triangle.

Circuncentro (pág. 201) Punto de concurrencia de las bisectrices perpendiculares de los lados de un triángulo; este es el centro del *circuncírculo* (*círculo circunscrito*) del triángulo.

Closed-form formula for a sequence See *Function formula for a sequence.*

Fórmula cerrada de una sucesión Ver *Fórmula de la función de una sucesión.*

Combined recursive formula (p. 489) A *recursive formula* of the form $A_n = rA_{n-1} + b$. (Also called an *affine recurrence relation* or a *nonhomogeneous first-order linear difference equation.*)

Fórmula recurrente combinada (pág. 489) *Fórmula recurrente* del tipo $A_n = rA_{n-1} + b$. (También llamada *relación recurrente afín* o *ecuación diferencial lineal de primer orden no homogénea*).

Common difference (p. 485) The constant difference between any two consecutive terms in an *arithmetic sequence.*

Diferencia común (pág. 485) Diferencia constante entre dos términos consecutivos cualesquiera de una *sucesión aritmética.*

Common logarithm (p. 560) If $10^x = y$, then x is called the base 10 logarithm of y; it is often denoted $x = \log y$.

Logaritmo común (pág. 560) Si $10^x = y$, entonces x se llama logaritmo en base 10 de y; con frecuencia se indica $x = \log y$.

Common ratio (p. 487) The constant ratio of any two consecutive terms in a *geometric sequence.*

Razón común (pág. 487) Razón constante de dos términos consecutivos cualesquiera de una *sucesión geométrica.*

Completing the square (p. 350) The process by which a quadratic expression is rewritten in the form $a(x - h)^2 + k$, called a *complete square* or *vertex form.*

Completar el cuadrado (pág. 350) El proceso por el cual una expresión cuadrática es reescrita en la forma $a(x - h)^2 + k$, llamada *cuadrado completo* o *forma del vértice.*

Complex number (p. 355) Any complex number can be expressed in the form $a + bi$ where a and b are real numbers and $i = \sqrt{-1}$.

Número complejo (pág. 355) Todo número complejo puede expresarse con la forma $a + bi$ donde a y b son números reales e $i = \sqrt{-1}$.

Components of a translation (p. 210) The horizontal and vertical directed distances that all points are moved in a plane (left or right, up or down) under a translation.

Componentes de una traslación (pág. 210) Las distancias dirigidas horizontales y verticales en las que se mueven todos los puntos de un plano (derecha o izquierda, arriba o abajo) durante una traslación.

Composition of transformations (p. 208) The process of applying two transformations in succession. The transformation that maps the *original preimage* to the *final image* is called the *composite transformation.*

Composición de transformaciones (pág. 208) Proceso de aplicar dos transformaciones sucesivas. La transformación que relaciona la *preimagen original* con la *imagen final* se llama *transformación compuesta.*

Compound interest (p. 465) Interest that is applied to previous interest as well as to the original amount of money borrowed or invested.

Interés compuesto (pág. 465) Interés aplicado al interés anterior, así como también al monto inicial de dinero prestado o invertido.

Concentric circles (p. 397) Two or more circles in the same plane that have the same center.

Círculos concéntricos (pág. 397) Dos o más círculos en el mismo plano que tienen el mismo centro.

Glossary/Glosario

English	Español
Conclusion (p. 3) In an "if-then" statement, the condition that follows "then." Symbolically, in the statement $p \Rightarrow q$, the conclusion is q.	**Conclusión** (pág. 3) En una oración condicional, la condición que sigue al término "entonces". Simbólicamente, en una oración $p \Rightarrow q$, la conclusion es q.
Concurrent lines (p. 200) Three or more lines that intersect at a common point.	**Rectas concurrentes** (pág. 200) Tres o más rectas que se intersecan en un punto en común.
Conditional statement See *If-then statement*.	**Enunciado condicional** Ver *Oración condicional*.
Congruent figures (p. 162) Two figures are congruent if and only if they are similar with a scale factor of 1. Congruent figures have the same shape and size, regardless of position or orientation.	**Figuras congruentes** (pág. 162) Dos figuras son congruentes si y sólo si son semejantes con un factor de escala de 1. Las figuras congruentes tienen el mismo tamaño y la misma forma, sin importar su posición u orientación.
Consecutive integers (p. 15) Adjacent integers on a number line. These can be expressed symbolically as n and $n + 1$.	**Números enteros consecutivos** (pág. 15) Números enteros adyacentes en una recta numérica. Pueden expresarse simbólicamente como n y $n + 1$.
Constraint (p. 132) A limitation on values that variables may assume in a problem situation. For example, the linear constraint $3x + 5y < 21$ expresses a condition for acceptable combinations of values for the variables x and y.	**Restricción** (pág. 132) Una limitación en los valores que una variable puede asumir de una situación problemática. Por ejemplo, la restricción lineal $3x + 5y < 21$ expresa una condición sobre las combinaciones de valores aceptables para las variables x e y.
Contrapositive of an if-then statement (p. 22) Reverses the order and negates both parts of the if-then statement. In symbols, the contrapositive of $p \Rightarrow q$ is *not* $q \Rightarrow$ *not* p.	**Contrapositivo de una oración condicional** (pág. 22) Invierte el orden y niega ambas partes de una oración condicional. En símbolos, el contrapositivo de $p \Rightarrow q$ es *no* $q \Rightarrow$ *no* p.
Control chart (or, **run chart)** (p. 283) A type of plot over time where observations from an industrial process are plotted in order of occurrence and checked for patterns that indicate that the process has gone out of control.	**Diagrama de control** (pág. 283) Tipo de diagrama en el tiempo donde se registran las observaciones de un proceso industrial y se buscan patrones que indiquen que el proceso está fuera de control.
Control group (or, **comparison group)** (p. 77) In an experiment, a randomly selected group of subjects that gets no treatment, gets a placebo, or gets an established or standard treatment. Otherwise, the control group is treated the same as the group or groups that get the experimental treatment or treatments.	**Grupo de control (**o **grupo de comparación)** (pág. 77) En un experimento, un grupo de sujetos seleccionados al azar que no recibe tratamiento, recibe un placebo o recibe el tratamiento establecido o estándar. De otra manera, el grupo de control se trata de la misma manera que el grupo o los grupos que reciben el tratamiento experimental.
Converse of an if-then statement (p. 10) Reverses the order of the two parts of the if-then statement. In symbols, given the original statement $p \Rightarrow q$, its converse statement is $q \Rightarrow p$.	**Converso de un enunciado condicional** (pág. 10) Invierte el orden de las dos partes de una oración condicional. En símbolos, dado el enunciado original $p \Rightarrow q$, su enunciado converso es $q \Rightarrow p$.

Glossary/Glosario

English	Español

Corresponding angles (p. 36) In the diagram, transversal *t* cuts lines ℓ and *m*, forming angles 1 through 8. Pairs of corresponding angles are ∠1 and ∠5, ∠2 and ∠6, ∠3 and ∠7, and ∠4 and ∠8. Angles in each pair are in the same relative position with respect to each line and the transversal.

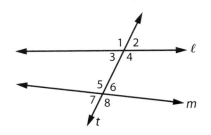

Cycle—function The graph of one period of a *periodic function*. In the case of circular motion, a cycle corresponds to one full revolution.

Cycle—iteration (p. 521) A sequence of numbers that repeats over and over when *iterating a function*.

Ángulos correspondientes (pág. 36) En el diagrama, la transversal *t* corta las líneas ℓ y *m*, formando los ángulos 1 a 8. Los pares de ángulos correspondientes son ∠1 y ∠5, ∠2 y ∠6, ∠3 y ∠7, y ∠4 y ∠8. Los ángulos en cada par están en la misma posición relativa con respecto a cada recta y a la transversal.

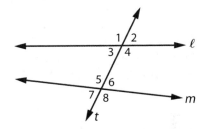

Ciclo—función La gráfica de un periodo de una *función periódica*. En el caso del movimiento circular, un ciclo corresponde a una revolución completa.

Ciclo—iteración (pág. 521) Secuencia de números que se repite una y otra vez en la *iteración de una función*.

· (D) ·

Deductive reasoning (p. 2) Reasoning strategy that involves reasoning *from* facts, definitions, and accepted properties *to* conclusions using principles of logic.

Degree measure of a circular arc (p. 401) The degree measure of a minor arc and the degree measure of its corresponding central angle are the same. The degree measure of a major arc is 360° minus the degree measure of its corresponding central angle.

Degree of a polynomial (p. 324) The highest exponent of the variable that appears in the polynomial expression.

Difference equation See *Recursive formula*.

Discrete dynamical system (p. 462) A situation (system) involving change (dynamical) in which the nature of the change is step-by-step (discrete).

Distance from a point to a line (p. 202) The length of the perpendicular segment from the point to the line.

Razonamiento deductivo (pág. 2) Estrategia de razonamiento que involucra el razonamiento a partir de hechos, definiciones y propiedades aceptadas para obtener conclusiones que usan principios de lógica.

Medida gradual de un arco circular (pág. 401) La medida gradual de un arco menor y la de su ángulo central correspondiente son iguales. La medida gradual de un arco mayor es 360° menos la medida gradual de su ángulo central correspondiente.

Grado de un polinomio (pág. 324) El mayor exponente de la variable que aparece en la expresión polinomial.

Ecuación de diferencia Ver *Fórmula recursiva*.

Sistema dinámico discreto (pág. 462) Situación (sistema) que involucra un cambio (dinámico) en la que la naturaleza del cambio se da paso a paso (discreto).

Distancia desde un punto a una recta (pág. 202) Longitud del segmento perpendicular desde el punto a la recta.

Glossary/Glosario

English	Español

Double blind (p. 78) An experiment that is both subject blind and evaluator blind.

Doble ciego (pág. 78) Experimento en el que tanto el sujeto como el evaluador son "ciegos".

· (E) ·

Equilic quadrilateral (p. 225) A quadrilateral with a pair of congruent opposite sides that, when extended, meet to form a 60° angle. The other two sides are called bases.

Cuadrilátero equílico (pág. 225) Cuadrilátero con un par de lados opuestos congruentes que, al extenderse, se encuentran para formar un ángulo de 60°. Los otros dos lados se llaman bases.

Evaluator blind (p. 78) An experiment in which the person who evaluates how well the treatment works does not know which treatment the subject received.

Evaluador ciego (pág. 78) Experimento en el cual la persona que evalúa qué tan bien funciona el tratamiento no sabe qué tratamiento recibe el sujeto.

Expected value (or, **expected number)** (p. 261) In probability, the long-run average or mean value of a probability distribution.

Valor esperado (o número esperado) (pág. 261) En probabilidad, el promedio a largo plazo o valor medio de una distribución de probabilidad.

Experiment (p. 77) A research study in which available subjects are randomly assigned to two or more different treatments in order to compare how responses to the treatments differ.

Experimento (pág. 77) Tipo de investigación en el que los sujetos son asignados en forma aleatoria a dos o más tratamientos distintos para comparar como difieren las respuestas a los tratamientos.

Explicit formula for a sequence See *Function formula for a sequence.*

Fórmula explícita de una sucesión Ver *Fórmula de la función de una sucesión.*

Exponential growth (p. 486) Growth that is modeled by a *geometric sequence* or an exponential function.

Crecimiento exponencial (pág. 486) Crecimiento basado en una *sucesión geométrica* o una función exponencial.

Exterior angle of a triangle (p. 46) The angle formed by the side of a triangle and the extension of an adjacent side.

Ángulo exterior de un triángulo (pág. 46) Ángulo que se forma por un lado del triángulo y la extensión de un lado adyacente.

Exterior angles on the same side of the transversal (p. 36) In the diagram, transversal t cuts lines ℓ and m, forming angles 1 through 8. Pairs of exterior angles on the same side of the transversal are $\angle 1$ and $\angle 7$, and $\angle 2$ and $\angle 8$.

Ángulos exteriores en el mismo lado de la transversal (pág. 36) En el diagrama, la transversal t corta las rectas ℓ y m, formando los ángulos 1 a 8. Los pares de ángulos exteriores en el mismo lado de la transversal son $\angle 1$ y $\angle 7$, y $\angle 2$ y $\angle 8$.

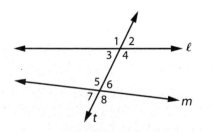

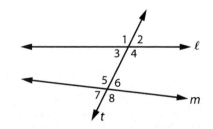

Exterior of a circle (p. 397) The set of all points in the plane of a circle whose distance from the center is greater than the circle's radius.

Exterior de un círculo (pág. 397) Conjunto de todos los puntos del plano de un círculo cuya distancia desde el centro es mayor que el radio del círculo.

Glossary/Glosario

English	Español

Factorial notation (p. 20) A compact way of writing the product of consecutive positive whole numbers. Symbolically, $n! = n \cdot (n-1) \cdot (n-2) \cdot \cdots \cdot 2 \cdot 1$.

False alarm (p. 294) In statistical process control, this is when a test signals that a process may be out of control when it is in control.

Feasible region (p. 136) In a linear programming problem, the feasible region is the set of all points whose coordinates satisfy all given constraints.

Finite differences table (p. 495) A table corresponding to a numerical sequence in which the first column of the table is a consecutive list of indices for the sequence, the second column is the corresponding terms of the sequence, the third column contains the differences of consecutive terms from the second column (called first differences), the fourth column contains the differences of consecutive terms in the third column (called second differences), and so on.

Fixed point of a function (p. 520) For the function f, a value x such that $f(x) = x$. When *iterating a function* if you reach that value, you never leave it.

Function formula for a sequence (p. 489) A non-recursive formula that expresses the nth term in a sequence as a function of n. (Also called an *explicit formula* or a *closed-form formula*.)

Notación factorial (pág. 20) Forma compacta de escribir el producto de números enteros positivos consecutivos. En símbolos, $n! = n \cdot (n-1) \cdot (n-2) \cdot \cdots \cdot 2 \cdot 1$.

Falsa alarma (pág. 294) En control de proceso estadístico, ésta ocurre cuando una prueba señala que el proceso puede estar fuera de control cuando está bajo control.

Zona factible (pág. 136) En problemas de programación lineal, la zona factible es el conjunto de todos los puntos cuyas coordenadas satisfacen todas las limitaciones dadas.

Tabla de diferencias finitas (pág. 495) Tabla correspondiente a una sucesión numérica en la que la primera columna de la tabla es una lista consecutiva de los índices de la sucesión, la segunda columna son los términos correspondientes de la secuencia, la tercera columna contiene las diferencias de los términos consecutivos de la segunda columna (llamada primera diferencia), la cuarta columna contiene las diferencias de los números consecutivos de la tercera columna (llamada segunda diferencia) y así sucesivamente.

Punto fijo de una función (pág. 520) Para la función f, una valor x tal que $f(x) = x$. En el proceso de *iteración de una función*, cuando se alcanza ese valor, nunca se deja.

Fórmula de la función de una sucesión (pág. 489) Fórmula no recurrente que expresa el término nth en una sucesión como una función de n. (También llamada *fórmula explícita* o *fórmula cerrada*).

Geometric growth (p. 486) Growth that is modeled by a *geometric sequence*.

Geometric mean (p. 186) The geometric mean of two positive integers a and b is the positive number x such that $\frac{a}{x} = \frac{x}{b}$ or $x = \sqrt{ab}$.

Geometric sequence (p. 485) A sequence of numbers in which the ratio of any two consecutive terms is a fixed constant. Symbolically, $a_{n+1} = r \cdot a_n$.

Crecimiento geométrico (pág. 486) Crecimiento basado en una *sucesión geométrica*.

Media geométrica (pág. 186) La media geométrica de dos enteros positivos a y b es el número positivo x tal que $\frac{a}{x} = \frac{x}{b}$ ó $x = \sqrt{ab}$.

Sucesión geométrica (pág. 485) Sucesión de números en la que la razón de cualquier par de números consecutivos es una constante fija. Simbólicamente, se presenta así: $a_{n+1} = r \cdot a_n$.

Glossary/Glosario

English	Español

Geometric series (p. 493) A *series* whose terms are those of a *geometric sequence*.

Serie geométrica (pág. 493) *Serie* cuyos términos son los de una *sucesión geométrica*.

Global maximum or minimum point (p. 343) A global maximum point for a function $f(x)$ is a pair $(a, f(a))$ with the property that $f(a) \geq f(x)$ for all x. The pair $(b, f(b))$ is a global minimum point if $f(b) \leq f(x)$ for all x.

Punto global máximo o mínimo (pág. 343) El punto global máximo de una función $f(x)$ es un par $(a, f(a))$ con la propiedad que $f(a) \geq f(x)$ para toda x. El par $(b, f(b))$ es el punto global mínimo si $f(b) \leq f(x)$ para toda x.

Graphical iteration (p. 519) A graphical representation of *iterating a function*, in which the graph of $y = x$ is drawn on the same set of coordinate axes as the graph of the function being iterated and the process of iteration is shown graphically by moving vertically to the graph of the function, then horizontally to the graph of $y = x$, then vertically to the graph of the function, then horizontally to the graph of $y = x$, and so on.

Iteración gráfica (pág. 519) Representación gráfica de la *iteración de una función*, en la que la gráfica de $y = x$ se dibuja en el mismo conjunto de ejes de coordenadas que la de la función que se quiere iterar, y el proceso de iteración se muestra gráficamente desplazándose verticalmente a la gráfica de la función, luego en forma horizontal a la gráfica de $y = x$, luego verticalmente a la gráfica de la función, luego horizontalmente a la gráfica de $y = x$ y así sucesivamente.

Great circle (p. 48) A circle on the surface of a sphere formed by a plane passing through the center of the sphere.

Gran círculo (pág. 48) Círculo en la superficie de una esfera formado por un plano que pasa por el centro de la esfera.

· (H) ·

Horizontal asymptote (p. 367) A line with equation $y = k$ is a horizontal asymptote for the graph of a function $f(x)$ whenever the values of $f(x)$ approach k as a limit as $x \rightarrow +\infty$ or $x \rightarrow -\infty$.

Asíntota horizontal (pág. 367) Una recta con ecuación $y = k$ es una asíntota horizontal para la gráfica de una función $f(x)$ cuando los valores de $f(x)$ se aproximan a k como $x \rightarrow +\infty$ o $x \rightarrow -\infty$.

Hypothesis of an if-then statement (p. 10) The condition that follows "if." Symbolically, in an if-then statement $p \Rightarrow q$, p is the hypothesis.

Hipótesis de una oración condicional (pág. 10) La condición que sigue al "Si". Simbólicamente, en una oración condicional $p \Rightarrow q$, p es la hipótesis donde q es la conclusión.

· (I) ·

If and only if statement (p. 21) A combination of an if-then statement and its converse. In symbols, "p if and only if q" is written as $p \Leftrightarrow q$, and is understood to mean $p \Rightarrow q$ and $q \Rightarrow p$.

Oración Si y sólo si (pág. 21) Combinación de oraciones condicionales y su inverso. En símbolos, "p si y solo si q" se escribe $p \Leftrightarrow q$, y se supone que significa $p \Rightarrow q$ y $q \Rightarrow p$.

If-then statement (p. 10) Frequently used in deductive arguments because if the hypothesis is satisfied then the conclusion follows. If-then statements can be represented symbolically as $p \Rightarrow q$ (read "if p, then q" or "p implies q"), where p represents the hypothesis and q represents the conclusion.

Oración condicional (pág. 10) Frecuentemente usada en los argumentos deductivos porque si se satisface la hipótesis, entonces sigue la conclusión. Las oraciones condicionales pueden representarse simbólicamente como $p \Rightarrow q$ (se lee "si p, entonces q" o "p implica q"), donde p representa la hipótesis y q representa la conclusión.

Incenter (p. 202) The point of concurrency of the bisectors of the angles of a triangle; this is the center of the *incircle* (*inscribed circle*) of the triangle.

Incentro (pág. 202) Punto donde se unen las bisectrices de los ángulos de un triángulo; éste es el centro del *incentro* (*círculo inscrito*) del triángulo.

Glossary/Glosario

English	Español

Independent events (p. 308) In probability, two events A and B are said to be independent if the probability that B occurs does not change depending on whether or not A occurred.

Eventos independientes (pág. 308) En probabilidad, se dice que dos eventos A y B son independientes si la probabilidad de que B ocurra no cambia si A ocurre o no.

Inductive reasoning (p. 2) Reasoning strategy used to discover general patterns or principles based on evidence from experiments or several cases.

Razonamiento inductivo (pág. 2) Estrategia de razonamiento que se usa para descubrir patrones o principios generales, basándose en pruebas de experimentos o de otros casos.

Inequality (p. 108) A statement like $3x + 5y < 9$ or $t^2 + 2 \geq 4$ composed of numbers or algebraic expressions connected by an inequality symbol $(<, \leq, >, \geq)$. The solution of an inequality is all values of the variable(s) for which the statement is true.

Desigualdad (pág. 108) Oración como $3x + 5y < 9$ ó $t^2 + 2 \geq 4$ compuesta por números o expresiones algebraicas relacionadas por un símbolo de desigualdad $(<, \leq, >, \geq)$. La solución de una desigualdad son todos los valores para la o las variables que hacen verdadera la oración.

Inscribed angle in a circle (p. 455) An angle whose vertex is on the circle and whose sides contain chords of the circle.

Ángulo inscrito de un círculo (pág. 455) Ángulo cuyo vértice está en el círculo y cuyos lados contienen cuerdas del círculo.

Interior angles on the same side of the transversal (p. 36) In the diagram, transversal t cuts lines ℓ and m, forming angles 1 through 8. Pairs of interior angles on the same side of the transversal are $\angle 4$ and $\angle 6$, and $\angle 3$ and $\angle 5$.

Ángulos interiores en el mismo lado de la transversal (pág. 36) En el diagrama, la transversal t corta las rectas ℓ y m, formando los ángulos 1 a 8. Los pares de ángulos interiores en el mismo lado de la transversal son $\angle 4$ y $\angle 6$, y $\angle 3$ y $\angle 5$.

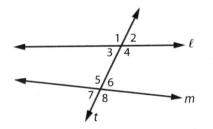

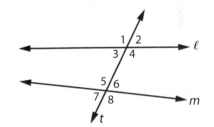

Interior of a circle (p. 397) The set of all points in the plane of a circle whose distance from the center is less than the circle's radius.

Interior de un círculo (pág. 397) Conjunto de todos los puntos del plano de un círculo cuya distancia desde el centro es menor que el radio del círculo.

Interval (p. 116) All numbers on a coordinate line between two specified endpoints. The *closed* interval $[a, b]$ is all numbers x such that $a \leq x \leq b$. The *open* interval (a, b) is all numbers x such that $a < x < b$.

Intervalo (pág. 116) Todos los números de una recta de coordenadas entre dos extremos especificados. El intervalo *cerrado* $[a, b]$ son todos los números x tal que $a \leq x \leq b$. El intervalo *abierto* (a, b) son todos los números x tal que $a < x < b$.

Inverse cosine function (p. 584) The inverse cosine or arccos function is defined as $\cos^{-1} k = x$ if $\cos x = k$ and $0 \leq x \leq \pi$.

Función coseno inverso (pág. 584) La función coseno inverso o arcocoseno se define como $\cos^{-1} k = x$ si $\cos x = k$ y $0 \leq x \leq \pi$.

Inverse function (p. 537) For a given function f, if the function g has domain equal to the range of f, range equal to the domain of f, and $g(f(x)) = x$ for all x, then g is called the inverse of f.

Función inversa (pág. 537) Para una función dada f, si la función g tiene un dominio igual al rango de f, rango igual al dominio de f y $g(f(x)) = x$ para toda x, entonces g se llama la inversa de f.

Glossary/Glosario

English	Español

Inverse sine function (p. 579) The inverse sine or arcsin function is defined as $\sin^{-1} k = x$ if $\sin x = k$ and $-\frac{\pi}{2} \leq x \leq \frac{\pi}{2}$.

Función seno inverso (pág. 579) La función seno inverso o arcoseno se define como $\operatorname{sen}^{-1} k = x$ si $\operatorname{sen} x = k$ y $-\frac{\pi}{2} \leq x \leq \frac{\pi}{2}$.

Inverse of an if-then statement (p. 21) The negation of the hypothesis and conclusion in an if-then statement. In symbols, the inverse of $p \Rightarrow q$ is not $p \Rightarrow$ not q.

Elnverso de una oración Si y sólo si (pág. 21) Negación de la hipótesis y la conclusión en una oración condicional. En símbolos, el inverso de $p \Rightarrow q$ es no $p \Rightarrow$ no q.

Inverse tangent function (p. 587) The inverse tangent or arctan function is defined as $\tan^{-1} k = x$ if $\tan x = k$ and $-\frac{\pi}{2} < x < \frac{\pi}{2}$.

Función tangente inversa (pág. 587) La función tangente inversa o arcotangente se define como $\tan^{-1} k = x$ si $\tan x = k$ y $-\frac{\pi}{2} < x < \frac{\pi}{2}$.

Isosceles trapezoid (p. 66) A quadrilateral with exactly one pair of parallel sides and the nonparallel sides congruent.

Trapecio isósceles (pág. 66) Cuadrilátero con exactamente un par de lados paralelos y lados no paralelos congruentes.

Iterating a function (p. 514) The process of sequentially feeding the outputs of a function back into itself as inputs.

Iteración de una función (pág. 514) Proceso de reingresar secuencialmente los resultados de una función en sí misma como valor de entrada.

Iteration (p. 462) The process of repeating the same procedure or computation over and over.

Iteración (pág. 462) Proceso de repetir el mismo procedimiento o cálculo una y otra vez.

— L —

Law of Cosines (p. 168) In any triangle ABC with sides of lengths a, b, and c opposite $\angle A$, $\angle B$, and $\angle C$, respectively: $c^2 = a^2 + b^2 - 2ab \cos C$.

Ley del coseno (pág. 168) En todo triángulo ABC con lados de longitud a, b y c opuestos a $\angle A$, $\angle B$ y $\angle C$, respectivamente: $c^2 = a^2 + b^2 - 2ab \cos C$.

Law of Sines (p. 168) In any triangle ABC with sides of lengths a, b, and c opposite $\angle A$, $\angle B$, and $\angle C$, respectively: $\frac{\sin A}{a} = \frac{\sin B}{b} = \frac{\sin C}{c}$.

Ley del seno (pág. 168) En todo triángulo ABC con lados de longitud a, b y c opuestos a $\angle A$, $\angle B$ y $\angle C$, respectivamente: $\frac{\sin A}{a} = \frac{\sin B}{b} = \frac{\sin C}{c}$.

Line reflection (p. 209) A transformation that maps each point P of the plane onto an image point P' as follows: If point P is not on line ℓ, then ℓ is the perpendicular bisector of $\overline{PP'}$. If point P is on ℓ, then $P' = P''$. That is, P is its own image.

Recta de reflexión (pág. 209) Transformación que representa cada punto P del plano en un punto imagen P' de la siguiente manera: Si el punto P no está en la recta ℓ, entonces ℓ es la bisectriz perpendicular de $\overline{PP'}$. Si el punto P está en ℓ, entonces $P' = P''$. Es decir, P es su propia imagen.

Linear pair (p. 30) A pair of adjacent angles whose noncommon sides are opposite rays.

Par lineal (pág. 30) Par de ángulos adyacentes cuyos lados no comunes son rayos opuestos.

Linear programming (p. 128) A mathematical procedure to find values of variables that satisfy a set of linear *constraints* and optimize the value of a linear *objective function*.

Programación lineal (pág. 128) UProcedimiento matemático en el que la tarea es encontrar los valores de variables que satisfacen un grupo de *restricciones* lineales y optimizan el valor de una *función objetiva* lineal.

Linear velocity (p. 421) The distance that a point on a revolving circle moves in a unit of time.

Velocidad lineal (pág. 421) Distancia que un punto recorre en una unidad de tiempo en un círculo rotativo.

Glossary/Glosario

English	**Español**

Local maximum or minimum point (p. 324) A local maximum point for a function $f(x)$ is a pair $(a, f(a))$ with the property that $f(a) \geq f(x)$ for all x in an open interval containing a. The pair $(b, f(b))$ is a local minimum point if $f(b) \leq f(x)$ for all x in an open interval containing a.

Punto local máximo o mínimo (pág. 324) El punto local máximo para una función $f(x)$ es un par $(a, f(a))$ con la propiedad que $f(a) \geq f(x)$ para toda x en un intervalo abierto que contiene a. El par $(b, f(b))$ es el punto local mínimo si $f(b) \leq f(x)$ para toda x en un intervalo abierto que contiene a.

Logically equivalent statements (p. 22) Two statements p and q are logically equivalent if each implies the other. In symbols, $p \Rightarrow q$ and $q \Rightarrow p$.

Enunciados lógicamente equivalentes (pág. 22) Dos oraciones p y q son equivalentes desde el punto de vista lógico si cada una implica la otra. Simbólicamente, se representa así: $p \Rightarrow q$ y $q \Rightarrow p$.

Logistic equation (or logistic map) (p. 518) An equation of the form $f(x) = rx(1 - x)$.

Ecuación logística (pág. 518) Ecuación con la forma $f(x) = rx(1 - x)$.

Lurking variable (p. 79) A variable that helps to explain the association between the conditions or treatments and the response, but is not the explanation that the study was designed to test.

Variable escondida (pág. 79) Variable que ayuda a explicar la asociación entre las condiciones o tratamientos y la respuesta, pero que no es la explicación que el estudio debía probar.

(M)

Major arc of a circle (p. 401) An arc with degree measure greater than 180°.

Arco mayor de un círculo (pág. 401) Arco con una medida mayor de 180°.

Minor arc of a circle (p. 401) An arc with degree measure less than 180°.

Arco menor de un círculo (pág. 401) Arco con una medida menor de 180°.

Modus ponens (Latin: mode that affirms) (p. 10) A fundamental principle of logic. If an if-then statement is true in general and the hypothesis is known to be true in a particular case, then the conclusion is also true in that case. In symbols, $p \Rightarrow q$, given p, conclude q. Also called Affirming the Hypothesis.

Modus ponens (del Latín "modo que afirma") (pág. 10) Principio fundamental de la lógica. Si una oración condicional es verdadera en general y la hipótesis es verdadera en un caso en particular, entonces la conclusión es verdadera en ese caso. En símbolos, $p \Rightarrow q$, dado p, se concluyes q. También se conoce como "afirmar la hipótesis".

Mutually exclusive events (or, disjoint events) (p. 305) Two events are said to be mutually exclusive if it is impossible for both of them to occur on the same trial.

Eventos mutuamente excluyentes (o eventos desunidos) (pág. 305) Se dice que dos eventos son mutuamente excluyentes si es imposible que ambos ocurran en el mismo experimento.

(N)

Negation of a statement (p. 21) A statement that negates the given statement. In symbols, the negation of statement p is *not p*.

Negación de una oración (pág. 21) Oración que niega una oración dada. En símbolos, la negación de la oración p *no* es p.

Normal distribution (p. 237) A theoretical probability distribution that is bell-shaped, symmetric, continuous, and defined for all real numbers.

Distribución normal (pág. 237) Distribución de probabilidad teórica que es tiene la forma de una campana, y es simétrica, continua y definida para todos los números reales.

Glossary/Glosario

English	Español

(O)

Objective function (p. 137) In a linear programming problem, an algebraic expression like $7x - 3y$ whose value is to be optimized within the constraints of the problem.

Función objetiva (pág. 137) En un problema de programación lineal, es una expresión algebraica como $7x - 3y$ cuyo valor debe ser optimizado dentro de las restricciones del problema.

Observational study (p. 89) A statistical study in which the conditions to be compared are already present in the subjects that are observed.

Estudio observacional (pág. 89) Estudio estadístico en el que las condiciones que se comparan están presentes, en ese momento, en los sujetos que serán observados.

Odds (p. 278) An alternative way of expressing a probability. When outcomes are equally likely, the odds of an event are the number of favorable outcomes to the number of unfavorable outcomes. For example, if the odds that an event occurs are 3 to 5, then the probability the event occurs is $\frac{3}{(3 + 5)}$, or $\frac{3}{8}$.

Posibilidades (pág. 278) Forma alternativa de expresar una probabilidad. Cuando los resultados son igualmente posibles, las posibilidades de un evento son el número de resultados favorables al número de resultados desfavorables. Por ejemplo, si las posibilidades de que un evento ocurra son 3 a 5, entonces la probabilidad de que ocurra el evento es $\frac{3}{(3 + 5)}$, ó $\frac{3}{8}$.

Orientation of a figure (p. 214) Determined by the clockwise or counterclockwise cyclic labeling of at least three points on a figure.

Orientación de una figura (pág. 214) Está determinada por la clasificación del ciclo horario o antihorario de al menos tres puntos de una figura.

(P)

Parallelogram (p. 20) A quadrilateral that has two pairs of opposite sides the same length (congruent), or equivalently, a quadrilateral that has two pairs of parallel sides.

Paralelogramo (pág. 20) Cuadrilátero que tiene dos pares de lados opuestos de la misma longitud (congruentes), o de manera equivalente, cuadrilátero que tiene dos pares de lados paralelos.

Percentile (p. 241) A value x in a distribution lies at the pth percentile if $p\%$ of the values in the distribution are less than or equal to x.

Percentil (pág. 241) Un valor x de una distribución se encuentra en el percentil $p.º$ si $p\%$ de los valores de la distribución son menores que o iguales a x.

Period (p. 434) The length of a smallest interval (in the domain) that contains a cycle of a periodic graph.

Período (pág. 434) Longitud del intervalo más corto (en el dominio) que contiene un ciclo en una gráfica periódica.

Periodic graph (p. 434) A graph of a pattern of change that repeats itself over and over again.

Gráfica periódica (pág. 434) Gráfica de un patrón de cambio que se repite una y otra vez.

Perpendicular bisector of a segment (p. 198) A line perpendicular to the segment at its midpoint.

Bisectriz perpendicular de un segmento (pág. 198) Recta perpendicular del segmento en su punto medio.

Placebo (p. 77) A sham or empty treatment that to subjects of an experiment appears to be the real treatment.

Placebo (pág. 77) Tratamiento simulado o falso para los sujetos de un experimento que parece ser el tratamiento real.

Placebo effect (p. 78) The phenomenon that people tend to do better when given a treatment, even if it is a placebo.

Efecto placebo (pág. 78) Fenómeno por el que las personas tienden a sentirse mejor con un tratamiento, incluso si es un placebo.

Glossary/Glosario

English	Español

English

Polynomial expression (p. 327) An algebraic expression in the general form $a_nx^n + a_{n-1}x^{n-1} + \cdots + a_1x + a_0$, where $a_n, a_{n-1}, \ldots, a_1, a_0$ are constants.

Polynomial function (p. 321) A function whose rule can be expressed in the form $f(x) = a_nx^n + a_{n-1}x^{n-1} + \cdots + a_1x + a_0$.

Postulates (p. 31) Mathematical statements that are accepted as true without proof. Also called axioms.

Present value (p. 476) The amount of money that, if invested today at a fixed *compound interest* rate, would give the same yield as a number of regular payments in the future such that at exactly the end of the payment period the *balance* is zero.

Prime number (p. 10) An integer greater than 1 that has exactly two factors, 1 and itself.

Principal (p. 465) In finance, the amount of money borrowed or invested.

Proportion (p. 66) A statement of equality between ratios.

Español

Expresión polinomial (pág. 327) Una expresión polinomial es cualquier expresión algebraica con la forma general $a_nx^n + a_{n-1}x^{n-1} + \cdots + a_1x + a_0$, donde $a_n, a_{n-1}, \ldots, a_1, a_0$ son constantes.

Función polinomial (pág. 321) Función cuya regla puede ser expresada en la forma $f(x) = a_nx^n + a_{n-1}x^{n-1} + \cdots + a_1x + a_0$.

Postulados (pág. 31) Enunciados matemáticos que son aceptados como verdaderos sin evidencia. También se les llama axiomas.

Valor actual (pág. 476) La cantidad de dinero que, si se invierte hoy a una tasa fija de *interés compuesto*, daría el mismo rendimiento en cuanto al número dado de pagos regulares en el futuro, de forma tal que al final del período de pago el *saldo* sería cero.

Número primo (pág. 10) Un entero mayor que 1 que tiene exactamente dos factores, 1 y sí mismo.

Capital (pág. 465) En finanzas, la cantidad de dinero que se pide prestado o se invierte.

Proporción (pág. 66) Un enunciado de igualdad entre razones.

Q

Quadratic formula (p. 353) The formula $x = \dfrac{-b \pm \sqrt{b^2 - 4ac}}{2a}$ that gives the solutions of any quadratic equation in the form $ax^2 + bx + c = 0$, where a, b, and c are constants and $a \neq 0$.

Fórmula cuadrática (pág. 353) La fórmula $x = \dfrac{-b \pm \sqrt{b^2 - 4ac}}{2a}$ que da las soluciones de cualquier ecuación cuadrática en la forma $ax^2 + bx + c = 0$, donde a, b y c son constantes y $a \neq 0$.

R

Radian (p. 427) The measure of a central angle of a circle that intercepts an arc equal in length to the radius of the circle. One radian equals $\dfrac{180}{\pi}$ degrees, which is approximately 57.2958°.

Random sample of size *n* (p. 89) A sample selected by a method equivalent to writing the name of every member of the population on a card, mixing the cards well, and drawing n cards.

Randomization distribution (p. 84) In an experiment, a distribution of possible differences between the mean responses from two treatments, generated by assuming that each response would have been the same had each subject been assigned to the other treatment.

Radian (pág. 427) Medida del ángulo central de un círculo que intercepta un arco de igual longitud que el radio del círculo. Un radian equivale a $\dfrac{180}{\pi}$ grados, lo cual es aproximadamente 57.2958°.

Muestra aleatoria de tamaño *n* (pág. 89) Muestra que se obtiene por un método equivalente a escribir el nombre de cada miembro de la población en una tarjeta, mezclarlas bien y elegir n tarjetas.

Distribución aleatoria (pág. 84) En un experimento, la distribución de diferencias posibles entre las respuestas medias de dos tratamientos, generadas al suponer que cada respuesta hubiera sido la misma si a cada uno de los sujetos se le hubiera asignado el otro tratamiento.

Glossary/Glosario

Randomization test (or, **permutation test)** (p. 85) A statistical test that can be used to determine whether the difference in the mean response from two treatments in an experiment is statistically significant.

Rare event (p. 267) An event that lies in the outer 5% of a distribution. In a waiting-time distribution, rare events typically are in the upper 5% of the distribution. In a binomial distribution, rare events may be those in the upper 2.5% and lower 2.5%.

Rational expression (p. 369) A quotient of two polynomial expressions.

Rational function (p. 364) A rational function is a function with rule that can be expressed as the quotient of two polynomials.

Recursion (p. 462) A sequential process in which a step is described in terms of previous steps.

Recursive formula (p. 467) A formula involving *recursion*. (Also called a recurrence relation or a difference equation.)

Recursive formula for a sequence (p. 483) A formula that expresses a given term in a sequence as a function of previous terms.

Regular polygon (p. 4) A polygon in which all sides are congruent and all angles are congruent.

Remote interior angles of a triangle (p. 46) The two angles of a triangle that are not adjacent to a given exterior angle.

Repelling fixed point (p. 521) A *fixed point* such that function iteration sequences move away from it (except for a sequence that begins at the fixed point).

Response variable (p. 76) In an experiment, the outcome to be measured.

Rigid transformation (p. 208) A transformation of points in the plane that preserves all distances. Such a transformation repositions a figure in a plane without changing its shape or size.

Prueba aleatoria (pág. 85) Prueba estadística que se puede usar para determinar si la diferencia en la respuesta media de dos tratamientos de un experimento es estadísticamente significativa.

Evento casual (pág. 267) Evento que ocurre en el 5% externo de una distribución. En una distribución de tiempo de espera, los eventos casuales normalmente se hallan en el 5% superior de la distribución. En una distribución binomial, los eventos casuales pueden ser aquellos que se encuentran en el 2.5% superior y 2.5% inferior.

Expresión racional (pág. 369) El cociente de dos expresiones polinomiales.

Función racional (pág. 364) Una función racional es una función con una regla que se puede expresar como el cociente de dos polinomios.

Recursión (pág. 462) Proceso secuencial en el cual un paso es descrito en términos de los pasos previos.

Fórmula recurrente (pág. 467) Fórmula que involucra *recursión*. (También llamada relación recurrente o ecuación de diferencia).

Fórmula recurrente de una sucesión (pág. 483) Fórmula que expresa un término dado en una sucesión como una función de los términos previos.

Polígono regular (pág. 4) Polígono con todos los lados y los ángulos congruentes.

Ángulos interiores remotos de un triángulo (pág. 46) Los dos ángulos de un triángulo que no son adyacentes a un ángulo exterior dado.

Punto fijo de repulsión (pág. 521) *Punto fijo* tal que las sucesiones de iteración de la función se alejan de él (a excepción de la sucesión que comienza en el punto fijo).

Variable de respuesta (pág. 76) En un experimento, el resultado que se debe medir.

Transformación rígida (pág. 208) Transformación de los puntos en un plano que conserva todas las distancias. Tal transformación reposiciona una figura en un plano sin cambiar el tamaño o la forma de la figura.

Glossary/Glosario

English	Español

Rotation (p. 208) A transformation that "turns" all points in a plane through a specified angle about a fixed point called the rotation center. That is, if points P' and Q' are the images of points P and Q under a counterclockwise rotation about point C, then $CP = CP'$, $CQ = CQ'$, y m$\angle PCP'$ = m$\angle QCQ'$.

Rotación (pág. 208) Transformación que "gira" todos los puntos en un plano a través de un ángulo específico con relación a un punto fijo llamado centro de rotación. Es decir, si los puntos P' y Q' son las imágenes de los puntos P y Q en una rotación antihoraria alrededor del punto C, entonces $CP = CP'$, $CQ = CQ'$, y m$\angle PCP'$ = m$\angle QCQ'$.

(S)

Sample survey (or, poll) (p. 89) Observation of a random sample in order to estimate a characteristic of the larger population from which the sample was taken.

Encuesta por muestreo (pág. 89) Observación de una muestra aleatoria para estimar una característica de la población total a partir de la muestra tomada.

Scale factor of a size transformation (p. 165) A positive constant that scales (multiplies) all lengths (or distances) in the plane. A scale factor greater than 1 produces enlarged figures, and a scale factor less than 1 produces reduced figures; in both cases, the figures transformed by the size transformation are similar to the original.

Factor de escala de una transformación de (pág. 165) Constante positiva que aumenta (multiplica) todas las longitudes (o distancias) en el plano. Una factor de escala mayor que 1 produce figuras ampliadas, y un factor de escala menor que 1 produce figuras reducidas; en ambos caso, las figuras transformadas son semejantes a la original.

Scientific notation (p. 571) Expression of a number in the form $a \cdot 10^k$, where a has absolute value between 1 and 10 and k is an integer. For example, 3.245×10^3 or 3.245×10^{-3} are expressed in scientific notation.

Notación científica (pág. 571) Expresión de un número en la forma $a \cdot 10^k$, donde a tiene un valor absoluto entre 1 y 10 y k es un número entero. Por ejemplo, 3.245×10^3 ó 3.245×10^{-3}, están expresados en notación científica.

Sequential change (p. 462) Change that occurs step-by-step.

Cambio secuencial (pág. 462) Cambio que ocurre paso a paso.

Series (p. 493) An expression in which the terms of a sequence are added together.

Serie (pág. 493) Expresión en la que los términos de una sucesión son sumados juntos.

Sierpinski Triangle (p. 188) A fractal that begins at the initial stage as an equilateral triangle. At each iterative step, in each remaining triangle, the middle triangle(s) formed by connecting the midpoints of each side are removed.

Triángulo de Sierpinski (pág. 188) Fractal que comienza en la etapa inicial como un triángulo equilátero. En cada paso de la iteración, en cada triángulo restante, se quitan el/los triángulo(s) del medio formado(s) al conectar los puntos medios de cada lado.

Similar figures (p. 164) Figures that are related by a size transformation or by a similarity transformation. Such figures have the same shape, regardless of position or orientation.

Figuras semejantes (pág. 164) Figuras relacionadas por una transformación de tamaño o por una transformación de semejanza. Tales figuras tienen la firma forma, sin importar la posición u orientación.

Similar polygons (p. 165) A special case of similar figures. Corresponding angles have the same measure and the ratios of lengths of corresponding sides is a constant.

Polígonos semejantes (pág. 165) Caso especial de figuras semejantes. Los ángulos correspondientes tiene la misma medida y la longitud de los radios de los lados correspondientes es una constante.

Similarity transformation (p. 208) Composite of a size transformation and a rigid transformation. Such a transformation resizes a figure in a plane without changing its shape.

Transformación de semejanza (pág. 208) Combinación de una transformación de tamaño y una transformación rígida. Tal transformación cambia las medidas de una figura en el plano sin cambiar su forma.

Glossary/Glosario

English	Español

Size transformation (p. 177) A transformation with center C and magnitude $k > 0$ that maps each point P of the plane onto an image point P' as follows: Point C is its own image. For $P \neq C$, the image point P' is on $\overline{CP}$ and $CP' = k \cdot CP$.

Transformación de tamaño (pág. 177) Una transformación con centro C y magnitud $k > 0$ que representa cada punto P en un plano sobre un punto de imagen P' de la siguiente forma: el punto C es su propia imagen. Para $P \neq C$, la imagen del punto P' está en $\overline{CP}$, y $CP' = k \cdot CP$.

Spherical geometry (p. 48) The geometry on a sphere in which all "lines" (shortest paths on the surface) are great circles.

Geometría esférica (pág. 48) Geometría en una esfera en la que todas las "rectas" (los caminos más cortos de la superficie) son grandes círculos.

Standardized value (or, **z-score) (p. 243)** The (positive or negative) number of standard deviations a given value lies from the mean in a distribution.

Valor estandarizado (o valor z) (pág. 243) En una distribución, el número (positivo o negativo) de desviaciones estándar de un número dado a partir de la media.

Statistically significant (p. 85) In an experiment, the conclusion that it is unreasonable to attribute the difference in mean response from the treatments solely to the particular random assignment of treatments to subjects. The researcher may conclude that one treatment causes a larger mean response than the other.

Estadísticamente significativo (pág. 85) En un experimento, la conclusión de que no es razonable atribuir la diferencia de la respuesta media al tratamiento sólo a la asignación aleatoria particular de los tratamientos a los pacientes. El investigador puede concluir que el experimento establece que un tratamiento causa una respuesta media mayor que el otro.

Subject blind (p. 78) An experiment in which the subjects do not know which treatment they are getting.

Sujeto ciego (pág. 78) Experimento en el cual los sujetos no saben qué tratamiento reciben.

Subjects (p. 77) The available group of people (or animals, plants, or objects) to which treatments are applied in an experiment.

Sujetos (pág. 77) Grupo de personas disponibles (o animales, plantas u objetos) a los que se somete a un tratamiento en un experimento.

Supplementary angles (p. 35) A pair of angles whose measures add to 180°.

Ángulos suplementarios (pág. 35) Par de ángulos cuyas medidas suman 180°.

· (T) ·

Tangent line to a circle (p. 397) A line that intersects a circle in only one point.

Rectas tangentes de un círculo (pág. 397) Recta que interseca un círculo sólo en un punto.

Theorem (p. 32) In mathematics, a statement that has been proved true.

Teorema (pág. 32) En matemáticas, enunciado que se ha probado como verdadero.

Translation (p. 208) A transformation that "slides" all points in the plane the same distance (magnitude) and same direction. That is, if points P' and Q' are the images of points P and Q under a translation, then $PP' = QQ'$ and $\overline{PP'} \parallel \overline{QQ'}$.

Traslación (pág. 208) Transformación que "desliza" todos los puntos de un plano la misma distancia (magnitud) y en la misma dirección. Es decir, si los puntos P' y Q' son imágenes de los puntos P y Q en una traslación, entonces $PP' = QQ'$ y $\overline{PP'} \parallel \overline{QQ'}$.

Transmission factor (p. 443) The number by which the speed of the driver in a pulley system is multiplied to get the speed of the follower.

Factor de transmisión (pág. 443) Número por el que la velocidad del conductor en un sistema de poleas se multiplica para obtener la velocidad del seguidor.

Transversal (p. 35) A line that intersects two coplanar lines in two distinct points.

Transversal (pág. 35) Recta que interseca dos rectas coplanares en dos puntos distintos.

Glossary/Glosario

English

Trapezoid (p. 10) A quadrilateral with two opposite sides parallel.

Treatments (p. 76) The conditions to be compared in an experiment. Treatments should be randomly assigned to subjects.

Trial (p. 260) In probability, one repetition of a random process.

· (V)

Valid argument (p. xx) An argument that uses correct rules of logic. When the premises (hypotheses) are true, and the argument is valid, then the conclusion must be true.

Venn diagram (p. 20) A diagram where mutually exclusive events are represented by non-overlapping circles and events that are not mutually exclusive are represented by overlapping circles.

Vertex form of a quadratic See *Completing the square.*

Vertical angles (p. 30) Two angles whose sides form two pairs of opposite rays. When two lines or two segments intersect, vertical angles are formed.

Vertical asymptote (p. 367) A line with equation $x = k$ is a vertical asymptote for the graph of a function $f(x)$ whenever values of $f(x)$ approach $+\infty$ or $-\infty$ as $x \to k$ (from one side only, or from both sides).

· (X)

x-bar chart (p. 300) A control chart where the means of samples of measurements, rather than individual measurements, are plotted.

· (Z)

Zeroes of polynomials (p. 329) A number k is a zero of the polynomial $f(x) = a_n x^n + a_{n-1} x^{n-1} + \cdots + a_1 x + a_0$ if $f(x) = 0$. The number k will be an x-intercept of the graph of f; k is also called a root of the polynomial.

Español

Trapecio (pág. 10) Cuadrilátero con dos lados opuestos paralelos.

Tratamientos (pág. 76) Condiciones que se deben comparar en un experimento. Los tratamientos deben aplicarse a los sujetos en forma aleatoria.

Prueba (pág. 260) En probabilidad, una repetición de un proceso aleatorio.

Argumento válido (pág. xx) Argumento que utiliza reglas correctas de la lógica. Cuando las premisas (hipótesis) son verdaderas, y el argumento es válido, entonces la conclusión debe ser verdadera.

Diagrama de Venn (pág. 20) Diagrama en el que los eventos mutuamente excluyentes se representan mediante círculos que no se superponen y los eventos que no son mutuamente excluyentes se representan mediante círculos superpuestos.

Forma de vértice de una expresión cuadrática Ver *Completar el cuadrado.*

Ángulos opuestos por el vértice (pág. 30) Dos ángulos cuyos lados forman dos pares de rayos opuestos. Cuando dos líneas o dos segmentos se intersecan, se forman ángulos verticales.

Asíntota vertical (pág. 367) Una recta con ecuación $x = k$ es una asíntota vertical para el gráfico de una función $f(x)$ cuando los valores de $f(x)$ tiendan a $+\infty$ ó $-\infty$, en tanto $x \to k$ (de un lado solamente, o de ambos lados).

Gráfica de barras x (pág. 300) Tipo de diagrama de control en el que las medias de las muestras de mediciones, en vez de ser mediciones individuales, son combinadas.

Cero de un polinomio (pág. 329) Un número k es cero de un polinomio $a_n x^n + a_{n-1} x^{n-1} + \cdots + a_1 x + a_0$ si $f(x) = 0$. El número k serán una intercepción en x de gráfica de f; k es también llamado raíz del polinomio.

Index of Mathematical Topics

Index of Mathematical Topics (continued)

Index of Mathematical Topics (continued)

Index of Mathematical Topics (continued)

Index of Mathematical Topics (continued)

Index of Contexts

Index of Contexts (continued)

Index of Contexts (continued)

Photo Credits